RESEARCH PROGRESS IN ALZHEIMER'S DISEASE AND DEMENTIA, VOL. 3

RESEARCH PROGRESS IN ALZHEIMER'S DISEASE AND DEMENTIA, VOL. 3

MIAO-KUN SUN
EDITOR

Nova Biomedical Books
New York

For permission to use material from this book please contact us:
Telephone 631-231-7269; Fax 631-231-8175
Web Site: http://www.novapublishers.com

NOTICE TO THE READER

The Publisher has taken reasonable care in the preparation of this book, but makes no expressed or implied warranty of any kind and assumes no responsibility for any errors or omissions. No liability is assumed for incidental or consequential damages in connection with or arising out of information contained in this book. The Publisher shall not be liable for any special, consequential, or exemplary damages resulting, in whole or in part, from the readers' use of, or reliance upon, this material. Any parts of this book based on government reports are so indicated and copyright is claimed for those parts to the extent applicable to compilations of such works.

Independent verification should be sought for any data, advice or recommendations contained in this book. In addition, no responsibility is assumed by the publisher for any injury and/or damage to persons or property arising from any methods, products, instructions, ideas or otherwise contained in this publication.

This publication is designed to provide accurate and authoritative information with regard to the subject matter covered herein. It is sold with the clear understanding that the Publisher is not engaged in rendering legal or any other professional services. If legal or any other expert assistance is required, the services of a competent person should be sought. FROM A DECLARATION OF PARTICIPANTS JOINTLY ADOPTED BY A COMMITTEE OF THE AMERICAN BAR ASSOCIATION AND A COMMITTEE OF PUBLISHERS.

LIBRARY OF CONGRESS CATALOGING-IN-PUBLICATION DATA
Available upon request

ISBN 13: 978-1-60021-960-3
ISBN 10: 1-60021-960-8

Published by Nova Science Publishers, Inc. ✦ *New York*

CONTENTS

PREFACE

Miao-Kun Sun

Blanchette Rockefeller Neurosciences Institute, USA.

RESEARCH PROGRESS IN ALZHEIMER'S DISEASE AND DEMENTIA (VOLUME 3)

Dementia, including Alzheimer's disease (AD), the most common form of memory deficits in the elderly, progressively robs the patients of their cognitive ability, i.e., the ability to learn, memorize, reason, communicate, make judgments, and carry out daily activities. AD is characterized pathologically by extracellular amyloid plaques containing amyloid β peptide (Aβ) in the brain and intracellular neurofibrillary tangles containing hyperphosphorylated microtubule protein tau, pathophysiologically by synaptic dysfunction, and clinically by a progressive loss of memory.

The main focuses of research efforts in AD and dementia are defining the underlying pathogenic mechanisms and developing methods that are reliable for the diagnosis of early AD and therapies that directly target the underlying causes of the disorders. Accumulation of Aβ is still believed to play a critical role in the AD pathogenesis, including those patients with familial early-onset AD, a rare disease, and late-onset AD, the sporadic and common form of the disorder. Identifying the genetic risk factors, the disease loci, and their underlying pathogenic mechanisms in AD is essential. Significant progress has been made as to identifying gene expression abnormalities in the progression of AD and our understanding of tauopathy in AD, a dynamic interaction between intracellular Aβ and tau hyperphosphorylation, which may act as effectors causing cell damage. Mutations in *PSEN1* and *PSEN2* genes, which encode presenilins, the catalytic subunits of γ-secretase, underlie the majority of cases of early-onset familial AD and their roles in AD pathogenesis are getting better understood. Specific inhibitors targeting the active site of γ-secretase in sub-cellular membrane micro-domain involved in amyloid precursor protein processing are promising as a novel therapeutic strategy. In late-onset AD, apolipoprotein E, the major cholesterol transporter, is the only currently known genetic risk factor, suggesting an involvement of neuronal cholesterol in AD pathogenesis. Although the molecular mechanisms underlying intracellular Aβ pathogenic cascade(s) have not been clarified, accumulated intraneuronal Aβ is likely to be a target for AD therapeutics. Intraneuronal Aβ accumulation occurs early and correlates with cognitive and behavioral deficits in the disorder. Emerging evidence suggests that lipoprotein receptors play an important role in regulation of neuronal processes leading to AD. The potential benefits of reducing brain cholesterol levels with statins, however, remain to be evaluated. Successful AD therapies depend on a reliable diagnosis of early AD and development of therapeutic strategies that treat the underlying cause of the disease. One of such diagnostic approaches is *in vivo* visualization of amyloid-like structures with positron emission tomography, detecting the pathological deposits in the brain. Cathepsin B plays an antiamyloidogenic and neuroprotective function *in vivo* and enhancing its activity reduces Aβ load and may represent an effective therapeutic strategy. The value of experience in enriched, complex environments for prolonged periods has been suggested since it reduces Aβ deposits in the brain and improves learning and memory. Some chapters are also devoted to the research progress in such important topics as the fragile X syndrome, a neurodevelopmental disorder with cognitive defects, category learning in Parkinson's disease, and roles of cerebrovascular disease and hypertension in onset and progression of dementia.

All these new developments further indicate the multi-disciplinary nature of the study of AD and dementia. The emergence of an effective cure of AD and dementia depends on how well we understand the underlying pathogenic mechanisms. Our hope is that effective therapeutic agents that target memory-relevant AD pathogenesis and other dementic disorders are developed soon, through the intensive research efforts worldwide, as evidenced in this book volume.

FOREWORD

Miao-Kun Sun

Blanchette Rockefeller Neurosciences Institute, USA.

Alzheimer's disease (AD), the most common form of neurodegenerative disorder in the elderly, is characterized pathologically by extracellular amyloid plaques and intracellular neurofibrillary tangles, pathophysiologically by synaptic dysfunction, and clinically by a progressive decline in cognition. Currently, AD has no cure and its prevalence is predicted to triple by 2050 with the rapid increase in the aging population, unless more effective treatments are developed. Since the publication of the second book volume, the rapid progress in the research fields of AD and dementia continues through the intensive efforts of research scientists worldwide. This third book volume contains 15 chapters, bringing together a presentation of research frontiers in current AD/dementia research. The topics include molecular genetics of AD, gene expression abnormalities in AD progression, presenilins, tauopathy in AD, single neuron gene expression abnormalities in AD, intracellular Aβ-induced neurodegeneration, roles of lipoprotein receptors in AD onset and progression, cholesterol and tau hyperphosphorylation, AD diagnostics and therapeutic strategies, *in vivo* visualization of amyloid-like structures, cathepsin B, antiamyloidogenesis and neuroprotection, environmental enrichment, Fragile X mental retardation gene and dementia, category learning in Parkinson's disease, cerebrovascular disease and dementia, and dementia and hypertension. These chapters cover current advances in our understanding of the pathogenic mechanisms underlying AD and dementia, in the diagnosis of early AD and dementia, and in the development of therapeutic agents that target memory-relevant AD pathogenesis. The book will be highly valuable to students and scientists worldwide who are interested in the scientific research progress in AD and dementia.

In: Research Progress in Alzheimer's Disease and Dementia   ISBN 978-1-60021-960-3
Editor: Miao-Kun Sun, pp. 1-23   © 2008 Nova Science Publishers, Inc.

Chapter I

MOLECULAR GENETICS OF ALZHEIMER'S DISEASE

Odity Mukherjee[1,2], Petra Nowotny[1] and Alison Goate[1,*]
[1]Dept. of Psychiatry, Washington University School of Medicine, St. Louis,
MO 63110, USA;
[2]National Center for Biological Sciences, Bangalore, India.

ABSTRACT

Alzheimer's Disease (AD) is the most common cause of dementia in the elderly. The disease affects ~3-5% of the population above the age of 65 years and nearly 40% above the age of 85 years. In the past decade many advances in the understanding of the etiology of AD have been reported. Familial early-onset AD is a rare disorder, which is caused by mutations in one of three genes. These mutations all implicate the longer forms of ß-amyloid, a proteolytic processing product of the amyloid precursor protein, in disease pathogenesis. Current linkage and association studies are focused on identifying genetic risk factors for late-onset AD, the sporadic and common form of the disease. In this group of people the only confirmed genetic risk factor is the $\varepsilon 4$ allele of the *Apolipoprotein E* gene. Like the mutations causing early-onset AD, *APOE4* implicates ß-amyloid as a central factor in the disease and thus a major target for drug development. However, 50% of AD cases do not carry an *APOE4* allele suggesting that there are other genetic or environmental factors still to be discovered.

---

* Correspondence concerning this article should be addressed to: Dr. Goate, Dept. of Psychiatry, Washington University School of Medicine, 660 S. Euclid Ave, St. Louis, MO 63110 Email: goate@icarus.wustl.edu.

INTRODUCTION

Alzheimer's disease (AD) is an age dependent irreversible neurodegenerative disorder. Early symptoms include amnesia (loss of short-term memory), which usually manifests as minor forgetfulness becoming steadily more pronounced with disease progression. As the illness progresses, cognitive impairment extends to the domains of language (aphasia), skilled movements (apraxia), recognition (agnosia) and functions closely related to the frontal and temporal lobes of the brain as they become disconnected from the limbic system (e.g. decision-making and planning). The pathological process underlying the disease is results in neuronal loss in the temporoparietal and frontal cortice, together with an inflammatory response to the deposition of amyloid plaques and neurofibrillary tangles. The course and progression of this disease is highly variable and can be anywhere from 7-20 years.

Although the risk of developing AD increases with age, the symptoms are not part of normal aging. AD is the most common cause of dementia among the elderly ($\geq$ 65years),. AD is classified into two main groups based on the age-of-onset and familial aggregation, namely familial AD (FAD) and late-onset AD (LOAD). In FAD, the disease segregates in families in an autosomal dominant manner with onset usually before the age of 60 years. FAD is rare, representing less than 1% of all AD cases (Ezquerra et al., 1999), while LOAD is common and has a later age-of-onset (usually after 65 years). Although different in their age at presentation, both forms of the disease have the same clinical features and pathological lesions: neuronal loss and the presence of β-amyloid plaques and neurofibrillary tangles.

The prevalence of AD is around 1.5% at age 65 years and doubles every four years, to reach 30% at age 80 years (Gorelick 2004). Currently, approximately 4 million Americans are above the age of 85 years. Studies predict, that unless more effective treatments can be developed, by 2050 more than 13.2 million people will have AD in the USA alone (Hebert et al., 2003). Nationally the annual cost of caring for AD patients is $100 billion (Ernst and Hay 1994). It is hypothesized that a five year delay in the onset of the disease would result in half as many cases within one generation (Brookmeyer et al., 1998).

Many research groups across the world are involved in deciphering the biological underpinnings of this disease. These groups are looking into three main aspects of the disease: 1) causes/risk factors, 2) diagnosis, biomarkers of disease and 3) treatment/care giving. Research into the basic biology of aging and the nervous system is aimed at understanding the differences between a healthy brain and an AD brain. Identification and assessment of factors influencing the risk of developing AD and understanding how these factors cause certain nerve cells to die or lose their ability to function and communicate with neighboring nerve cells is the crux of this research effort. The second area of research involves designing methods and technologies for early identification of dementia within the general population. A central part of this research effort is to identify biomarkers, improve ways to assess patient function and enhance neuroimaging techniques for early detection of dementia. Finally, a third group of researchers are involved in the discovery and development of drugs and interventions to prevent disease or improve treatment and management of symptoms in AD patients. Several of these drugs are currently in clinical trials. All these efforts have improved our understanding of this devastating disease. The findings have also helped gain knowledge about normal brain functioning in healthy elderly individuals and ways to minimize age related cognitive decline.

GENETIC RISK FACTORS FOR ALZHEIMER'S DISEASE

Familial Alzheimer's Disease

Complete or partial trisomy of chromosome 21 leads to Down Syndrome. All individuals with complete trisomy of chromosome 21 develop AD pathology by middle age (Wisniewski et al., 1985). In contrast, individuals who have a partial trisomy of chromosome 21 only develop AD neuropathology when the *APP* gene is present in three copies (Prasher et al., 1998). The *APP* gene is located on the long arm on chromosome 21 (21q21.2) and consists of 18 coding exons (Hattori et al., 2000) that can be alternatively spliced to generate seven multi-domain proteins (Yoshikai et al., 1990).

Having three copies of the *APP* gene causes elevated levels of circulating Aβ peptide (Schupf et al., 2001) leading to premature accumulation of Aβ in amyloid plaques in the Down Syndrome brain (Kida et al., 1995; Wisniewski et al., 1985) and an early age-of-onset of AD (Hyman 1992; Zigman et al., 1996).

A second group of individuals who will develop AD with certainty are the children of affected individuals in kindreds with early onset AD. One hundred percent of the children who inherit the disease allele from their AD affected parent will develop disease. Statistically, half the children will inherit the disease allele. Studies of these FAD kindreds have been extremely successful over the past two decades resulting in major new insights into the causes of disease and the molecular mechanisms underlying that risk. Rare cases of AD are caused by fully penetrant mutations in three genes: *amyloid precursor protein (APP), Presenilin 1 (PSEN1)* and *Presenilin 2 (PSEN2)* (Goate et al., 1991; Levy-Lahad et al., 1995; Rogaev et al., 1995; Sherrington et al., 1995) APP is the precursor to β-amyloid (Aβ) and the *presenilin* genes code for proteins that are components of the γ-secretase enzyme that cleaves N-terminally truncated fragments of APP within the transmembrane domain to generate the ß-amyloid fragment. The majority of FAD mutations lead to increased production of Aβ42 (ß-amyloid that is 42 amino acids in length) by modifying the processing of APP, resulting in increased β-amyloid deposition in the brain (Scheuner et al., 1996).

Since the discovery of the first *APP* mutation causing FAD by Goate and coworkers (1991), a total of 27 different pathogenic mutations in *APP* have been reported, accounting for ~ 10 % of all FAD cases (http://www.molgen.ua.ac.be/ADMutations/). Several of these mutations lead to a spectrum of clinical phenotypes including both dementia and hemorrhagic stroke. The first *APP* mutation (E693Q) to be reported was identified in a large Dutch kindred with hereditary cerebral hemorrhage with amyloidosis (HCHWA), resulting in an autosomal dominant form of vascular amyloidosis with Aß deposition in the cerebral blood vessels, leading to hemorrhagic strokes and dementia (Levy et al., 1990; van Duinen et al., 1987). This mutation occurs within the Aß sequence but close to the α-secretase cleavage site of APP.

Most *APP* mutations occur at codons near the β or γ-secretase cleavage sites flanking the Aß sequence. The mutations near the γ-secretase cleavage site result in an increase in the ratio of Aβ42 to Aβ40 while mutations at the ß-secretase cleavage site, like the "Swedish" mutation, K670N/M671L, result in an increase in total Aß species without altering the ratio (Citron et al., 1992; De Strooper and Annaert 2000). Individuals with this mutation have both neuritic plaques and cerebral amyloid angiopathy (CAA). Carriers of the Flemish mutation (A692G), another intra-Aβ mutation, suffer from intracerebral hemorrhage, and individuals who survive, develop a progressive dementia with features of AD (Hendriks et al., 1992). This mutation leads to an increased total Aß and Aß/p3 ratios, suggesting that the mutation affects the α-secretase cleavage. *In vitro* studies of mutant and wild-type synthetic Aβ peptides have shown that the Dutch mutation accelerates protofibril formation while the Flemish peptide displays increased solubility and decreased fibrillogenesis rates compared to the wild type (Haass et al., 1994; Watson et al., 1999). Other pathogenic intra-Aβ mutations have been discovered including the Italian mutation (E693K) with a clinical presentation similar to the Dutch patients (Miravalle et al., 2000) and the Iowa mutation (D694N), which has a clinical presentation of progressive dementia and severe cerebral amyloid angiopathy (Grabowski et al., 2001). The cellular effects of these mutations on Aβ formation have not yet been determined. In addition to the above pathogenic missense mutations, duplication of *APP* has recently been shown to lead to a familial disorder characterized clinically by hemorrhagic strokes as well as dementia and pathologically by neuritic plaques and CAA (Rovelet-Lecrux et al., 2006). Like the Swedish mutation, *APP* duplication leads to an increase in total Aß levels.

The *PSEN1* gene contains 12 exons and spans 84kb on the long arm of chromosome 14 (14q24.2). The full-length protein is composed of 467 amino acids with 8-9 transmembrane domains (Laudon et al., 2005; Li and Greenwald 1996; Li and Greenwald 1997; Li and Greenwald 1998). The *Presenilin* genes were identified using either positional cloning (*PSEN1*) or a combination of positional cloning and a candidate gene approach (*PSEN2*). Mutations in *PSEN1* increase the ratio of Aβ42 to Aβ40 and can result in very early-onset of disease (26-76 yrs; (Dermaut et al., 1999; Gustafson et al., 1998; Xia et al., 1997). These mutations occur throughout the molecule but appear to have similar effects on Aß levels. To date over 161 mutations have been identified in several hundred families, resolving the genetic basis of a large proportion of FAD cases (*http://www.molgen.ua.ac.be/ ADMutations/*). PSEN2 is a homologous protein to PSEN1, encoded by a gene on chromosome 1q42.13 with 12 exons spanning 25kb. Mutations in *PSEN2* are the rarest of the known causes of FAD with just 11 identified mutations (*http://www.molgen.ua.ac.be/ ADMutations/*). The known mutations in *PSEN2* generally result in a later age-of-onset (40-75yrs) than homologous mutations in *PSEN1* and may exhibit incomplete penetrance (Ezquerra et al., 2003).

Several FAD mutations have been used to create transgenic mouse models that exhibit age dependent Aß deposition in cerebral vessels and/or cerebral cortex. These studies have helped in the elucidation of the pathological mechanisms of the disease mutations. Transgenic mice overexpressing the *APP* mutation E693Q have been shown to cause Aβ deposition in the cerebral vasculature inducing hemorrhages (Herzig et al., 2004). However, when these mice were crossed with transgenic mice overexpressing mutations in the *PSEN1* gene, the Aβ42/Aβ40 ratio is increased and the amyloid pathology redistributes to the parenchyma (Herzig et al., 2004). A similar result was also obtained at the E693G site in the Aβ sequence (also called the "Arctic" mutation) (Cheng et al., 2004). Together, these human and transgenic mouse studies suggest that elevated levels of total Aβ or increased protofibril formation lead to mixed dementia pathology (AD and CAA), while elevation of Aβ42/Aβ40 ratio results only in AD pathology. These findings suggest that the underlying pathologies are specific to the mutations.

There was a long-standing debate about the primacy of plaques vs. tangles, the two pathological hallmarks of AD, in the disease pathogenesis. This was resolved by the discovery of mutations in the Microtubule Associayed Protein Tau (*MAPT*) gene, which can also cause dementia (Hutton et al., 1998; Poorkaj et al., 1998). It has been shown that missense and splicing mutations in *MAPT* are associated with inherited forms of frontotemporal dementia with parkinsonism, progressive supranuclear palsy and Pick's disease, but not AD. These data showed that tangles could be directly initiated by *MAPT* mutations, resulting a disease with tangles but no plaques. Studies in double transgenic mice which carried mutations in *MAPT* and *APP* showed that elevated Aβ increased the formation of tau deposits in neurons, but not the opposite (Lewis et al., 2001).

Late-Onset Alzheimer's Disease

While we have some knowledge about the causes of the early onset familial form of AD, age is the single most important risk factor for LOAD (Ritchie and Kildea 1995) and, to date, apolipoprotein E *(APOE)* is the only known genetic risk factor for LOAD. The *APOE* gene is located on chromosome 19. ApoE carries and clears lipids in the bloodstream. The gene has three alleles — ε2, ε3 and ε4 — and inheritance of the ε4 allele is regarded as a risk factor for developing LOAD. Further, it is hypothesized that the ε2 allele acts as a protective factor for AD and ε3 plays a neutral role in disease development. The *APOE* polymorphisms have been genotyped in many populations, and consistently show evidence for association with LOAD (Bertram et al., 2007; Finckh et al., 2003). Most individuals homozygous for the *APOE4* allele have been shown to develop LOAD by 80 years of age (Corder et al., 1993). Additionally, in certain populations, like European-Americans, a dose dependent effect is observed. Individuals, heterozygous for the *APOE4* allele, exhibit a threefold increase in risk, while homozygotes show nearly an eightfold increase in risk. Further, it has been shown that the allelic architecture at the *APOE* locus may also explain some of the variance seen in age-of-onset in kindreds with known FAD mutations: mutation carriers who have an *APOE4* allele have an earlier age-of-onset than relatives with a disease causing mutation but no *APOE4* allele (Pastor et al., 2003). A number of hypotheses regarding interactions between APOE and Aβ underlying the pathogenesis of LOAD have been proposed. Patients carrying at least one *APOE4* allele have a greater number of plaques than patients without an *APOE4* allele (Schmechel et al., 1993). *In vitro*, APOE4 binds to Aβ with higher affinity than APOE3 (Strittmatter et al., 1993). There is also evidence that APOE and Aβ may compete for clearance through the same receptor (Kounnas et al., 1995). Mouse models that overexpress *APP* carrying an FAD mutation only show thioflavin positive Aβ (amyloid) deposition when the *APOE* gene is expressed (Bales et al., 1997). A study by Holtzman *et al.* suggests that APOE4 may influence fibril formation and clearance of Aβ, causing increased Aβ deposition (Holtzman et al., 2000). The same group also showed that mice with *APOE4* alleles developed earlier and more severe pathological phenotypes (Fryer et al., 2003). *In vitro* experiments show that APOE3 binds to tau with a higher affinity than APOE4, suggesting that APOE may also have some effect on neurofibrillary tangles (Strittmatter et al., 1994). Some studies also suggest that promoter variants in *APOE* are associated with LOAD risk (Wang et al., 2000). *APOE2*, which is the rarest allele in most populations, seems to be protective for AD, resulting in higher age-of-onset of disease. Mouse studies also suggest that Aß cannot form amyloid deposits in the presence of APOE2 (Fryer et al., 2003). Mayeux et al. showed that the biological effects of head injury may increase risk for AD through a synergistic relationship with the *APOE4* allele (Mayeux et al., 1995). The *APOE* genotype has also been implicated as a risk factor in a number of other diseases including coronary artery disease and CAA (Contois et al., 1996). *APOE4* is certainly a major risk factor for LOAD, however, there are likely to be other factors, because *APOE4* shows only a modest effect on risk in Amish and Hispanic patients (Pericak-Vance et al., 1996; Tang et al., 1998) and approximately 50% of Caucasian AD patients do not carry an *APOE4* allele.

SEARCH FOR NOVEL PUTATIVE LOCI

Due to certain disease specific characteristics, together with the development of relatively inexpensive and high-throughput genotyping technologies, the search for novel AD genes has led to a steep increase in the number of laboratories studying AD genetics. To date many whole genome screens using either linkage or association based methodologies have been reported. Additionally, numerous candidate gene association studies have also been performed.

Linkage Studies

Linkage studies identify regions of the genome harboring disease genes by examining the patterns of allele-transmission or sharing in families. These studies require familial samples with multi-generational pedigrees providing the greatest statistical power. Thus, the characteristic late onset of LOAD makes it difficult to collect such samples. As a result, many linkage studies of LOAD are underpowered. Despite these difficulties, several groups have identified linked regions by performing genome-wide genetic linkage studies in LOAD families using affected sibling pairs (ASPs) (Blacker et al., 2003; Kehoe et al., 1999; Myers et al., 2002; Pericak-Vance et al., 1997). Table 1 summarizes the recent linkage screens for AD. Many of these studies used overlapping or identical samples with either a set of different genetic markers or analytical methods (Bertram and Tanzi 2004).

Pericak-Vance et al. (1997) used a two-stage design for their linkage study. The first set of 16 LOAD families was screened with markers at 10-cM intervals. Regions of the genome showing positive linkage were subsequently investigated in an additional sample set of 38 families. The strongest evidence of linkage was found on chromosome 12 (multipoint LOD score [MLS] =3.9), and moderate evidence of linkage was found on chromosomes 4, 6, and 20. In a replication effort they increased the number of families to 466 and found evidence for another locus on chromosome 9 (MLS=4.3) (Pericak-Vance et al., 2000). In 1999, Kehoe et al. reported the results of the first stage of their two-stage screen of LOAD affected sibling pairs (ASPs). In the first stage, 292 ASPs were screened with markers at approximately 20-cM intervals. Regions with an multi-point lod score (MLS) greater than 1 were then screened with a denser set of markers in a total of 450 ASPs (Myers et al. 2002). The strongest evidence for linkage was found on chromosome 10 (MLS=3.9), and suggestive linkage was observed on chromosomes 1 (MLS=2.67), 9 (MLS=2.38), and 19 (MLS=1.79). Blacker et al. (2003) performed a 9-cM screen of 437 families. They identified significant linkage on chromosome 19, and suggestive linkage in 12 regions on chromosomes 1, 3, 4, 5, 6, 9, 10, 11, 14, 15, and 21. The linkage on chromosome 12 (Pericak-Vance et al., 1997) has been replicated by several studies (Rogaeva et al., 1998; Wu et al., 1998). In a separate study in Caribbean Hispanic families, evidence for linkage on chromosome 12 was also found (MLS=3.15; (Mayeux et al., 2002). Although there appears to be replication of several chromosomal regions in these studies it should be noted that many of the studies used overlapping datasets and thus the results are not truly independent.

Table 1. Results of genome screens and linkage studies

Study	Chromosome[a]	Results[b]
Pericak-Vance et al. 1997[c]	4, 6, **12**, 20	MLS:3.9
Wu et al. 1998	12	MLS:1.9
Rogaeva et al. 1998	12	NPLS:3.5
Zubenko et al. 1998[c]	1, 10, 12, 19, X	All P<0.05
Kehoe et al. 1999[c]	**1**, 5, **9**, **10**, 12, 14, **19**, 21	All MLS~2
Pericak-Vance et al. 2000[c]	9	MLS:4.3
Bertram et al. 2000	10	TLS:3.4
Ertekin-Taner et al. 2000	10	MLS:3.9
Mayeux et al. 2002	12	TLS:3.15
Myers et al. 2002[c]	1, 5, 6, 9, **10**, 12, 19, 21, X	MLS:3.9
Blacker et al. 2003[c]	1, 3, 4, 5, 6, 9, 10, 11, 14, 15, 21	All MLS≥2
Farrer et al. 2003[c]	2, 9, 10, 12	All P<0.05
Sillen et al. 2005[c]	4, 5, **19**	MLS:2.99
Rademakers et al. 2005[c]	7	MLS:3.39
Sillen et al. 2005[c]	4, 5, **19**	MLS:2.99
Grupe et al. 2007[c]	1, 2, 7, 10, 14, 15, 17, **19**, 20, 22	All P<0.05

MLS=multipoint LOD score; NPLS=nonparametric linkage score; TLS=two-point LOD score.
[a]The strongest finding is printed in bold;
[b]Result is for the strongest finding;
[c]These studies are whole genome screens.

Endophenotypes

The use of an endophenotype for studying complex disease confers several advantages, providing greater power because it is less heterogeneous than clinical diagnosis and more directly affected by genetic variations. A useful endophenotype should be associated with the disorder, associated with heritable and non-heritable risk factors in clinically unaffected individuals and correlated with relative risk. Many studies have shown variation in Aβ levels for both FAD (plasma Aβ) and LOAD (CSF Aβ) cases. Given that the central hypothesis of AD pathology is an abnormal aggregation of Aβ peptides into insoluble forms (e.g. oligomers and plaques) as causal for Alzheimer's disease, variations in Aβ levels serve as an important endophenotype for AD. Additionally, age-at-onset, *APOE* genotype, neuroimaging and clinical profile are other useful endophenotypes. Additional evidence for a LOAD locus on chromosome 10 has come from studies using a quantitative endophenotype, plasma Aβ42 levels. Ertekin-Taner et al. (2000) reported that high plasma Aβ levels are a heritable trait, and identified strong evidence for linkage to high plasma Aβ levels on chromosome 10 (MLS=3.9). This finding is consistent with the linkage findings in AD ASPs reported by Myers et al., (2000).

Further, research in quantitative neuroimaging has yielded some promising results. In a recent study, abnormally low positron emission tomography (PET) measurements of cerebral metabolic rate of glucose (CMRgl) were used as a quantitative presymptomatic endophenotype to help evaluate the individual and aggregate effect of putative genetic and non-genetic modifiers of AD risk (Reiman et al., 2005).

Li et al. performed a genome screen to identify regions influencing age-of-onset in LOAD and Parkinson's disease and identified linkage around *APOE* on chromosome 19 (Li et al., 2002). The study also implicated a region of chromosome 10 identified in a prior report (Bertram et al., 2000).

Homogeneous Populations

To overcome the possibility of introducing genetic heterogeneity resulting in reduced power to detect disease loci, several researchers have used relatively homogeneous populations (Farrer et al., 2003; Hahs et al., 2006; Sillen et al., 2006). These studies have reported significant evidence of linkage on chromosome 9, 10, 12, 19 and 5 and moderate to suggestive LOD scores on chromosomes 2, 3 and 4 (Farrer et al., 2003; Hahs et al., 2006). Another useful method of reducing heterogeneity is to perform linkage analysis in a single, large multiplex kindred. Rademakers et al. performed a whole genome linkage scan in a single Dutch multiplex family with a mean age-of-onset of 68 yrs and found strong evidence of linkage (LOD = 3.39) with markers at chromosome 7q36 (Rademakers et al., 2005). They performed additional analyses that led to the identification of 3 additional Dutch families, who shared the same disease haplotypes and narrowed the candidate region to 9.4cM.

All the genome screens performed to date have consistently identified linkage to chromosome 19 near *APOE*. In addition, regions of chromosomes 6, 9, 10,12, 19 and 21 appear to be most promising for LOAD or related phenotypes (reported in 3 or more studies).

Candidate Genes

Association studies have some advantages over linkage studies, because they have greater power to detect disease loci. In addition, association studies can be performed using either family-based samples or case-control series. Case-control samples are easily collected and provide considerable statistical power, but may be subject to an increase in spurious associations due to population stratification if they are not carefully ascertained. Family-based samples, generally in the form of parent-offspring trios or ASPs, are not subject to the problem of stratification, but are difficult to collect given the late age-at-onset of AD. A recent study comparing the power of the two methods showed that parent-offspring trios and unrelated cases and controls yielded higher odds ratios and more significant test values than ASPs when looking at known risk loci for type II diabetes. However, subsequent simulation studies suggest that no one strategy is ideal in every situation; the optimal ascertainment strategy depends on the underlying disease model, which is unknown (Howson et al., 2005).

Many positional candidate genes have been identified using information from the linkage studies. Additionally, several biological candidate genes for LOAD have also been identified. Since the known FAD genes directly implicate Aß metabolism and Aß aggregation in AD pathogenesis, efforts to better characterize the role of Aβ have led to the identification of a large number of genes, which are involved in Aβ production, aggregation, degradation and clearance. Many of these genes are found under linkage peaks, making them both positional and biological candidate genes. *Ubiquilin* and *ABCA1* are strong biological candidate genes located under a linkage peak on chromosome 9. Family based association studies have shown positive association with AD and Ubiquilin (Bertram et al., 2005), however, few subsequent studies replicated this observation with just two of the nine populations tested showing evidence for association (Brouwers et al., 2006; Slifer et al., 2005; Smemo et al., 2006). Similar results were also obtained at the *ABCA1* gene locus, with association being observed in some studies, but not others (Katzov et al., 2004; Li et al., 2004b; Shibata et al., 2006; Wollmer et al., 2003). Positional and biological candidate genes on chromosomes 10 and 12 also show the same trend. A detailed summary of more than 1,000 LOAD association studies can be found at http://www.alzgene.org (Bertram et al., 2007). Alzgene also provides a meta-analysis of association for each SNP genotyped in at least four datasets. The website is updated frequently, and thus provides an interesting and dynamic view of LOAD association studies.

Despite these vast efforts, no single gene has yet emerged that exhibits the consistency and reliability of the *APOE* gene (Bertram and Tanzi 2004).

FUTURE RESEARCH

Large Scale Whole Genome Initiatives

With the advent of cheap high-throughput genotyping technology, whole genome association studies will be more feasible to perform in both existing and newly ascertained samples. Whole genome studies provide increased power and efficiency compared to family-based linkage scans and are viewed by many scientists as a critical new tool for the identification of novel susceptibility loci for complex diseases (Risch and Merikangas 1996). These studies have the potential to identify novel genetic risk factors that will increase our understanding of the disease pathogenesis. However, these whole genome studies face a number of difficulties. Care must be taken to design these studies to deal with the statistical issues such as multiple testing and power estimates to identify true positive results and minimizing false positive results. In addition, researchers must be careful to use well-defined phenotypes, appropriately matched controls and sample sizes. Use of quantitative endophenotypes should be increased to improve the signal-to-noise ratio. It is also important to account for other sources of error such as population stratification and genotyping error (Ehm et al., 2005).

Recently large-scale association studies for Parkinson's disease (PD) and LOAD have been reported. These studies employed multiple approaches to identify susceptibility loci, either attempting to adequately sample the linkage disequilibrium structure or to screen the putative functional polymorphisms in linkage regions. A 2-stage approach was used by Maraganore et al to perform a whole genome linkage disequilibrium screen for Parkinson's disease (Maraganore et al., 2005). 443 discordant sibling pairs were screened with ~ 200,000 SNPs. 1,793 SNPs were identified to be positively associated with PD. These were subsequently genotyped in an additional cohort of 332 matched case-control pairs. The most significant association was detected for SNPs within a known PD susceptibility gene (PARK10). Although this study used a large number of SNPs and a fairly large cohort of individuals new genome association chips will assess more than one million SNPs and sample sizes will be more than one thousand cases and one thousand controls.

While a genome-wide linkage disequilibrium screen of LOAD has not yet been reported, three studies focusing on the large scale screening of putative functional polymorphisms have had some success. These studies performed association studies in three large case-control series using SNPs across linkage peaks. First, a large number of markers were tested in a single sample. Then markers, which showed significant association, were genotyped in at least two additional case-control samples to test for replication. With this approach, SNPs in *GAPD* on chromosome 12 and in paralogs on other chromosomes showed evidence for association with LOAD (Li et al., 2004a). This group also used the same approach to identify a SNP on chromosome 10 in the linkage region that replicated association across multiple datasets (Grupe et al., 2006) and SNPs in *DAPK1* on chromosome 9 that were associated with LOAD in multiple datasets. In the second study the authors also showed that these SNPs were associated with *DAPK1* allele-specific expression (Li et al., 2006). Recently in a genome-wide, gene-centric association study with putative functional variants and a large set of samples, the most significant association was with three markers on chromosome 19, which are in LD with *APOE* (Grupe et al., 2007). These results suggest that large-scale association studies may lead to the identification of novel susceptibility loci for LOAD but it is likely that no other loci will have the impact on risk observed with *APOE* alleles.

Functional Studies

Genetic and functional studies have shown that risk for sporadic forms of the disease may be influenced by variation in expression levels of the same genes that carry fully penetrant mutations in the familial forms of the same disorder (Hardy 2005). For example, mutations in the *PRNP* gene have been shown to segregate with Creutzfeldt-Jakob disease (Owen et al., 1990), while polymorphisms upstream of *PRNP* exon 1 and a missense polymorphism (met/val129) have been shown to be associated with risk for the sporadic form of Creutzfeldt-Jakob disease (Mead et al., 2001). Similarly, missense and splicing mutations in the *MAPT* gene have been implicated in frontotemporal dementia (Hutton et al., 1998) while common polymorphisms and haplotypes influence risk for several sporadic tauopathies (progressive supranuclear palsy and corticobasal degeneration) (Baker et al., 1999; Houlden et al., 2001). Mutations in the *α-synuclein* gene cause familial PD (Zarranz et al., 2004) and polymorphisms that alter the expression of α-synuclein influence risk for sporadic PD (Chiba-Falek, 2003). These studies suggest that in many neurodegenerative disorders familial early-onset forms of the disease are caused by mutations in the gene encoding the protein that is deposited in the brain, while polymorphisms that lead to overexpression of the same gene may lead to sporadic or late onset forms of the same disorder. A similar mechanism is hypothesized for AD as a comparison of known risk factors for AD and PD provides striking parallels (Hardy 2005); 1) *APP*, like *α-synuclein*, codes for a deposited protein and mutations in both genes have been shown to cause familial early-onset forms of AD and PD, respectively. 2) Variation in the copy number of *α-synuclein* has been shown to cause familial PD (Chartier-Harlin et al., 2004; Ibanez et al., 2004; Singleton et al., 2003) and also duplication of *APP* causes AD (Rovelet-Lecrux et al., 2006).

Table 2. A summary of selected SNPs in known risk factors for AD from alzgene.org

Gene	Polymorphism	Chromosome/ Position	Association		Meta-analysis
			Positive Populations	Negative Populations	OR (95% CI) **
APOE	E3 vs. E4	19/50100904	34	2	**3.68 (3.31,4.11)**
	rs405509	19 50100676	5	10	**0.79 (0.71,0.87)**
	rs440446	19/50101007	3	1	**0.58 (0.5,0.7)**
	rs449647	19/50100404	14	20	**0.72 (0.6,0.8)**
	rs769446	See Lambert et al 1998	3	9	0.85 (0.7,1)
PSEN1	-48 C/T	14/72672861	2	5	0.85 (0.67,1.08)
	rs165932	14/72734606	3	31	**0.93 (0.87,0.98)**
	rs362373 (E318G)*	See Mattila et al 1998	1	4	1.37 (0.6,3.1)
PSEN2	5' in/del*	1/223364999	0	3	1.01 (0.82,1.25)
	rs8383	1/223390285	1	2	1.23 (0.88,1.74)

*Putative functional polymorphism;

**Significant results from the meta-analysis are in bold.

Based on these similarities it may be hypothesized that like α-synuclein in PD, subtle changes in levels of expression of APP would affect risk for sporadic LOAD. Furthermore, based on the phenotype observed in the duplication families and in DS, overexpression of APP is likely to be associated with both neuritic plaques and CAA and thus will be associated with both dementia and hemorrhagic strokes, while overexpression of the presenilins may lead to increased risk for neuritic plaques and dementia but not CAA or strokes. Only a handful of polymorphisms in the known risk factors for AD have been investigated in multiple studies (Table 2).

Several studies have reported an association between common promoter polymorphisms in *APP* and increased risk for LOAD but these findings have not been replicated by others (Athan et al., 2002; Lahiri et al., 2005). An alternative approach has been to sequence the *APP* promoter in a large number of AD cases to identify rare variants and then test these *in vitro* for their effects on APP expression. One such study identified three rare polymorphisms that showed a nearly two-fold increase in neuronal APP transcriptional activity *in vitro* (Theuns et al., 2006). These variants were observed in AD cases but not controls.

In an association study to investigate the role of *APP* in the risk for LOAD, 44 common SNPs, spanning 300 kb around *APP*, were genotyped in a large case-control series (Nowotny et al., 2007). No significant association was found but it cannot be ruled out that one or multiple rare variants increase APP expression. Another caveat in this study is the selection criteria of the LOAD cases, which may have excluded individuals with strokes who are most likely to carry a risk factor in the *APP* gene (Rovelet-Lecrux et al., 2006).

Promoter variations in the *PSEN1* gene have also been reported to be associated with increased risk for AD. Higher levels of *PSEN1* gene expression are hypothesized to increase γ-secretase levels leading to higher Aβ levels and increased risk for AD (Lambert et al., 2001; Theuns et al., 2000). No association has been found in the *PSEN2* gene so far.

Although the results so far are not consistent, the hypothesis that variation in the expression of the known familial AD risk factors can lead to increase risk for LOAD warrants further investigation, especially given the data in other neurodegenerative diseases.

Design and Development of Quantitative Endophenotypes

The use of quantitative endophenotypes has greatly aided the search for genetic risk factors in complex disease. The use of cholesterol levels in coronary artery disease and various electrophysiological characteristics in alcoholism provide good examples (Bierut et al., 2002; Sing and Moll 1989). Quantitative endophenotypes like age-of-onset and various neuropsychiatric tests have been used to reduce heterogeneity of the sample, but they are not considered biomarkers for AD. The hypothesis that AD is a result of an imbalance between Aβ production and clearance leading to a gradual accumulation of Aβ and followed by widespread neuronal cell death suggests that Aβ levels may be good biomarkers for AD. Plasma Aβ levels have been shown to increase in individuals with FAD (Scheuner et al., 1996) and LOAD (Ertekin-Taner et al., 2004; Ertekin-Taner et al., 2000; Ertekin-Taner et al., 2003). However, the finding that plasma Aβ levels are increased in individuals with LOAD is disputed (DeMattos et al., 2002; Freeman et al., 2007; Fukumoto et al., 2003). This makes it unclear how the results of these studies using plasma Aβ as a phenotype apply to genetic risk for LOAD. Furthermore several studies have reported that BMI and creatinine levels correlate with plasma Aß levels suggesting that many factors unrelated to AD may influence plasma Aß levels. While plasma Aβ may be an interesting phenotype in its own right, it does not seem to be a useful biomarker for LOAD and many other proteins and compounds are being considered (Frey et al., 2005).

Levels of tau and Aβ42 in CSF have been shown to correlate with AD status (Sunderland et al., 2003). These traits are promising, though alone they lack the specificity necessary to be effective biomarkers. Many researchers are currently working on identifying other molecules or combinations of molecules in CSF that may serve as biomarkers for AD (Blasko et al., 2006). Recent studies have shown that CSF Aß levels may be a useful endophenotype for genetic studies. Sequencing of the known FAD genes in individuals with extreme Aß levels (top and bottom 10th percentiles) led to the identification of an individual carrying a known *PSEN1* FAD mutation (Kauwe et al., 2007). This individual had a family history of AD but the mean age-of-onset in the family was 69 yrs and thus had not previously been screened for *PSEN1* mutations. CSF Aß may also be useful in identifying more common variation with lower penetrance that influences risk for LOAD.

Imaging of Aβ in the brain using Pittsburgh compound B (PIB) has shown that PIB retention is correlated with the presence of disease (Klunk et al., 2004). PIB imaging of amyloid plaques may soon be applied as a diagnostic tool (Mintun 2005) and pilot studies investigating the utility of this phenotype in genetic studies are underway. The development of valid biomarkers for AD will refine the phenotype, creating more homogenous samples and greatly improving our ability to detect disease loci.

Genetic Testing and Pharmacogenetics

Predictive genetic testing is clinically available for mutations in the FAD genes but they are recommended only for at-risk individuals, above the age of eighteen years, with a clear family history and an early age-of-onset of disease. *APOE4* is a risk factor for LOAD and a test is available but not recommended for general use because it cannot be used for prediction or risk assessment (Liddell et al., 2001; Schutte 2006).

Current therapies for AD are based on neurotransmitter-replacement therapies that treat disease symptoms but do not address the underlying causes of disease. The increasing knowledge about the pathogenic pathway has revealed many potential therapeutic targets. Several different strategies are being pursued including inhibition of the enzymes β- and γ-secretase, which generate Aβ42, preventing oligomerization of Aβ, anti-amyloid immunotherapy and use of anti-inflammatory agents.

Clinicians have known for decades that not all patients respond similarly to drugs and that doses need to be optimized for each individual. Drug response may be influenced by non-genetic factors such as age, gender, diet/exercise, hepatic/renal function, nicotine and alcohol use. However, even when these factors are taken into account considerable variation remains and may be attributable to inherent genetic variation. Pharmacokinetic and pharmacodynamic pathways are likely to be important sites of functional variation influencing drug response. Pharmacokinetics refers to the absorption, distribution, metabolism and excretion of a drug. Variation in genes that influence pharmacokinetics can result in differences in the rate of metabolism of a drug, thereby affecting efficacy and/or susceptibility to adverse drug reactions. Pharmocodynamics are affected by a wide variety of gene families including receptors, ion channels, enzymes and immune system genes. Variation in these genes can cause changes in the drug target pathways, which may affect efficacy. An increased understanding of a patient's genotype and its effect on drug response will in the future, allow a physician to choose an effective drug and to optimize the dose in a timely manner.

CONCLUSION

Dominant mutations in three genes have been shown to cause FAD by increasing the production of Aβ42. The only known genetic risk factor of LOAD is *APOE*, which has also been shown to affect Aβ fibril formation. Additionally, *APOE* has also been shown to affect the age-of-onset of AD in both FAD and sporadic forms of the disease.

Significant linkage has been observed in regions of chromosomes 9, 10, and 12 in a number of studies and many positional and biological candidate genes have been tested for association with disease. However, only the *APOE* gene has shown consistent positive association with LOAD. Several novel risk loci for AD have been identified recently using the new technology and analytical tools of whole genome association studies. In addition, the successful identification of risk loci in other neurodegenerative disorders has revealed promising new hypotheses for AD, suggesting that variation in the expression levels of APP, PSEN1, PSEN2, and APOE either through cis or trans variation be subjected to further scrutiny in LOAD. Finally, the development of AD biomarkers such as CSF Aβ42 and PIB retention in the brain will refine the AD phenotype providing additional power to detect disease loci. These new methods and hypotheses will accelerate our search for genetic factors and other variants that modify risk for AD.

REFERENCES

Athan ES, Lee JH, Arriaga A, Mayeux RP, Tycko B. 2002. Polymorphisms in the promoter of the human APP gene: functional evaluation and allele frequencies in Alzheimer disease. *Arch Neurol 59*(11):1793-9.

Baker M, Litvan I, Houlden H, Adamson J, Dickson D, Perez-Tur J, Hardy J, Lynch T, Bigio E, Hutton M. 1999. Association of an extended haplotype in the tau gene with progressive supranuclear palsy. *Hum Mol Genet 8*(4):711-5.

Bales KR, Verina T, Dodel RC, Du Y, Altstiel L, Bender M, Hyslop P, Johnstone EM, Little SP, Cummins DJ and others. 1997. Lack of apolipoprotein E dramatically reduces amyloid beta-peptide deposition. *Nat Genet 17*(3):263-4.

Bertram L, Blacker D, Mullin K, Keeney D, Jones J, Basu S, Yhu S, McInnis MG, Go RC, Vekrellis K and others. 2000. Evidence for genetic linkage of Alzheimer's disease to chromosome 10q. *Science 290*(5500):2302-3.

Bertram L, Hiltunen M, Parkinson M, Ingelsson M, Lange C, Ramasamy K, Mullin K, Menon R, Sampson AJ, Hsiao MY and others. 2005. Family-based association between Alzheimer's disease and variants in UBQLN1. *N Engl J Med 352*(9):884-94.

Bertram L, McQueen MB, Mullin K, Blacker D, Tanzi RE. 2007. Systematic meta-analyses of Alzheimer disease genetic association studies: the AlzGene database. *Nat Genet 39*(1):17-23.

Bertram L, Tanzi RE. 2004. Alzheimer's disease: one disorder, too many genes? *Hum Mol Genet 13 Spec* No 1:R135-41.

Bierut LJ, Saccone NL, Rice JP, Goate A, Foroud T, Edenberg H, Almasy L, Conneally PM, Crowe R, Hesselbrock V and others. 2002. Defining alcohol-related phenotypes in humans. The Collaborative Study on the Genetics of Alcoholism. *Alcohol Res Health 26*(3):208-13.

Blacker D, Bertram L, Saunders AJ, Moscarillo TJ, Albert MS, Wiener H, Perry RT, Collins JS, Harrell LE, Go RC and others. 2003. Results of a high-resolution genome screen of 437 Alzheimer's disease families. *Hum Mol Genet 12*(1):23-32.

Blasko I, Lederer W, Oberbauer H, Walch T, Kemmler G, Hinterhuber H, Marksteiner J, Humpel C. 2006. Measurement of thirteen biological markers in CSF of patients with Alzheimer's disease and other dementias. *Dement Geriatr Cogn Disord 21*(1):9-15.

Brookmeyer R, Gray S, Kawas C. 1998. Projections of Alzheimer's disease in the United States and the public health impact of delaying disease onset. *Am J Public Health 88*(9):1337-42.

Brouwers N, Sleegers K, Engelborghs S, Bogaerts V, van Duijn CM, De Deyn PP, Van Broeckhoven C, Dermaut B. 2006. The UBQLN1 polymorphism, UBQ-8i, at 9q22 is not associated with Alzheimer's disease with onset before 70 years. *Neurosci Lett 392*(1-2):72-4.

Chartier-Harlin MC, Kachergus J, Roumier C, Mouroux V, Douay X, Lincoln S, Levecque C, Larvor L, Andrieux J, Hulihan M and others. 2004. Alpha-synuclein locus duplication as a cause of familial Parkinson's disease. *Lancet 364*(9440):1167-9.

Cheng IH, Palop JJ, Esposito LA, Bien-Ly N, Yan F, Mucke L. 2004. Aggressive amyloidosis in mice expressing human amyloid peptides with the Arctic mutation. *Nat Med 10*(11):1190-2.

Chiba-Falek O, Nussbaum RL. 2003. Regulation of alpha-synulcein expression: implications for Parkinson's disease. *Cold Spring Harb Symp Quant Biol* 68:409-15

Citron M, Oltersdorf T, Haass C, McConlogue L, Hung AY, Seubert P, Vigo-Pelfrey C, Lieberburg I, Selkoe DJ. 1992. Mutation of the beta-amyloid precursor protein in familial Alzheimer's disease increases beta-protein production. *Nature 360*(6405):672-4.

Contois JH, Anamani DE, Tsongalis GJ. 1996. The underlying molecular mechanism of apolipoprotein E polymorphism: relationships to lipid disorders, cardiovascular disease, and Alzheimer's disease. *Clin Lab Med 16*(1):105-23.

Corder EH, Saunders AM, Strittmatter WJ, Schmechel DE, Gaskell PC, Small GW, Roses AD, Haines JL, Pericak-Vance MA. 1993. Gene dose of apolipoprotein E type 4 allele and the risk of Alzheimer's disease in late onset families. *Science 261*(5123):921-3.

De Strooper B, Annaert W. 2000. Proteolytic processing and cell biological functions of the amyloid precursor protein. *J Cell Sci 113* (Pt 11):1857-70.

DeMattos RB, Bales KR, Parsadanian M, O'Dell MA, Foss EM, Paul SM, Holtzman DM. 2002. Plaque-associated disruption of CSF and plasma amyloid-beta (Abeta) equilibrium in a mouse model of Alzheimer's disease. *J Neurochem 81*(2):229-36.

Dermaut B, Cruts M, Slooter AJ, Van Gestel S, De Jonghe C, Vanderstichele H, Vanmechelen E, Breteler MM, Hofman A, van Duijn CM and others. 1999. The Glu318Gly substitution in presenilin 1 is not causally related to Alzheimer disease. *Am J Hum Genet 64*(1):290-2.

Ehm MG, Nelson MR, Spurr NK. 2005. Guidelines for conducting and reporting whole genome/large-scale association studies. *Hum Mol Genet 14*(17):2485-8.

Ernst RL, Hay JW. 1994. The US economic and social costs of Alzheimer's disease revisited. *Am J Public Health 84*(8):1261-4.

Ertekin-Taner N, Allen M, Fadale D, Scanlin L, Younkin L, Petersen RC, Graff-Radford N, Younkin SG. 2004. Genetic variants in a haplotype block spanning IDE are significantly associated with plasma Abeta42 levels and risk for Alzheimer disease. *Hum Mutat 23*(4):334-42.

Ertekin-Taner N, Graff-Radford N, Younkin LH, Eckman C, Baker M, Adamson J, Ronald J, Blangero J, Hutton M, Younkin SG. 2000. Linkage of plasma Abeta42 to a quantitative locus on chromosome 10 in late-onset Alzheimer's disease pedigrees. *Science 290*(5500):2303-4.

Ertekin-Taner N, Ronald J, Asahara H, Younkin L, Hella M, Jain S, Gnida E, Younkin S, Fadale D, Ohyagi Y and others. 2003. Fine mapping of the alpha-T catenin gene to a quantitative trait locus on chromosome 10 in late-onset Alzheimer's disease pedigrees. *Hum Mol Genet 12*(23):3133-43.

Ezquerra M, Carnero C, Blesa R, Gelpi JL, Ballesta F, Oliva R. 1999. A presenilin 1 mutation (Ser169Pro) associated with early-onset AD and myoclonic seizures. *Neurology 52*(3):566-70.

Ezquerra M, Lleo A, Castellvi M, Queralt R, Santacruz P, Pastor P, Molinuevo JL, Blesa R, Oliva R. 2003. A novel mutation in the PSEN2 gene (T430M) associated with variable expression in a family with early-onset Alzheimer disease. *Arch Neurol 60*(8):1149-51.

Farrer LA, Bowirrat A, Friedland RP, Waraska K, Korczyn AD, Baldwin CT. 2003. Identification of multiple loci for Alzheimer disease in a consanguineous Israeli-Arab community. *Hum Mol Genet 12*(4):415-22.

Finckh U, van Hadeln K, Muller-Thomsen T, Alberici A, Binetti G, Hock C, Nitsch RM, Stoppe G, Reiss J, Gal A. 2003. Association of late-onset Alzheimer disease with a genotype of PLAU, the gene encoding urokinase-type plasminogen activator on chromosome 10q22.2. *Neurogenetics 4*(4):213-7.

Freeman SH, Raju S, Hyman BT, Frosch MP, Irizarry MC. 2007. Plasma Abeta levels do not reflect brain Abeta levels. *J Neuropathol Exp Neurol 66*(4):264-71.

Frey HJ, Mattila KM, Korolainen MA, Pirttila T. 2005. Problems associated with biological markers of Alzheimer's disease. *Neurochem Res 30*(12):1501-10.

Fryer JD, Taylor JW, DeMattos RB, Bales KR, Paul SM, Parsadanian M, Holtzman DM. 2003. Apolipoprotein E markedly facilitates age-dependent cerebral amyloid angiopathy and spontaneous hemorrhage in amyloid precursor protein transgenic mice. *J Neurosci 23*(21):7889-96.

Fukumoto H, Tennis M, Locascio JJ, Hyman BT, Growdon JH, Irizarry MC. 2003. Age but not diagnosis is the main predictor of plasma amyloid beta-protein levels. *Arch Neurol 60*(7):958-64.

Goate A, Chartier-Harlin MC, Mullan M, Brown J, Crawford F, Fidani L, Giuffra L, Haynes A, Irving N, James L and others. 1991. Segregation of a missense mutation in the amyloid precursor protein gene with familial Alzheimer's disease. *Nature 349*(6311):704-6.

Gorelick PB. 2004. Risk factors for vascular dementia and Alzheimer disease. *Stroke 35*(11 Suppl 1):2620-2.

Grabowski TJ, Cho HS, Vonsattel JP, Rebeck GW, Greenberg SM. 2001. Novel amyloid precursor protein mutation in an Iowa family with dementia and severe cerebral amyloid angiopathy. *Ann Neurol 49*(6):697-705.

Grupe A, Abraham R, Li Y, Rowland C, Hollingworth P, Morgan A, Jehu L, Segurado R, Stone D, Schadt E and others. 2007. Evidence for novel susceptibility genes for late-onset Alzheimer's disease from a genome-wide association study of putative functional variants. *Hum Mol Genet.*

Grupe A, Li Y, Rowland C, Nowotny P, Hinrichs AL, Smemo S, Kauwe JS, Maxwell TJ, Cherny S, Doil L and others. 2006. A scan of chromosome 10 identifies a novel locus showing strong association with late-onset Alzheimer disease. *Am J Hum Genet 78*(1):78-88.

Gustafson L, Brun A, Englund E, Hagnell O, Nilsson K, Stensmyr M, Ohlin AK, Abrahamson M. 1998. A 50-year perspective of a family with chromosome-14-linked Alzheimer's disease. *Hum Genet 102*(3):253-7.

Haass C, Hung AY, Selkoe DJ, Teplow DB. 1994. Mutations associated with a locus for familial Alzheimer's disease result in alternative processing of amyloid beta-protein precursor. *J Biol Chem 269*(26):17741-8.

Hahs DW, McCauley JL, Crunk AE, McFarland LL, Gaskell PC, Jiang L, Slifer SH, Vance JM, Scott WK, Welsh-Bohmer KA and others. 2006. A genome-wide linkage analysis of dementia in the Amish. *Am J Med Genet B Neuropsychiatr Genet 141*(2):160-6.

Hardy J. 2005. Expression of normal sequence pathogenic proteins for neurodegenerative disease contributes to disease risk: 'permissive templating' as a general mechanism underlying neurodegeneration. *Biochem Soc Trans 33*(Pt 4):578-81.

Hattori M, Fujiyama A, Taylor TD, Watanabe H, Yada T, Park HS, Toyoda A, Ishii K, Totoki Y, Choi DK and others. 2000. The DNA sequence of human chromosome 21. *Nature 405*(6784):311-9.

Hebert LE, Scherr PA, Bienias JL, Bennett DA, Evans DA. 2003. Alzheimer disease in the US population: prevalence estimates using the 2000 census. *Arch Neurol 60*(8):1119-22.

Hendriks L, van Duijn CM, Cras P, Cruts M, Van Hul W, van Harskamp F, Warren A, McInnis MG, Antonarakis SE, Martin JJ and others. 1992. Presenile dementia and cerebral haemorrhage linked to a mutation at codon 692 of the beta-amyloid precursor protein gene. *Nat Genet 1*(3):218-21.

Herzig MC, Winkler DT, Burgermeister P, Pfeifer M, Kohler E, Schmidt SD, Danner S, Abramowski D, Sturchler-Pierrat C, Burki K and others. 2004. Abeta is targeted to the vasculature in a mouse model of hereditary cerebral hemorrhage with amyloidosis. *Nat Neurosci 7*(9):954-60.

Holtzman DM, Fagan AM, Mackey B, Tenkova T, Sartorius L, Paul SM, Bales K, Ashe KH, Irizarry MC, Hyman BT. 2000. Apolipoprotein E facilitates neuritic and cerebrovascular plaque formation in an Alzheimer's disease model. *Ann Neurol 47*(6):739-47.

Houlden H, Baker M, Morris HR, MacDonald N, Pickering-Brown S, Adamson J, Lees AJ, Rossor MN, Quinn NP, Kertesz A and others. 2001. Corticobasal degeneration and progressive supranuclear palsy share a common tau haplotype. *Neurology 56*(12):1702-6.

Howson JM, Barratt BJ, Todd JA, Cordell HJ. 2005. Comparison of population- and family-based methods for genetic association analysis in the presence of interacting loci. *Genet Epidemiol 29*(1):51-67.

Hutton M, Lendon CL, Rizzu P, Baker M, Froelich S, Houlden H, Pickering-Brown S, Chakraverty S, Isaacs A, Grover A and others. 1998. Association of missense and 5'-splice-site mutations in tau with the inherited dementia FTDP-17. *Nature 393*(6686):702-5.

Hyman BT. 1992. Down syndrome and Alzheimer disease. *Prog Clin Biol Res 379*:123-42.

Ibanez P, Bonnet AM, Debarges B, Lohmann E, Tison F, Pollak P, Agid Y, Durr A, Brice A. 2004. Causal relation between alpha-synuclein gene duplication and familial Parkinson's disease. *Lancet 364*(9440):1169-71.

Katzov H, Chalmers K, Palmgren J, Andreasen N, Johansson B, Cairns NJ, Gatz M, Wilcock GK, Love S, Pedersen NL and others. 2004. Genetic variants of ABCA1 modify Alzheimer disease risk and quantitative traits related to beta-amyloid metabolism. *Hum Mutat 23*(4):358-67.

Kauwe JS, Jacquart S, Chakraverty S, Wang J, Mayo K, Fagan AM, Holtzman DM, Morris JC, Goate AM. 2007. Extreme cerebrospinal fluid amyloid beta levels identify family with late-onset Alzheimer's disease presenilin 1 mutation. *Ann Neurol 61*(5):446-53.

Kehoe P, Wavrant-De Vrieze F, Crook R, Wu WS, Holmans P, Fenton I, Spurlock G, Norton N, Williams H, Williams N and others. 1999. A full genome scan for late onset Alzheimer's disease. *Hum Mol Genet 8*(2):237-45.

Kida E, Choi-Miura NH, Wisniewski KE. 1995. Deposition of apolipoproteins E and J in senile plaques is topographically determined in both Alzheimer's disease and Down's syndrome brain. *Brain Res 685*(1-2):211-6.

Klunk WE, Engler H, Nordberg A, Wang Y, Blomqvist G, Holt DP, Bergstrom M, Savitcheva I, Huang GF, Estrada S and others. 2004. Imaging brain amyloid in Alzheimer's disease with Pittsburgh Compound-B. *Ann Neurol 55*(3):306-19.

Kounnas MZ, Moir RD, Rebeck GW, Bush AI, Argraves WS, Tanzi RE, Hyman BT, Strickland DK. 1995. LDL receptor-related protein, a multifunctional ApoE receptor, binds secreted beta-amyloid precursor protein and mediates its degradation. *Cell* *82*(2):331-40.

Lahiri DK, Ge YW, Maloney B, Wavrant-De Vrieze F, Hardy J. 2005. Characterization of two APP gene promoter polymorphisms that appear to influence risk of late-onset Alzheimer's disease. *Neurobiol Aging* *26*(10):1329-41.

Lambert JC, Mann DM, Harris JM, Chartier-Harlin MC, Cumming A, Coates J, Lemmon H, StClair D, Iwatsubo T, Lendon C. 2001. The -48 C/T polymorphism in the presenilin 1 promoter is associated with an increased risk of developing Alzheimer's disease and an increased Abeta load in brain. *J Med Genet* *38*(6):353-5.

Laudon H, Hansson EM, Melen K, Bergman A, Farmery MR, Winblad B, Lendahl U, von Heijne G, Naslund J. 2005. A nine-transmembrane domain topology for presenilin 1. *J Biol Chem* *280*(42):35352-60.

Levy E, Carman MD, Fernandez-Madrid IJ, Power MD, Lieberburg I, van Duinen SG, Bots GT, Luyendijk W, Frangione B. 1990. Mutation of the Alzheimer's disease amyloid gene in hereditary cerebral hemorrhage, Dutch type. *Science* *248*(4959):1124-6.

Levy-Lahad E, Wasco W, Poorkaj P, Romano DM, Oshima J, Pettingell WH, Yu CE, Jondro PD, Schmidt SD, Wang K and others. 1995. Candidate gene for the chromosome 1 familial Alzheimer's disease locus. *Science* *269*(5226):973-7.

Lewis J, Dickson DW, Lin WL, Chisholm L, Corral A, Jones G, Yen SH, Sahara N, Skipper L, Yager D and others. 2001. Enhanced neurofibrillary degeneration in transgenic mice expressing mutant tau and APP. *Science* *293*(5534):1487-91.

Li X, Greenwald I. 1996. Membrane topology of the C. elegans SEL-12 presenilin. *Neuron* *17*(5):1015-21.

Li X, Greenwald I. 1997. HOP-1, a Caenorhabditis elegans presenilin, appears to be functionally redundant with SEL-12 presenilin and to facilitate LIN-12 and GLP-1 signaling. *Proc Natl Acad Sci U S A* *94*(22):12204-9.

Li X, Greenwald I. 1998. Additional evidence for an eight-transmembrane-domain topology for Caenorhabditis elegans and human presenilins. *Proc Natl Acad Sci U S A* *95*(12):7109-14.

Li Y, Grupe A, Rowland C, Nowotny P, Kauwe JS, Smemo S, Hinrichs A, Tacey K, Toombs TA, Kwok S and others. 2006. DAPK1 variants are associated with Alzheimer's disease and allele-specific expression. *Hum Mol Genet* *15*(17):2560-8.

Li Y, Nowotny P, Holmans P, Smemo S, Kauwe JS, Hinrichs AL, Tacey K, Doil L, van Luchene R, Garcia V and others. 2004a. Association of late-onset Alzheimer's disease with genetic variation in multiple members of the GAPD gene family. *Proc Natl Acad Sci U S A* *101*(44):15688-93.

Li Y, Tacey K, Doil L, van Luchene R, Garcia V, Rowland C, Schrodi S, Leong D, Lau K, Catanese J and others. 2004b. Association of ABCA1 with late-onset Alzheimer's disease is not observed in a case-control study. *Neurosci Lett* *366*(3):268-71.

Li YJ, Scott WK, Hedges DJ, Zhang F, Gaskell PC, Nance MA, Watts RL, Hubble JP, Koller WC, Pahwa R and others. 2002. Age at onset in two common neurodegenerative diseases is genetically controlled. *Am J Hum Genet* *70*(4):985-93.

Liddell MB, Lovestone S, Owen MJ. 2001. Genetic risk of Alzheimer's disease: advising relatives. *Br J Psychiatry* *178*(1):7-11.

Maraganore DM, de Andrade M, Lesnick TG, Strain KJ, Farrer MJ, Rocca WA, Pant PV, Frazer KA, Cox DR, Ballinger DG. 2005. High-resolution whole-genome association study of Parkinson disease. *Am J Hum Genet 77*(5):685-93.

Mayeux R, Lee JH, Romas SN, Mayo D, Santana V, Williamson J, Ciappa A, Rondon HZ, Estevez P, Lantigua R and others. 2002. Chromosome-12 mapping of late-onset Alzheimer disease among Caribbean Hispanics. *Am J Hum Genet 70*(1):237-43.

Mayeux R, Ottman R, Maestre G, Ngai C, Tang MX, Ginsberg H, Chun M, Tycko B, Shelanski M. 1995. Synergistic effects of traumatic head injury and apolipoprotein-epsilon 4 in patients with Alzheimer's disease. *Neurology 45*(3 Pt 1):555-7.

Mead S, Mahal SP, Beck J, Campbell T, Farrall M, Fisher E, Collinge J. 2001. Sporadic--but not variant--Creutzfeldt-Jakob disease is associated with polymorphisms upstream of PRNP exon 1. *Am J Hum Genet 69*(6):1225-35.

Mintun MA. 2005. Utilizing advanced imaging and surrogate markers across the spectrum of Alzheimer's disease. *CNS Spectr 10*(11 Suppl 18):13-6.

Miravalle L, Tokuda T, Chiarle R, Giaccone G, Bugiani O, Tagliavini F, Frangione B, Ghiso J. 2000. Substitutions at codon 22 of Alzheimer's abeta peptide induce diverse conformational changes and apoptotic effects in human cerebral endothelial cells. *J Biol Chem 275*(35):27110-6.

Myers A, Holmans P, Marshall H, Kwon J, Meyer D, Ramic D, Shears S, Booth J, DeVrieze FW, Crook R and others. 2000. Susceptibility locus for Alzheimer's disease on chromosome 10. *Science 290*(5500):2304-5.

Myers A, Wavrant De-Vrieze F, Holmans P, Hamshere M, Crook R, Compton D, Marshall H, Meyer D, Shears S, Booth J and others. 2002. Full genome screen for Alzheimer disease: stage II analysis. *Am J Med Genet 114*(2):235-44.

Nowotny P, Simcock X, Bertelsen S, Hinrichs AL, Kauwe JS, Mayo K, Smemo S, Morris JC, Goate A. 2007. Association studies testing for risk for late-onset Alzheimer's disease with common variants in the beta-amyloid precursor protein (APP). *Am J Med Genet B Neuropsychiatr Genet.*

Owen F, Poulter M, Shah T, Collinge J, Lofthouse R, Baker H, Ridley R, McVey J, Crow TJ. 1990. An in-frame insertion in the prion protein gene in familial Creutzfeldt-Jakob disease. *Brain Res Mol Brain Res 7*(3):273-6.

Pastor P, Roe CM, Villegas A, Bedoya G, Chakraverty S, Garcia G, Tirado V, Norton J, Rios S, Martinez M and others. 2003. Apolipoprotein Eepsilon4 modifies Alzheimer's disease onset in an E280A PS1 kindred. *Ann Neurol 54*(2):163-9.

Pericak-Vance MA, Bass MP, Yamaoka LH, Gaskell PC, Scott WK, Terwedow HA, Menold MM, Conneally PM, Small GW, Vance JM and others. 1997. Complete genomic screen in late-onset familial Alzheimer disease. Evidence for a new locus on chromosome 12. *Jama 278*(15):1237-41.

Pericak-Vance MA, Grubber J, Bailey LR, Hedges D, West S, Santoro L, Kemmerer B, Hall JL, Saunders AM, Roses AD and others. 2000. Identification of novel genes in late-onset Alzheimer's disease. *Exp Gerontol 35*(9-10):1343-52.

Pericak-Vance MA, Johnson CC, Rimmler JB, Saunders AM, Robinson LC, D'Hondt EG, Jackson CE, Haines JL. 1996. Alzheimer's disease and apolipoprotein E-4 allele in an Amish population. *Ann Neurol 39*(6):700-4.

Poorkaj P, Bird TD, Wijsman E, Nemens E, Garruto RM, Anderson L, Andreadis A, Wiederholt WC, Raskind M, Schellenberg GD. 1998. Tau is a candidate gene for chromosome 17 frontotemporal dementia. *Ann Neurol 43*(6):815-25.

Prasher VP, Farrer MJ, Kessling AM, Fisher EM, West RJ, Barber PC, Butler AC. 1998. Molecular mapping of Alzheimer-type dementia in Down's syndrome. *Ann Neurol 43*(3):380-3.

Rademakers R, Cruts M, Sleegers K, Dermaut B, Theuns J, Aulchenko Y, Weckx S, De Pooter T, Van den Broeck M, Corsmit E and others. 2005. Linkage and association studies identify a novel locus for Alzheimer disease at 7q36 in a Dutch population-based sample. *Am J Hum Genet 77*(4):643-52.

Reiman EM, Chen K, Alexander GE, Caselli RJ, Bandy D, Osborne D, Saunders AM, Hardy J. 2005. Correlations between apolipoprotein E epsilon4 gene dose and brain-imaging measurements of regional hypometabolism. *Proc Natl Acad Sci U S A 102*(23):8299-302.

Risch N, Merikangas K. 1996. The future of genetic studies of complex human diseases. *Science 273*(5281):1516-7.

Ritchie K, Kildea D. 1995. Is senile dementia "age-related" or "ageing-related"?--evidence from meta-analysis of dementia prevalence in the oldest old. *Lancet 346*(8980):931-4.

Rogaev EI, Sherrington R, Rogaeva EA, Levesque G, Ikeda M, Liang Y, Chi H, Lin C, Holman K, Tsuda T and others. 1995. Familial Alzheimer's disease in kindreds with missense mutations in a gene on chromosome 1 related to the Alzheimer's disease type 3 gene. *Nature 376*(6543):775-8.

Rogaeva E, Premkumar S, Song Y, Sorbi S, Brindle N, Paterson A, Duara R, Levesque G, Yu G, Nishimura M and others. 1998. Evidence for an Alzheimer disease susceptibility locus on chromosome 12 and for further locus heterogeneity. *Jama 280*(7):614-8.

Rovelet-Lecrux A, Hannequin D, Raux G, Le Meur N, Laquerriere A, Vital A, Dumanchin C, Feuillette S, Brice A, Vercelletto M and others. 2006. APP locus duplication causes autosomal dominant early-onset Alzheimer disease with cerebral amyloid angiopathy. *Nat Genet 38*(1):24-6.

Scheuner D, Eckman C, Jensen M, Song X, Citron M, Suzuki N, Bird TD, Hardy J, Hutton M, Kukull W and others. 1996. Secreted amyloid beta-protein similar to that in the senile plaques of Alzheimer's disease is increased in vivo by the presenilin 1 and 2 and APP mutations linked to familial Alzheimer's disease. *Nat Med 2*(8):864-70.

Schmechel DE, Saunders AM, Strittmatter WJ, Crain BJ, Hulette CM, Joo SH, Pericak-Vance MA, Goldgaber D, Roses AD. 1993. Increased amyloid beta-peptide deposition in cerebral cortex as a consequence of apolipoprotein E genotype in late-onset Alzheimer disease. *Proc Natl Acad Sci U S A 90*(20):9649-53.

Schupf N, Patel B, Silverman W, Zigman WB, Zhong N, Tycko B, Mehta PD, Mayeux R. 2001. Elevated plasma amyloid beta-peptide 1-42 and onset of dementia in adults with Down syndrome. *Neurosci Lett 301*(3):199-203.

Schutte DL. 2006. Alzheimer disease and genetics: anticipating the questions. *Am J Nurs 106*(12):40-7; quiz 47-8.

Sherrington R, Rogaev EI, Liang Y, Rogaeva EA, Levesque G, Ikeda M, Chi H, Lin C, Li G, Holman K and others. 1995. Cloning of a gene bearing missense mutations in early-onset familial Alzheimer's disease. *Nature 375*(6534):754-60.

Shibata N, Kawarai T, Lee JH, Lee HS, Shibata E, Sato C, Liang Y, Duara R, Mayeux RP, St George-Hyslop PH and others. 2006. Association studies of cholesterol metabolism genes (CH25H, ABCA1 and CH24H) in Alzheimer's disease. *Neurosci Lett 391*(3):142-6.

Sillen A, Forsell C, Lilius L, Axelman K, Bjork BF, Onkamo P, Kere J, Winblad B, Graff C. 2006. Genome scan on Swedish Alzheimer's disease families. *Mol Psychiatry 11*(2):182-6.

Sing CF, Moll PP. 1989. Genetics of variability of CHD risk. *Int J Epidemiol 18*(3 Suppl 1):S183-95.

Singleton AB, Farrer M, Johnson J, Singleton A, Hague S, Kachergus J, Hulihan M, Peuralinna T, Dutra A, Nussbaum R and others. 2003. alpha-Synuclein locus triplication causes Parkinson's disease. *Science 302*(5646):841.

Slifer MA, Martin ER, Haines JL, Pericak-Vance MA. 2005. The ubiquilin 1 gene and Alzheimer's disease. *N Engl J Med 352*(26):2752-3; author reply 2752-3.

Smemo S, Nowotny P, Hinrichs AL, Kauwe JS, Cherny S, Erickson K, Myers AJ, Kaleem M, Marlowe L, Gibson AM and others. 2006. Ubiquilin 1 polymorphisms are not associated with late-onset Alzheimer's disease. *Ann Neurol 59*(1):21-6.

Strittmatter WJ, Saunders AM, Goedert M, Weisgraber KH, Dong LM, Jakes R, Huang DY, Pericak-Vance M, Schmechel D, Roses AD. 1994. Isoform-specific interactions of apolipoprotein E with microtubule-associated protein tau: implications for Alzheimer disease. *Proc Natl Acad Sci U S A 91*(23):11183-6.

Strittmatter WJ, Saunders AM, Schmechel D, Pericak-Vance M, Enghild J, Salvesen GS, Roses AD. 1993. Apolipoprotein E: high-avidity binding to beta-amyloid and increased frequency of type 4 allele in late-onset familial Alzheimer disease. *Proc Natl Acad Sci USA 90*(5):1977-81.

Sunderland T, Linker G, Mirza N, Putnam KT, Friedman DL, Kimmel LH, Bergeson J, Manetti GJ, Zimmermann M, Tang B and others. 2003. Decreased beta-amyloid1-42 and increased tau levels in cerebrospinal fluid of patients with Alzheimer disease. *Jama 289*(16):2094-103.

Tang MX, Stern Y, Marder K, Bell K, Gurland B, Lantigua R, Andrews H, Feng L, Tycko B, Mayeux R. 1998. The APOE-epsilon4 allele and the risk of Alzheimer disease among African Americans, whites, and Hispanics. *Jama 279*(10):751-5.

Theuns J, Brouwers N, Engelborghs S, Sleegers K, Bogaerts V, Corsmit E, De Pooter T, van Duijn CM, De Deyn PP, Van Broeckhoven C. 2006. Promoter mutations that increase amyloid precursor-protein expression are associated with Alzheimer disease. *Am J Hum Genet 78*(6):936-46.

Theuns J, Del-Favero J, Dermaut B, van Duijn CM, Backhovens H, Van den Broeck MV, Serneels S, Corsmit E, Van Broeckhoven CV, Cruts M. 2000. Genetic variability in the regulatory region of presenilin 1 associated with risk for Alzheimer's disease and variable expression. *Hum Mol Genet 9*(3):325-31.

van Duinen SG, Castano EM, Prelli F, Bots GT, Luyendijk W, Frangione B. 1987. Hereditary cerebral hemorrhage with amyloidosis in patients of Dutch origin is related to Alzheimer disease. *Proc Natl Acad Sci U S A 84*(16):5991-4.

Wang JC, Kwon JM, Shah P, Morris JC, Goate A. 2000. Effect of APOE genotype and promoter polymorphism on risk of Alzheimer's disease. *Neurology 55*(11):1644-9.

Watson DJ, Selkoe DJ, Teplow DB. 1999. Effects of the amyloid precursor protein Glu693-->Gln 'Dutch' mutation on the production and stability of amyloid beta-protein. *Biochem J 340* (Pt 3):703-9.

Wisniewski KE, Wisniewski HM, Wen GY. 1985. Occurrence of neuropathological changes and dementia of Alzheimer's disease in Down's syndrome. *Ann Neurol 17*(3):278-82.

Wollmer MA, Streffer JR, Lutjohann D, Tsolaki M, Iakovidou V, Hegi T, Pasch T, Jung HH, Bergmann K, Nitsch RM and others. 2003. ABCA1 modulates CSF cholesterol levels and influences the age at onset of Alzheimer's disease. *Neurobiol Aging 24*(3):421-6.

Wu WS, Holmans P, Wavrant-DeVrieze F, Shears S, Kehoe P, Crook R, Booth J, Williams N, Perez-Tur J, Roehl K and others. 1998. Genetic studies on chromosome 12 in late-onset Alzheimer disease. *Jama 280*(7):619-22.

Xia W, Zhang J, Kholodenko D, Citron M, Podlisny MB, Teplow DB, Haass C, Seubert P, Koo EH, Selkoe DJ. 1997. Enhanced production and oligomerization of the 42-residue amyloid beta-protein by Chinese hamster ovary cells stably expressing mutant presenilins. *J Biol Chem 272*(12):7977-82.

Yoshikai S, Sasaki H, Doh-ura K, Furuya H, Sakaki Y. 1990. Genomic organization of the human amyloid beta-protein precursor gene. *Gene 87*(2):257-63.

Zarranz JJ, Alegre J, Gomez-Esteban JC, Lezcano E, Ros R, Ampuero I, Vidal L, Hoenicka J, Rodriguez O, Atares B and others. 2004. The new mutation, E46K, of alpha-synuclein causes Parkinson and Lewy body dementia. *Ann Neurol 55*(2):164-73.

Zigman WB, Schupf N, Sersen E, Silverman W. 1996. Prevalence of dementia in adults with and without Down syndrome. *Am J Ment Retard 100*(4):403-12.

In: Research Progress in Alzheimer's Disease and Dementia   ISBN 978-1-60021-960-3
Editor: Miao-Kun Sun, pp. 25-58   © 2008 Nova Science Publishers, Inc.

Chapter II

GENE EXPRESSION ABNORMALITIES MARK THE PROGRESSION OF ALZHEIMER'S DISEASE

Stephen D. Ginsberg[1,2,3,*], Shaoli Che[1,2], Scott E. Counts[4] and Elliott J. Mufson[4]

[1]Center for Dementia Research, Nathan Kline Institute, USA;
[2]Department of Psychiatry, [3]Department of Physiology & Neuroscience, New York University School of Medicine, Orangeburg, NY 10962, USA;
[4]Department of Neurological Sciences, Rush University Medical Center, Chicago, IL, USA.

ABSTRACT

Advancements in functional genomics have led to the development of high-throughput gene profiling techniques to quantify expression levels of dozens, to hundreds, to thousands of transcripts simultaneously within discrete brain regions and phenotypically-identified specific individual cell types from animal models of neurodegeneration as well as postmortem human brain tissues from normal people and those with neurodegenerative disorders. A major focus of our ongoing research program is to analyze select classes of genes from homogeneous cell types within a defined region without potential contamination by expression profiles of adjacent neuronal and nonneuronal cells in the brains of subjects with and without neurologic dysfunction. The precise resolution afforded by single cell and population cell RNA analysis in combination with microarrays and real-time quantitative polymerase-chain reaction (qPCR)-based examination allows for relative gene expression level comparisons across cell types under different experimental conditions and during stages of disease progression. Gene expression analysis performed in the hippocampal formation and cholinergic basal forebrain (CBF) from postmortem Alzheimer's disease (AD) brain

---
* Correspondence concerning this article should be addressed to: Dr. Stephen D. Ginsberg, Ph.D., Center for Dementia Research, Nathan Kline Institute, New York University School of Medicine, 140 Old Orangeburg Road, Orangeburg, NY 10962. 845-398-2170 (phone); 845-398-5422 (FAX); ginsberg@nki.rfmh.org.

revealed that selectively vulnerable cell types share putative pathogenetic alterations in similar classes of transcripts that have downstream functional implications for pharmacogenomic development of rational therapies to stall or reverse the progression of dementia. Thus, expression profiles of vulnerable neurons may reveal important clues towards the understanding of the molecular pathogenesis of dementing illness, and aid in identifying mechanisms underlying human neurologic conditions including mild cognitive impairment (MCI) and AD.

Keywords: aging, expression profiling, microarray, mild cognitive impairment, molecular fingerprint, neurodegeneration, qPCR, postmortem human brain, RNA amplification.

ABBREVIATIONS

3Rtau	three-repeat tau
4Rtau	four-repeat tau
AAA-ATPase	ATPase associated with diverse cellular activities
Abeta	amyloid-beta protein
ACTB	beta-actin
AD	Alzheimer's disease
ALS	amyotrophic lateral sclerosis
AO	acridine orange
APP	amyloid-ß protein precursor
aRNA	amplified antisense RNA
BDNF	brain-derived neurotrophic factor
CBF	cholinergic basal forebrain
CHAT	choline acetyltransferase
CREB	cyclic AMP response element binding protein
CTSD	cathepsin D
DS	Down's syndrome
EALS	endosomal-autophagic-lysosomal system
ECD	extracellular domain
ESTs	expressed sequence-tagged cDNAs
FAD	familial forms of Alzheimer's disease
FTLD	frontotemporal lobar degeneration
FTLD-U	frontotemporal lobar degeneration with ubiquitin-positive, tau-negative inclusions
FTDP-17	chromosome 17-linked frontotemporal dementia and parkinsonism
GAPDH	glyceraldehyde-3-phosphate dehydrogenase
GCS	Global Cognitive Score
GluRs	glutamate receptors
HSA 21	human chromosome 21
LCM	laser capture microdissection
mAChRs	muscarinic acetylcholine receptors
MCI	mild cognitive impairment

MMSE	Mini-Mental State Examination
MND	motor neuron disease
nAChRs	nicotinic acetylcholine receptors
NB	nucleus basalis
NFTs	neurofibrillary tangles
NGF	nerve growth factor
NTs	neuropil threads
PGRN	progranulin
PPP2R1B	protein phosphatase 2, regulatory subunit A, beta isoform
PSEN1	presenilin 1
PSEN2	presenilin 2
qPCR	quantitative polymerase-chain reaction
Ribo-SPIA	RNA-based single-primer isothermal amplification
SPs	senile plaques
TDP-43	TAR DNA-binding protein 43
TC	terminal continuation
TK	tyrosine kinase
TS	thioflavine-S
VCP	valosin containing protein
VPS10	vacuolar protein sorting 10

INTRODUCTION

Dementia characterized by memory loss and cognitive decline describes a syndrome associated with a range of diseases that progressively impair brain functions and rob the afflicted of their ability to learn, reason, make judgments, communicate, and carry out activities of daily living. Dementia crosses social, economic, ethnic, or geographical boundaries and the full impact upon society has only begun to be appreciated. Alzheimer's disease (AD) accounts for approximately 50%-60% of all people diagnosed with dementia. Aging is the greatest risk factor for AD. The likelihood of developing AD doubles approximately every five years beginning at the age of 65 and by age 85 the risk of dementia approaches nearly 50% (Evans et al., 1989; Hebert et al., 2001). An estimated 4.5 million Americans have AD and another 19 million have a family member suffering from this disease. These numbers have more than doubled since 1980 and will continue to grow as the percentage of elderly people increases in the USA. It is estimated that the number of individuals with AD could range from 11-16 million by the year 2050. A worldwide estimate of the cost of caring for demented individuals (based upon a demented population of over 29 million people) was approximately 315 billion dollars in 2005 (Wimo et al., 2007), a staggering sum that will only increase with the projected greater census of demented persons in the years to come.

Another clinical pathological entity, termed mild cognitive impairment (MCI), describes a population of people whose memory or other aspects of cognition are not normal but who do not meet the clinical diagnosis of dementia (Petersen, 2004; Winblad et al., 2004). MCI may mark the earliest stages where a person transitions from a normal aging course towards dementia and ultimately AD. Since the duration of dementing illness can vary from 3 to 20 years, it is imperative that we learn more about the molecular pathogenesis underlying the progressive neurodegeneration that leads to AD. This information is crucial for the development of rational therapies that delay the onset and progression of AD and other related dementing illnesses. In these disorders thebiological substrates or mechanisms underlying the loss of specific types of neurons and synapses continue to remain elusive. The overall goal of this research effort is to understand and characterize the molecular and cellular events that cause cell-type specific neuronal damage, or selective vulnerability.

AD is identified clinically by progressive cognitive decline, loss of executive function, and memory deficits eventually leading to incapacitating dementia prior to death. It is characterized pathologically by the deposition of filamentous material in intracellular and extracellular compartments in the form of neurofibrillary tangles (NFTs), neuropil threads (NTs), and senile plaques (SPs), predominantly within areas of the forebrain which include the hippocampus and neocortex (Ginsberg, 2007; Ginsberg et al., 1999b; Mufson et al., 2006; Selkoe, 1997; Trojanowski and Lee, 2005). Although there is widespread decline in various neurotransmitter systems as AD progresses, the most notable and consistent deficits along with associated cell loss are associated with long cholinergic projection neurons arising from the nucleus basalis (NB) (Davies and Maloney, 1976; Mufson et al., 2003; Whitehouse et al., 1982), glutamatergic neurons within the entorhinal cortex and neocortex, (Hyman et al., 1984, 1990), glutamatergic layer II/III and V corticocortical projection neurons of secondary association cortex (Hof and Morrison, 2004; Morrison and Hof, 1992), and the cortical projecting noradrenergic locus coeruleus neurons (Grudzien et al., 2007) leading to regionally-specific connectivity-based synaptic disconnection syndromes. A final diagnosis of AD is based upon a postmortem neuropathologic examination of the patient's brain to determine whether the clinical findings are associated with the presence of abundant SPs and NFTs in select brain regions (Hyman and Trojanowski, 1997; Mirra et al., 1991). Our laboratory and others have developed innovative advances in functional genomics and molecular neuroscience to evaluate the neurodegenerative processes that underlie the pathophysiology of the progression of AD.

GENETICS OF DEMENTING ILLNESS

In the AD field there are numerous reports indicating genetic association with presumed disease susceptibility genes (Bertram et al., 2007). Unfortunately, this literature is extremely confusing, and at present, equivocal in terms of the importance of most of these candidate genes. To date, genetic studies of the familial forms of Alzheimer's disease (FAD) along with the more prevalent sporadic form of AD have demonstrated that the entity designated as AD is a heterogeneous disorder with differing etiologies that share similar clinical and pathological phenotypes (Ginsberg et al., 1999b, 2006b; Skovronsky et al., 2006). In addition to AD, several other neurological disorders display the pathological hallmarks of SP deposition and NFT accumulation. For example, Down's syndrome (DS) patients typically develop AD pathology by their fourth decade of life, and SPs have been identified in DS patients by early adolescence (Hirayama et al., 2003; Leverenz and Raskind, 1998). The coincidence of AD pathology in DS and the localization of the amyloid-beta protein precursor (APP) gene to human chromosome 21 (HSA 21) was one of the initial observations underlying the genetic analyses of FAD on the HSA 21 locus. Triplication of the APP gene appears to be particularly critical for the development of AD in the context of DS. Early onset AD recently has been identified in families in which APP is duplicated along with as few as four additional genes flanking this locus (Rovelet-Lecrux et al., 2006). In DS, the onset of dementia can be promoted by rare APP polymorphisms (Margallo-Lana et al., 2004). Interestingly, in a DS individual with partial trisomy 21 who possessed a normal level of two copies of APP, AD pathology was not found even beyond 78 years of age (Prasher et al., 1998).

Presently, 32 mutations in the APP gene account for a minor percentage of FAD kindreds (27 deemed to be pathogenic; Alzheimer Disease Mutation Database; www.molgen.ua.ac.be/ADMutations), and provide genetic evidence for the abnormal function of APP processing and amyloid-beta protein (Abeta) deposition in the pathogenesis of AD (Goate et al., 1991; Levy et al., 1990; Rovelet-Lecrux et al., 2006; Selkoe, 1996). Furthermore, mice over expressing FAD-related APP transgenes display increased Abeta peptide {particularly Abeta (1-42) production} and plaque deposition (Borchelt et al., 1996; Games et al., 1995; Hsiao et al., 1996). Autosomal dominant mutations in genes encoding presenilin 1 (PSEN1) on HSA 14 and presenilin 2 (PSEN2) on HSA 1 account for the majority of FAD kindreds identified to date (Finckh et al., 2005; Rogaev et al., 1995; Sherrington et al., 1995). PSEN1 and PSEN2 are transmembrane proteins of approximately 50 kDa that share 67% sequence homology, and are localized primarily to the endoplasmic reticulum and Golgi apparatus (Kovacs et al., 1996; Rogaev et al., 1995; Sherrington et al., 1995). PSEN1 is hypothesized to be an integral component of the gamma secretase complex (along with nicastrin, pen-2, and aph-1, among others) that mediates the intramembrane proteolysis of APP to generate Abeta peptides and carboxy-terminal fragments of APP (Iwatsubo, 2004; Pasternak et al., 2003). Cell culture and transgenic mouse studies have also detected an interaction between mutations in the PSEN1 and PSEN2 genes observed in FAD kindreds and increased production of Abeta (1-42) (Borchelt et al., 1996; Citron et al., 1997; Duff et al., 1996). Presently, 165 mutations (4 are non-pathogenic) have been identified within the PSEN1 gene, and 12 mutations (1 non-pathogenic) have been detected in the PSEN2 gene (Alzheimer Disease Mutation Database).

The genetic risk factor with the highest log ratio for the development of AD is the APOE ε4 allele located on HSA 19 which was found to be common to many family members who developed AD late in life (Bennett et al., 2003; Strittmatter and Roses, 1995). Three major alleles have been identified; APOE ε2, ε3, and ε4, with the ε3 allele being the most common. Individuals homozygous for the APOE ε4 allele are more likely to develop sporadic AD or FAD at an earlier age of onset compared to heterozygous individuals or people with no copies of the ε4 allele (Blacker et al., 1997; Corder et al., 1993). A greater APOE ε2 allele dosage may decrease the risk for AD, but is associated with a higher risk of hemorrhage due to cerebral amyloid angiopathy (Corder et al., 1994). APOE is a 34 kDa glycoprotein that is synthesized principally in the liver and functions in lipid transport, notably cholesterol, and metabolic pathways (Mahley, 1988). APOE binds to soluble forms of the Abeta peptide *in vitro*, and isoform-specific interactions have been demonstrated between APOE and amyloid fibril formation (Sanan et al., 1994; Wisniewski et al., 1994). APOE also binds the microtubule-associated protein tau in its nonphosphorylated state *in vitro* in an isoform-specific manner, with the APO ε3 allele binding with a higher affinity to tau than the APO ε4 allele (Strittmatter et al., 1994). The brain is enriched in APOE mRNA and protein, with astrocytes being the primary cell type for protein localization (Corder et al., 1994; Strittmatter et al., 1994). APOE immunoreactivity has also been localized to NFT and SP lesions within the AD brain and other neurodegenerative disorders (Bao et al., 1996; Benzing and Mufson, 1995; Namba et al., 1991). APOE, notably the APO ε4 allele, may act as a pathological chaperone to increase the deposition, or block the reuptake, of soluble Abeta peptides and/or hyperphosphorylated tau.

Converging lines of biochemical, cell biological, epidemiological, and genetic evidence have highlighted the involvement of lipoprotein receptors in the pathogenesis of sporadic AD. LR11, also known as SorLA, is a mosaic receptor member of the vacuolar protein sorting 10 (VPS10) family that contains a cluster of 11 low density lipoprotein receptor type A ligand-binding repeats (Yamazaki et al., 1996). LR11/SorLA is a multifunctional APOE receptor expressed predominantly in brain. LR11/SorLA is encoded by the SORL1 gene, and mapping studies have demonstrated that SORL1 genetic variants are associated with an increased risk of AD (Lee et al., 2007; Rogaeva et al., 2007), making it a promising candidate risk factor for late-onset AD. LR11/SorLA gene expression is down regulated in AD by microarray assessment in postmortem human brains (Scherzer et al., 2004), and further validation at the protein level has demonstrated a very strong association between sporadic AD, but not FAD, and reduced LR11/SorLA protein levels, most notably a preferential loss of LR11/SorLA in regions vulnerable to AD pathology (Dodson et al., 2006; Offe et al., 2006). Moreover, LR11/SorLA has the ability to regulate Abeta levels in cell culture systems, interacts with APP, and alters APP trafficking and processing (Andersen et al., 2006; Offe et al., 2006). LR11/SorLA also colocalizes with endocytic markers, and suggests a mechanism by which this multifunctional mosaic receptor may regulate levels of Abeta by altering the trafficking of APP through the endocytic pathway (Offe et al., 2006). This mechanism is relevant to the pathogenesis of AD, as enlargement of early endosomes in vulnerable cerebral cortex, hippocampal, and cholinergic basal forebrain (CBF) neurons in is one of the earliest known pathologic events in AD (Nixon, 2005; Nixon and Cataldo, 2006). In summary, converging genetic, cell/animal model system, and postmortem human observations suggest that LR11/SorLA may represent an important and novel mediator of AD pathogenesis.

Tau is a low molecular weight microtubule-associated protein found in the central and peripheral nervous system, and is localized primarily to axonal compartments in normal brain (Binder et al., 1985; Couchie et al., 1992). Abnormally phosphorylated tau is observed within neurofibrillary lesions (NFTs, NTs, and dystrophic neurites in corona of SPs) of the AD brain and other tangle-bearing disorders including Pick's disease, progressive supranuclear palsy, and corticobasal degeneration, among others (Ginsberg et al., 1999b; Goedert and Jakes, 2005). Cloning of the tau gene revealed that multiple tau isoforms are produced from a single gene on HSA 17 through alternative mRNA splicing (Goedert et al., 1989a, 1989b). Six isoforms of tau protein are found in the adult human brain: 3 isoforms with 3 tandem microtubule binding repeats {three-repeat tau (3Rtau)} and 3 isoforms with 4 tandem microtubule binding repeats {four-repeat tau (4Rtau)} of 31 or 32 amino acids in the carboxy-terminus of the molecule, and these tandem repeat regions contain microtubule binding domains (Goedert et al., 1989a, 1989b; Goode and Feinstein, 1994). Tau isoforms also differ by 29 or 58 amino acid inserts (0, 1, or 2 inserts) in the amino-terminal region of the molecule (Goedert et al., 1989a, 1989b; Goode and Feinstein, 1994). Tau promotes the polymerization of tubulin monomers into microtubules (Goode and Feinstein, 1994), and phosphorylation negatively regulates tau binding to microtubules (Drecshel et al., 1992). Mutations in the human tau gene have been identified in a group of frontotemporal lobar degeneration (FTLD) cases termed chromosome 17-linked frontotemporal dementia and parkinsonism (FTDP-17) (Goedert and Jakes, 2005; Hutton et al., 1998; Lee et al., 2001; Poorkaj et al., 1998). At present, 62 different mutations (21 non-pathogenic) within the tau gene that cause FTD-17 have been identified (Alzheimer Disease Mutation Database), including missense mutations in exons 9, 10, 12, and 13, as well as point mutations in the 5' splice donor site of exon 10 (Goedert and Jakes, 2005; Ingram and Spillantini, 2002; Mott et al., 2005). Many of these mutations result in the intraneuronal accumulation of hyperphosphorylated tau and NFTs. Neuronal cell loss is also observed, although cell death does not always occur through an NFT-bearing mechanism (Bergmann et al., 1996; Spillantini et al., 1998). FTDP-17 kindreds display a wide phenotypic variety that may reflect the function (i.e., dysfunction, and/or toxic gain of function) of individual tau mutations.

FTLDs are a heterogeneous group of neurodegenerative disorders that are gaining additional recognition due to breakthroughs in the genetics of dementing illness. FTLDs comprise a class of neurodegenerative disorders that is clinically and pathologically distinct from AD, although some individual cases display overlap (Liscic et al., 2007). In fact, FTLD can be mistaken for AD, particularly in its clinical presentation. FTLDs present with diverse clinical, genetic, and neuropathological features, and may account for nearly 20% of early onset dementia cases (McKhann et al., 2001). Using consensus criteria, the FTLDs have been classified into three broad groups: 1) tauopathies (including FTDP-17, see above; Pick's disease, corticobasal degeneration, progressive supranuclear palsy, among others), 2) ubiquitin-positive, tau-negative FTLDs, and 3) FTLDs without discernable pathology (also termed dementia lacking distinctive histopathology) (McKhann et al., 2001). FTLDs tend to manifest with behavioral/emotional problems along with language dysfunction and can present with or without motor neuron disease (MND) leading to cognitive decline and dementia (Josephs et al., 2006; Talbot and Ansorge, 2006). For example, a form of FTLD termed frontotemporal lobar degeneration with ubiquitin-positive, tau-negative inclusions (FTLD-U) is a common pathological hallmark of FTLD with and without MND (Lipton et al., 2004; Mukherjee et al., 2006). Recently, the genetic basis of FTLD-U not linked to tau mutations was discovered with 59 mutations (24 non-pathogenic) (Alzheimer Disease Mutation Database) in the progranulin (PGRN) gene (Baker et al., 2006; Cruts et al., 2006; Gass et al., 2006; Mackenzie et al., 2006). The PGRN gene encodes a precursor glycoprotein which can be cleaved to form a family of small (6 kDa) peptides termed granulins (He and Bateman, 2003). The normative function(s) of PGRN and the granulins in the central nervous system remains unknown. Interestingly, TAR DNA-binding protein 43 (TDP-43), a nuclear protein involved in exon skipping (Ayala et al., 2006; Buratti et al., 2004), has been identified recently as the major pathological hallmark protein of FTLD-U with and without

MND, including familial FTLD-U arising from PRGN mutations as well as FTLD-U arising from rare mutations in the valosin containing protein (VCP), a member of the ATPase associated with diverse cellular activities (AAA-ATPase) family (Forman et al., 2006; Neumann et al., 2006, 2007). The ubiquitinated protein in FTLD-U is not the mutated PRGN or VCP, but TDP-43, making it a pathological hallmark of familial and sporadic forms of FTLD-U, as well as sporadic forms of amyotrophic lateral sclerosis (ALS) (Arai et al., 2006; Neumann et al., 2006). Thus, TDP-43 proteinopathies define a novel class of neurodegenerative entities that are negative for Abeta, tau, and other pathological hallmarks implicated previously in neurodegenerative disorders such as AD and FTDP-17.

REGIONAL GENE EXPRESSION ASSESSMENTS WITHIN THE AD BRAIN

New developments in molecular and cellular approaches to neuroscience have enabled the initiation of high throughput analysis of the aged brain under normative and pathological conditions. To evaluate molecular events associated with the mechanisms underlying the pathobiology of AD and related disorders in animal models of neurodegeneration and human postmortem tissues, microarray analysis along with associated downstream genetic studies are performed at the regional and cellular levels to characterize transcriptional patterns, or mosaics, that may provide insight into some of the mechanism(s) underlying neuropathology. The rationale is to apply high throughput functional genomics and proteomics based approaches to neurodegenerative disease research to develop valid and reliable biomarkers for rational pharmacotherapeutic drug development and disease prevention and/or symptom reduction.

Regional analysis of gene expression is a widely used paradigm due to the relatively large amounts of RNA that can be extracted from carefully dissected frozen tissue from animal models as well as postmortem human brain tissues, as evidenced by reports on amyloid over expression in transgenic mice (Dickey et al., 2003; Reddy et al., 2004; Wu et al., 2006) and several neurodegenerative disorders including AD (Blalock et al., 2004; Brooks et al., 2007; Colangelo et al., 2002; Dunckley et al., 2006; Loring et al., 2001; Lukiw, 2004). An advantage of regional gene expression analysis is that in most cases, extracted RNA is sufficient to generate significant hybridization signal intensity for microarray analysis, enabling the analysis of hundreds to thousands of targets without requiring RNA amplification (Ginsberg et al., 2006d). However, expression profiles garnered from regional dissections cannot discriminate molecular signatures from admixed neuronal populations and nonneuronal populations within the region of interest. Novel and highly effective RNA amplification procedures have been developed to analyze gene expression profiles of single neurons and homogeneous neuronal populations (Che and Ginsberg, 2006; Ginsberg, 2005; Ginsberg et al., 2006d). An advantage of single cell expression profiling and homogeneous population expression profiling is that individual cell types can be identified and microaspirated based upon their signature neurochemical phenotype. For example, CBF neurons (Counts et al., 2006a; Ginsberg et al., 2006a, 2006c; Mufson et al., 2006), midbrain dopaminergic neurons (Fasulo and Hemby, 2003; Greene et al., 2005; Tang et al., 2003), and astrocytes (Burbach et al., 2004a, 2004b) can be demarcated by selective expression of phenotypic markers and isolated for microdissection, RNA amplification, and subsequent microarray analysis. In addition, cells that lack a distinct and/or selective phenotype can be analyzed using a variety of cytomorphological histochemical stains including cresyl violet, hematoxylin & eosin, and thionin (Ginsberg and Che, 2004; Ginsberg et al., 2006d; Kamme et al., 2003; Luo et al., 1999; Vincent et al., 2002) for downstream genetic applications. The ability to differentiate adjacent and admixed cell types is a critical aspect of single cell and population cell microaspiration methodologies, and enables the discrimination of neuronal subtypes as well as neurons from glia, vascular epithelia, and other nonneuronal cell types within the brain.

CELL ACQUISITION FOR FUNCTIONAL GENOMIC APPROACHES

Single cell isolation and homogeneous population cell accrual are ideal for experiments designed to evaluate potential molecular pathogenetic mechanisms underlying the selective vulnerability of specific neuronal populations affected in AD and other neurodegenerative disorders. AD is hypothesized to present clinically once an undetermined threshold number of critical hippocampal, neocortical, and basocortical neurons lose the ability to perform normative functions and subsequently fail to respond to fluctuations in the external and internal milieu (Ginsberg, 2007; Mufson et al., 2006). Degenerating neurons become progressively disconnected from their afferent and efferent projection sites, eventually succumbing to frank neurodegeneration. The brain is a complex structure with heterogeneous neuronal (e.g., principal neurons and interneurons) and nonneuronal cell populations (e.g., glial cells, epithelial cells, inflammatory cells, and vascular elements). The development of a series of molecular and cellular criteria that differentiates selectively vulnerable neurons from relatively spared neurons is critical. An important factor that determines specificity of functional genomics methods is the identification and purity of captured cells for subsequent downstream genetic analyses. As such, single cell and population cell molecular fingerprinting require accurate, nondestructive isolation of cells from optimally prepared tissue sections (Ginsberg et al., 2006b, 2006d; Ginsberg and Mirnics, 2006).

Effective and reproducible microdissection methodologies include laser capture microdissection (LCM) and microaspiration. LCM employs a high-energy laser source that separates desired cells from the remainder of a tissue section, and facilitates transfer of the identified cells to a microfuge tube for downstream genetic analysis (Bonner et al., 1997; Emmert-Buck et al., 1996). There are two principal means of LCM, positive extraction and negative extraction. Positive extraction (a method used by the PixCell IIe from Arcturus) employs a near-infrared laser source directly on the cell(s) of interest for the purpose of microaspiration. Negative extraction (or non-contact laser extraction) procedures employ a laser source to cut around the area of interest within a tissue section, and the microdissected material is catapulted into a microfuge tube (a method utilized by the P.A.L.M. system, P.A.L.M. Microlaser Technologies). Single cells as well as hundreds of cells and other elements can be acquired quickly via LCM. Individual cells and pooled populations of cells can be visualized by immunocytochemical and/or histochemical procedures for optimal identification of specific cells of interest for subsequent downstream genetic analyses including microarray studies and qPCR in animal models of neurodegenerative disorders and postmortem human AD brain tissues (Ginsberg et al., 2006d; Ginsberg and Mirnics, 2006; Lombardino et al., 2006; McClain et al., 2005; Mikulowska-Mennis et al., 2002; Vincent et al., 2002).

Microaspiration is another technique to isolate individual neurons and populations of homogeneous cells. This procedure entails visualizing individual cells or their processes using an inverted microscope workstation connected to a micromanipulator and microcontrolled vacuum source on an air table). Individual cell(s) are patched onto using a microelectrode and excised. Microaspiration results in accurate dissection of the neurons of interest with minimal disruption of the surrounding neuropil (Figure 1) (Ginsberg et al., 1999a, 2000, 2006a, 2006c; Hemby et al., 2002, 2003; Mufson et al., 2002). Microaspiration enables precise dissections of single elements including individual neurons and their processes. Single cells can be used alone, or pooled with other cells for qPCR and/or RNA amplification and subsequent microarray analysis, including analysis of postmortem AD tissues (Counts et al., 2006a; Ginsberg et al., 1999a, 2000, 2004, 2006a, 2006b, 2006c; Mufson et al., 2002, 2006). Microaspiration provides a very accurate dissection of single cells and homogeneous populations of cells, but is more labor intensive than LCM and has a significantly lower throughput potential (Ginsberg et al., 2006d; Ginsberg and Mirnics, 2006).

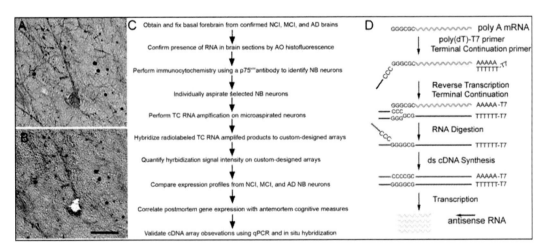

Figure 1. Experimental design, microaspiration, and TC RNA amplification. A. Representative p75[NTR]–immunoreactive NB neuron prior to microaspiration. B. Same tissue section shown in A, illustrating the site of the microaspirated neuron. Scale bar: A-B, 50 um. C. Schematic overview of the experimental design. D. Illustration of the TC RNA amplification method. A TC primer and a poly d(T) primer are added to the mRNA population to be amplified (green rippled line). First strand synthesis (blue line) occurs as an mRNA-cDNA hybrid is formed following reverse transcription. After an RNase H digestion step to remove the original mRNA template strand, second strand synthesis (red line) is performed using *Taq* polymerase. The resultant double stranded (ds) product is utilized as template for *in vitro* transcription, yielding linear RNA amplification of antisense orientation (yellow rippled lines). Adapted from (Ginsberg et al., 2006c).

STRATEGIES FOR RNA AMPLIFICATION

To generate a significant amount of RNA sufficient to perform microarray analysis and other genetic analyses, an RNA amplification technique is often necessary when expression profiling from single neurons, groups of neurons, or microdissected regions. PCR-based amplification methods are not optimal, as exponential amplification can skew the original quantitative relationships between genes from an initial population (Kacharmina et al., 1999). Linear RNA amplification is a strategy that has been used successfully to generate enough input RNA for robust hybridization signal intensity on multiple array platforms. Amplified antisense RNA (aRNA) amplification, developed by Eberwine and colleagues (Eberwine et al., 1992, 2001, 2002) utilizes a T7 RNA polymerase based amplification procedure that enables quantitation of the relative abundance of gene expression levels. aRNA products maintain a proportional representation of the size and complexity of input mRNAs (Eberwine et al., 1992; VanGelder et al., 1990). aRNA synthesis amplifies genetic signals from limited amounts of fresh, frozen, or fixed tissues and cells, and has been used successfully to analyze molecular fingerprints from AD and control neurons including mRNAs accessed from SPs and NFT-bearing neurons (Cheetham et al., 1997; Chow et al., 1998; Ginsberg et al., 1999a, 2000; Hemby et al., 2003). Although the aRNA procedure consists of a complicated series of steps, successful results have been generated with microaspirated animal model and postmortem human brain tissue samples utilizing a wide variety of microarray platforms, and several kits that use aRNA technology to amplify small amounts of RNA are available commercially (Ginsberg, 2005; Ginsberg and Mirnics, 2006).

A new technology for RNA-based single-primer isothermal amplification (Ribo-SPIA) yielding high fidelity RNA amplification for gene expression analysis has been developed by NuGEN, and is of interest to molecular neuroscientists performing microarray evaluations. Ribo-SPIA is a linear RNA amplification procedure that enables the formation of a double stranded cDNA as a substrate for subsequent single-primer isothermal amplification, effectively generating multiple copies of single stranded DNA products that are complementary to the initial input mRNA source without *in vitro* transcription (Dafforn et al., 2004; Kurn et al., 2005). A single Ribo-SPIA amplification can generate amplified RNA for multiple hybridization experiments from less than about five nanograms of total RNA (Dafforn et al., 2004).

A novel methodology termed terminal continuation (TC) RNA amplification has been developed in our laboratory to amplify RNA from minute amounts of starting material (Che and Ginsberg, 2004, 2006; Ginsberg, 2005). In the TC RNA amplification scheme, an RNA synthesis promoter is attached to the 3' and/or 5' region of cDNA utilizing the TC mechanism (Che and Ginsberg, 2004, 2006). The orientation of amplified RNAs is 'antisense', or a novel 'sense' orientation, and one round of TC RNA amplification is sufficient for downstream genetic analyses (Che and Ginsberg, 2004, 2006; Ginsberg and Mirnics, 2006) (Figure 1). TC RNA amplification is utilized for many downstream applications including gene expression profiling, microarray analysis, cDNA library/subtraction library construction, and microRNA profiling. Synthesized sense TC amplified RNA can also be used as a template for *in vitro* protein translation and proteomic applications.

MICROARRAY PLATFORMS

Technical advances have enabled the development of numerous microarray platforms which are the substrate for high throughput analysis of dozens to hundreds to thousands of genes simultaneously. Microarrays represent miniaturized, high-density dot-blots that take advantage of complementary hybridization between nucleic acids (Brown and Botstein, 1999; Eisen and Brown, 1999; Schena et al., 1995). Synthesis of cDNA microarrays entails adhering cDNAs or expressed sequence-tagged cDNAs (ESTs) to solid supports such as glass slides, plastic slides, or nylon membranes. A parallel technology uses photolithography to adhere oligonucleotides to array media (Lockhart et al., 1996). RNA extracted from experimental sources is used to generate labeled probes via biotinylated, fluorescent, or radioactive labeling methods. Arrays are washed to remove nonspecific background hybridization, and imaged using a laser scanner for biotinylated/fluorescently labeled probes and a phosphor imager for radioactively labeled probes. A target-labeled probe complex emits a quantifiable signal that is proportional to the abundance of the labeled probe in the sample. The specific signal intensity (minus background) is expressed as a ratio of the total hybridization signal intensity, reducing variation across array platforms due to differences in specific activity of the probe and absolute quantity of probe present. Quantification of hybridization signal intensity is performed to evaluate relative expression levels of each cDNA, EST, or oligonucleotide feature on the array platform. Gene expression is then assessed using statistical and informatics modules that coordinate statistical analyses. Computational analysis is critical due to the large number of data points that are generated from a single assay (Almudevar et al., 2006; Olson, 2006). An important caveat of microarray analysis is that coordinate changes in proteins encoded by the genes of interest are common, but not absolute (Gygi et al., 1999).

EXPRESSION PROFILE ANALYSIS OF NFTS IN AD HIPPOCAMPAL CA1 NEURONS

The pathogenesis of NFTs in AD and related neurodegenerative disorders remains unknown, and the molecular pathophysiology of these pathologic hallmark lesions is being evaluated in postmortem human brains as well as in animal models of tauopathy (Andorfer et al., 2003; Ginsberg et al., 2000, 2004, 2006a; Gotz et al., 2001; Ramsden et al., 2005). Our research endeavor has employed a single cell microarray analysis paradigm to identify transcripts that are differentially regulated in CA1 neurons that bear NFTs in AD relative to non-tangle bearing CA1 neurons in normal aged control brains. The underlying hypothesis of this work is that alterations in the expression of specific transcripts will reflect mechanisms underlying the formation of NFTs and their biological consequences in affected neurons (Ginsberg, 2007; Ginsberg et al., 2006b; Mufson et al., 2006). The impetus for this functional genomics foray into pathological hallmarks of AD originated from quantitative analysis of hippocampal tissue sections double labeled for acridine orange (AO) histofluorescence, a marker for the presence of RNA species in tissues, and thioflavine-S (TS) demonstrating that approximately 80% of TS labeled NFTs are also AO-positive (Ginsberg et al., 1997, 1998). Single cell microarray analysis was performed using both high-density platforms to identify a wide group of regulated transcripts as well as employing a custom-designed array platform to target several relevant classes of transcripts for a more in depth characterization of AD and control neurons. Notably, total hybridization signal intensity on the custom-designed array platform is down regulated in single AD NFT-bearing neurons compared to normal CA1 neurons by approximately 30% (Ginsberg et al., 2000, 2004), consistent with studies of total polyadenylated mRNA expression in AD using alternate methods (Griffin et al., 1990; Harrison et al., 1991). Single cell microarray results indicate that relative to normal CA1 neurons, NFT-bearing neurons in AD display a significant down regulation in multiple classes of transcripts implicated in the neuropathology of AD including synaptic-related markers, protein phosphatases and kinases, endosomal-autophagic-lysosomal system (EALS) markers, and dopamine receptors, among others (Ginsberg et al., 2000, 2006d).

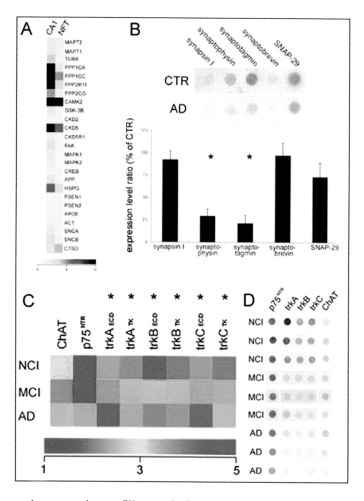

Figure 2. Representative expression profiling results in CA1 pyramidal neurons and CBF neurons. A. Expression profile analysis of select transcripts in NFT-bearing neurons obtained from AD brains in comparison with non-tangle bearing neurons from control brains is depicted in a color-coded dendrogram. Down regulation of several protein phosphatases is observed including protein phosphatase 1 subunits (PPP1CA, PPP1CC) and protein phosphatase 2 subunits (PPP2R1B, PPP2CA).

Down regulation of several kinases (GSK-3B, FAK, MAPK1, and MAPK2), and synaptic-related markers (SNCA, SNCB) are also found. One transcript, the lysosomal hydrolase CTSD, is up regulated in NFT-bearing CA1 neurons in AD brains as compared to non-tangle bearing CA1 neurons in normal control brains. B. Representative gene array (top panel) and histogram (bottom panel) illustrating down-regulation of synaptophysin and synaptotagmin I expression in AD cholinergic NB neurons as compared to aged controls. No alterations in expression levels were seen for synapsin-1, synaptobrevin, or SNAP-29. *, p < .001 via ANOVA with Neuman-Keuls post hoc test for multiple comparisons. C. Expression profile analysis of CHAT, p75[NTR], trkA, trkB, and trkC, derived from individual NBneurons from NCI, MCI, and AD subjects. Dendrogram with a color-coded scale illustrates relative expression levels. No significant differences are found for CHAT and p75[NTR] gene expression. In contrast, statistically significant down regulation (asterisk) of trkA, trkB, and trkC are observed in MCI and AD. ESTs identifying extracellular domain (ECD) and tyrosine kinase (TK) domains display down regulation. The decrement of trk gene expression in MCI is intermediate relative to AD, indicating a step down effect in expression levels from NCI to MCI to AD. D. Representative custom-designed arrays illustrate expression level differences among NCI, MCI, and AD cases for trk levels. Abbreviations: Note the use of the NCBI-Unigene annotation. ACT, alpha-1-antichymotrypsin; APOE, apolipoprotein E; APP, amyloid-beta precursor protein; CAMK2, calcium/calmodulin-dependent protein kinase II, alpha; CDK2, cyclin-dependent kinase 2; CDK5, cyclin-dependent kinase 5; CDK5R1, cyclin-dependent kinase 5, regulatory subunit 1 (p35); CTSD, cathepsin D; CREB, cAMP responsive element binding protein; CTSD, cathepsin D; FAK, focal adhesion kinase; GSK-3B, glycogen synthase kinase-3 beta; HSPG, heparan sulfate proteoglycan; MAPK1, mitogen-activated protein kinase 1 (p44); MAPK2, mitogen-activated protein kinase 2 (p42); MAPT1, three-repeat tau; MAPT2, four-repeat tau; PPP1CA, protein phosphatase 1, catalytic subunit, alpha isoform; PPP1CC, protein phosphatase 1, catalytic subunit, gamma isoform; PPP2R1B, protein phosphatase 2, regulatory subunit A, beta isoform; PPP2CA, protein phosphatase 2, catalytic subunit, alpha isoform; PPP2CG, protein phosphatase 2, catalytic subunit, gamma isoform; PSEN1, presenilin 1; PSEN2, presenilin 2; SNCA, alpha-synuclein; SNCB, beta-synuclein; TUBB, beta-tubulin. Adapted from (Ginsberg and Che, 2004; Ginsberg et al., 2006c).

Synaptic loss is considered one of the hallmark features of AD. In this regard, reduction in gene expression levels of synaptic-related markers occurs consistently in NFT-bearing CA1 neurons, implicating a role for these lesions in synaptic damage. Synaptic-related markers that are down regulated on our array platforms include synaptophysin, synaptotagmin I, synapsin I, α-synuclein, and ß-synuclein (Ginsberg, 2007; Ginsberg et al., 2000, 2004) (Figure 2). These data are consistent with observations that several synaptic-related markers (including synaptophysin) mRNA levels are decreased in the AD hippocampus by qPCR and in situ hybridization (Callahan et al., 1999; Gutala and Reddy, 2004). Moreover, selective down regulation of synaptic-related proteins appears to be an early manifestation of AD, as loss of synaptophysin protein correlates with cognitive decline (Counts et al., 2006b; Heffernan et al., 1998; Shimohama et al., 1997; Sze et al., 1997, 2000).

In addition, mRNAs for protein phosphatase 1 and protein phosphatase 2 subunits displayed significant down regulation in CA1 tangle-bearing neurons as compared to neurons without NFTs, consistent with reports implicating reduced protein phosphatase expression and activity as a potential contributing mechanism towards NFT formation (Liu et al., 2005; Sontag et al., 2004; Vogelsberg-Ragaglia et al., 2001). Notably, down regulation of several independent ESTs linked to a single protein phosphatase subunit mRNA was found, including all five ESTs linked to the protein phosphatase 2, regulatory subunit A, beta isoform (PPP2R1B) on a high-density microarray (Ginsberg et al., 2000). These observations are consistent with a comparable down regulation observed on a custom-designed cDNA array platform (Figure 2) (Ginsberg et al., 2000, 2004, 2006b). Tau hyperphosphorylation in AD and related tauopathies is likely due to dysfunction in protein phosphorylation and dephosphorylation through decreases in protein phosphatase abundance and/or activity, as well as concomitant increases in tau kinases (Goedert et al., 2006; Iqbal and Grundke-Iqbal, 2005; Liu et al., 2005). Importantly, developing pharmacotherapeutic interventions that attenuate abnormal tau hyperphosphorylation through protein phosphatase and/or kinase modulation may become a viable and rational therapy for the treatment of disorders with profuse neurofibrillary pathology including AD and FTLDs.

Activation of cellular programs converging on the EALS pathways is a prominent neuropathological feature of AD and related disorders. Specifically, dysfunction of the endocytic pathway in vulnerable neurons is one of the earliest known intracellular changes occurring in AD and DS (Nixon, 2005; Nixon and Cataldo, 2006). Interestingly, quantitative assessment of high-density cDNA microarrays in our laboratory revealed several ESTs are up regulated in individual NFT-bearing CA1 pyramidal neurons in AD brains as compared to normal CA1 neurons in age-matched control brains, including the lysosomal hydrolase cathepsin D (CTSD) (Ginsberg et al., 2000, 2004). CTSD has been demonstrated to be up regulated in endosomal and lysosomal compartments in AD brain using alternate methods, and may be implicated in the pathogenesis of the disease (Cataldo et al., 1991, 1995, 1997). An approximate two-fold up regulation of CTSD expression is observed on our custom-designed array platform, and hyperphosphorylated tau positive NFTs co-localize with increased CTSD immunoreactivity in the same CA1 neurons (Ginsberg et al., 1999b, 2000, 2006b). These data add to the growing literature on the importance of evaluating the EALS pathway in AD and DS, as endosomal alterations actually precede clinical symptoms of AD and appear prior to abundant amyloid and tau accumulation (Cataldo et al., 2000; Nixon, 2005). Moreover, enlarged endosomes are observed in neurons within adult DS brain, and in distinct populations of cortical neurons in perinatal and infant cases of DS, decades before amyloid and tau pathology become evident (Cataldo et al., 2000).

In terms of chemically-defined neurotransmitter systems affected in single neurons in AD, a 2-4 fold decrease in the expression of the mRNAs for dopamine receptors DRD1-DRD5 and the dopamine transporter is observed in NFT-bearing neurons in AD versus non-tangle bearing neurons in control brains (Ginsberg et al., 2000, 2004, 2006b). These observations are consistent with results displaying decreased dopamine receptor binding and immunocytochemistry in the AD forebrain (Joyce et al., 1993; Kumar and Patel, 2007; Ryoo and Joyce, 1994). Notably, single cell gene expression analysis results illustrate the advantages of employing single cell dopamine receptor mRNA assessments since antibodies and ligand-based studies have not been able to discriminate unequivocally between dopamine receptor subtypes. Furthermore, the effects of aging on dopamine receptor mRNA expression levels in hippocampal CA1 pyramidal neurons and entorhinal cortex layer II stellate cells have been evaluated in a cohort of normal control postmortem human brains aged 19-95 years (Hemby et al., 2003). Results indicate a significant age-related decline for DRD1-DRD5 mRNAs in CA1 pyramidal neurons (Hemby et al., 2003). The down regulation of dopamine receptor subtypes appears to be relatively selective, as no decrement in other mRNAs including beta-actin (ACTB), 3Rtau, and 4Rtau is observed in CA1 pyramidal neurons in the same subjects (Ginsberg, 2007; Hemby et al., 2003). No significant changes in dopamine receptor subtype expression are observed in stellate cells across the same cohort. Deficits in dopaminergic neurotransmission contribute to cognitive decline associated with normal aging in the hippocampus (Amenta et al., 2001; Rinne et al., 1990; Volkow et al., 1998) and may be relevant towards understanding aspects of the pathophysiology associated with attention and memory deficits in progressive, late-onset neurodegenerative disorders such as AD.

EXPRESSION PROFILE ANALYSIS OF SPS

Although extensive analysis of SPs has been performed, little data exists on the non-proteinaceous components of these lesions. The presence of RNA species (including mRNA, rRNA, and tRNA) in SPs was evaluated using AO histofluorescence, alone or in combination with TS staining and immunocytochemistry in AD brains and related neurodegenerative disorders that display abundant SPs (Ginsberg et al., 1997, 1998). Quantitative analysis revealed that approximately 55% of TS-stained SPs also contain AO labeling (Ginsberg et al., 1997, 1998). The sequestration of RNA species to SPs in AD and related disorders prompted single cell analysis of SPs in AD brains. Expression profiles garnered from extracellular SPs was compared to individual CA1 neurons and surrounding neuropil of normal control brains using single cell RNA amplification coupled with custom-designed cDNA array analysis. Results indicate that SPs contain two distinct pools of genes with varying expression levels. One pool of transcripts contains high abundance genes including APP, tau, bcl-2, bax, protein phosphatase subunits, and several ionotropic glutamate receptors (GluRs) (Ginsberg et al., 1999a, 2004, 2006b). A second pool of transcripts contains low abundance genes including neurofilament subunits and glial-enriched mRNAs (e.g., glial fibrillary acidic protein, interleukin-1, and the receptor for advanced glycation end-products) (Ginsberg et al., 1999a, 2004, 2006b). The presence of mRNA species in extracellular SPs was validated by combining TS staining with *in situ* hybridization histochemistry using a probe directed against cyclic AMP response element binding protein (CREB). In addition, a PCR-based strategy was employed to identify APP isoforms from individual SPs (Ginsberg et al., 1999a). These datasets indicate that multiple mRNA species are found in individual, extracellular SPs of the AD hippocampus. Although expression profiles amplified from SPs are predominantly neuronal, relatively low levels of glial-derived mRNAs are found in SPs. However, expression profiling of microglia and astrocytes has been successful in other paradigms (Burbach et al., 2004a, 2004b; Gebicke-Haerter, 2005; Nakagawa and Schwartz, 2004). Furthermore, microglial cells have been identified within SPs, and astrocytes and their processes are observed around SPs (Christie et al., 1996; Ginsberg et al., 1997; Itagaki et al., 1989; Vehmas et al., 2003). In summary, microarray, PCR, and AO histofluorescence observations suggest that SPs sequester the remnants of degenerating neurons (Ginsberg et al., 1999a, 2006b).

SINGLE CELL ANALYSIS OF CBF NEURONS IN AD

CBF neurons of the septal/diagonal band and NB nuclei supply the majority of cholinergic fibers to the hippocampal formation and cerebral cortex, respectively, are a key component of mnemonic and attentional brain circuits, and their degeneration correlates with disease duration and cognitive decline (Auld et al., 2002; Bartus et al., 1982; Baxter and Chiba, 1999; Bierer et al., 1995; Mesulam et al., 1983; Mufson et al., 1989). Progressive pathogenesis of CBF neurons suggests that deficits in basocortical cholinergic neurotransmission contribute to the severe cognitive abnormalities seen in advanced AD (Bartus, 2000; Mufson et al., 2003, 2007; Whitehouse et al., 1982). CBF neurons require primarily nerve growth factor (NGF) and the binding of NGF with the low-affinity pan-neurotrophin receptor p75^{NTR} and the high-affinity receptor tyrosine kinase, trkA, and to a lesser degree, brain-derived neurotrophic factor (BDNF) which binds to the trkB receptor for their survival and biological activity (Kaplan and Miller, 2000; Mufson et al., 2007; Sofroniew et al., 2001). NGF and BDNF are produced by neurons in the hippocampus and neocortex, bind receptors on cholinergic axon terminals, and are retrogradely transported to cholinergic neuron cell bodies located within the basal forebrain (Sofroniew et al., 2001). These receptors mediate the binding, internalization, and retrograde transport of target derived NGF and BDNF from the cortex/hippocampus to CBF consumer neurons (Kaplan and Miller, 2000; Teng and Hempstead, 2004). Since trkA and p75^{NTR} protein levels are reduced within CBF neurons of people with MCI and mild AD, deficits in their gene expression may drive NB neurodegeneration (Counts and Mufson, 2005; Mufson et al., 2006).

A single cell molecular fingerprinting paradigm was performed using individual CBF neurons microaspirated from postmortem tissue samples obtained from 34 subjects clinically characterized antemortem with no cognitive impairment (NCI), MCI, or AD. These cases were obtained from the Religious Orders Study (ROS), an ongoing longitudinal clinicopathological study of aging and dementia in Catholic nuns, priests, and brothers (Bennett et al., 2002; Mufson et al., 2000, 2002, 2006). Single cell acquisition and terminal continuation (TC) RNA amplification was coupled with custom-designed cDNA arrays and validation with real-time qPCR and *in situ* hybridization (Ginsberg, 2005; Ginsberg et al., 2006b; Ginsberg and Mirnics, 2006). Quantitative analysis revealed a significant down regulation of trkA, trkB, and trkC gene expression within individual neurons microaspirated from AD and MCI as compared to NCI (Ginsberg et al., 2006c; Mufson et al., 2007). An intermediate reduction was observed in MCI, with the greatest decrement in AD compared to control NCI subjects. Moreover, down regulation was found for two separate ESTs for each trk gene {e.g., ESTs targeted to the extracellular domain (ECD) and tyrosine kinase (TK) domain} (Figure 2) (Ginsberg et al., 2006c). By contrast, regulation of choline acetyltransferase (CHAT) and glyceraldehyde-3-phosphate dehydrogenase (GAPDH) mRNA was not observed across clinical conditions. These observations indicate a relative selectivity in the alteration of high-affinity neurotrophin receptors within single NB neurons during prodromal stages of AD. Importantly, trkA, trkB, and trkC down regulation are associated with cognitive decline as measured by a Global Cognitive Score (GCS) and the Mini-Mental State Examination (MMSE) (Ginsberg et al., 2006c; Mufson et al., 2007). In contrast, there is a lack of regulation of p75[NTR] expression, and no association between p75[NTR] expression and cognitive decline (Counts et al., 2004; Ginsberg et al., 2006b, 2006c; Mufson et al., 2007). These results suggest that the onset of neurotrophic dysfunction in CBF neurons occurs during the earliest stages of cognitive decline, and that deficits in trk expression are associated with the clinical presentation of the disease. Thus, trk defects may be a biomarker for the transition from NCI to MCI, and from MCI to frank AD.

CBF neurons receive cholinergic inputs and express both nicotinic acetylcholine receptors (nAChRs) and muscarinic acetylcholine receptors (mAChRs) which may play a role in the regulation of NB neuronal activity, particularly during the progression of AD. There is virtually no information detailing whether defects in nAChR and mAChR expression occur in cholinergic NB neurons during disease progression. Individual NB neurons derived from tissue sections obtained postmortem from the ROS cohort were analyzed by single cell molecular fingerprinting using custom-designed microarrays with validation via real-time qPCR. The findings from these experiments indicate that cholinergic NB neurons displayed a significant up regulation of the α7 nicotinic acetylcholine receptor (CHRNA7) expression in AD subjects compared to NCI and MCI (Counts et al., 2007). No differences in gene expression levels were found for other nAChRs (nicotinic acetylcholine receptor alpha subunits α1-α6 and beta subunits ß1-ß4) and mAChRs (muscarinic acetylcholine receptor subunits m1-m5) across the cohort. Moreover, CHRNA7 expression levels were inversely associated with antemortem GCS and MMSE cognitive performance tests (Counts et al., 2007). An advantage of the current paradigm is that the target mAChR and nAChR cDNA sequences on the custom-designed arrays are non-overlapping. This provides optimal receptor subunit specificity and sensitivity, and avoids potential confounds inherent in studies where mAChRs and nAChRs are detected by radioligands which cannot discriminate between individual subunits (Gotti et al., 2006). CHRNA7 up regulation may signal a compensatory response to maintain basocortical cholinergic tone during the progression of AD. Paradoxically, increased CHRNA7 expression may contribute to neurodegeneration observed in AD. Notably, CHRNA7 binds and/or interacts with APP and Abeta peptides (Small et al., 2007; Wang et al., 2000), and cell surface interactions between CHRNA7 and Abeta peptides may promote endocytosis, subsequent intraneuronal Abeta accumulation, and possibly SP formation (Nagele et al., 2002). Thus, CHRNA7 expression may be an early biomarker for the progression of AD, arising as a compensatory neuroprotective response that is offset by interactions with APP and/or Abeta peptides, eventually leading to cholinergic dysfunction.

Attempts to analyze molecular and cellular alterations in specific tau isoforms within vulnerable neuronal populations have been hindered by the lack of antemortem, clinically well-characterized cases. Recently, our group initiated single cell gene expression profiling to assess the expression levels of the six tau isoforms (MAPT1-MAPT6) of CBF neurons within the NB during the course of AD (Counts and Mufson, 2005; Ginsberg et al., 2006a; Mufson et al., 2002). Tau transcript and other cytoskeletal elements (including neurofilament subunits, and tubulin, among others) expression levels did not differ significantly across groups. However, when the ratios of 3Rtau/4Rtau were calculated, a significant difference in the proportion of 3Rtau/4Rtau mRNA was found in MCI and AD relative to NCI. Specifically, a decrement in the expression ratio of 3Rtau relative to 4Rtau was observed in both MCI and AD CBF neurons in all tau transcripts (e.g., 3Rtau/4Rtau 0 amino terminal insert, 1 amino terminal insert, and 2 amino terminal inserts) (Ginsberg et al., 2006a). The shift is due to a decrease in 3Rtau as opposed to an increase in 4Rtau levels. In addition, this shift in 3Rtau/4Rtau ratio was present in NB neurons from MCI and AD, suggesting that tau isoform mRNA dysregulation impacts neuronal function and marks a transition from normal cognition to prodromal AD. There were no differences in total 3Rtau or 4Rtau expression between microaspirated CA1 neurofilament-immunoreactive normal aged control and hyperphosphorylated tau-immunoreactive NFTs from AD brains (Ginsberg et al., 2000, 2006a). Similar to observations within CBF neurons, there was a shift in the 3Rtau/4Rtau ratio in CA1 pyramidal neurons microaspirated from AD brains. In contrast to AD, age related differences within CA1 pyramidal neurons and entorhinal cortex layer II/III stellate cells obtained from a cohort of normal controls aged 19-92 years were not observed in overall tau expression levels or the 3Rtau/4Rtau ratio (Ginsberg et al., 2006a; Hemby et al., 2003). The functional significance for the observed shift in the 3Rtau/4Rtau ratio in vulnerable neurons remains unknown. Studies indicate that 3Rtau and 4Rtau may play different roles in select neurons (King et al., 2000; Levy et al., 2005), and could be dysregulated differentially during the pathogenesis of various neurodegenerative diseases. In summary, these data suggest a subtle, yet pervasive change in gene dosage of 3Rtau and 4Rtau within vulnerable neurons in MCI and AD, which does not occur during normal aging. Shifts in the ratio of tau genes may be a fundamental mechanism whereby normal tau expression is dysregulated, leading to NFT formation.

CONCLUSION

Methodological and technological advancements in functional genomics procedures, including microaspiration, RNA amplification, microarray optimization, and qPCR have led to an increase in the number of studies of single cell gene expression studies within the brain. Notably, simultaneous quantitative assessment of multiple transcripts by microaspiration, RNA amplification, and custom-designed cDNA array analysis provides a paradigm whereby the genetic signature of anatomically defined cells within a specific brain region can be differentiated from neighboring structures (Galvin, 2004; Ginsberg, 2005, 2007; Ginsberg et al., 2006b, 2006d; Ginsberg and Mirnics, 2006). The unprecedented resolution afforded by single cell RNA analysis in combination with microarrays and qPCR-based analyses allows for relative gene expression level comparisons across cell types under different experimental conditions and disease states. Importantly, this technology enables quantitative analyses of vulnerable cell types during the progression of clinical impairment in human neurologic disease. A mosaic of gene expression levels in a homogeneous population of single neurons may be more informative than patterns derived from whole brain or regional tissue dissections, as each neuronal subtype is likely to have a unique molecular signature under normative and pathological conditions. In addition, analysis of single neurons/homogeneous populations avoids potential overlap and intermingling of expression profiles. In this chapter we provide evidence of the ability of single cell mRNA technology to discriminate the genetic signature of projection neurons located in the cholinergic NB during the progression of AD as well as in the hippocampus and entorhinal cortex in aging and AD. In conclusion, single cell mRNA analysis as presented herein has the potential for biomarker detection as well as development of novel pharmacotherapeutic agents that target vulnerable gene(s) and gene products within specific cell types in the aged and diseased brain.

ACKNOWLEDGEMENTS

Support for this project comes from NIH grants NS48447 AG14449, AG10161, AG09466, AG17617, and AG26032 and the Alzheimer's Association. We thank Dr. Melissa J. Alldred, Irina Elarova, Shaona Fang, and Nadeem Muhammad for expert technical assistance. We express our appreciation to the families of the patients studied and to the altruism and support of the hundreds of nuns, priests and brothers participating in the Religious Orders Study. A list of participating groups can be found at the website: http://www.rush.edu/rumc/page-R12394.html.

REFERENCES

Almudevar A, Klebanov LB, Qiu X, Salzman P, Yakovlev AY. 2006. Utility of correlation measures in analysis of gene expression. *NeuroRx 3*:384-395.

Amenta F, Mignini F, Ricci A, Sabbatini M, Tomassoni D, Tayebati SK. 2001. Age-related changes of dopamine receptors in the rat hippocampus: a light microscope autoradiography study. *Mech Ageing Dev 122*:2071-2083.

Andersen OM, Schmidt V, Spoelgen R, Gliemann J, Behlke J, Galatis D, McKinstry WJ, Parker MW, Masters CL, Hyman BT, Cappai R, Willnow TE. 2006. Molecular dissection of the interaction between amyloid precursor protein and its neuronal trafficking receptor SorLA/LR11. *Biochemistry 45*:2618-2628.

Andorfer C, Kress Y, Espinoza M, de Silva R, Tucker KL, Barde Y-A, Duff K, Davies P. 2003. Hyperphosphorylation and aggregation of tau in mice expressing normal human tau isoforms. *J Neurochem 86*:582-590.

Arai T, Hasegawa M, Akiyama H, Ikeda K, Nonaka T, Mori H, Mann D, Tsuchiya K, Yoshida M, Hashizume Y, Oda T. 2006. TDP-43 is a component of ubiquitin-positive tau-negative inclusions in frontotemporal lobar degeneration and amyotrophic lateral sclerosis. *Biochem Biophys Res Commun 351*:602-611.

Auld DS, Kornecook TJ, Bastianetto S, Quirion R. 2002. Alzheimer's disease and the basal forebrain cholinergic system: relations to beta-amyloid peptides, cognition, and treatment strategies. *Prog Neurobiol 68*:209-245.

Ayala YM, Pagani F, Baralle FE. 2006. TDP43 depletion rescues aberrant CFTR exon 9 skipping. *FEBS Lett 580*:1339-1344.

Baker M, Mackenzie IR, Pickering-Brown SM, Gass J, Rademakers R, Lindholm C, Snowden J, Adamson J, Sadovnick AD, Rollinson S, Cannon A, Dwosh E, Neary D, Melquist S, Richardson A, Dickson D, Berger Z, Eriksen J, Robinson T, Zehr C, Dickey CA, Crook R, McGowan E, Mann D, Boeve B, Feldman H, Hutton M. 2006. Mutations in progranulin cause tau-negative frontotemporal dementia linked to chromosome 17. *Nature 442*:916-919.

Bao F, Arai H, Matsushita S, Higuchi S, Sasaki H. 1996. Expression of apolipoprotein E in normal and diverse neurodegenerative disease brain. *Neuroreport 7*:1733-1739.

Bartus RT. 2000. On neurodegenerative diseases, models, and treatment strategies: lessons learned and lessons forgotten a generation following the cholinergic hypothesis. *Exp Neurol 163*:495-529.

Bartus RT, Dean RL, 3rd, Beer B, Lippa AS. 1982. The cholinergic hypothesis of geriatric memory dysfunction. *Science 217*:408-414.

Baxter MG, Chiba AA. 1999. Cognitive functions of the basal forebrain. *Curr Opin Neurobiol 9*:178-183.

Bennett DA, Wilson RS, Schneider JA, Evans DA, Aggarwal NT, Arnold SE, Cochran EJ, Berry-Kravis E, Bienias JL. 2003. Apolipoprotein E epsilon4 allele, AD pathology, and the clinical expression of Alzheimer's disease. *Neurology 60*:246-252.

Bennett DA, Wilson RS, Schneider JA, Evans DA, Beckett LA, Aggarwal NT, Barnes LL, Fox JH, Bach J. 2002. Natural history of mild cognitive impairment in older persons. *Neurology 59*:198-205.

Benzing WC, Mufson EJ. 1995. Apolipoprotein E immunoreactivity within neurofibrillary tangles: relationship to tau and PHF in Alzheimer's disease. *Exp Neurol 132*:162-171.

Bergmann M, Kuchelmeister K, Schmid KW, Kretzschmar HA, Schroder R. 1996. Different variants of frontotemporal dementia: a neuropathological and immunohistochemical study. *Acta Neuropathol (Berl) 92*:170-179.

Bertram L, McQueen MB, Mullin K, Blacker D, Tanzi RE. 2007. Systematic meta-analyses of Alzheimer disease genetic association studies: the AlzGene database. Nat Genet 39:17-23.

Bierer LM, Haroutunian V, Gabriel S, Knott PJ, Carlin LS, Purohit DP, Perl DP, Schmeidler J, Kanof P, Davis KL. 1995. Neurochemical correlates of dementia severity in Alzheimer's disease: relative importance of the cholinergic deficits. *J Neurochem 64*:749-760.

Binder LI, Frankfurter A, Rebhun LI. 1985. The distribution of tau in the mammalian central nervous system. *J Cell Biol 101*:1371-1378.

Blacker D, Haines JL, Rodes L, Terwedow H, Go RC, Harrell LE, Perry RT, Bassett SS, Chase G, Meyers D, Albert MS, Tanzi R. 1997. ApoE-4 and age at onset of Alzheimer's disease: the NIMH genetics initiative. *Neurology 48*:139-147.

Blalock EM, Geddes JW, Chen KC, Porter NM, Markesbery WR, Landfield PW. 2004. Incipient Alzheimer's disease: microarray correlation analyses reveal major transcriptional and tumor suppressor responses. *Proc Natl Acad Sci USA101*:2173-2178.

Bonner RF, Emmert-Buck M, Cole K, Pohida T, Chuaqui R, Goldstein S, Liotta LA. 1997. Laser capture microdissection: molecular analysis of tissue. *Science 278*:1481-1483.

Borchelt DR, Thinakaran G, Eckman CB, Lee MK, Davenport F, Ratovitsky T, Prada C-M, Kim G, Seekins S, Yager D, Slunt HH, Wang R, Seeger M, Levey AI, Gandy SE, Copeland NG, Jenkins NA, Price DL, Younkin SG, Sisodia SS. 1996. Familial Alzheimer's disease-linked presenilin 1 variants elevate Aß1-42/40 ratio in vitro and in vivo. *Neuron 17*:1005-1013.

Brooks WM, Lynch PJ, Ingle CC, Hatton A, Emson PC, Faull RL, Starkey MP. 2007. Gene expression profiles of metabolic enzyme transcripts in Alzheimer's disease. *Brain Res 1127*:127-135.

Brown PO, Botstein D. 1999. Exploring the new world of the genome with DNA microarrays. *Nat Genet 21*:33-37.

Buratti E, Brindisi A, Pagani F, Baralle FE. 2004. Nuclear factor TDP-43 binds to the polymorphic TG repeats in CFTR intron 8 and causes skipping of exon 9: a functional link with disease penetrance. *Am J Hum Genet 74*:1322-1325.

Burbach GJ, Dehn D, Del Turco D, Staufenbiel M, Deller T. 2004a. Laser microdissection reveals regional and cellular differences in GFAP mRNA upregulation following brain injury, axonal denervation, and amyloid plaque deposition. *Glia 48*:76-84.

Burbach GJ, Dehn D, Nagel B, Del Turco D, Deller T. 2004b. Laser microdissection of immunolabeled astrocytes allows quantification of astrocytic gene expression. *J Neurosci Methods 138*:141-148.

Callahan LM, Vaules WA, Coleman PD. 1999. Quantitative decrease in synaptophysin message expression and increase in cathepsin D message expression in Alzheimer disease neurons containing neurofibrillary tangles. *J Neuropathol Exp Neurol 58*:275-287.

Cataldo AM, Barnett JL, Berman SA, Li J, Quarless S, Bursztajn S, Lippa C, Nixon RA. 1995. Gene expression and cellular content of cathepsin D in Alzheimer's disease brain: evidence for early up-regulation of the endosomal-lysosomal system. *Neuron 14*:671-680.

Cataldo AM, Barnett JL, Picroni C, Nixon RA. 1997. Increased neuronal endocytosis and protease delivery to early endosomes in sporadic Alzheimer's disease: neuropathologic evidence for a mechanism of increased ß-amyloidogenesis. *J Neurosci 17*:6142-6151.

Cataldo AM, Paskevich PA, Kominami E, Nixon RA. 1991. Lysosomal hydrolases of different classes are abnormally distributed in brains of patients with Alzheimer disease. *Proc Natl Acad Sci USA 88*:10998-11002.

Cataldo AM, Peterhoff CM, Troncoso JC, Gomez-Isla T, Hyman BT, Nixon RA. 2000. Endocytic pathway abnormalities precede amyloid beta deposition in sporadic Alzheimer's disease and Down syndrome: differential effects of APOE genotype and presenilin mutations. *Am J Pathol 157*:277-286.

Che S, Ginsberg SD. 2004. Amplification of transcripts using terminal continuation. *Lab Invest 84*:131-137.

Che S, Ginsberg SD. 2006. RNA amplification methodologies. In: McNamara PA, editor. *Trends in RNA Research*. Hauppauge: Nova Science Publishing, pp 277-301.

Cheetham JE, Coleman PD, Chow N. 1997. Isolation of single immunohistochemically identified whole neuronal cell bodies from post-mortem human brain for simultaneous analysis of multiple gene expression. *J Neurosci Methods 77*:43-48.

Chow N, Cox C, Callahan LM, Weimer JM, Guo L, Coleman PD. 1998. Expression profiles of multiple genes in single neurons of Alzheimer's disease. *Proc Natl Acad Sci USA 95*:9620-9625.

Christie RH, Freeman M, Hyman BT. 1996. Expression of the macrophage scavenger receptor, a multifunctional lipoprotein receptor, in microglia associated with senile plaques in Alzheimer's disease. *Am J Pathol 148*:399-403.

Citron M, Westaway D, Xia W, Carlson G, Diehl T, Levesque G, Johnson-Wood K, Lee MK, Seubert P, Davis A, Kholodenko D, Motter R, Sherrington R, Perry B, Yao H, Strome R, Lieberburg I, Rommens J, Kim S, Schenk D, Fraser P, St. George-Hyslop P, Selkoe DJ. 1997. Mutant presenilins of Alzheimer's disease increase production of 42-residue amyloid ß-protein in both transfected cells and transgenic mice. *Nature Med 3*:67-72.

Colangelo V, Schurr J, Ball MJ, Pelaez RP, Bazan NG, Lukiw WJ. 2002. Gene expression profiling of 12633 genes in Alzheimer hippocampal CA1: transcription and neurotrophic factor down-regulation and up-regulation of apoptotic and pro-inflammatory signaling. *J Neurosci Res 70*:462-473.

Corder EH, Saunders AM, Risch NJ, Strittmatter WJ, Schmechel DE, Gaskell Jr. PC, Rimmler JB, Locke PA, Conneally PM, Schmader KE, Small GW, Roses AD, Haines JL, Pericak-Vance MA. 1994. Protective effect of apolipoprotein E type 2 allele for late onset Alzheimer disease. *Nature Genet 7*:180-184.

Corder EH, Saunders AM, Strittmatter WJ, Schmechel DE, Gaskell PC, Small GW, Roses AD, Haines JL, Pericak-Vance MA. 1993. Gene dose of apolipoprotein E type 4 allele and the risk of Alzheimer's disease in late onset families. *Science 261*:921-923.

Couchie D, Mavilia C, Georgieff IS, Liem RK, Shelanski ML, Nunez J. 1992. Primary structure of high molecular weight tau present in the peripheral nervous system. *Proc Natl Acad Sci USA 89*:4378-4381.

Counts SE, Chen EY, Che S, Ikonomovic MD, Wuu J, Ginsberg SD, DeKosky ST, Mufson EJ. 2006a. Galanin fiber hypertrophy within the cholinergic nucleus basalis during the progression of Alzheimer's disease. *Dement Geriatr Cogn Disord 21*:205-214.

Counts SE, He B, Che S, Ikonomovic MD, DeKosky ST, Ginsberg SD, Mufson EJ. 2007. a7 nicotinic receptor up-regulation in cholinergic basal forebrain neurons in early stage Alzheimer's disease. *Arch Neurol, in press.*

Counts SE, Mufson EJ. 2005. The role of nerve growth factor receptors in cholinergic basal forebrain degeneration in prodromal Alzheimer's disease. *J Neuropath Exp Neurol 64*:263-272.

Counts SE, Nadeem M, Lad SP, Wuu J, Mufson EJ. 2006b. Differential expression of synaptic proteins in the frontal and temporal cortex of elderly subjects with mild cognitive impairment. *J Neuropathol Exp Neurol 65*:592-601.

Counts SE, Nadeem M, Wuu J, Ginsberg SD, Saragovi HU, Mufson EJ. 2004. Reduction of cortical TrkA but not p75(NTR) protein in early-stage Alzheimer's disease. *Ann Neurol 56*:520-531.

Cruts M, Gijselinck I, van der Zee J, Engelborghs S, Wils H, Pirici D, Rademakers R, Vandenberghe R, Dermaut B, Martin JJ, van Duijn C, Peeters K, Sciot R, Santens P, De Pooter T, Mattheijssens M, Van den Broeck M, Cuijt I, Vennekens K, De Deyn PP, Kumar-Singh S, Van Broeckhoven C. 2006. Null mutations in progranulin cause ubiquitin-positive frontotemporal dementia linked to chromosome 17q21. *Nature 442*:920-924.

Dafforn A, Chen P, Deng G, Herrler M, Iglehart D, Koritala S, Lato S, Pillarisetty S, Purohit R, Wang M, Wang S, Kurn N. 2004. Linear mRNA amplification from as little as 5 ng total RNA for global gene expression analysis. *BioTechniques 37*:854-857.

Davies P, Maloney AJ. 1976. Selective loss of central cholinergic neurons in Alzheimer's disease. *Lancet 2*:1403.

Dickey CA, Loring JF, Montgomery J, Gordon MN, Eastman PS, Morgan D. 2003. Selectively reduced expression of synaptic plasticity-related genes in amyloid precursor protein + presenilin-1 transgenic mice. *J Neurosci 23*:5219-5226.

Dodson SE, Gearing M, Lippa CF, Montine TJ, Levey AI, Lah JJ. 2006. LR11/SorLA expression is reduced in sporadic Alzheimer disease but not in familial Alzheimer disease. *J Neuropathol Exp Neurol 65*:866-872.

Drecshel DN, Hyman AA, Cobb MH, Kirschner M. 1992. Modulation of the dynamic instability of tubulin assembly by the microtubule associated protein tau. *Mol Biol Cell 3*:1147-1154.

Duff K, Eckman C, Zehr C, Yu X, Prada C-M, Perez-tur J, Hutton M, Buee L, Harigaya Y, Yager D, Morgan D, Gordon MN, Holcomb L, Refolo L, Zenk B, Hardy J, Younkin S. 1996. Increased amyloid-ß42(43) in brains of mice expressing mutant presenilin 1. *Nature 383*:710-713.

Dunckley T, Beach TG, Ramsey KE, Grover A, Mastroeni D, Walker DG, LaFleur BJ, Coon KD, Brown KM, Caselli R, Kukull W, Higdon R, McKeel D, Morris JC, Hulette C, Schmechel D, Reiman EM, Rogers J, Stephan DA. 2006. Gene expression correlates of neurofibrillary tangles in Alzheimer's disease. *Neurobiol Aging 27*:1359-1371.

Eberwine J, Belt B, Kacharmina JE, Miyashiro K. 2002. Analysis of subcellularly localized mRNAs using in situ hybridization, mRNA amplification, and expression profiling. *Neurochem Res 27*:1065-1077.

Eberwine J, Kacharmina JE, Andrews C, Miyashiro K, McIntosh T, Becker K, Barrett T, Hinkle D, Dent G, Marciano P. 2001. mRNA expression analysis of tissue sections and single cells. *J Neurosci 21*:8310-8314.

Eberwine J, Yeh H, Miyashiro K, Cao Y, Nair S, Finnell R, Zettel M, Coleman P. 1992. Analysis of gene expression in single live neurons. *Proc Natl Acad Sci USA89*:3010-3014.

Eisen MB, Brown PO. 1999. DNA arrays for analysis of gene expression. *Methods Enzymol 303*:179-205.

Emmert-Buck MR, Bonner RF, Smith PD, Chuaqui RF, Zhuang Z, Goldstein SR, Weiss RA, Liotta LA. 1996. Laser capture microdissection. *Science 274*:998-1001.

Evans DA, Funkenstein HH, Albert MS, Scherr PA, Cook NR, Chown MJ, Hebert LE, Hennekens CH, Taylor JO. 1989. Prevalence of Alzheimer's disease in a community population of older persons. Higher than previously reported. *JAMA 262*:2551-2256.

Fasulo WH, Hemby SE. 2003. Time-dependent changes in gene expression profiles of midbrain dopamine neurons following haloperidol administration. *J Neurochem 87*:205-219.

Finckh U, Kuschel C, Anagnostouli M, Patsouris E, Pantes GV, Gatzonis S, Kapaki E, Davaki P, Lamszus K, Stavrou D, Gal A. 2005. Novel mutations and repeated findings of mutations in familial Alzheimer disease. *Neurogenetics 6*:85-89.

Forman MS, Mackenzie IR, Cairns NJ, Swanson E, Boyer PJ, Drachman DA, Jhaveri BS, Karlawish JH, Pestronk A, Smith TW, Tu PH, Watts GD, Markesbery WR, Smith CD, Kimonis VE. 2006. Novel ubiquitin neuropathology in frontotemporal dementia with valosin-containing protein gene mutations. *J Neuropathol Exp Neurol 65*:571-581.

Galvin JE. 2004. Neurodegenerative diseases: pathology and the advantage of single-cell profiling. *Neurochem Res 29*:1041-1051.

Games D, Adams D, Alessandrini R, Barbour R, Berthelette P, Blackwell C, Carr T, Clemens J, Donaldson T, Gillespie F, Guido T, Hagoplan S, Johnson-Wood K, Khan K, Lee M, Leibowitz P, Lieberburg I, Little S, Masliah E, McConlogue L, Montoya-Zavala M, Mucke L, Paganini L, Penniman E, Power M, Schenk D, Seubert P, Snyder B, Soriano F, Tan H, Vitale J, Wadsworth S, Wolozin B, Zhao J. 1995. Alzheimer-type neuropathology in transgenic mice overexpressing V717F ß-amyloid precursor protein. *Nature 373*:523-527.

Gass J, Cannon A, Mackenzie IR, Boeve B, Baker M, Adamson J, Crook R, Melquist S, Kuntz K, Petersen R, Josephs K, Pickering-Brown SM, Graff-Radford N, Uitti R, Dickson D, Wszolek Z, Gonzalez J, Beach TG, Bigio E, Johnson N, Weintraub S, Mesulam M, White CL, 3rd, Woodruff B, Caselli R, Hsiung GY, Feldman H, Knopman D, Hutton M, Rademakers R. 2006. Mutations in progranulin are a major cause of ubiquitin-positive frontotemporal lobar degeneration. *Hum Mol Genet 15*:2988-3001.

Gebicke-Haerter PJ. 2005. Microarrays and expression profiling in microglia research and in inflammatory brain disorders. *J Neurosci Res 81*:327-341.

Ginsberg SD. 2005. RNA amplification strategies for small sample populations. *Methods 37*:229-237.

Ginsberg SD. 2007. Expression profile analysis of brain aging. In: Riddle DR, editor. *Brain Aging: Models, Methods and Mechanisms*. New York: CRC Press, pp 159-185.

Ginsberg SD, Che S. 2004. Combined histochemical staining, RNA amplification, regional, and single cell analysis within the hippocampus. *Lab Invest 84*:952-962.

Ginsberg SD, Che S, Counts SE, Mufson EJ. 2006a. Shift in the ratio of three-repeat tau and four-repeat tau mRNAs in individual cholinergic basal forebrain neurons in mild cognitive impairment and Alzheimer's disease. *J Neurochem 96*:1401-1408.

Ginsberg SD, Che S, Counts SE, Mufson EJ. 2006b. Single cell gene expression profiling in Alzheimer's disease. *NeuroRx 3*:302-318.

Ginsberg SD, Che S, Wuu J, Counts SE, Mufson EJ. 2006c. Down regulation of trk but not p75 gene expression in single cholinergic basal forebrain neurons mark the progression of Alzheimer's disease. *J Neurochem 97*:475-487.

Ginsberg SD, Crino PB, Hemby SE, Weingarten JA, Lee VM-Y, Eberwine JH, Trojanowski JQ. 1999a. Predominance of neuronal mRNAs in individual Alzheimer's disease senile plaques. *Ann Neurol 45*:174-181.

Ginsberg SD, Crino PB, Lee VM-Y, Eberwine JH, Trojanowski JQ. 1997. Sequestration of RNA in Alzheimer's disease neurofibrillary tangles and senile plaques. *Ann Neurol 41*:200-209.

Ginsberg SD, Elarova I, Ruben M, Tan F, Counts SE, Eberwine JH, Trojanowski JQ, Hemby SE, Mufson EJ, Che S. 2004. Single cell gene expression analysis: implications for neurodegenerative and neuropsychiatric disorders. *Neurochem Res 29*:1054-1065.

Ginsberg SD, Galvin JE, Chiu T-S, Lee VM-Y, Masliah E, Trojanowski JQ. 1998. RNA sequestration to pathological lesions of neurodegenerative disorders. *Acta Neuropathol 96*:487-494.

Ginsberg SD, Hemby SE, Lee VM-Y, Eberwine JH, Trojanowski JQ. 2000. Expression profile of transcripts in Alzheimer's disease tangle-bearing CA1 neurons. *Ann Neurol 48*:77-87.

Ginsberg SD, Hemby SE, Mufson EJ, Martin LJ. 2006d. Cell and tissue microdissection in combination with genomic and proteomic applications. In: Zaborszky L, Wouterlood FG, Lanciego JL, editors. *Neuroanatomical Tract Tracing 3: Molecules, Neurons, and Systems*. New York: Springer, pp. 109-141.

Ginsberg SD, Mirnics K. 2006. Functional genomic methodologies. *Prog Brain Res 158*:15-40.

Ginsberg SD, Schmidt ML, Crino PB, Eberwine JH, Lee VM-Y, Trojanowski JQ. 1999b. Molecular pathology of Alzheimer's disease and related disorders. In: Peters A, Morrison JH, editors. *Cerebral Cortex, vol 14 Neurodegenerative and Age-related Changes in Structure and Function of Cerebral Cortex*. New York: Kluwer Academic/Plenum, pp. 603-653.

Goate A, Chartier-Harlin MC, Mullan M, Brown J, Crawford F, Fidani L, Giuffra L, Haynes A, Irving N, James L, Mant R, Newton P, Rooke K, Roques P, Talbot C, Pericak-Vance M, Roses A, Williamson R, Rossor M, Owen M, Hardy J. 1991. Segregation of a missense mutation in the amyloid precursor protein gene with familial Alzheimer's disease. *Nature 349*:704-706.

Goedert M, Jakes R. 2005. Mutations causing neurodegenerative tauopathies. *Biochim Biophys Acta 1739*:240-250.

Goedert M, Klug A, Crowther RA. 2006. Tau protein, the paired helical filament and Alzheimer's disease. *J Alzheimers Dis 9*:195-207.

Goedert M, Spillantini MG, Jakes R, Rutherford D, Crowther RA. 1989a. Multiple isoforms of human microtubule-associated protein tau: sequences and localization in neurofibrillary tangles of Alzheimer's disease. *Neuron 3*:519-526.

Goedert M, Spillantini MG, Potier MC, Ulrich J, Crowther RA. 1989b. Cloning and sequencing of the cDNA encoding an isoform of microtubule-associated protein tau containing four tandem repeats: differential expression of tau protein mRNAs in human brain. *EMBO J 8*:393-399.

Goode BL, Feinstein SC. 1994. Identification of a novel microtubule binding and assembly domain in the developmentally regulated inter-repeat region of tau. *J Cell Biol 124*:769-782.

Gotti C, Zoli M, Clementi F. 2006. Brain nicotinic acetylcholine receptors: native subtypes and their relevance. *Trends Pharmacol Sci 27*:482-491.

Gotz J, Chen F, Barmettler R, Nitsch RM. 2001. Tau filament formation in transgenic mice expressing P301L tau. *J Biol Chem 276*:529-534.

Greene JG, Dingledine R, Greenamyre JT. 2005. Gene expression profiling of rat midbrain dopamine neurons: implications for selective vulnerability in parkinsonism. *Neurobiol Dis 18*:19-31.

Griffin WS, Ling C, White CL III, Morrison-Bogorad M. 1990. Polyadenylated messenger RNA in paired helical filament-immunoreactive neurons in Alzheimer disease. *Alzheimer Dis Assoc Disord 4*:69-78.

Grudzien A, Shaw P, Weintraub S, Bigio E, Mash DC, Mesulam MM. 2007. Locus coeruleus neurofibrillary degeneration in aging, mild cognitive impairment and early Alzheimer's disease. *Neurobiol Aging 28*:327-335.

Gutala RV, Reddy PH. 2004. The use of real-time PCR analysis in a gene expression study of Alzheimer's disease post-mortem brains. *J Neurosci Methods 132*:101-107.

Gygi SP, Rochon Y, Franza BR, Aebersold R. 1999. Correlation between protein and mRNA abundance in yeast. *Mol Cell Biol 19*:1720-1730.

Harrison PJ, Barton AJ, Najlerahim A, McDonald B, Pearson RC. 1991. Regional and neuronal reductions of polyadenylated messenger RNA in Alzheimer's disease. *Psychol Med 21*:855-866.

He Z, Bateman A. 2003. Progranulin (granulin-epithelin precursor, PC-cell-derived growth factor, acrogranin) mediates tissue repair and tumorigenesis. *J Mol Med 81*:600-612.

Hebert LE, Beckett LA, Scherr PA, Evans DA. 2001. Annual incidence of Alzheimer disease in the United States projected to the years 2000 through 2050. *Alzheimer Dis Assoc Disord 15*:169-173.

Heffernan JM, Eastwood SL, Nagy Z, Sanders MW, McDonald B, Harrison PJ. 1998. Temporal cortex synaptophysin mRNA is reduced in Alzheimer's disease and is negatively correlated with the severity of dementia. *Exp Neurol 150*:235-239.

Hemby SE, Ginsberg SD, Brunk B, Arnold SE, Trojanowski JQ, Eberwine JH. 2002. Gene expression profile for schizophrenia: discrete neuron transcription patterns in the entorhinal cortex. *Arch Gen Psychiat 59*:631-640.

Hemby SE, Trojanowski JQ, Ginsberg SD. 2003. Neuron-specific age-related decreases in dopamine receptor subtype mRNAs. *J Comp Neurol 456*:176-183.

Hirayama A, Horikoshi Y, Maeda M, Ito M, Takashima S. 2003. Characteristic developmental expression of amyloid beta40, 42 and 43 in patients with Down syndrome. *Brain Dev 25*:180-185.

Hof PR, Morrison JH. 2004. The aging brain: morphomolecular senescence of cortical circuits. *Trends Neurosci 27*:607-613.

Hsiao K, Chapman P, Nilsen S, Eckman C, Harigaya Y, Younkin S, Yang F, Cole G. 1996. Correlative memory deficits, Abeta elevation, and amyloid plaques in transgenic mice. *Science 274*:99-102.

Hutton M, Lendon CL, Rizzu P, Baker M, Froelich S, Houlden H, Pickering-Brown S, Chakraverty S, Isaacs A, Grover A, Hackett J, Adamson J, Lincoln S, Dickson D, Davies P, Petersen RC, Stevens M, de Graaff E, Wauters E, van Baren J, Hillebrand M, Joosse M, Kwon JM, Nowotny P, Che LK, Norton J, Morris JC, Reed LA, Trojanowski J, Basun H, Lannfelt L, Neystat M, Fahn S, Dark F, Tannenberg T, Dodd PR, Andreadis A, Snowden J, Craufurd D, Neary D, Owen F, Oostra BA, Hardy J, Goate A, van Swieten H, Mann D, Lynch T, Heutink P. 1998. Association of missense and 5'-splice-site mutations in tau with the inherited dementia FTDP-17. *Nature 393*:702-705.

Hyman BT, Trojanowski JQ. 1997. Consensus recommendations for the postmortem diagnosis of Alzheimer disease from the National Institute on Aging and the Reagan

Institute Working Group on diagnostic criteria for the neuropathological assessment of Alzheimer disease. *J Neuropathol Exp Neurol 56*:1095-1097.

Hyman BT, Van Hoesen GW, Damasio AR. 1990. Memory-related neural systems in Alzheimer's disease: an anatomic study. *Neurology 40*:1721-1730.

Hyman BT, Van Hoesen GW, Damasio AR, Barnes CL. 1984. Alzheimer's disease: cell-specific pathology isolates the hippocampal formation. *Science 225*:1168-1170.

Ingram EM, Spillantini MG. 2002. Tau gene mutations: dissecting the pathogenesis of FTDP-17. *Trends Mol Med 8*:555-562.

Iqbal K, Grundke-Iqbal I. 2005. Metabolic/signal transduction hypothesis of Alzheimer's disease and other tauopathies. *Acta Neuropathol (Berl) 109*:25-31.

Itagaki S, McGeer PL, Akiyama H, Zhu S, Selkoe D. 1989. Relationship of microglia and astrocytes to amyloid deposits of Alzheimer disease. *J Neuroimmunol 24*:173-182.

Iwatsubo T. 2004. The gamma-secretase complex: machinery for intramembrane proteolysis. *Curr Opin Neurobiol 14*:379-383.

Josephs KA, Parisi JE, Knopman DS, Boeve BF, Petersen RC, Dickson DW. 2006. Clinically undetected motor neuron disease in pathologically proven frontotemporal lobar degeneration with motor neuron disease. *Arch Neurol 63*:506-512.

Joyce JN, Kaeger C, Ryoo H, Goldsmith S. 1993. Dopamine D2 receptors in the hippocampus and amygdala in Alzheimer's disease. *Neurosci Lett 154*:171-174.

Kacharmina JE, Crino PB, Eberwine J. 1999. Preparation of cDNA from single cells and subcellular regions. *Methods Enzymol 303*:3-18.

Kamme F, Salunga R, Yu J, Tran DT, Zhu J, Luo L, Bittner A, Guo HQ, Miller N, Wan J, Erlander M. 2003. Single-cell microarray analysis in hippocampus CA1: demonstration and validation of cellular heterogeneity. *J Neurosci 23*:3607-3615.

Kaplan DR, Miller FD. 2000. Neurotrophin signal transduction in the nervous system. *Curr Opin Neurobiol 10*:381-391.

King ME, Gamblin TC, Kuret J, Binder LI. 2000. Differential assembly of human tau isoforms in the presence of arachidonic acid. *J Neurochem 74*:1749-1757.

Kovacs DM, Fausett HJ, Page KJ, Kim T-W, Moir RD, Merriam DE, Hollister RD, Hallmark OG, Mancini R, Felsenstein KM, Hyman BT, Tanzi RE, Wasco W. 1996. Alzheimer-associated presenilins 1 and 2: neuronal expression in brain and localization to intracellular membranes in mammalian cells. *Nature Med 2*:224-229.

Kumar U, Patel SC. 2007. Immunohistochemical localization of dopamine receptor subtypes (D1R-D5R) in Alzheimer's disease brain. *Brain Res 1131*:187-196.

Kurn N, Chen P, Heath JD, Kopf-Sill A, Stephens KM, Wang S. 2005. Novel isothermal, linear nucleic acid amplification systems for highly multiplexed applications. *Clin Chem 51*:1973-1981.

Lee JH, Cheng R, Schupf N, Manly J, Lantigua R, Stern Y, Rogaeva E, Wakutani Y, Farrer L, St George-Hyslop P, Mayeux R. 2007. The association between genetic variants in SORL1 and Alzheimer disease in an urban, multiethnic, community-based cohort. *Arch Neurol 64*:501-506.

Lee VM, Goedert M, Trojanowski JQ. 2001. Neurodegenerative tauopathies. *Annu Rev Neurosci 24*:1121-1159.

Leverenz JB, Raskind MA. 1998. Early amyloid deposition in the medial temporal lobe of young Down syndrome patients: a regional quantitative analysis. *Exp Neurol 150*:296-304.

Levy E, Carman MD, Fernandez-Madrid IJ, Power MD, Lieberburg I, van Duinen SG, Bots GT, Luyendijk W, Frangione B. 1990. Mutation of the Alzheimer's disease amyloid gene in hereditary cerebral hemorrhage, Dutch type. *Science 248*:1124-1126.

Levy SF, Leboeuf AC, Massie MR, Jordan MA, Wilson L, Feinstein SC. 2005. Three- and four-repeat tau regulate the dynamic instability of two distinct microtubule subpopulations in qualitatively different manners. Implications for neurodegeneration. *J Biol Chem 280*:13520-13528.

Lipton AM, White CL, 3rd, Bigio EH. 2004. Frontotemporal lobar degeneration with motor neuron disease-type inclusions predominates in 76 cases of frontotemporal degeneration. *Acta Neuropathol (Berl) 108*:379-385.

Liscic RM, Storandt M, Cairns NJ, Morris JC. 2007. Clinical and psychometric distinction of frontotemporal and Alzheimer dementias. *Arch Neurol 64*:535-540.

Liu F, Grundke-Iqbal I, Iqbal K, Gong CX. 2005. Contributions of protein phosphatases PP1, PP2A, PP2B and PP5 to the regulation of tau phosphorylation. *Eur J Neurosci 22*:1942-1950.

Lockhart DJ, Dong H, Byrne MC, Follettie MT, Gallo MV, Chee MS, Mittmann M, Wang C, Kobayashi M, Horton H, Brown EL. 1996. Expression monitoring by hybridization to high density oligonucleotide arrays. *Nat Biotechnol 14*:1675-1680.

Lombardino AJ, Hertel M, Li XC, Haripal B, Martin-Harris L, Pariser E, Nottebohm F. 2006. Expression profiling of intermingled long-range projection neurons harvested by laser capture microdissection. *J Neurosci Methods 157*:195-207.

Loring JF, Wen X, Lee JM, Seilhamer J, Somogyi R. 2001. A gene expression profile of Alzheimer's disease. *DNA Cell Biol 20*:683-695.

Lukiw WJ. 2004. Gene expression profiling in fetal, aged, and Alzheimer hippocampus: a continuum of stress-related signaling. *Neurochem Res 29*:1287-1297.

Luo L, Salunga RC, Guo H, Bittner A, Joy KC, Galindo JE, Xiao H, Rogers KE, Wan JS, Jackson MR, Erlander MG. 1999. Gene expression profiles of laser-captured adjacent neuronal subtypes. *Nat Med 5*:117-122.

Mackenzie IR, Baker M, Pickering-Brown S, Hsiung GY, Lindholm C, Dwosh E, Gass J, Cannon A, Rademakers R, Hutton M, Feldman HH. 2006. The neuropathology of frontotemporal lobar degeneration caused by mutations in the progranulin gene. *Brain 129*:3081-3090.

Mahley RW. 1988. Apolipoprotein E: cholesterol transport protein with expanding role in cell biology. *Science 240*:622-630.

Margallo-Lana M, Morris CM, Gibson AM, Tan AL, Kay DW, Tyrer SP, Moore BP, Ballard CG. 2004. Influence of the amyloid precursor protein locus on dementia in Down syndrome. *Neurology 62*:1996-1998.

McClain KL, Cai YH, Hicks J, Peterson LE, Yan XT, Che S, Ginsberg SD. 2005. Expression profiling using human tissues in combination with RNA amplification and microarray analysis: assessment of Langerhans cell histiocytosis. *Amino Acids 28*:279-290.

McKhann GM, Albert MS, Grossman M, Miller B, Dickson D, Trojanowski JQ. 2001. Clinical and pathological diagnosis of frontotemporal dementia: report of the Work Group on Frontotemporal Dementia and Pick's Disease. *Arch Neurol 58*:1803-1809.

Mesulam MM, Mufson EJ, Levey AI, Wainer BH. 1983. Cholinergic innervation of cortex by the basal forebrain: cytochemistry and cortical connections of the septal area, diagonal band nuclei, nucleus basalis (substantia innominata), and hypothalamus in the rhesus monkey. *J Comp Neurol 214*:170-197.

Mikulowska-Mennis A, Taylor TB, Vishnu P, Michie SA, Raja R, Horner N, Kunitake ST. 2002. High-quality RNA from cells isolated by laser capture microdissection. *BioTechniques 33*:176-179.

Mirra SS, Heyman A, McKeel D, Sumi SM, Crain BJ, Brownlee LM, Vogel FS, Hughes JP, van Belle G, Berg L. 1991. The Consortium to Establish a Registry for Alzheimer's Disease (CERAD). Part II. Standardization of the neuropathologic assessment of Alzheimer's disease. *Neurology 41*:479-486.

Morrison JH, Hof PR. 1992. The organization of the cerebral cortex: from molecules to circuits. In: Magistretti PJ, editor. *Discussions in Neuroscience, Volume 9*. Geneva: FESN-Elsevier.

Mott RT, Dickson DW, Trojanowski JQ, Zhukareva V, Lee VM, Forman M, Van Deerlin V, Ervin JF, Wang DS, Schmechel DE, Hulette CM. 2005. Neuropathologic, biochemical, and molecular characterization of the frontotemporal dementias. *J Neuropathol Exp Neurol 64*:420-428.

Mufson EJ, Bothwell M, Kordower JH. 1989. Loss of nerve growth factor receptor-containing neurons in Alzheimer's disease: a quantitative analysis across subregions of the basal forebrain. *Exp Neurol 105*:221-232.

Mufson EJ, Counts SE, Che S, Ginsberg SD. 2006. Neuronal gene expression profiling: uncovering the molecular biology of neurodegenerative disease. *Prog Brain Res 158*:197-222.

Mufson EJ, Counts SE, Fahnestock M, Ginsberg SD. 2007. NGF family of neurotrophins and their receptors: early involvement in the progression of Alzheimer's disease. In: Dawbarn D, Allen SJ, editors. *Neurobiology of Alzheimer's Disease*, Third Edition. Oxford: Oxford University Press, pp. 283-321.

Mufson EJ, Counts SE, Ginsberg SD. 2002. Single cell gene expression profiles of nucleus basalis cholinergic neurons in Alzheimer's disease. *Neurochem Res 27*:1035-1048.

Mufson EJ, Ginsberg SD, Ikonomovic MD, DeKosky ST. 2003. Human cholinergic basal forebrain: chemoanatomy and neurologic dysfunction. *J Chem Neuroanat 26*:233-242.

Mufson EJ, Ma SY, Cochran EJ, Bennett DA, Beckett LA, Jaffar S, Saragovi HU, Kordower JH. 2000. Loss of nucleus basalis neurons containing trkA immunoreactivity in individuals with mild cognitive impairment and early Alzheimer's disease. *J Comp Neurol 427*:19-30.

Mukherjee O, Pastor P, Cairns NJ, Chakraverty S, Kauwe JS, Shears S, Behrens MI, Budde J, Hinrichs AL, Norton J, Levitch D, Taylor-Reinwald L, Gitcho M, Tu PH, Tenenholz Grinberg L, Liscic RM, Armendariz J, Morris JC, Goate AM. 2006. HDDD2 is a familial frontotemporal lobar degeneration with ubiquitin-positive, tau-negative inclusions caused by a missense mutation in the signal peptide of progranulin. *Ann Neurol 60*:314-322.

Nagele RG, D'Andrea MR, Anderson WJ, Wang HY. 2002. Intracellular accumulation of beta-amyloid(1-42) in neurons is facilitated by the alpha 7 nicotinic acetylcholine receptor in Alzheimer's disease. *Neuroscience 110*:199-211.

Nakagawa T, Schwartz JP. 2004. Gene expression profiles of reactive astrocytes in dopamine-depleted striatum. *Brain Pathol 14*:275-280.

Namba Y, Tomonaga M, Kawasaki H, Otomo E, Ikeda K. 1991. Apolipoprotein E immunoreactivity in cerebral amyloid deposits and neurofibrillary tangles in Alzheimer's disease and kuru plaque amyloid in Creutzfeldt-Jakob disease. *Brain Res 541*:163-166.

Neumann M, Mackenzie IR, Cairns NJ, Boyer PJ, Markesbery WR, Smith CD, Taylor JP, Kretzschmar HA, Kimonis VE, Forman MS. 2007. TDP-43 in the ubiquitin pathology of frontotemporal dementia with VCP gene mutations. *J Neuropathol Exp Neurol 66*:152-157.

Neumann M, Sampathu DM, Kwong LK, Truax AC, Micsenyi MC, Chou TT, Bruce J, Schuck T, Grossman M, Clark CM, McCluskey LF, Miller BL, Masliah E, Mackenzie IR, Feldman H, Feiden W, Kretzschmar HA, Trojanowski JQ, Lee VM. 2006. Ubiquitinated TDP-43 in frontotemporal lobar degeneration and amyotrophic lateral sclerosis. *Science 314*:130-133.

Nixon RA. 2005. Endosome function and dysfunction in Alzheimer's disease and other neurodegenerative diseases. *Neurobiol Aging 26*:373-382.

Nixon RA, Cataldo AM. 2006. Lysosomal system pathways: genes to neurodegeneration in Alzheimer's disease. *J Alzheimers Dis 9*:277-289.

Offe K, Dodson SE, Shoemaker JT, Fritz JJ, Gearing M, Levey AI, Lah JJ. 2006. The lipoprotein receptor LR11 regulates amyloid beta production and amyloid precursor protein traffic in endosomal compartments. *J Neurosci 26*:1596-1603.

Olson NE. 2006. The microarray data analysis process - from raw data to biological significance. *NeuroRx 3*: 373-383.

Pasternak SH, Bagshaw RD, Guiral M, Zhang S, Ackerley CA, Pak BJ, Callahan JW, Mahuran DJ. 2003. Presenilin-1, nicastrin, amyloid precursor protein, and gamma-secretase activity are co-localized in the lysosomal membrane. *J Biol Chem 278*:26687-26894.

Petersen RC. 2004. Mild cognitive impairment as a diagnostic entity. *J Intern Med 256*:183-194.

Poorkaj P, Bird TD, Wijsman E, Nemens E, Garruto RM, Anderson L, Andreadis A, Wiederholt WC, Raskind M, Schellenberg GD. 1998. Tau is a candidate gene for chromosome 17 frontotemporal dementia. *Ann Neurol 43*:815-825.

Prasher VP, Farrer MJ, Kessling AM, Fisher EM, West RJ, Barber PC, Butler AC. 1998. Molecular mapping of Alzheimer-type dementia in Down's syndrome. *Ann Neurol 43*:380-383.

Ramsden M, Kotilinek L, Forster C, Paulson J, McGowan E, SantaCruz K, Guimaraes A, Yue M, Lewis J, Carlson G, Hutton M, Ashe KH. 2005. Age-dependent neurofibrillary tangle formation, neuron loss, and memory impairment in a mouse model of human tauopathy (P301L). *J Neurosci 25*:10637-10647.

Reddy PH, McWeeney S, Park BS, Manczak M, Gutala RV, Partovi D, Jung Y, Yau V, Searles R, Mori M, Quinn J. 2004. Gene expression profiles of transcripts in amyloid precursor protein transgenic mice: up-regulation of mitochondrial metabolism and apoptotic genes is an early cellular change in Alzheimer's disease. *Hum Mol Genet 13*:1225-1240.

Rinne JO, Lonnberg P, Marjamaki P. 1990. Age-dependent decline in human brain dopamine D1 and D2 receptors. *Brain Res 508*:349-352.

Rogaev EI, Sherrington R, Rogaeva EA, Levesque G, Ikeda M, Liang Y, Chi H, Lin C, Holman K, Tsuda T, Mar L, Sorbi S, Nacmlas B, Placentini S, Amaducci L, Chumakov I, Cohen D, Lannfelt L, Fraser PE, Rommens JM, St. George-Hyslop PH. 1995. Familial Alzheimer's disease in kindreds with missense mutations in a gene on chromosome 1 related to the Alzheimer's disease type 3 gene. *Nature 376*:775-778.

Rogaeva E, Meng Y, Lee JH, Gu Y, Kawarai T, Zou F, Katayama T, Baldwin CT, Cheng R, Hasegawa H, Chen F, Shibata N, Lunetta KL, Pardossi-Piquard R, Bohm C, Wakutani Y, Cupples LA, Cuenco KT, Green RC, Pinessi L, Rainero I, Sorbi S, Bruni A, Duara R, Friedland RP, Inzelberg R, Hampe W, Bujo H, Song YQ, Andersen OM, Willnow TE, Graff-Radford N, Petersen RC, Dickson D, Der SD, Fraser PE, Schmitt-Ulms G, Younkin S, Mayeux R, Farrer LA, St George-Hyslop P. 2007. The neuronal sortilin-related receptor SORL1 is genetically associated with Alzheimer disease. *Nat Genet 39*:168-177.

Rovelet-Lecrux A, Hannequin D, Raux G, Meur NL, Laquerriere A, Vital A, Dumanchin C, Feuillette S, Brice A, Vercelletto M, Dubas F, Frebourg T, Campion D. 2006. APP locus duplication causes autosomal dominant early-onset Alzheimer disease with cerebral amyloid angiopathy. *Nat Genet 38*:24-26.

Ryoo HL, Joyce JN. 1994. Loss of dopamine D2 receptors varies along the rostrocaudal axis of the hippocampal complex in Alzheimer's disease. *J Comp Neurol 348*:94-110.

Sanan DA, Weisgraber K, Russell SJ, Mahley RW, Huang D, Saunders A, Schmechel D, Wisniewski T, Frangione B, Roses AD, Strittmatter WJ. 1994. Apolipoprotein E associates with Aß amyloid peptide to form novel monofibrils: isoform apoE4 associates more efficiently than apoE3. *J Clin Invest 94*:860-869.

Schena M, Shalon D, Davis RW, Brown PO. 1995. Quantitative monitoring of gene expression patterns with a complementary DNA microarray. *Science 270*:467-470.

Scherzer CR, Offe K, Gearing M, Rees HD, Fang G, Heilman CJ, Schaller C, Bujo H, Levey AI, Lah JJ. 2004. Loss of apolipoprotein E receptor LR11 in Alzheimer disease. *Arch Neurol 61*:1200-1205.

Selkoe DJ. 1996. Amyloid-ß-protein and the genetics of Alzheimer's disease. *J Biol Chem 271*:18295-18298.

Selkoe DJ. 1997. Alzheimer's disease: genotypes, phenotypes, and treatments. *Science 275*:630-631.

Sherrington R, Rogaev EI, Liang Y, Rogaeva EA, Levesque G, Ikeda M, Chi H, Lin C, Li G, Holman K, Tsuda T, Mar L, Foncin J-F, Brunl AC, Montesi MP, Sorbi S, Rainero I, Pinessi L, Nee L, Chumakov I, Pollen D, Brookes A, Sanseau P, Pollinsky RJ, Wasco W, Da Silva HAR, Haines JL, Pericak-Vance MA, Tanzi RE, Roses AD, Fraser PE,

Rommens JM, St. George-Hyslop PH. 1995. Cloning of a gene bearing missense mutations in early-onset familial Alzheimer's disease. *Nature 375*:754-760.

Shimohama S, Kamiya S, Taniguchi T, Akagawa K, Kimura J. 1997. Differential involvement of synaptic vesicle and presynaptic plasma membrane proteins in Alzheimer's disease. *Biochem Biophys Res Comm 236*:239-242.

Skovronsky DM, Lee VM-Y, Trojanowski JQ. 2006. Neurodegenerative diseases: new concepts of pathogenesis and their therapeutic implications. *Annu Rev Pathol Mech Dis 1*:151-170.

Small DH, Maksel D, Kerr ML, Ng J, Hou X, Chu C, Mehrani H, Unabia S, Azari MF, Loiacono R, Aguilar MI, Chebib M. 2007. The beta-amyloid protein of Alzheimer's disease binds to membrane lipids but does not bind to the alpha7 nicotinic acetylcholine receptor. *J Neurochem 101:* 1527-1538.

Sofroniew MV, Howe CL, Mobley WC. 2001. Nerve growth factor signaling, neuroprotection, and neural repair. *Annu Rev Neurosci 24*:1217-1281.

Sontag E, Luangpirom A, Hladik C, Mudrak I, Ogris E, Speciale S, White CL III. 2004. Altered expression levels of the protein phosphatase 2A ABalphaC enzyme are associated with Alzheimer disease pathology. *J Neuropathol Exp Neurol 63*:287-301.

Spillantini MG, Bird TD, Ghetti B. 1998. Frontotemporal dementia and Parkinsonism linked to chromosome 17: a new group of tauopathies. *Brain Pathol 8*:387-402.

Strittmatter WJ, Roses AD. 1995. Apolipoprotein E and Alzheimer disease. *Proc Natl Acad Sci USA 92*:4725-4727.

Strittmatter WJ, Saunders AM, Goedert M, Weisgraber KH, Dong L-M, Jakes R, Huang DY, Pericak-Vance M, Schmechel D, Roses AD. 1994. Isoform-specific interactions of apolipoprotein E with microtubule-associated protein tau: implications for Alzheimer's disease. *Proc Natl Acad Sci USA 91*:11183-11186.

Sze CI, Bi H, Kleinschmidt-DeMasters BK, Filley CM, Martin LJ. 2000. Selective regional loss of exocytotic presynaptic vesicle proteins in Alzheimer's disease brains. *J Neurol Sci 175*:81-90.

Sze CI, Troncoso JC, Kawas C, Mouton P, Price DL, Martin LJ. 1997. Loss of the presynaptic vesicle protein synaptophysin in hippocampus correlates with cognitive decline in Alzheimer disease. *J Neuropathol Exp Neurol 56*:933-944.

Talbot K, Ansorge O. 2006. Recent advances in the genetics of amyotrophic lateral sclerosis and frontotemporal dementia: common pathways in neurodegenerative disease. *Hum Mol Genet 15*:R182-R187.

Tang WX, Fasulo WH, Mash DC, Hemby SE. 2003. Molecular profiling of midbrain dopamine regions in cocaine overdose victims. *J Neurochem 85*:911-924.

Teng KK, Hempstead BL. 2004. Neurotrophins and their receptors: signaling trios in complex biological systems. *Cell Mol Life Sci 61*:35-48.

Trojanowski JQ, Lee VM. 2005. The Alzheimer's brain: finding out what's broken tells us how to fix it. *Am J Pathol 167*:1183-1188.

VanGelder R, von Zastrow M, Yool A, Dement W, Barchas J, Eberwine J. 1990. Amplified RNA (aRNA) synthesized from limited quantities of heterogeneous cDNA. *Proc Natl Acad Sci USA87*:1663-1667.

Vehmas AK, Kawas CH, Stewart WF, Troncoso JC. 2003. Immune reactive cells in senile plaques and cognitive decline in Alzheimer's disease. *Neurobiol Aging* 24:321-331.

Vincent VA, DeVoss JJ, Ryan HS, Murphy GM, Jr. 2002. Analysis of neuronal gene expression with laser capture microdissection. *J Neurosci Res 69*:578-586.

Vogelsberg-Ragaglia V, Schuck T, Trojanowski JQ, Lee VM. 2001. PP2A mRNA expression is quantitatively decreased in Alzheimer's disease hippocampus. *Exp Neurol 168*:402-412.

Volkow ND, Wang GJ, Fowler JS, Ding YS, Gur RC, Gatley J, Logan J, Moberg PJ, Hitzemann R, Smith G, Pappas N. 1998. Parallel loss of presynaptic and postsynaptic dopamine markers in normal aging. *Ann Neurol 44*:143-147.

Wang HY, Lee DH, D'Andrea MR, Peterson PA, Shank RP, Reitz AB. 2000. beta-Amyloid(1-42) binds to alpha7 nicotinic acetylcholine receptor with high affinity. Implications for Alzheimer's disease pathology. *J Biol Chem 275*:5626-5632.

Whitehouse PJ, Price DL, Struble RG, Clark AW, Coyle JT, Delong MR. 1982. Alzheimer's disease and senile dementia: loss of neurons in the basal forebrain. *Science 215*:1237-1239.

Wimo A, Winblad B, Jönsson L. 2007. An estimate of the total worldwide societal costs of dementia in 2005. *Alzheimer's & Dementia 3*:81-91.

Winblad B, Palmer K, Kivipelto M, Jelic V, Fratiglioni L, Wahlund LO, Nordberg A, Backman L, Albert M, Almkvist O, Arai H, Basun H, Blennow K, de Leon M, DeCarli C, Erkinjuntti T, Giacobini E, Graff C, Hardy J, Jack C, Jorm A, Ritchie K, van Duijn C, Visser P, Petersen RC. 2004. Mild cognitive impairment--beyond controversies, towards a consensus: report of the International Working Group on Mild Cognitive Impairment. *J Intern Med 256*:240-246.

Wisniewski T, Castano EM, Golabek A, Vogel T, Frangione B. 1994. Acceleration of Alzheimer's fibril formation by apolipoprotein E *in vitro*. *Am J Pathol 145*:1030-1035.

Wu ZL, Ciallella JR, Flood DG, O'Kane TM, Bozyczko-Coyne D, Savage MJ. 2006. Comparative analysis of cortical gene expression in mouse models of Alzheimer's disease. *Neurobiol Aging 27*:377-386.

Yamazaki H, Bujo H, Kusunoki J, Seimiya K, Kanaki T, Morisaki N, Schneider WJ, Saito Y. 1996. Elements of neural adhesion molecules and a yeast vacuolar protein sorting receptor are present in a novel mammalian low density lipoprotein receptor family member. *J Biol Chem 271*:24761-24768.

In: Research Progress in Alzheimer's Disease and Dementia   ISBN 978-1-60021-960-3
Editor: Miao-Kun Sun, pp. 59-77   © 2008 Nova Science Publishers, Inc.

Chapter III

PRESENILINS

Gopal Thinakaran[*]

Departments of Neurobiology, Neurology and Pathology, The University of Chicago, Chicago, IL 60637, U.S.A.

ABSTRACT

Mutations in *PSEN1* and *PSEN2* genes account for the majority of cases of early-onset familial Alzheimer disease. *PSEN* genes encode polytopic membrane proteins termed presenilins, which function as the catalytic subunit of γ-secretase. Sequential cleavage of amyloid precursor protein by BACE and γ-secretase releases highly fibrillogenic β-amyloid peptides, which accumulate in the brains of aged individuals and patients with Alzheimer's disease. Familial Alzheimer's disease-associated presenilin variants are thought to exert their pathogenic function by modulating the relative abundance of Aβ40 and Aβ42 peptides. In addition to amyloid precursor protein, γ-secretase is also responsible for intramembranous proteolysis of wide spectrum of type I membrane protein substrates including Notch receptors. The biology of PS1, its role in γ-secretase activity, and recent developments in the cell biology of PS1 with respect to Alzheimer's disease pathogenesis are discussed here.

INTRODUCTION

Genetic linkage and mutations within homologous genes named *PSEN1* (chromosome 14) and *PSEN2* (chromosome 1) were first identified in 1995 in several early-onset familial Alzheimer's disease (FAD) kindreds (Levy-Lahad et al. 1995; Rogaev et al. 1995; Sherrington et al. 1995). Since then 161 mutations (>355 families) in *PSEN1* and 9 mutations (18 families) in *PSEN2* that co-segregate with FAD have been identified. Mutations in *PSEN*

---

[*] Correspondence concerning this article should be addressed to: Gopal Thinakaran, Department of Neurobiology, The University of Chicago, Knapp R212 924 East 57th street, Chicago, IL. 60637. Phone: (773) 834-3752; Fax: (773) 834-3808; Email: gopal@uchicago.edu.

genes are autosomal dominant, highly penetrant, and cause Alzheimer's disease (AD) symptoms before the age of 65. In general, mutations in *PSEN2* are associated with a later age of onset compared to *PSEN1* (mean familial age of onset 57.1 years and 44.1 years, respectively) and cause slower disease progression (Bertram and Tanzi 2004). Even though FAD-linked mutations in amyloid precursor protein (*APP*) and *PSEN* genes account for less than 5% of total AD cases, the phenocopies of these FAD mutations are reminiscent of late-onset sporadic AD.

PSEN1 and *PSEN2* encode 467 and 448 amino acid-long highly conserved polytopic transmembrane proteins with >65% sequence identity, termed presenilin 1 (PS1) and presenilin 2 (PS2), respectively. Both genes are ubiquitously expressed in the brain and peripheral tissues in adult human and rodent, although *PSEN1* is relatively expressed at higher levels than *PSEN2*. Moreover, *PSEN1* is expressed earlier than *PSEN2* during mouse embryonic development indicating differential regulation of these proteins during development (Lee et al. 1996). As discussed below, PS1 and PS2 are subunits of an enzyme, termed γ-secretase, which cleaves several type I membrane proteins including APP and Notch receptors within their transmembrane domain. In the case of APP, γ-secretase cleavage generates 39-43 amino acid-long β-amyloid peptides (Aβ), which accumulate in the brains of aged individuals and patients with AD. Although the mode of action (gain of function or loss of function) is still being debated, FAD-linked mutations in PS shift the cleavage site in APP in a manner that elevates the levels of highly amyloidogenic Aβ42 peptides and in some cases decrease the levels of the more abundant Aβ40 peptides. Moreover, FAD mutations exhibit partial loss of function in physiological activities associated with other transmembrane substrates. PS have been the focus of much scrutiny because of their central role in AD pathogenesis, and inhibition of γ-secretase activity has been considered as a potential therapeutic target for the treatment of AD. In addition, several studies have identified physiological functions of PS1 beyond AD including apoptosis, calcium homeostasis, neurite outgrowth, and synaptic plasticity [reviewed in (Thinakaran and Parent 2004; Parks and Curtis 2007)]. This chapter mainly focuses on recent advances in the cell biology of PS, and discusses the function of PS as it relates to AD.

PROTEIN TOPOLOGY

Determination of PS protein topology is of particular interest because it may facilitate a better understanding of the structural and functional relationship of γ-secretase activity. The transmembrane (TM) topology of PS1 has long been debated, and a few topology models have been proposed based on different experimental approaches. Most of the studies used antibodies, engineered N-glycosylation acceptor sites, protease digestion, and gene fusions with reporters, to map the cytosolic or lumen regions of the protein. PS1 and PS2 contain ten stretches of hydrophobic residues (HR) that can potentially function as TM domains. An eight TM topology model with N- and C-termini, and a hydrophilic loop domain between TM 6 and 7 facing the cytosol, was originally proposed (Doan et al. 1996). While there is uniform agreement between various models in cytosolic location of the N-terminus and the TM assignments of the first six HR, the models differ with respect to HR seven through ten as membrane spanning domains and the orientation of the C-terminus. In agreement with the eight TM model, recent studies using glycosylation acceptor sequences, amino acid substitutions, and biotinylation strategies confirmed the luminal orientation of the first hydrophilic loop, and cytosolic orientation of N-terminus and the large hydrophilic loop. However, in contrast to the eight TM model, the C-terminus was found oriented to the lumen suggesting that an HR near the C-terminus functions as the ninth TM segment (Laudon et al. 2005; Spasic et al. 2006).

ENDOPROTEOLYSIS OF PRESENILINS AND ACCUMULATION OF STABLE DERIVATIVES

PS1 is synthesized as a 42- to 43-kD polypeptide that undergoes highly regulated endoproteolytic processing within the large cytoplasmic loop domain connecting putative TM segments 6 and 7 to generate stable 27- to 28-kD N-terminal (NTF) and 16- to 17-kD C-terminal (CTF) fragments (Thinakaran et al. 1996) by an uncharacterized proteolytic activity. Endoproteolytic processing of PS is highly conserved during evolution and, perhaps represents a critical event that regulates the stability of PS1 and the biological activity of PS. While the nascent full length PS1 molecule is relatively short-lived with a half-life of 1-2 h, endoproteolytically processed derivatives (NTF and CTF) have a half-life of >24 h (Podlisny et al. 1997; Ratovitski et al. 1997). Moreover, the endoproteolytic event signifies the activation step in the process of PS1 maturation as it assembles with other γ-secretase subunits nicastrin, APH-1, and PEN-2 (described below) (Iwatsubo 2004). Exception to this initial activation event is the maturation of FAD-associated PS1ΔE9 variant, which lacks a region including the endoproteolytic cleavage site encoded by exon 9. PS1ΔE9 holoprotein is metabolically stable, forms a complex with other γ-secretase subunits and generates functional γ-secretase activity.

In transfected cells only a fraction of overexpressed PS1 is converted to stable NTF and CTF, whereas the vast majority of nascent PS1 holoprotein is highly unstable and undergoes rapid degradation. The process of PS1 endoproteolysis is a tightly regulated and saturable event, with PS1 NTF and CTF accumulating in 1:1 stoichiometry (Thinakaran et al. 1996; Thinakaran et al. 1997). Transgenic overexpression of human PS1 in mice replaces endogenous mouse PS1 by a highly selective and compensatory mechanism, and the extent of replacement is proportional to the level of exogenous PS1 (Thinakaran et al. 1996; Thinakaran et al. 1997), because exogenous and endogenous PS compete for limiting levels of the other γ-secretase subunits (discussed below). In cells co-expressing PS1 and PS2, the assemblies consist of either of PS1 derivatives or PS2 derivatives but not mixed assemblies (for example, PS1NTF•PS2CTF). However, expression of chimeric PS1/PS2 holoprotein is endoproteolysed and forms heteromeric assemblies made of PS1NTF.PS2CTF (Saura et al. 1999). Furthermore, exogenous PS1 NTF does not co-assemble with endogenous PS1 CTF. Nevertheless, co-expression of exogenous NTF and CTF can reconstitute functional γ-secretase in PS-deficient cells (Laudon et al. 2004; Stromberg et al. 2005). These findings indicate that association between N- and C-terminal domains of PS1 holoprotein occurs prior to endoproteolysis; and following assembly, PS-derived NTF/CTF do not exchange between γ-secretase complexes containing either PS1 or PS2.

Experimental deletion and replacement mutants and domain swap experiments have been useful in identifying amino acid residues that are critical for PS1 endoproteolysis as well as γ-secretase activity. Deletions and substitutions near the putative endoproteolytic cleavage sites between Thr291 and Ala299 (Podlisny et al. 1997) abolished PS1 endoproteolysis, but the resulting stable holoprotein still retained γ-secretase activity (Steiner et al. 1999). In contrast, aspartate residues at position D275 (in TM6) and D385 (in TM7) of PS1 are critical for both PS1 endoproteolysis and γ-secretase function (Wolfe et al. 1999). Furthermore, residues critical for both PS1 endoproteolysis and γ-secretase activity have been identified within TM1 of PS1 (Brunkan et al. 2005). These findings have been inconclusive with reference to the correspondence between PS endoproteolysis and γ-secretase activities. With a few exceptions, well-characterized and highly potent γ-secretase inhibitors do not affect PS1 endoproteolysis, providing more definite proof that PS endoproteolysis and γ-secretase activity are pharmacologically distinct (Beher et al. 2001). The enzyme activity responsible for PS1 endoproteolysis has not been identified. Based on the available data one cannot exclude the possibility that PS1 endoproteolysis may be an autocatalytic event, which occurs during the maturation of unstable nascent PS1 holoprotein into stable derivatives. Clues from deletion analysis of domains far from the endoproteolytic site are consistent with a potential conformational change associated with PS1 endoproteolysis and maturation. For example, deletion of TM1 through TM2 (PS1ΔM12) resulted in an endoproteolysis-defective mutant, which unlike PS1 holoprotein is extremely stable (Leem et al. 2002). Interestingly, a large hydrophilic loop domain connecting the TM domain 6 and 7 (residues 304-371) of PS1, which includes a caspase cleavage site (D345) and serves as the interaction domain for several PS-associated proteins, is dispensable for PS1 endoproteolysis and γ-secretase activity (Saura et al. 2000).

INTRAMEMBRANOUS PROTEOLYSIS OF TYPE I MEMBRANE PROTEINS

In the past few years there has been accumulating interest in understanding regulated cleavage of type I membrane proteins within their transmembrane domains. Aβ40 and Aβ42 peptides are released from APP by intramembranous cleavage at two major sites within the TM. In keeping with the nomenclature of previously described α- and β-secretase cleavage of APP within the extracellular domain, the intramembranous cleavage of APP was termed the "γ-secretase" cleavage. The realization that cleavage at one of the sites that corresponds to +42 residue of Aβ is enhanced 2-fold in FAD cases (Scheuner et al. 1996) led to increased scrutiny of this cleavage process. De Strooper and colleagues first reported a direct role for PS1 in γ-secretase cleavage when they noted loss of Aβ secretion and accumulation of APP C-terminal fragments (CTF) in *PS1*[-/-] neurons (De Strooper et al. 1998). Soon after, a striking similarity emerged between PS-mediated cleavage of APP and the proteolytic activation of Notch receptor (De Strooper et al. 1999; Struhl and Greenwald 1999; Mumm et al. 2000). In both cases, membrane tethered CTFs, rather than the full-length proteins, serve as the substrates for γ-secretase cleavage. Struhl and Adachi systematically examined the requirements for γ-secretase cleavage and concluded that PS1 can mediate sequence-independent cleavage of a diverse set of transmembrane proteins with short extracellular domains. Consistent with an ectodomain shedding event immediately preceding γ-secretase cleavage of APP and Notch, the cleavage efficiency of experimental transmembrane proteins was found inversely proportional to the length of their extracellular domain (Struhl and Adachi 2000).

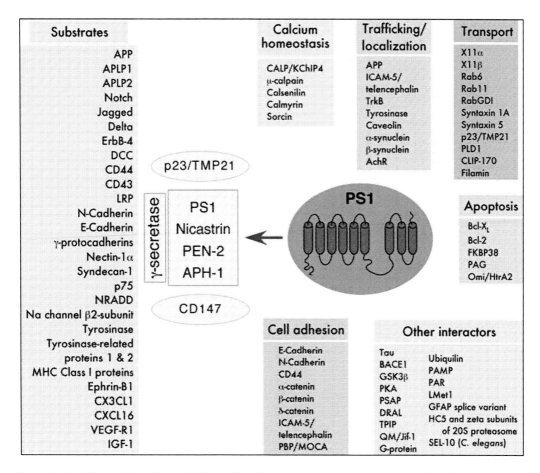

Figure.1. Multifaceted functions of PS1 mediated through the interacting proteins. The figure represents the multiple roles of PS1 in cellular functions. PS1 associates with nicastrin, APH-1 and PEN-2 to form the γ-secretase, which cleaves a set of type I membrane protein substrates including APP and Notch. Transmembrane proteins CD147 and p23/TMP21 have been shown to interact with γ-secretase complex and modulate Aβ production. In addition, PS1 interacts with several proteins that are involved in important physiological functions such as calcium homeostasis, vesicular transport, cell adhesion, etc. Trafficking of certain membrane proteins, including some γ-secretase substrates also seems to be influenced by PS1 deficiency, inhibition of γ-secretase activity, or expression of FAD-linked PS1 variants.

As expected from the relaxed sequence specificity of γ-secretase, a wide range of type I transmembrane substrates has been described, extending the physiological role for PS1 beyond the nervous system and AD (Figure 1). Substrates of the γ-secretase include homologues of APP (APLP1 and APLP2), Notch1 homologues, Notch ligands Delta and Jagged, the receptor tyrosine kinase ErbB-4, cell surface adhesion protein CD44, the mucin-type molecule CD43, low-density lipoprotein receptor-related protein, cell adhesion receptors N- and E-cadherins, cadherin-related gamma-protocadherins, synaptic adhesion protein nectin-1α, netrin receptor DCC, cell surface heparin sulphate proteoglycan syndecan-1, p75 neurotrophin receptor and its homolog NRADD, the voltage-gated sodium channel β2-subunit, tyrosinase and tyrosinase-related proteins 1 and 2, etc. As with the case of APP and Notch1, γ-secretase cleavage of these additional substrates is preceded by cleavage(s) within their extracellular domain. In several cases γ-secretase cleavage releases an intracellular domain analogous to Notch intracellular domain that can translocate into the nucleus. It remains to be determined whether intracellular domains of all γ-secretase substrates engage in the modulation of gene expression upon gaining entry into the nucleus. For example, γ-secretase cleavage of DCC terminates the cAMP/PKA signaling cascade that persists as long as the DCC CTF remains tethered to the membrane (Parent et al. 2005).

PS1 STABILITY AND FUNCTION IN γ-SECRETASE ACTIVITY REQUIRES OTHER COMPONENTS

As described above, overexpression of PS1 alone neither substantially increases the levels of mature PS1 derivatives nor elevates Aβ generation in cultured cell lines and transgenic mice. Based on these findings, a model was proposed wherein the abundance of mature PS1 fragments is regulated by interaction with limiting cellular factor(s) (Thinakaran et al. 1997). Genetic and biochemical approaches have identified three additional proteins that are crucial for the stability of PS1 as well as γ-secretase activity. Goutte and colleagues used genetic screens to identify two genes, named *aph-1* and *aph-2* (anterior pharynx defective), which act in the GLP-1/Notch pathway during the early stages of *C. elegans* embryogenesis (Goutte et al. 2000; Goutte et al. 2002). A type I transmembrane protein termed Nicastrin, which is the mammalian homolog of *aph-2*, was identified simultaneously by biochemical methods as a protein bound to PS1 (Yu et al. 2000). An independent *C. elegans* genetic screen identified *aph-1* and *pen-2* as enhancers of sel-12/Presenilin function, and showed that *aph-2*, *aph-1* and *pen-2* are required for Notch signaling, PS1 accumulation, and γ-secretase activity (Francis et al. 2002). APH-1 is a multipass transmembrane protein encoded by two (human) or three (rodent) genes that can be alternatively spliced. PEN-2 is a protein with two transmembrane domains encoded by one gene. It is now clear that PS, nicastrin, APH-1, and PEN-2 are stoichiometric components of high molecular weight γ-secretase complex. Co-expression of these four transmembrane proteins is sufficient to reconstitute γ-secretase activity in yeast, which lacks these mammalian orthologs (Edbauer et al. 2003). Furthermore, co-expression of all four proteins is sufficient to overcome the limitation in generating high levels of PS-derived NTF and CTF in transfected cells (Kim et al. 2003; Kimberly et al. 2003; Takasugi et al. 2003). Thus, PS1 endoproteolysis, stability and accumulation of PS1 NTF/CTF are regulated by the availability of stoichiometric levels of nicastrin, APH-1 and PEN-2. Most interestingly, biogenesis, maturation, stability, and the steady state levels of γ-secretase components are co-dependent. Down regulation or targeted gene disruption of any one of these components affects maturation and stability of other subunits, indicating that their assembly into a high molecular weight complex is a highly regulated process that occurs during biosynthesis of these polypeptides. For example, the heavily glycosylated type I membrane protein nicastrin does not mature and exit the ER in cells lacking PS1 expression (Leem et al. 2002). PS1 deficiency also leads to altered intracellular trafficking of PEN-2 and APH-1, as well as their destabilization (Wang et al. 2004; Zhang et al. 2005). On the other hand, PS1 fails to undergo endoproteolysis to generate stable NTF and CTF in nicastrin[-/-] cells or when PEN-2 is downregulated by RNAi (Li et al. 2003; Luo et al. 2003; Zhang et al. 2005).

The temporal sequence of γ-secretase assembly is only beginning to unravel at this time, as is the structure of the active enzyme. Available evidence supports the formation of an early intermediate sub-complex made of APH-1 and nicastrin (LaVoie et al. 2003). Rer1p (retrieval to ER 1 protein) expression controls the formation of this gamma-secretase subcomplex by competing with APH-1 during active recycling between the endoplasmic reticulum and Golgi (Spasic et al. 2007). The proximal C-terminus region of PS1 holoprotein then binds to this subcomplex by interacting with nicastrin TM domain (Kaether et al. 2004). During the final step in the assembly, PEN-2 associates with the complex by interaction with TM 4 of PS1 2 (Kim and Sisodia 2005; Watanabe et al. 2005), concurrent with PS1 endoproteolysis. The observation that membrane-permeable γ-secretase inhibitors markedly increase cell surface levels of PS1 and PEN-2 without affecting that of nicastrin also implies a tighter association between PS1 and PEN-2 (Wang et al. 2004). Despite the identification of the core components, the precise stoichiometry of the active γ-secretase complex remains obscure, and the use of different biochemical purification methods and detergents has led to the apparent size discrepancy of active γ-secretase complexes, with estimates ranging from 250 kDa (Kimberly et al. 2003) to 2MDa (Li et al. 2000).

PS1 FUNCTIONS AS THE CATALYTIC CENTER OF γ-SECRETASE

The exact functional contribution of each γ-secretase subunit to enzyme activity still remains elusive. Two lines of investigation strongly support the notion that PS1 may form the catalytic center of γ-secretase. First, Wolfe and colleagues identified the presence of two highly conserved aspartate residues in transmembrane domains 6 (D257 in PS1 and D263 in PS2) and 7 (D385 in PS1 and D366 in PS2) that are indispensable for γ-secretase activity, and suggested that γ-secretase is a transmembrane aspartyl protease (Wolfe et al. 1999). Second, it was found that highly specific transition-state analogue inhibitors of γ-secretase specifically bound to PS1 NTF/CTF heterodimer (Li et al. 2000). Interestingly, APP and Notch can interact with PS1 in the presence of active site γ-secretase inhibitors, revealing the presence of a docking site within PS1 that is distinct from the catalytic site (Esler et al. 2002; Berezovska et al. 2003). The extracellular domain of nicastrin interacts with ectodomain cleaved APP and Notch, and thus functions as the γ-secretase substrate receptor (Shah et al. 2005). The widely expressed cell surface type I transmembrane glycoprotein CD147 (also called basigin and EMMPRIN) appears to function as a regulatory subunit of the γ-secretase complex (Zhou et al. 2005). Downregulation of CD147 expression caused a modest increase in Aβ production. Interestingly, unlike the integral γ-secretase components, overexpression or downregulation of CD147 did not affect the stability of γ-secretase complex (Zhou et al. 2005). Similarly, a recent study reported that p23/TMP21, a member of the p24 family of transmembrane proteins involved in vesicle trafficking between the ER and Golgi apparatus binds to γ-secretase complex. Knockdown of p23/TMP21 expression did not affect the steady-state levels of γ-secretase subunits, but altered APP trafficking and increased generation of Aβ40 and Aβ42 peptides without affecting ε-cleavage of APP or Notch (Chen et al. 2006; Vetrivel et al. 2007). Despite these recent advances, it is still intriguing how FAD-associated point mutations that are widely scattered throughout the protein, many of which are located far away from the putative catalytic site, selectively alter the cleavage site preference in APP in a manner that increases Aβ42 production and or decrease Aβ40 production.

SUBCELLULAR LOCALIZATION OF PS1

PS1 has been localized to multiple organelles including the endoplasmic reticulum (ER), ER/Golgi intermediate compartments, Golgi apparatus, endosomes, lysosomes, phagosomes, plasma membrane, and mitochondria. Quantitative immunoelectron microscopy estimates of endogenous PS1 in CHO cells showed that the vast majority (52%) of PS1 is present in pre-Golgi membranes that include nuclear envelope, ER and vesicular-tubular clusters that are positive for COP1, whereas only about 1% of total label was localized in the Golgi complex (Rechards et al. 2003). A significant amount of PS1 (25%) was localized in the plasma membrane and 13% in endocytic compartments. However, a recent biochemical study estimated that only 6% of PS1 and γ-secretase activity exists at the cell surface (Chyung et al. 2005). Consistent with the later estimates, cell fractionation studies show that the majority of the mature components of endogenous γ-secretase complex are present in intracellular organelles (Vetrivel et al. 2004). Furthermore, non-ionic detergent extraction revealed the presence of presenilin and other γ-secretase subunits in cholesterol- and sphingolipid-rich, detergent-resistant membrane microdomains of post-Golgi, TGN and endosome membranes. Association of γ-secretase components with detergent-resistant membranes is sensitive to cholesterol depletion, fulfilling a stringent criterion expected of bona fide lipid raft associated proteins. Using magnetic immunoisolation, active and mature components of γ-secretase complex were found to co-reside in lipid raft microdomains with VAMP-4 (TGN), syntaxin 6 (TGN vesicles) and syntaxin 13 (late endosomes). Interestingly, the cell-surface raft-associated protein SNAP-23 does not co-reside with γ-secretase subunits, further validating intracellular compartmentalization of γ-secretase complex (Vetrivel et al. 2004).

DIFFERENTIAL FUNCTIONS OF WILD TYPE AND FAD-ASSOCIATED PS1 AND PS2

FAD-linked mutations in PS intriguingly influence γ-secretase cleavage by an elusive mechanism that modulates the proteolysis of APP to selectively enhance the generation of highly amyloidogenic Aβ42 peptides (Borchelt et al. 1996; Scheuner et al. 1996). Precisely how FAD-linked PS mutations influence Aβ42 production is still not understood. Altered conformation has been suggested as a mechanism by which FAD-associated PS variants may influence specificity of cleavage site within APP, thus elevating Aβ42 production. For example, it has been shown that FAD-associated mutations change the proximity of N- and C-termini of PS1 (Berezovska et al. 2005). On the other hand, non-steroidal anti-inflammatory drugs such as sulindac sulfide, ibuprofen, indomethacin and flurbiprofen, which specifically lower Aβ42 levels without affecting Aβ40 production (Weggen et al. 2001), decrease the proximity of PS1 N- and C-terminus and PS1 to APP C-terminus (Lleo et al. 2004). Nevertheless, how these proximity measures of FAD mutants relate to conformational changes in the catalytic site or the substrate-docking site of γ-secretase in a manner that fosters elevated Aβ42 production remains to be understood. Recent studies also suggest that the adverse property of FAD-linked PS alleles is not limited to altering cleavage site specificity of substrates APP and Notch. For example, large-scale gene expression profiling in brains of conditional PS1 knockout mice and transgenic mice expressing wild type or FAD-linked mutant PS1 suggests that the FAD-linked PS1 variant produces transcriptome changes primarily by gain of aberrant function (Mirnics et al. 2005). Furthermore, the expression and activity of neprilysin, an Aβ degrading enzyme, is regulated by γ-secretase activity. *In vitro* studies show that transcription from neprilysin gene promoter can be activated by cytosolic domains released from APP, APLP1 or APLP2 by γ-secretase cleavage, and FAD-associated PS1 mutations increase neprilysin levels in brains of patients with mutant PS1 alleles (Pardossi-Piquard et al. 2005). Finally, since Aβ42 activates neutral sphingomyelinase and Aβ40 inhibits hydroxymethyl-CoA reductase, an indirect role for PS in maintaining cholesterol and sphingomyelin levels through Aβ40 and Aβ42 production has been proposed (Grimm et al. 2005). As expected from increased production of Aβ42, FAD-associated PS1 mutants specifically increase cellular cholesterol and decrease sphingomyelin levels.

In addition to causing a shift in APP cleavage site, FAD-associated PS1 mutations may show partial loss of function in some other physiological activities. For example, a recent study by Wang et al. found that melanin synthesis in FAD-associated *PSEN1* M146V knock-in mice was impaired, which was consistent with their observation that γ-secretase inhibitor blocked melanin synthesis (Wang et al. 2006). Interestingly, PS form ER Ca^{2+} leak channels that account for about 80% of passive Ca^{2+} leak from the endoplasmic reticulum. FAD-linked PS mutations disrupt this function, supporting a potential role for Ca^{2+} homeostasis in AD pathogenesis (Tu et al. 2006).

PS1 REGULATES TRAFFICKING OF SELECT MEMBRANE PROTEINS

In addition to its function as the catalytic subunit of γ-secretase, PS directly or indirectly regulates the trafficking of select membrane proteins. As mentioned above, PS1 deficiency resulted in abnormal intracellular trafficking of the other three γ-secretase components, nicastrin, APH-1 and PEN-2. In addition, PS1 deficiency in neurons accelerated the secretion of α- and β-secretase cleaved APP ectodomain (Naruse et al. 1998). Further analysis revealed that PS1 regulates biosynthetic secretory trafficking of APP. Absence of PS1 or the expression of a loss of function PS1 variant resulted in increased budding/generation of APP-containing vesicles from both ER and TGN with a concomitant increase in complex glycosylation and cell surface appearance of APP (Leem et al. 2002; Cai et al. 2003). In addition, the half-life and steady-state residence of full length APP and APP CTFs at the cell surface were greatly increased (Kim et al. 2001; Kaether et al. 2002). Interestingly, FAD-linked PS1 variants significantly reduced budding of APP-containing vesicles from both ER and TGN, resulting in decreased delivery of APP to the cell surface (Cai et al. 2003). These findings raised the possibility that FAD-linked PS1 variants may influence APP processing by increasing the residence time of APP at the TGN, consequently prolonging their availability for cleavage by β- and γ-secretases within the TGN. Direct evidence to support a trafficking role of PS1, independent of its function in γ-secretase activity, emerged from analysis of membrane proteins that are not substrates for γ-secretase cleavage. For example, complex oligosaccharide modification and brain-derived neurotrophic factor-induced phosphorylation of the neurotrophin receptor TrkB were severely affected in neurons lacking PS1 expression (Naruse et al. 1998). Furthermore, neuron specific intercellular adhesion molecule (ICAM-5)/telencephalin accumulated intracellularly in autophagic vacuoles and displayed extended half-life in the absence of PS1 (Annaert et al. 2001). Similarly, α- and β-synuclein were found mislocalized in autophagic organelles in PS1-deficient neurons but not in neurons treated with selective γ-secretase inhibitors (Wilson et al. 2004). Remarkably, increased assembly and cell surface delivery of nicotinic acetylcholine receptors (a mutimeric polytopic membrane protein complex) was observed in cells expressing a loss of function PS1 mutant that exhibited accelerated cell surface delivery of APP and slower kinetics of Aβ secretion (Leem et al. 2002). While a role for PS1 in regulating protein trafficking remains attractive, the growing number of γ-secretase substrates raises the possibility of impaired turnover of CTFs derived from type I membrane proteins indirectly influencing protein trafficking in cells lacking PS1 expression or γ-secretase activity. Indeed, a recent study demonstrated that PS deficiency resulted in mislocalization of post-Golgi tyrosinase-containing vesicles; and such an abnormal trafficking of tyrosinase is γ-secretase-dependent and accompanied by simultaneous accumulation of its C-terminal fragment (Wang et al. 2006). On the other hand, there is a possibility that PS1 indirectly regulates protein trafficking via its interaction with protein trafficking factors. For example, PS1 has been shown to interact with small factors such as Rab11, Rab6 and Rab GDI that are involved in regulation of vesicular transport (Dumanchin et al. 1999; Scheper et al. 2000; Scheper et al. 2004) and modulation of Rab6-mediated transport has been shown to affect APP processing.

Recently Cai et al. also showed that PS1 interacted with phospholipase D1 (PLD1), a phospholipid-modifying enzyme that regulates membrane trafficking events (Cai et al. 2006; Cai et al. 2006). The results demonstrated that this interaction recruited PLD1 to the Golgi/TGN and thus possibly modulated APP trafficking, since overexpression of PLD1 promoted generation of APP-containing vesicles from the TGN.

PS-INTERACTING PROTEINS

Over the past several years many investigators employed yeast two-hybrid assays and candidate approaches to identify proteins that interact with various domains of PS (Van Gassen et al. 2000) (Figure 1). As an outcome, several PS interacting proteins have been identified, including members of a family of armadillo-related proteins such as β-catenin; cell surface transmembrane protein E-cadherin; neuronal cell adhesion molecule telencephalin; filamin, an actin binding protein; PBP/MOCA, a protein with limited homology to Dock180; the enzyme glycogen synthase kinase-3β; microtubule-associated protein tau; calcium binding proteins such as calsenilin, calmyrin, sorcin, mu-calpain and CALP/KChIP4; anti-apoptotic molecule Bcl-X_L; Rab11 and Rab6, small GTPases involved in regulation of vesicular transport; RabGDI, a regulatory factor in vesicular transport; PLD1, a phospholipid-modifying enzyme involved in membrane trafficking events; syntaxin 1A, a t-SNARE localized in the synaptic plasma membrane; syntaxin 5, a t-SNARE that mediates transport between the ER and Golgi; adaptor proteins X11α and X11β; CLIP-170, the microtubule plus-end-tracking protein; brain G-protein, G_o; Ubiquilin, a protein containing ubiquitin-related domains; HC5 and ZETA subunits of the catalytic 20S proteasome; TPIP, a tetratricopeptide repeat containing protein; PAG, a protein of the thioredoxin peroxidase family, PSAP, a PDZ-like protein, QM/Jif-1, a negative regulator of c-Jun; DRAL, an LIM-domain protein; proliferation-associated gene product, a protein of the thioredoxin peroxidase family; β-secretase, BACE1; PAMP and PARL, two novel putative metalloproteases; Omi/HtrA2, a serine protease involved in the mammalian cellular stress response; Met1, a novel putative methyltransferase; mitochondrial immunophilin FKBP38; a splice variant of glial fibrillary acidic protein, etc. The *C. elegans* PS homologue SEL-12 was recently reported to interact with SEL-10, a Cdc4p-related protein. In many instances the physiological role for the identified interaction between the putative protein with PS1 or PS2 is not clearly defined. For example, the PS interaction with the anti-apoptotic Bcl2 family member Bcl-X_L offers a potential mechanism by which PSs might regulate apoptosis (Passer et al. 1999). However, it is unclear at present whether an increased apoptotic response associated with the expression of FAD-linked PS variants noted in several studies can be attributed to differential interaction of mutant PS1 or PS2 with Bcl-X_L. Similarly, the absence of PS1 or the expression of FAD-linked PS1 mutant results in increased glycogen synthase kinase-3β activity, enhanced kinesin light chain phosphorylation, and concomitant reduction in kinesin-based axonal transport (Pigino et al. 2003). But it remains unclear whether PS1·glycogen synthase kinase-3β interaction plays a direct role in regulating kinesin-based axonal transport. Finally, it is somewhat puzzling that neither regulated metabolism of PS nor the enhanced production of Aβ42 by FAD mutants appears to be influenced by any of the reported PS interacting proteins.

CONCLUSION

Mutations in *PSEN1* and *PSEN2* genes co-segregate with early onset FAD cases and genetic ablation of these genes eliminates Aβ production in transgenic mice. Abolishment of Aβ production by inhibiting γ-secretase is therefore considered a potential therapeutic strategy for the treatment of AD. To this end, several pharmacological inhibitors, which specifically target processed PS fragments have been developed. However, because several other functionally important substrates of γ-secretase cleavage including Notch receptors are critical for embryonic development and diverse physiological functions, generalized inhibition of γ-secretase could potentially result in severe consequences due to mechanism-based toxicity. By logical design and high throughput screening it is highly desirable to develop inhibitors that specifically target proteolytic processing of APP but not other substrates. Recent studies suggest the use of separate active sites by γ-secretase in the proteolytic processing of APP and Notch. Further, APP and Notch processing have been shown to occur in spatially distinct sites. Therefore, development of specific inhibitors targeting the active site of γ-secretase involved in APP processing or targeting the γ-secretase localized in subcellular membrane microdomains involved in APP processing is promising as a novel therapeutic strategy. The use of non-steroidal drugs, NSAIDs, has been shown to be effective in specifically reducing the levels of Aβ42 peptides without affecting Aβ40 production and Notch processing. The mechanistic underpinnings of changes in Aβ40 and Aβ42 levels by FAD-associated PS variants are still being explored. Altered conformation and proximity of PS1-derived fragments themselves or with the substrate APP have been proposed as possible pathogenic functions of FAD-associated PS1 variants. It is still intriguing how widely scattered FAD-associated PS1 mutants have the same functional effect on APP processing. PS1 has been shown to be involved in the subcellular trafficking of APP and FAD-linked PS1 variants increase the retention of substrate in compartments where γ-secretase was localized. Moreover, pathogenic mutations in PS1 have also been reported to impair ER Ca^{2+} leak function of PS1, but how this function is related to AD pathogenesis remains to be understood. Similarly, several PS interacting proteins have been identified but the functional relevance of such interactions is still not completely elucidated. Since the association between PS and FAD was identified a decade ago, we have gained significant insights into these proteins and their essential role in AD pathogenesis, and despite the advances finding a cure for the devastating AD still remains a challenge.

ACKNOWLEDGMENTS

Research in the author's laboratory is supported by grants from the National Institutes of Health, the Alzheimer's Association and the American Health Assistance Foundation.

REFERENCES

Annaert, W.G., C. Esselens, V. Baert, C. Boeve, G. Snellings, P. Cupers, K. Craessaerts and B. De Strooper. Interaction with Telencephalin and the amyloid precursor protein predicts a ring structure for presenilins. *Neuron 32*: 579-589, 2001.

Beher, D., J.D. Wrigley, A. Nadin, G. Evin, C.L. Masters, T. Harrison, J.L. Castro and M.S. Shearman. Pharmacological knock-down of the presenilin 1 heterodimer by a novel γ-secretase inhibitor: implications for presenilin biology. *J Biol Chem 276*: 45394-45402, 2001.

Berezovska, O., A. Lleo, L.D. Herl, M.P. Frosch, E.A. Stern, B.J. Bacskai and B.T. Hyman. Familial Alzheimer's disease presenilin 1 mutations cause alterations in the conformation of presenilin and interactions with amyloid precursor protein. *J Neurosci 25*: 3009-3017, 2005.

Berezovska, O., P. Ramdya, J. Skoch, M.S. Wolfe, B.J. Bacskai and B.T. Hyman. Amyloid precursor protein associates with a nicastrin-dependent docking site on the presenilin 1-gamma-secretase complex in cells demonstrated by fluorescence lifetime imaging. *J Neurosci 23*: 4560-4566, 2003.

Bertram, L. and R.E. Tanzi. The current status of Alzheimer's disease genetics: what do we tell the patients? *Pharmacol Res 50*: 385-396, 2004.

Borchelt, D.R., G. Thinakaran, C.B. Eckman, M.K. Lee, F. Davenport, T. Ratovitsky, C.M. Prada, G. Kim, S. Seekins, D. Yager, H.H. Slunt, R. Wang, M. Seeger, A.I. Levey, S.E. Gandy, N.G. Copeland, N.A. Jenkins, D.L. Price, S.G. Younkin and S.S. Sisodia. Familial Alzheimer's disease-linked presenilin 1 variants elevate Abeta1-42/1-40 ratio in vitro and in vivo. *Neuron 17*: 1005-1013, 1996.

Brunkan, A.L., M. Martinez, J. Wang, E.S. Walker, D. Beher, M.S. Shearman and A.M. Goate. Two domains within the first putative transmembrane domain of presenilin 1 differentially influence presenilinase and gamma-secretase activity. *J Neurochem 94*: 1315-1328, 2005.

Cai, D., J.Y. Leem, J.P. Greenfield, P. Wang, B.S. Kim, R. Wang, K.O. Lopes, S.H. Kim, H. Zheng, P. Greengard, S.S. Sisodia, G. Thinakaran and H. Xu. Presenilin-1 regulates intracellular trafficking and cell surface delivery of β-amyloid precursor protein. *J Biol Chem 278*: 3446-3454, 2003.

Cai, D., W.J. Netzer, M. Zhong, Y. Lin, G. Du, M. Frohman, D.A. Foster, S.S. Sisodia, H. Xu, F.S. Gorelick and P. Greengard. Presenilin-1 uses phospholipase D1 as a negative regulator of beta-amyloid formation. *Proc Natl Acad Sci U S A 103*: 1941-1946, 2006.

Cai, D., M. Zhong, R. Wang, W.J. Netzer, D. Shields, H. Zheng, S.S. Sisodia, D.A. Foster, F.S. Gorelick, H. Xu and P. Greengard. Phospholipase D1 corrects impaired betaAPP trafficking and neurite outgrowth in familial Alzheimer's disease-linked presenilin-1 mutant neurons. *Proc Natl Acad Sci U S A 103*: 1936-1940, 2006.

Chen, F., H. Hasegawa, G. Schmitt-Ulms, T. Kawarai, C. Bohm, T. Katayama, Y. Gu, N. Sanjo, M. Glista, E. Rogaeva, Y. Wakutani, R. Pardossi-Piquard, X. Ruan, A. Tandon, F. Checler, P. Marambaud, K. Hansen, D. Westaway, P. St George-Hyslop and P. Fraser. TMP21 is a presenilin complex component that modulates γ-secretase but not ε-secretase activity. *Nature 440*: 1208-1212, 2006.

Chyung, J.H., D.M. Raper and D.J. Selkoe. gamma -secretase exists on the plasma membrane as an intact complex that accepts substrates and effects intramembrane cleavage. *J Biol Chem 280*: 4383-4392, 2005.

De Strooper, B., W. Annaert, P. Cupers, P. Saftig, K. Craessaerts, J.S. Mumm, E.H. Schroeter, V. Schrijvers, M.S. Wolfe, W.J. Ray, A. Goate and R. Kopan. A presenilin-1-dependent γ-secretase-like protease mediates release of Notch intracellular domain. *Nature 398*: 518-522, 1999.

De Strooper, B., P. Saftig, K. Craessaerts, H. Vanderstichele, G. Guhde, W. Annaert, K. Von Figura and F. Van Leuven. Deficiency of presenilin-1 inhibits the normal cleavage of amyloid precursor protein. *Nature 391*: 387-390, 1998.

Doan, A., G. Thinakaran, D.R. Borchelt, H.H. Slunt, T. Ratovitsky, M. Podlisny, D.J. Selkoe, M. Seeger, S.E. Gandy, D.L. Price and S.S. Sisodia. Protein topology of presenilin 1. *Neuron 17*: 1023-1030, 1996.

Dumanchin, C., C. Czech, D. Campion, M.H. Cuif, T. Poyot, C. Martin, F. Charbonnier, B. Goud, L. Pradier and T. Frebourg. Presenilins interact with rab11, a small GTPase involved in the regulation of vesicular transport. *Hum Mol Genet 8*: 1263-1269, 1999.

Edbauer, D., E. Winkler, J.T. Regula, B. Pesold, H. Steiner and C. Haass. Reconstitution of γ-secretase activity. *Nat Cell Biol 5*: 486-488, 2003.

Esler, W.P., W.T. Kimberly, B.L. Ostaszewski, W. Ye, T.S. Diehl, D.J. Selkoe and M.S. Wolfe. Activity-dependent isolation of the presenilin-γ-secretase complex reveals nicastrin and a γ substrate. *Proc Natl Acad Sci U S A 99*: 2720-2725, 2002.

Francis, R., G. McGrath, J. Zhang, D.A. Ruddy, M. Sym, J. Apfeld, M. Nicoll, M. Maxwell, B. Hai, M.C. Ellis, A.L. Parks, W. Xu, J. Li, M. Gurney, R.L. Myers, C.S. Himes, R. Hiebsch, C. Ruble, J.S. Nye and D. Curtis. aph-1 and pen-2 are required for Notch pathway signaling, gamma-secretase cleavage of betaAPP, and presenilin protein accumulation. *Dev Cell 3*: 85-97, 2002.

Goutte, C., W. Hepler, K.M. Mickey and J.R. Priess. aph-2 encodes a novel extracellular protein required for GLP-1-mediated signaling. *Development 127*: 2481-2492, 2000.

Goutte, C., M. Tsunozaki, V.A. Hale and J.R. Priess. APH-1 is a multipass membrane protein essential for the Notch signaling pathway in Caenorhabditis elegans embryos. *Proc Natl Acad Sci U S A 99*: 775-779, 2002.

Grimm, M.O., H.S. Grimm, A.J. Patzold, E.G. Zinser, R. Halonen, M. Duering, J.A. Tschape, B.D. Strooper, U. Muller, J. Shen and T. Hartmann. Regulation of cholesterol and sphingomyelin metabolism by amyloid-beta and presenilin. *Nat Cell Biol 7*: 1118-1123, 2005.

Iwatsubo, T. The γ-secretase complex: machinery for intramembrane proteolysis. *Curr Opin Neurobiol 14*: 379-383, 2004.

Kaether, C., A. Capell, D. Edbauer, E. Winkler, B. Novak, H. Steiner and C. Haass. The presenilin C-terminus is required for ER-retention, nicastrin-binding and gamma-secretase activity. *Embo J 23*: 4738-4748, 2004.

Kaether, C., S. Lammich, D. Edbauer, M. Ertl, J. Rietdorf, A. Capell, H. Steiner and C. Haass. Presenilin-1 affects trafficking and processing of betaAPP and is targeted in a complex with nicastrin to the plasma membrane. *J Cell Biol 158*: 551-561, 2002.

Kim, S.H., T. Ikeuchi, C. Yu and S.S. Sisodia. Regulated hyperaccumulation of presenilin-1 and the "γ-secretase" complex. Evidence for differential intramembranous processing of transmembrane substrates. *J Biol Chem 278*: 33992-34002, 2003.

Kim, S.H., J.Y. Leem, J.J. Lah, H.H. Slunt, A. Levey, G. Thinakaran and S.S. Sisodia. Multiple effects of aspartate mutant presenilin 1 on the processing and trafficking of amyloid precursor protein. *J Biol Chem 276*: 43343-43350, 2001.

Kim, S.H. and S.S. Sisodia. Evidence that the "NF" motif in transmembrane domain 4 of presenilin 1 is critical for binding with PEN-2. *J Biol Chem 280*: 41953-41966, 2005.

Kimberly, W.T., M.J. LaVoie, B.L. Ostaszewski, W. Ye, M.S. Wolfe and D.J. Selkoe. γ-secretase is a membrane protein complex comprised of presenilin, nicastrin, Aph-1, and Pen-2. *Proc Natl Acad Sci U S A 100*: 6382-6387, 2003.

Laudon, H., E.M. Hansson, K. Melen, A. Bergman, M.R. Farmery, B. Winblad, U. Lendahl, G. von Heijne and J. Naslund. A Nine-transmembrane Domain Topology for Presenilin 1. *J Biol Chem 280*: 35352-35360, 2005.

Laudon, H., P.M. Mathews, H. Karlstrom, A. Bergman, M.R. Farmery, R.A. Nixon, B. Winblad, S.E. Gandy, U. Lendahl, J. Lundkvist and J. Naslund. Co-expressed presenilin 1 NTF and CTF form functional gamma-secretase complexes in cells devoid of full-length protein. *J Neurochem 89*: 44-53, 2004.

LaVoie, M.J., P.C. Fraering, B.L. Ostaszewski, W. Ye, W.T. Kimberly, M.S. Wolfe and D.J. Selkoe. Assembly of the γ-secretase complex involves early formation of an intermediate sub-complex of Aph-1 and Nicastrin. *J Biol Chem 278*: 37213-37222, 2003.

Lee, M.K., H.H. Slunt, L.J. Martin, G. Thinakaran, G. Kim, S.E. Gandy, M. Seeger, E. Koo, D.L. Price and S.S. Sisodia. Expression of presenilin 1 and 2 (PS1 and PS2) in human and murine tissues. *J Neurosci 16*: 7513-7525, 1996.

Leem, J.Y., C.A. Saura, C. Pietrzik, J. Christianson, C. Wanamaker, L.T. King, M.L. Veselits, T. Tomita, L. Gasparini, T. Iwatsubo, H. Xu, W.N. Green, E.H. Koo and G. Thinakaran. A role for presenilin 1 in regulating the delivery of amyloid precursor protein to the cell surface. *Neurobiol Dis 11*: 64-82, 2002.

Leem, J.Y., S. Vijayan, P. Han, D. Cai, M. Machura, K.O. Lopes, M.L. Veselits, H. Xu and G. Thinakaran. Presenilin 1 is required for maturation and cell surface accumulation of nicastrin. *J Biol Chem 277*: 19236-19240, 2002.

Levy-Lahad, E., W. Wasco, P. Poorkaj, D.M. Romano, J. Oshima, W.H. Pettingell, C.E. Yu, P.D. Jondro, S.D. Schmidt, K. Wang, A.C. Crowley, Y.-H. Fu, S.Y. Guenette, D. Galas, E. Nemens, E.M. Wijsman, T.D. Bird, G.D. Schellenberg and R.E. Tanzi. Candidate gene for the chromosome 1 familial Alzheimer's disease locus. *Science 269*: 973-977, 1995.

Li, T., G. Ma, H. Cai, D.L. Price and P.C. Wong. Nicastrin is required for assembly of presenilin/γ-secretase complexes to mediate Notch signaling and for processing and trafficking of β-amyloid precursor protein in mammals. *J Neurosci 23*: 3272-3277, 2003.

Li, Y.M., M.T. Lai, M. Xu, Q. Huang, J. DiMuzio-Mower, M.K. Sardana, X.P. Shi, K.C. Yin, J.A. Shafer and S.J. Gardell. Presenilin 1 is linked with γ-secretase activity in the detergent solubilized state. *Proc Natl Acad Sci U S A 97*: 6138-6143, 2000.

Li, Y.M., M. Xu, M.T. Lai, Q. Huang, J.L. Castro, J. DiMuzio-Mower, T. Harrison, C. Lellis, A. Nadin, J.G. Neduvelil, R.B. Register, M.K. Sardana, M.S. Shearman, A.L. Smith, X.P. Shi, K.C. Yin, J.A. Shafer and S.J. Gardell. Photoactivated γ-secretase inhibitors directed to the active site covalently label presenilin 1. *Nature 405*: 689-694, 2000.

Lleo, A., O. Berezovska, L. Herl, S. Raju, A. Deng, B.J. Bacskai, M.P. Frosch, M. Irizarry and B.T. Hyman. Nonsteroidal anti-inflammatory drugs lower Abeta42 and change presenilin 1 conformation. *Nat Med 10*: 1065-1066, 2004.

Luo, W.J., H. Wang, H. Li, B.S. Kim, S. Shah, H.J. Lee, G. Thinakaran, T.W. Kim, G. Yu and H. Xu. PEN-2 and APH-1 coordinately regulate proteolytic processing of presenilin 1. *J Biol Chem 278*: 7850-7854, 2003.

Mirnics, K., Z. Korade, D. Arion, O. Lazarov, T. Unger, M. Macioce, M. Sabatini, D. Terrano, K.C. Douglass, N.F. Schor and S.S. Sisodia. Presenilin-1-dependent transcriptome changes. *J Neurosci 25*: 1571-1578, 2005.

Mumm, J.S., E.H. Schroeter, M.T. Saxena, A. Griesemer, X. Tian, D.J. Pan, W.J. Ray and R. Kopan. A ligand-induced extracellular cleavage regulates γ-secretase-like proteolytic activation of Notch1. *Mol Cell 5*: 197-206, 2000.

Naruse, S., G. Thinakaran, J.-J. Luo, J.W. Kusiak, T. Tomiata, T. Iwatsubo, X. Qian, D.D. Ginty, D.L. Price, D.R. Borchelt and P.C. Wong. Effects of PS1 deficiency on membrane protein trafficking in neurons. *Neuron 21*: 1213-1221, 1998.

Pardossi-Piquard, R., A. Petit, T. Kawarai, C. Sunyach, C. Alves da Costa, B. Vincent, S. Ring, L. D'Adamio, J. Shen, U. Muller, P. St George Hyslop and F. Checler. Presenilin-dependent transcriptional control of the Abeta-degrading enzyme neprilysin by intracellular domains of betaAPP and APLP. *Neuron 46*: 541-554, 2005.

Parent, A.T., N.Y. Barnes, Y. Taniguchi, G. Thinakaran and S.S. Sisodia. Presenilin attenuates receptor-mediated signaling and synaptic function. *J Neurosci 25*: 1540-1549, 2005.

Parks, A.L. and D. Curtis. Presenilin diversifies its portfolio. *Trends Genet 23*: 140-150, 2007.

Passer, B.J., L. Pellegrini, P. Vito, J.K. Ganjei and L. D'Adamio. Interaction of Alzheimer's Presenilin-1 and Presenilin-2 with Bcl-X(L). A potential role in modulating the threshold of cell death. *J Biol Chem 274*: 24007-24013, 1999.

Pigino, G., G. Morfini, A. Pelsman, M.P. Mattson, S.T. Brady and J. Busciglio. Alzheimer's presenilin 1 mutations impair kinesin-based axonal transport. *J Neurosci 23*: 4499-4508, 2003.

Podlisny, M.B., M. Citron, P. Amarante, R. Sherrington, W. Xia, J. Zhang, T. Diehl, G. Levesque, P. Fraser, C. Haass, E.H. Koo, P. Seubert, P. St. George-Hyslop, D.B. Teplow and D.J. Selkoe. Presenilin proteins undergo heterogeneous endoproteolysis between Thr291 and Ala299 and occur as stable N- and C-terminal fragments in normal and Alzheimer brain tissue. *Neurobiol Dis 3*: 325-337, 1997.

Ratovitski, T., H.H. Slunt, G. Thinakaran, D.L. Price, S.S. Sisodia and D.R. Borchelt. Endoproteolytic processing and stabilization of wild-type and mutant presenilin. *J Biol Chem 272*: 24536-24541, 1997.

Rechards, M., W. Xia, V.M. Oorschot, D.J. Selkoe and J. Klumperman. Presenilin-1 exists in both pre- and post-Golgi compartments and recycles via COPI-coated membranes. *Traffic 4*: 553-565, 2003.

Rogaev, E.I., R. Sherrington, E.A. Rogaeva, G. Levesque, M. Ikeda, Y. Liang, H. Chi, C. Lin, K. Holman, T. Tsuda, L. Mar, S. Sorbi, B. Nacmias, S. Piacentini, L. Amaducci, I. Chumakov, D. Cohen, L. Lannfelt, P.E. Fraser, J.M. Rommens and P.H. St. George-Hyslop. Familial Alzheimer's disease in kindreds with missense mutations in a gene on chromosome 1 related to the Alzheimer's disease type 3 gene. *Nature 376*: 775-778, 1995.

Saura, C.A., T. Tomita, F. Davenport, C.L. Harris, T. Iwatsubo and G. Thinakaran. Evidence that intramolecular associations between Presenilin domains are obligatory for endoproteolytic processing. *J. Biol. Chem 274*: 13818-13823, 1999.

Saura, C.A., T. Tomita, S. Soriano, M. Takahashi, J.Y. Leem, T. Honda, E.H. Koo, T. Iwatsubo and G. Thinakaran. The non-conserved hydrophilic loop domain of presenilin (PS) is neither required for PS endoproteolysis nor enhanced Aβ42 production mediated by familial Alzheimer's disease-linked PS variants. *J Biol Chem 275*: 17136-17142., 2000.

Scheper, W., R. Zwart and F. Baas. Rab6 membrane association is dependent of Presenilin 1 and cellular phosphorylation events. *Brain Res Mol Brain Res 122*: 17-23, 2004.

Scheper, W., R. Zwart, P. Sluijs, W. Annaert, W.A. Gool and F. Baas. Alzheimer's presenilin 1 is a putative membrane receptor for rab GDP dissociation inhibitor. *Hum Mol Genet 9*: 303-310, 2000.

Scheuner, D., C. Eckman, M. Jensen, X. Song, M. Citron, N. Suzuki, T.D. Bird, J. Hardy, M. Hutton, W. Kukull, E. Larson, E. Levy-Lahad, M. Viitanen, E. Peskind, P. Poorkaj, G. Schellenberg, R. Tanzi, W. Wasco, L. Lannfelt, D. Selkoe and S. Younkin. Secreted amyloid β-protein similar to that in the senile plaques of Alzheimer's disease is increased in vivo by the presenilin 1 and 2 and APP mutations linked to familial Alzheimer's disease. *Nat Med 2*: 864-870, 1996.

Shah, S., S.F. Lee, K. Tabuchi, Y.H. Hao, C. Yu, Q. LaPlant, H. Ball, C.E. Dann, 3rd, T. Sudhof and G. Yu. Nicastrin functions as a gamma-secretase-substrate receptor. *Cell 122*: 435-447, 2005.

Sherrington, R., E.I. Rogaev, Y. Liang, E.A. Rogaeva, G. Levesque, M. Ikeda, H. Chi, C. Lin, G. Li, K. Holman, T. Tsuda, L. Mar, J.-F. Foncin, Bruni, A. C., M.P. Montesi, S. Sorbi, I. Rainero, L. Pinessi, L. Nee, I. Chumakov, D. Pollen, A. Brookes, P. Sansequ, R.J. Polinsky, W. Wasco, H.A.R. Da Silva, J.L. Haines, M.A. Pericak-Vance, R.E. Tanzi, A.D. Roses, P.E. Fraser, J.M. Rommens and P.H. St. George-Hyslop. Cloning of a gene bearing missense mutations in early-onset familial Alzheimer's disease. *Nature 375*: 754-760, 1995.

Spasic, D., T. Raemaekers, K. Dillen, I. Declerck, V. Baert, L. Serneels, J. Fullekrug and W. Annaert. Rer1p competes with APH-1 for binding to nicastrin and regulates gamma-secretase complex assembly in the early secretory pathway. *J Cell Biol 176*: 629-640, 2007.

Spasic, D., A. Tolia, K. Dillen, V. Baert, B. De Strooper, S. Vrijens and W. Annaert. Presenilin-1 maintains a nine-transmembrane topology throughout the secretory pathway. *J Biol Chem 281*: 26569-26577, 2006.

Steiner, H., H. Romig, B. Pesold, U. Philipp, M. Baader, M. Citron, H. Loetscher, H. Jacobsen and C. Haass. Amyloidogenic Function of the Alzheimer's Disease-Associated Presenilin 1 in the Absence of Endoproteolysis. *Biochemistry 38*: 14600-14605, 1999.

Stromberg, K., E.M. Hansson, H. Laudon, S. Bergstedt, J. Naslund, J. Lundkvist and U. Lendahl. gamma-Secretase complexes containing N- and C-terminal fragments of different presenilin origin retain normal gamma-secretase activity. *J Neurochem 95*: 880-890, 2005.

Struhl, G. and A. Adachi. Requirements for Presenilin-dependent cleavage of Notch and other transmembrane proteins. *Molecular Cell 6*: 625-636, 2000.

Struhl, G. and I. Greenwald. Presenilin is required for activity and nuclear access of Notch in Drosophila. *Nature 398*: 522-525, 1999.

Takasugi, N., T. Tomita, I. Hayashi, M. Tsuruoka, M. Niimura, Y. Takahashi, G. Thinakaran and T. Iwatsubo. The role of presenilin cofactors in the γ-secretase complex. *Nature 422*: 438-441, 2003.

Thinakaran, G., D.R. Borchelt, M.K. Lee, H.H. Slunt, L. Spitzer, G. Kim, T. Ratovitsky, F. Davenport, C. Nordstedt, M. Seeger, J. Hardy, A.I. Levey, S.E. Gandy, N.A. Jenkins, N.G. Copeland, D.L. Price and S.S. Sisodia. Endoproteolysis of presenilin 1 and accumulation of processed derivatives in vivo. *Neuron 17*: 181-190, 1996.

Thinakaran, G., C.L. Harris, T. Ratovitski, F. Davenport, H.H. Slunt, D.L. Price, D.R. Borchelt and S.S. Sisodia. Evidence that levels of presenilins (PS1 and PS2) are coordinately regulated by competition for limiting cellular factors. *J Biol Chem 272*: 28415-28422, 1997.

Thinakaran, G. and A.T. Parent. Identification of the role of presenilins beyond Alzheimer's disease. *Pharmacol Res 50*: 411-418, 2004.

Tu, H., O. Nelson, A. Bezprozvanny, Z. Wang, S.F. Lee, Y.H. Hao, L. Serneels, B. De Strooper, G. Yu and I. Bezprozvanny. Presenilins form ER Ca2+ leak channels, a function disrupted by familial Alzheimer's disease-linked mutations. *Cell 126*: 981-993, 2006.

Van Gassen, G., W. Annaert and C. Van Broeckhoven. Binding partners of Alzheimer's disease proteins: are they physiologically relevant? *Neurobiol Dis 7*: 135-151, 2000.

Vetrivel, K.S., H. Cheng, W. Lin, T. Sakurai, T. Li, N. Nukina, P.C. Wong, H. Xu and G. Thinakaran. Association of γ-secretase with lipid rafts in post-golgi and endosome membranes. *J Biol Chem 279*: 44945-44954, 2004.

Vetrivel, K.S., P. Gong, J.W. Bowen, H. Cheng, Y. Chen, M. Carter, P.D. Nguyen, L. Placanica, F.T. Wieland, Y.M. Li, M.Z. Kounnas and G. Thinakaran. Dual roles of the transmembrane protein p23/TMP21 in the modulation of amyloid precursor protein metabolism. *Mol Neurodegener 2*: 4, 2007.

Wang, H., W.J. Luo, Y.W. Zhang, Y.M. Li, G. Thinakaran, P. Greengard and H. Xu. Presenilins and gamma-secretase inhibitors affect intracellular trafficking and cell surface localization of the gamma-secretase complex components. *J Biol Chem 279*: 40560-40566, 2004.

Wang, R., P. Tang, P. Wang, R.E. Boissy and H. Zheng. Regulation of tyrosinase trafficking and processing by presenilins: partial loss of function by familial Alzheimer's disease mutation. *Proc Natl Acad Sci U S A 103*: 353-358, 2006.

Watanabe, N., T. Tomita, C. Sato, T. Kitamura, Y. Morohashi and T. Iwatsubo. Pen-2 is incorporated into the gamma-secretase complex through binding to transmembrane domain 4 of presenilin 1. *J Biol Chem 280*: 41967-41975, 2005.

Weggen, S., J.L. Eriksen, P. Das, S.A. Sagi, R. Wang, C.U. Pietrzik, K.A. Findlay, T.E. Smith, M.P. Murphy, T. Bulter, D.E. Kang, N. Marquez-Sterling, T.E. Golde and E.H. Koo. A subset of NSAIDs lower amyloidogenic Abeta42 independently of cyclooxygenase activity. *Nature 414*: 212-216, 2001.

Wilson, C.A., D.D. Murphy, B.I. Giasson, B. Zhang, J.Q. Trojanowski and V.M. Lee. Degradative organelles containing mislocalized alpha-and beta-synuclein proliferate in presenilin-1 null neurons. *J Cell Biol 165*: 335-346, 2004.

Wolfe, M.S., W. Xia, B.L. Ostaszewski, T.S. Diehl, W.T. Kimberly and D.J. Selkoe. Two transmembrane aspartates in presenilin-1 required for presenilin endoproteolysis and γ-secretase activity. *Nature 398*: 513-517, 1999.

Yu, G., M. Nishimura, S. Arawaka, D. Levitan, L. Zhang, A. Tandon, Y.Q. Song, E. Rogaeva, F. Chen, T. Kawarai, A. Supala, L. Levesque, H. Yu, D.S. Yang, E. Holmes, P. Milman, Y. Liang, D.M. Zhang, D.H. Xu, C. Sato, E. Rogaev, M. Smith, C. Janus, Y. Zhang, R. Aebersold, L.S. Farrer, S. Sorbi, A. Bruni, P. Fraser and P. St George-Hyslop. Nicastrin modulates presenilin-mediated notch/glp-1 signal transduction and betaAPP processing. *Nature 407*: 48-54, 2000.

Zhang, Y.W., W.J. Luo, H. Wang, P. Lin, K.S. Vetrivel, F. Liao, F. Li, P.C. Wong, M.G. Farquhar, G. Thinakaran and H. Xu. Nicastrin Is Critical for Stability and Trafficking but Not Association of Other Presenilin/gamma-Secretase Components. *J Biol Chem 280*: 17020-17026, 2005.

Zhou, S., H. Zhou, P.J. Walian and B.K. Jap. CD147 is a regulatory subunit of the gamma-secretase complex in Alzheimer's disease amyloid beta-peptide production. *Proc Natl Acad Sci U S A 102*: 7499-7504, 2005.

In: Research Progress in Alzheimer's Disease and Dementia   ISBN 978-1-60021-960-3
Editor: Miao-Kun Sun, pp. 79-93   © 2008 Nova Science Publishers, Inc.

Chapter IV

TAUOPATHY IN ALZHEIMER'S DISEASE

Roland Brandt and Monika Hundelt*

Department of Neurobiology, University of Osnabrück, 49076 Osnabrück, Germany.

ABSTRACT

Pathologic tau modifications and filamentous tau inclusions are a histopathologic hallmark of Alzheimer's disease (AD) and other tauopathies. This chapter begins with a summary of data on the structure and function of the tau proteins as an important component of the neuronal cytoskeleton during neuronal development and brain function. The second part concentrates on alterations of tau during AD which include the development of a filamentous pathology, characteristic alterations in posttranslational modifications and functional changes. A brief discussion of natural and transgenic animal models follows since such models have an important role for studying changes of tau in AD and for testing potential therapeutics. The chapter ends with concluding remarks on the relationship between changes in tau and pathological mechanisms which point to disease-related alterations in the dynamic turnover of intracellular proteins which AD has in common with other neurodegenerative diseases such as Parkinson's disease and Huntington's disease.

ABBREVIATIONS:

AD,	Alzheimer's Disease
AGEs,	advanced glycation endproducts
APP,	amyloid precursor protein
CNS,	central nervous system

* Correspondence concerning this article should be addressed to: Prof. Dr. Roland Brandt, Department of Neurobiology, University of Osnabrück, Barbarastrasse 11, D-49076 Osnabrück, Germany. Phone: [+49] (541) 969-2338; Fax: [+49] (541) 969-2354; e-mail: brandt@biologie.uni-osnabrueck.de.

FTDP-17,   frontotemporal dementia with parkinsonism linked to chromosome 17
HD,   Huntington's disease
MAPs,   microtubule-associated proteins
NFTs,   neurofibrillary tangles
PD,   Parkinson's disease
PHFs,   paired helical filaments
PS1,   presenilin 1
SDS-PAGE, sodium dodecyl sulfate-polyacrylamide gel electrophoresis
SFs,   straight filaments

1. INTRODUCTION

Alzheimer's Disease (AD) is characterized by a progressive loss of memory and cognitive functions, resulting in a severe dementia and massive neuron loss. Histopathologically, AD is defined by the presence of extracellular amyloid plaques containing the aggregated APP (amyloid precursor protein) peptide fragment Aβ and intracellular neurofibrillary tangles (NFTs) composed of hyperphosphorylated tau proteins (for a review see Goedert and Spillantini, 2006). Filamentous tau inclusions are a neuropathological hallmark of a family of neurodegenerative diseases collectively known as tauopathies (for a review see Iqbal et al., 2005) and pathogenic mutations in the tau gene have been found in the hereditary tauopathy frontotemporal dementia with parkinsonism linked to chromosome 17 (FTDP-17). The mutations in tau have emphasized that tau-related pathology can be sufficient to cause dementia and may indicate a central role of tau pathology also in AD. Although tau mutations have not been identified in familial forms of AD, the fact that mutations in tau give rise to tau-inclusion tangles but not plaques and yet mutations in APP give rise to both plaques and tangles suggests that amyloid pathology occurs upstream of tau pathology and that pathological tau modifications act as effectors of cell death during the disease. This chapter attempts to summarize data on the role of the tau proteins during neuronal development and brain function on one side and tau protein pathology in Alzheimer's disease on the other side with the aim to highlight disease-related changes in structure and function of tau. It becomes evident that accumulation of misfolded and modified tau proteins are signs of pathological alterations in the dynamic turnover of cellular proteins.

2. STRUCTURE AND FUNCTION OF THE TAU PROTEINS

Tau proteins are microtubule-associated proteins (MAPs) that are abundant in the central and peripheral nervous system, where they are expressed predominantly in neurons. Human tau proteins are encoded by a single gene on chromosome 17q21 that consists of 16 exons. By alternative mRNA splicing of exons 2, 3, and 10, six tau isoforms are produced in the central nervous system (CNS) (Figure 1A). They differ by the presence or absence of one or two inserts in the aminoterminal half (0N, 1N, and 2N, respectively), and have either three or four microtubule-binding repeat motifs in the carboxyterminal half (3R and 4R-tau). In fetal brain, only the shortest isoform (3R/0N) is expressed, whereas all isoforms are present in adult brains. In mice, which are often used as animal models for AD, endogenous mouse tau is spliced only into the 4R isoform in the adult mouse brain (reviewed in Lee et al., 2005).

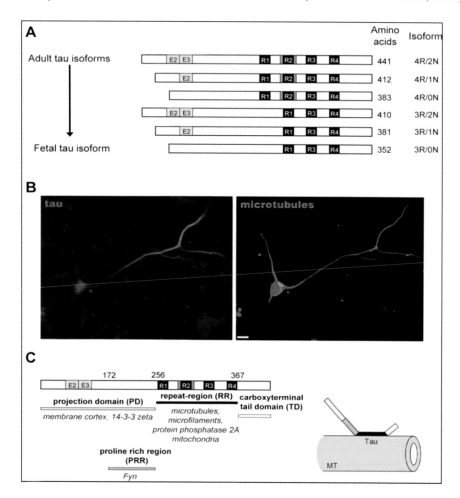

Figure 1. Structure and function of the tau proteins in the CNS. A. Schematic representation of the human tau isoforms. Alternatively spliced exons are shown in grey. The repeats (R1-R4) constitute the microtubule-binding region. B. Immunofluorescence micrograph showing the distribution of tau (left) and microtubules (right) in cultured human neurons. Tau exhibits a proximo-distal gradient in the axon. C. Schematic of the functional organization of tau protein. Some interactions that have been mapped to specific tau regions are indicated. MT, microtubule. For details see Brandt and Leschik, 2004.

Tau stimulates microtubule nucleation and growth in cell-free reactions, reduces microtubule instability, and promotes microtubule accumulation and stability in cultured cells (Weingarten et al., 1975, Drubin and Kirschner, 1986, Drechsel et al., 1992, Brandt and Lee, 1993). In the brain, tau is enriched in axons (Binder et al., 1985) and in cultured neurons it was found to be most associated with microtubules at the distal end of the axon close to the growth cone (Black et al., 1996, Kempf et al., 1996) (Figure 1B). This may suggest a role for tau in regulating axon formation and microtubule stability in the axon. However, experiments aimed to determine the role of tau expression for axonal development gave conflicting results. While some types of cultured neurons failed to extend axons after tau suppression using antisense oligonucleotides (Caceres and Kosik, 1990), in other neurons acute inactivation of tau by antibody microinjection had no effect on axon elongation (Tint et al., 1998). Furthermore, tau knockout mice develop normally indicating that tau is not essential for proper axon formation (Harada et al., 1994). These studies suggest that the function of tau in the growing axon extends beyond its classical microtubule-stabilizing function.

Based on amino acid composition and sequence, four regions of tau protein can be distinguished (Figure 1C): the aminoterminal projection domain (PD), which protrudes from the microtubule surface when tau is bound to microtubules, the proline-rich region (PRR), the repeat-region (RR), which contains either three (3R-tau) or four (4R-tau) imperfect 18-amino acid repeats with a single repeat as the basic microtubule interacting unit and the carboxyterminal tail domain (TD). Many direct interactions of tau with cellular proteins and organelles have been reported and include cytoskeletal components, organelles and the membrane cortex (with the latter being loosely defined as the plasma membrane and its associated protein components), kinases and phosphatases, extracellular and transmembrane proteins and others (for a review see Brandt and Leschik, 2004). In some instances, different regions of tau have been shown to interact with different proteins or organelles. This may point to a potential role of tau as a scaffolding protein that specifically localizes members of signal transduction mechanisms to axonal compartments.

Tau belongs to the major phosphoproteins in the brain. Most phosphorylation occurs at serine or threonine residues but also tyrosine-phosphorylation has been reported (Lee, 2005, Stoothoff and Johnson, 2005). In many cases, phosphorylation of tau decreases its affinity for microtubules and its activity to promote microtubule assembly. Phosphorylation affects also some other interactions of tau suggesting that tau's localization and intracellular interactions are regulated by specific phosphorylation events. Interestingly, in cultured neurons, a phosphorylation gradient was evident, with a gradual change from phosphorylated to dephosphorylated tau from the soma, through the axon, to the growth cone (Mandell and Banker, 1996, Maas et al., 2000). In addition to phosphorylation also other dynamic modifications may have a role in regulating tau's interactions. Of importance could be the O-glycosylation of selected residues, which occurs in many cytoskeletal proteins including tau (Arnold et al., 1996) and which may inversely regulate phosphorylation since the same sites can either be modified by O-glycosylation or phosphorylation (Liu et al., 2004).

3. TAU PROTEIN PATHOLOGY IN ALZHEIMER'S DISEASE

Neuropathological Profile

AD is characterized by a well-defined neuropathological profile which includes the formation of NFTs, neuritic plaques, and neuropil threads. The number of NFTs is closely correlated with the degree of dementia. The manner in which NFT formation spreads to various brain areas during the course of AD is not random but follows a stereotyped pattern which has been used to define six neuropathological stages, the Braak stages (Braak and Braak, 1991). Earliest NFTs are observed in the transentorhinal and entorhinal cortex (stages I and II; transentorhinal stages). A more extensive involvement of the entorhinal cortex and the formation of NFTs in the CA1 area of the hippocampus correspond to stages III and IV or to limbic stages. At stages I and II patients are cognitively unimpaired whereas subjects with limbic stages III and IV may have mild cognitive impairment. The main feature of stages V and VI is the development of abundant NFTs in neocortical association areas (isocortical stages). Subjects with stages V and VI meet the neuropathological criteria for diagnosis of AD and are severely demented. Intracellularly, the formation of NFTs is associated with abnormal phosphorylation of tau at selected sites and a relocalization from the axonal to the somatodendritic compartment (Figure 2A).

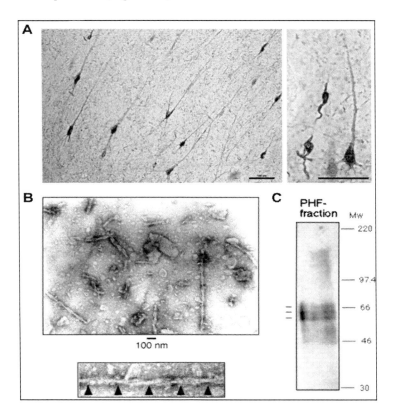

Figure 2. Tau in AD. A. Distribution of phosphorylated tau in the neocortex of a patient with AD. Tau was stained using an antibody against a disease-related phosphoepitope (AT8 antibody). Note the presence of intense tau staining in the somatodendritic compartment of affected neurons. A high power magnification showing neurons with damaged dendritic processes is shown on the right. B, C. Electron micrograph (B) and immunoblot (C) of PHFs isolated from an AD brain. For the immunoblot, a tau antibody that detects all isoforms of tau has been used. A high power electron micrograph demonstrating the periodicity of PHFs is shown at the bottom. Scale bar, 100 μm (A), 100 nm (B).

Filamentous Pathology

All tauopathies including AD share a common filamentous pathology. Ultrastructurally, the dominant components of neurofibrillary lesions in AD are paired helical filaments (PHFs) and straight filaments (SFs) (Figure 2B). PHFs are composed of two strands of filaments twisted around one another with a periodicity of 80 nm and a diameter varying from 8 to 20 nm (Crowther and Wischik, 1985), whereas SFs lack this helical periodicity (Crowther, 1991). Both PHFs and SFs are composed predominantly of abnormally hyperphosphorylated tau proteins (Lee et al., 1991). Analysis of PHFs purified from AD brains by sodium dodecyl sulfate-polyacrylamide gel electrophoresis (SDS-PAGE) has revealed three major bands of approximately 68, 64, and 60 kDa (Figure 2C) (Greenberg and Davies, 1990). Upon dephosphorylation six tau bands are seen indicating that PHF tau contains all six isoforms, each in a hyperphosphorylated state.

Hyperphosphorylation

Tau isolated from PHFs has a stoichiometry of phosphorylation of about 6-8 mol phosphate/mol tau, which is significantly higher than tau isolated from control brains (1.9 mol phosphate/mol tau) (Kenessey and Yen, 1993). While few if any phosphorylation sites appear to be unique to PHF-tau, the proportion of tau phosphorylation at any given site is significantly higher in PHF-tau than in biopsy-derived normal tau protein (Matsuo et al., 1994). Site-specific phosphorylation of tau can be regulated by concerted and sequential action of many protein kinases and phosphatases (Iqbal et al., 2005, Stoothoff and Johnson, 2005). These findings, and the changes in kinases and phosphatases observed in AD (Iqbal et al., 2005), suggest that tau hyperphosphorylation is likely to be caused by an imbalance of the complex protein phosphorylation and dephosphorylation systems in the diseased brain which results in less dynamic phosphorylation/dephosphorylation events and an accumulation of hyperphosphorylated tau. Many of the sites that have been identified to be highly phosphorylated in tau isolated from AD patients are located in regions that aminoterminally and carboxyterminally flank tau's repeat-region (the proline-rich region and the carboxyterminal tail domain; compare to Figure 1C) and which are recognized by phosphorylation-sensitive antibodies that are used for diagnosis of the disease (Stoothoff and Johnson, 2005).

N- and O-Glycosylation

Hyperphosphorylated tau proteins in AD brain are N-glycosylated (Wang et al., 1996) and PHF-tau contains high mannose-type sugar chains and truncated N-glycans in addition to a small amount of sialylated bi- and triantennary sugar chains (Sato et al., 2001). Normal tau is O-glycosylated by O-GlcNAc (see above). O-GlcNAcylation may be increased during Alzheimer's disease (Griffith and Schmitz, 1995).

Glycation

Glycation is a non-enzymatic posttranslational modification that involves a covalent linkage between a sugar and an amino group of a protein and occurs in several diseases. Subsequent oxidation, fragmentation or crosslinking leads then to the production of advanced glycation endproducts (AGEs). Tau is glycated in PHF-tau isolated from the brains of Alzheimer's disease patients (Ko et al., 1999) whereas soluble tau from either Alzheimer's disease or non-demented human brain is not glycated (Ledesma et al., 1994). Glycation is present in the repeat-region of tau (Ledesma et al., 1995).

Ubiquitination

In cells, short lived or damaged proteins become conjugated with multimers of ubiquitin which marks them for degradation in the proteosome. Under normal conditions, tau does not appear to become ubiquitinated. However, PHFs contain ubiquitin (Mori et al., 1987) and ubiquitin levels correlate strongly with the extent of neurofibrillary pathology in the cortex (Wang et al., 1991). Most PHF-tau appears to be monoubiquitinated (Morishima-Kawashima et al., 1993) which may not be a strong signal for ubiquitin-mediated degradation. However, recently it was shown that PHF-tau is also polyubiquitinated (Cripps et al., 2006).

Nitration

Oxidative and nitrative injury is implicated in the pathogenesis of several diseases and nitrated tau was detected in the insoluble tau fraction from AD brains (Horiguchi et al., 2003). Nitration occurs at Tyr29 in soluble tau and PHF-tau from severely affected brains of AD patients but not in tau from normal aged brain (Reynolds et al., 2006).

Proteolysis

PHFs are very resistant to degradation but evidence exists that during AD tau is specifically cleaved by multiple caspases. This includes cleavage at Asp421 in neurofibrillar pathologies by the apoptotic enzyme caspase-3 (Gamblin et al., 2003) as well as N-terminal truncation of tau at Asp13 by caspase-6 (Horowitz et al., 2004).

Functional Changes

A well studied consequence of tau hyperphosphorylation in AD is a reduction in its ability to interact with microtubules and a functional loss to promote microtubule assembly which can be mimicked by pseudohyperphosphorylation of tau (Eidenmüller et al., 2000, Eidenmüller et al., 2001). The amount of tau that binds to microtubules is reduced in AD brain and the degree of impairment in microtubule binding correlates with the extent of tau pathology (Bramblett et al., 1992). The ability of PHF-tau to bind to microtubules is significantly less than that of control tau (Yoshida and Ihara, 1993). Disease-like hyperphosphorylated tau also exhibits functional deficiencies in other interactions, e.g. binding to actin filaments (Selden and Pollard, 1983), binding to the membrane cortex (Maas et al., 2000), and interaction with protein phosphatase 2A (Eidenmüller et al., 2000). Evidence exists that disease-like tau may also gain functions that could be detrimental in the disease process. *In vitro* data indicate that hyperphosphorylated tau from AD brains is capable of associating with normal tau and the high molecular weight MAPs MAP1 and MAP2, which may sequester normal tau and these MAPs from microtubules (Alonso et al., 1996, Alonso et al., 1997). Interestingly, polymerization of hyperphosphorylated tau into filaments inhibits its ability to bind normal tau and dissociation of the filaments by ultrasonication restores this ability indicating that this gain of function effect operates only when tau is soluble (Alonso et al., 2006).

4. NATURAL AND TRANSGENIC ANIMAL MODELS FOR TAU PATHOLOGY IN ALZHEIMER'S DISEASE

Animal models are indispensable for studying the role of tau in AD and for testing possible therapeutics.

Some natural models for hyperphosphorylation or aggregation of tau are known. E.g., aggregation of tau has been described for aged bears, sheep, wolverines, and baboons (Cork et al., 1988, Nelson and Saper, 1995, Roertgen et al., 1996, Schultz et al., 2000). In sheep the deposition of altered tau at dendritic branching points may indicate a link between neurofibrillary pathology and dendritic remodeling (Nelson and Saper, 1995). Natural hyperphosphorylation of tau occurs in hibernating animals, either reversibly during torpor possibly as a protective mechanism (Arendt et al., 2003) or irreversibly upon aging (Härtig et al., 2005). Natural models provide the advantage that it becomes possible to correlate the process of tau hyperphosphorylation and aggregation with behavioral, morphological, and biochemical changes in more detail than it is possible in humans without the risk of inducing artificial effects as they may occur in transgenic animals.

A variety of transgenic animals as models for tauopathies have been produced on different evolutionary levels. These include the roundworm (*Caenorhabditis elegans*), the fruit fly (*Drosophila melanogaster*), and the mouse (*Mus musculus*) (reviewed in Lee et al., 2005). Most of these animal models express tau constructs with mutations that are found in the familial tauopathy FTDP-17. It should however be noted that the transfer of these results to the role of tau pathology in AD must be handled with caution, because tau is not mutated in AD and therefore altered tau might act in a different way in AD compared to FTDP-17.

Several transgenic mouse lines that express different isoforms of human tau in its unaltered state in the presence or absence of endogenous mouse tau have been produced (for an overview see Götz, 2001, Lee et al., 2005). The first tau transgenic mice expressed the longest human brain tau isoform at low level which was found to not induce formation of NFTs (Götz et al., 1995). More recently, a very elaborate mouse model that expresses all six isoforms of the adult human CNS in the absence of endogenous mouse tau has been produced (Andorfer et al., 2003). These mice develop NFTs composed of hyperphosphorylated tau and show neuronal cell death. Interestingly, cell death did not directly correlate with the formation of NFTs, indicating that neurodegeneration can occur independently of NFT formation (Andorfer et al., 2005). Using these mice it was shown that the mechanism of neurodegeneration involves the reexpression of cell cycle proteins, suggesting that tau pathology in AD may be linked to abnormal cell-cycle reentry in mature neurons (Andorfer et al., 2005). Very recently this hypothesis was confirmed in a different model in which transgenic mice with forced cell cycle activation were produced by oncogene expression (Park et al., 2007). These mice developed clear characteristics of tau pathology even with endogenous mouse tau.

Additional types of transgenic mice were produced with the aim that they develop a complete AD pathology, i.e. hyperphosphorylated tau, formation of NFTs, and development of senile plaques (reviewed e.g. in Games et al., 2006, McGowan et al., 2006). The results are difficult to interpret because of the inherent complexity but these models may allow to elucidate the functional interaction of Aβ and tau pathology. For example, using a triple-transgenic model expressing mutated presenilin 1 (PS1), mutated APP, and mutated tau it could be shown that Aβ deposition develops prior to tau aggregation (Oddo et al., 2003a) and that removal of Aβ also removed tau pathology (Oddo et al., 2006), which is in line with the so-called amyloid cascade hypothesis which states that tau pathology is downstream of Aβ. Synaptic dysfunction was observed already before formation of Aβ plaques and tau tangles, providing evidence that highly aggregated states of Aβ or tau are not essential for functional changes in the affected neurons (Oddo et al., 2003b).

5. CONCLUSION AND PROSPECTS

The neuropathological profile and posttranslational changes of tau protein during AD are well described (Table 1). However, the relationship between changes in tau and pathological mechanisms are still a matter of debate. E.g., it is still unclear whether increased phosphorylation or other modifications present a toxic insult, whether tau aggregation is required for tau-mediated degeneration or – in turn – represents a rescue attempt of the affected neurons, and how other disease-related changes contribute to the neurodegenerative process.

Alzheimer's disease (AD) as well as some other neurodegenerative disorders including Parkinson's disease (PD) and Huntington's disease (HD) are increasingly being realized to have in common pathological alterations in the dynamic turnover of intracellular proteins (Ross and Poirier, 2004). Increasing evidence including results from clinical trials indicate that these alterations significantly contribute to cellular dysfunction and neuronal death (Lansbury and Lashuel, 2006). In AD, changes in the dynamic turnover of proteins become evident as accumulation of misfolded tau proteins and pathological posttanslational modifications such as increased and less dynamic phosphorylation ('hyperphosphorylation'), glycosylation, ubiquitination and nitration (see Table 1).

A better understanding of the cellular mechanisms of the disease process by taking advantage of recent developments including new approaches to visualize the dynamics of disease-relevant proteins such as tau in living cells will help to identify critical events in the pathologic cascade and may pave the avenue for the development of drugs that interfere with these changes. Animal models that recapitulate key aspects of tau pathology will be very useful to test these drugs prior to clinical studies.

Table 1. Changes of tau during AD. See text for details

Feature	"Normal" tau	Tau in Alzheimer's disease
Intracellular distribution	Enriched in the axon	Accumulation in somatodendritic compartment
Aggregation state	Soluble/associated with cellular proteins and organelles	Neurofibrillar lesions composed of PHFs and SFs
Phosphorylation	Dynamic with a stoichiometry of about 1.9 mol phosphate/mol tau for isolated tau	Less dynamic with a stoichiometry of about 6-8 mol phosphate/mol tau in isolated PHFs; hyperphosphorylation clustered in regions that aminoterminally and carboxyterminally flank tau's repeat-region
N-glycosylation	No evidence for N-glycosylation	PHF-tau is N-glycosylated with high mannose-type sugar chains and truncated N-glycans
O-glycosylation	Tau is O-glycosylated by O-GlcNAc	May be increased during AD
Glycation	Not detected	PHF-tau is glycated; glycation is present in the repeat-region of tau
Ubiquitination	No evidence for ubiquitination	Mono- and polyubiquitination of PHF-tau
Nitration	No nitration at Tyr29 in tau from normal aged brain	Soluble tau and PHF-tau from severely affected brains of AD patients is nitrated at Tyr29
Proteolysis	No evidence for caspase-mediated cleavage	Caspase-mediated cleavage of PHF-tau at Asp421 and Asp13
Functional changes	Stimulation of microtubule nucleation and growth, reduction of microtubule instability; binding to actin filaments, the membrane cortex, and protein phosphatase 2A	Reduced ability of PHF-tau to bind to microtubules; soluble AD-like phosphorylated tau sequesters normal tau and MAP1 and MAP2; disease-like phosphorylated tau looses its ability to bind to actin filaments, the membrane cortex, and protein phosphatase 2A

ACKNOWLEDGEMENTS

This work was supported by the Ministry for Science and Culture of Lower Saxony and a grant of the Alzheimer Forschung Initiative e.V. (to M.H.).

REFERENCES

Alonso, A.C., Grundke-Iqbal, I. and Iqbal, K. Alzheimer's disease hyperphosphorylated tau sequesters normal tau into tangles of filaments and disassembles microtubules. *Nat Med 2:* 783-787, 1996.

Alonso, A.C., Grundke-Iqbal, I., Barra, H.S. and Iqbal, K. Abnormal phosphorylation of tau and the mechanism of Alzheimer neurofibrillary degeneration: sequestration of microtubule-associated proteins 1 and 2 and the disassembly of microtubules by the abnormal tau. *Proc Natl Acad Sci USA 94:* 298-303, 1997.

Alonso, A.C., Li, B., Grundke-Iqbal, I. and Iqbal, K. Polymerization of hyperphosphorylated tau into filaments eliminates its inhibitory activity. *Proc Natl Acad Sci USA 103:* 8864-8869, 2006.

Andorfer, C., Acker, C.M., Kress, Y., Hof, P.R., Duff, K. and Davies, P. Cell-cycle reentry and cell death in transgenic mice expressing nonmutant human tau isoforms. *J Neurosci 25:* 5446-5454, 2005.

Andorfer, C., Kress, Y., Espinoza, M., de Silva, R., Tucker, K.L., Barde, Y.A., Duff, K. and Davies, P. Hyperphosphorylation and aggregation of tau in mice expressing normal human tau isoforms. *J Neurochem 86:* 582-590, 2003.

Arendt, T., Stieler, J., Strijkstra, A.M., Hut, R.A., Rudiger, J., Van der Zee, E.A., Harkany, T., Holzer, M. and Härtig, W. Reversible paired helical filament-like phosphorylation of tau is an adaptive process associated with neuronal plasticity in hibernating animals. *J Neurosci 23:* 6972-6981, 2003.

Arnold, C.S., Johnson, G.V.W., Cole, R.N., Dong, D.L., Le, M. and Hart, G.W. The microtubule-associated protein tau is extensively modified with O-linked N-acetylglucosamine. *J Biol Chem 271:* 28741-28744, 1996.

Binder, L.I., Frankfurter, A. and Rebhun, L.I. The distribution of tau in the mammalian central nervous system. *J Cell Biol 101:* 1371-1378, 1985.

Black, M.M., Slaughter, T., Moshiach, S., Obrocka, M. and Fischer, I. Tau is enriched on dynamic microtubules in the distal region of growing axons. *J Neurosci 16:* 3601-3619, 1996.

Braak, H. and Braak, E. Neuropathological stageing of Alzheimer-related changes. *Acta Neuropathol (Berl) 82:* 239-259, 1991.

Bramblett, G.T., Trojanowski, J.Q. and Lee, V.M. Regions with abundant neurofibrillary pathology in human brain exhibit a selective reduction in levels of binding-competent tau and accumulation of abnormal tau-isoforms (A68 proteins). *Lab Invest 66:* 212-222, 1992.

Brandt, R. and Lee, G. Functional organization of microtubule associated protein tau: identification of regions which affect microtubule growth, nucleation, and bundle formation in vitro. *J Biol Chem 268:* 3414-3419, 1993.

Brandt, R. and Leschik, J. Functional interactions of tau and their relevance for Alzheimer's disease. *Current Alzheimer Research 1:* 255-269, 2004.

Caceres, A. and Kosik, K.S. Inhibition of neurite polarity by tau antisense oligonucleotides in primary cerebellar neurons. *Nature 343:* 461-463, 1990.

Cork, L.C., Powers, R.E., Selkoe, D.J., Davies, P., Geyer, J.J. and Price, D.L. Neurofibrillary tangles and senile plaques in aged bears. *J Neuropathol Exp Neurol 47:* 629-641, 1988.

Cripps, D., Thomas, S.N., Jeng, Y., Yang, F., Davies, P. and Yang, A.J. Alzheimer disease-specific conformation of hyperphosphorylated paired helical filament-Tau is polyubiquitinated through Lys-48, Lys-11, and Lys-6 ubiquitin conjugation. *J Biol Chem 281:* 10825-10838, 2006.

Crowther, R.A. Straight and paired helical filaments in Alzheimer disease have a common structural unit. *Proc Natl Acad Sci USA 88:* 2288-2292, 1991.

Crowther, R.A. and Wischik, C.M. Image reconstruction of the Alzheimer paired helical filament. *EMBO J 4:* 3661-3665, 1985.

Drechsel, D.N., Hyman, A.A., Cobb, M.H. and Kirschner, M.W. Modulation of the dynamic instability of tubulin assembly by the microtubule-associated protein tau. *Mol Biol Cell 3:* 1141-1154, 1992.

Drubin, D.G. and Kirschner, M.W. Tau protein function in living cells. *J Cell Biol 103:* 2739-2746, 1986.

Eidenmüller, J., Fath, T., Hellwig, A., Reed, J., Sontag, E. and Brandt, R. Structural and functional implications of tau hyperphosphorylation: information from phosphorylation-mimicking mutated tau proteins. *Biochemistry 39:* 13166-13175, 2000.

Eidenmüller, J., Fath, T., Maas, T., Pool, M., Sontag, E. and Brandt, R. Phosphorylation-mimicking glutamate clusters in the proline-rich region are sufficient to simulate the functional deficiencies of hyperphosphorylated tau protein. *Biochem J 357:* 759-767, 2001.

Gamblin, T.C., Chen, F., Zambrano, A., Abraha, A., Lagalwar, S., Guillozet, A.L., Lu, Y., Fu, Y., Garcia-Sierra, F., LaPointe, N., Miller, R., Berry, R.W., Binder, L.I. and Cryns, V.L. Caspase cleavage of tau: linking amyloid and neurofibrillary tangles in Alzheimer's disease. *Proc Natl Acad Sci USA 100:* 10032-10037, 2003.

Games, D., Buttini, M., Kobayashi, D., Schenk, D. and Seubert, P. Mice as models: transgenic approaches and Alzheimer's disease. *J Alzheimers Dis 9:* 133-149, 2006.

Goedert, M. and Spillantini, M.G. A century of Alzheimer's disease. *Science 314:* 777-781, 2006.

Götz, J. Tau and transgenic animal models. *Brain Res Rev 35:* 266-286, 2001.

Götz, J., Probst, A., Spillantini, M.G., Schafer, T., Jakes, R., Burki, K. and Goedert, M. Somatodendritic localization and hyperphosphorylation of tau protein in transgenic mice expressing the longest human brain tau isoform. *EMBO J 14:* 1304-1313, 1995.

Greenberg, S.G. and Davies, P. A preparation of Alzheimer paired helical filaments that displays distinct tau proteins by polyacrylamide gel electrophoresis. *Proc Natl Acad Sci USA 87:* 5827-5831, 1990.

Griffith, L.S. and Schmitz, B. O-linked N-acetylglucosamine is upregulated in Alzheimer brains. *Biochem Biophys Res Commun 213:* 424-431, 1995.

Harada, A., Oguchi, K., Okabe, S., Kuno, J., Terada, S. and Ohshima, T., Sato-Yoshitake R, Takei Y, Noda T, Hirokawa N. Altered microtubule organization in small-calibre axons of mice lacking tau protein. *Nature 369:* 488-491, 1994.

Härtig, W., Oklejewicz, M., Strijkstra, A.M., Boerema, A.S., Stieler, J. and Arendt, T. Phosphorylation of the tau protein sequence 199-205 in the hippocampal CA3 region of Syrian hamsters in adulthood and during aging. *Brain Res 1056:* 100-104, 2005.

Horiguchi, T., Uryu, K., Giasson, B.I., Ischiropoulos, H., LightFoot, R., Bellmann, C., Richter-Landsberg, C., Lee, V.M. and Trojanowski, J.Q. Nitration of tau protein is linked to neurodegeneration in tauopathies. *Am J Pathol 163:* 1021-1031, 2003.

Horowitz, P.M., Patterson, K.R., Guillozet-Bongaarts, A.L., Reynolds, M.R., Carroll, C.A., Weintraub, S.T., Bennett, D.A., Cryns, V.L., Berry, R.W. and Binder, L.I. Early N-terminal changes and caspase-6 cleavage of tau in Alzheimer's disease. *J Neurosci 24:* 7895-7902, 2004.

Iqbal, K., Alonso Adel, C., Chen, S., Chohan, M.O., El-Akkad, E., Gong, C.X., Khatoon, S., Li, B., Liu, F., Rahman, A., Tanimukai, H. and Grundke-Iqbal, I. Tau pathology in Alzheimer disease and other tauopathies. *Biochim Biophys Acta 1739:* 198-210, 2005.

Kempf, M., Clement, A., Faissner, A., Lee, G. and Brandt, R. Tau binds to the distal axon early in development of polarity in a microtubule- and microfilament-dependent manner. *J Neurosci 16:* 5583-5592, 1996.

Kenessey, A. and Yen, S.H. The extent of phosphorylation of fetal tau is comparable to that of PHF-tau from Alzheimer paired helical filaments. *Brain Res 629:* 40-46, 1993.

Ko, L.W., Ko, E.C., Nacharaju, P., Liu, W.K., Chang, E., Kenessey, A. and Yen, S.H. An immunochemical study on tau glycation in paired helical filaments. *Brain Res 830:* 301-313, 1999.

Lansbury, P.T. and Lashuel, H.A. A century-old debate on protein aggregation and neurodegeneration enters the clinic. *Nature 443:* 774-779, 2006.

Ledesma, M.D., Bonay, P. and Avila, J. Tau protein from Alzheimer's disease patients is glycated at its tubulin-binding domain. *J Neurochem:* 1658-1664, 1995.

Ledesma, M.D., Bonay, P., Colaco, C. and Avila, J. Analysis of microtubule-associated protein tau glycation in paired helical filaments. *J Biol Chem 269:* 21614-21619, 1994.

Lee, G. Tau and src family tyrosine kinases. *Biochim Biophys Acta 1739:* 323-330, 2005.

Lee, V.M., Balin, B.J., Otvos Jr., L. and Trojanowski, J.Q. A68: a major subunit of paired helical filaments and derivatized forms of normal tau. *Science 251:* 675-678, 1991.

Lee, V.M., Kenyon, T.K. and Trojanowski, J.Q. Transgenic animal models of tauopathies. *Biochim Biophys Acta 1739:* 251-259, 2005.

Liu, F., Iqbal, K., Grundke-Iqbal, I., Hart, G.W. and Gong, C.X. O-GlcNAcylation regulates phosphorylation of tau: a mechanism involved in Alzheimer's disease. *Proc Natl Acad Sci USA 101:* 10804-10809, 2004.

Maas, T., Eidenmüller, J. and Brandt, R. Interaction of tau with the neural membrane cortex is regulated by phosphorylation at sites that are modified in paired helical filaments. *J Biol Chem 275:* 15733-15740, 2000.

Mandell, J.W. and Banker, G.A. A spatial gradient of tau protein phosphorylation in nascent axons. *J Neurosci 16:* 5727-5740, 1996.

Matsuo, E.S., Shin, R.W., Billingsley, M.L., Van de Voorde, A., O'Connor, M., Trojanowski, J.Q. and Lee, V.M. Biopsy-derived adult human brain tau is phosphorylated at many of the same sites as Alzheimer's disease paired helical filament tau. *Neuron 13:* 989-1002, 1994.

McGowan, E., Eriksen, J. and Hutton, M. A decade of modeling Alzheimer's disease in transgenic mice. *Trends Genet 22:* 281-289, 2006.

Mori, H., Kondo, J. and Ihara, Y. Ubiquitin is a component of paired helical filaments in Alzheimer's disease. *Science 235:* 1641-1644, 1987.

Morishima-Kawashima, M., Hasegawa, M., Takio, K., Suzuki, M., Titani, K. and Ihara, Y. Ubiquitin is conjugated with amino-terminally processed tau in paired helical filaments. *Neuron 10:* 1151-1160, 1993.

Nelson, P.T. and Saper, C.B. Ultrastructure of neurofibrillary tangles in the cerebral cortex of sheep. *Neurobiol Aging 16:* 315-323, 1995.

Oddo, S., Caccamo, A., Kitazawa, M., Tseng, B.P. and LaFerla, F.M. Amyloid deposition precedes tangle formation in a triple transgenic model of Alzheimer's disease. *Neurobiol Aging 24:* 1063-1070, 2003a.

Oddo, S., Caccamo, A., Shepherd, J.D., Murphy, M.P., Golde, T.E., Kayed, R., Metherate, R., Mattson, M.P., Akbari, Y. and LaFerla, F.M. Triple-transgenic model of Alzheimer's disease with plaques and tangles: intracellular Abeta and synaptic dysfunction. *Neuron 39:* 409-421, 2003b.

Oddo, S., Caccamo, A., Tran, L., Lambert, M.P., Glabe, C.G., Klein, W.L. and Laferla, F.M. Temporal profile of amyloid-beta (Abeta) oligomerization in an in vivo model of Alzheimer disease: A link between Abeta and tau pathology. *J Biol Chem 281:* 1599-1604, 2006.

Reynolds, M.R., Reyes, J.F., Fu, Y., Bigio, E.H., Guillozet-Bongaarts, A.L., Berry, R.W. and Binder, L.I. Tau nitration occurs at tyrosine 29 in the fibrillar lesions of Alzheimer's disease and other tauopathies. *J Neurosci 26:* 10636-10645, 2006.

Roertgen, K.E., Parisi, J.E., Clark, H.B., Barnes, D.L., O'Brien, T.D. and Johnson, K.H. A beta-associated cerebral angiopathy and senile plaques with neurofibrillary tangles and cerebral hemorrhage in an aged wolverine (Gulo gulo). *Neurobiol Aging 17:* 243-247, 1996.

Ross, C.A. and Poirier, M.A. Protein aggregation and neurodegenerative disease. *Nat Med 10:* S10-17, 2004.

Sato, Y., Naito, I., Grundke-Iqbal, I., Iqbal, K. and Endo, T. Analysis of N-glycans of pathological tau: possible occurrence of aberrant processing of tau in Alzheimer's disease. *FEBS Lett 496:* 152-160, 2001.

Schultz, C., Dehghani, F., Hubbard, G.B., Thal, D.R., Struckhoff, G., Braak, E. and Braak, H. Filamentous tau pathology in nerve cells, astrocytes, and oligodendrocytes of aged baboons. *J Neuropathol Exp Neurol 59:* 39-52, 2000.

Selden, S.C. and Pollard, T.D. Phosphorylation of microtubule-associated proteins regulates their interaction with actin filaments. *J Biol Chem 258:* 7064-7071, 1983.

Stoothoff, W.H. and Johnson, G.V. Tau phosphorylation: physiological and pathological consequences. *Biochim Biophys Acta 1739:* 280-297, 2005.

Tint, I., Slaughter, T., Fischer, I. and Black, M.M. Acute inactivation of tau has no effect on dynamics of microtubules in growing axons of cultured sympathetic neurons. *J Neurosci 18:* 8660-8673, 1998.

Wang, G.P., Khatoon, S., Iqbal, K. and Grundke-Iqbal, I. Brain ubiquitin is markedly elevated in Alzheimer disease. *Brain Res 566:* 146-151, 1991.

Wang, J.Z., Grundke-Iqbal, I. and Iqbal, K. Glycosylation of microtubule-associated protein tau: an abnormal posttranslational modification in Alzheimer's disease. *Nat Med 2:* 871-875, 1996.

Weingarten, M.D., Lockwood, A.H., Hwo, S.Y. and Kirschner, M.W. A protein factor essential for microtubule assembly. *Proc Natl Acad Sci USA 72:* 1858-1862, 1975.

Yoshida, H. and Ihara, Y. Tau in paired helical filaments is functionally distinct from fetal tau: assembly incompetence of paired helical filament-tau. *J Neurochem 61:* 1183-1186, 1993.

In: Research Progress in Alzheimer's Disease and Dementia   ISBN 978-1-60021-960-3
Editor: Miao-Kun Sun, pp. 95-134   © 2008 Nova Science Publishers, Inc.

Chapter V

Intraneuronal β-Amyloid-Induced Neurodegeneration and Alzheimer's Dementia

Sarah L. Cole and Robert Vassar[*]

Department of Cell and Molecular Biology, Northwestern University, The Feinberg
School of Medicine, Chicago, Illinois 60611, USA.

ABSTRACT

A wealth of data suggests that the accumulation of intraneuronal beta amyloid peptide (Aβ) is an early neuropathological event in Alzheimer's disease (AD). Indeed, reports indicate that intraneuronal Aβ may act as an important initiating trigger factor in the development of well-described AD-associated pathology, such as Aβ plaque deposition and subsequent neuronal loss, which are observed later in the course of the disease. As such, this pool of intraneuronal Aβ may serve as an ideal target for future AD therapeutics. Here, we have attempted to assimilate this large body of data and we discuss the appearance, nature (monomeric, oligomeric and/or fibrillar) and subcellular localization of intraneuronal Aβ in both human brain and the brains of various transgenic (Tg) mouse models of AD. We describe how this pool of Aβ appears to correlate with significant cognitive and behavioral deficits prior to the appearance of Aβ plaque and neurofibrillary tangle (NFT) formation. Further, we provide insight into putative cellular and molecular mechanisms that link intraneuronal Aβ accumulation with such deficits. In addition, the relationship between intraneuronal and extracellular Aβ is discussed and we explore the potential that intraneuronal Aβ has as a putative drug target.

---

[*] Correspondence concerning this article should be addressed to: Robert Vassar, Email: r-vassar@northwestern.edu.

ABBREVIATIONS

Aβ,	Beta amyloid peptide;
AD,	Alzheimer's disease;
Tg,	transgenic;
NFT,	neurofibrillary tangle;
APP,	amyloid precursor protein;
BACE1,	β-site APP cleaving enzyme;
CTF,	C terminal fragment;
Aph1,	anterior pharynx defective 1;
PS,	presenilin;
Pen2,	resenilin enhancer-2;
AICD,	APP intracellular domain;
FAD,	familial AD;
DS,	Down's syndrome;
ADDLs,	Aβ derived diffusible ligands;
LTP,	long-term potentiation;
MCI,	mild cognitive impairment;
PHF,	paired helical filament;
ER/IC,	endoplasmic reticulum/intermediate compartment;
TGN,	trans-Golgi network;
EM,	electron microscopy;
MVB,	multivesicular body;
MWM,	Morris water maze;
ICV,	intracerebroventricular;
nAChR,	nicotinic acetylcholine receptor;
HSP,	heat shock protein;
GSK,	glycogen synthase kinase;
Cdk,	cyclin dependent kinase;
EGFR,	epidermal growth factor receptor;
EGF,	epidermal growth factor;
UPS,	ubiquitin-proteasome system.

THE AMYLOID HYPOTHESIS

AD is characterized by several pathological abnormalities including amyloid plaques, composed of Aβ, NFTs, composed of hyperphosphorylated tau, neuroinflammation, neuronal dysfunction and cell death. A unifying model of AD progression that links all of these diverse endpoints remains to be described. However, for over a decade, the prevailing view for the cellular and molecular pathogenesis of AD has centered on Aβ accumulation.

Aβ is generated as a result of the proteolytic activities of two enzymes, namely β- and γ-secretase that sequentially cleave amyloid precursor protein (APP) to yield a variety of Aβ peptides (Figure 1; reviewed in Sisodia et al., 1999; Selkoe, 2001a; Vassar, 2004). Initially, β-secretase (β-site APP Cleaving Enzyme 1; BACE1) cuts APP at the amino terminus of the Aβ domain to yield the membrane-bound C-terminal fragment (CTF), C99 and the secreted ectodomain, APPsβ. C99 is the substrate for γ-secretase, a protein complex comprising of nicastrin, anterior pharynx defective-1 (Aph1), presenilin (PS) and presenilin enhancer-2 (Pen2), which cleaves to generate an APP intracellular domain (AICD) and importantly, Aβ. The heterogeneity of γ-secretase cleavage produces Aβ peptides of varying length, ranging from 38-43 amino acid peptides. The more fibrillogenic 42 amino acid peptide (Aβ42) is the predominant species of Aβ in amyloid plaques. In an alternative non-amyloidogenic pathway, which precludes Aβ generation, α-secretase cleaves APP within the Aβ domain to liberate the membrane bound CTF, C83 and the secreted APP ectodomain, APPsα. C83, like C99, is a substrate for γ-secretase, which cleaves it to generate the non-amyloidogenic fragment p3 and AICD.

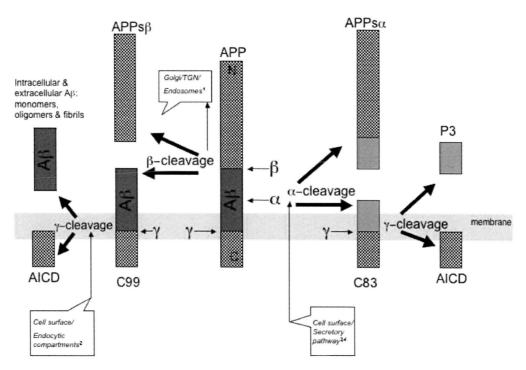

Figure 1. APP Processing (reviewed in Sisodia et al., 1999; Selkoe, 2001a; Vassar, 2004). APP is cleaved by the sequential actions of β- (BACE1) and γ-secretase (a complex of PS, nicastrin, APH1 and PEN2) to generate Aβ. Initial cleavage by BACE1 ([1]Vassar et al., 1999) yields APPsβ, a secreted molecule, and C99, a membrane-bound stub. C99 is then proteolyzed by γ-secretase ([2]Kaether et al., 2006) and Aβ peptides of varying lengths are generated, along with APP intracellular domains (AICD). Aβ exists in multiple forms including extracellular, aggregated Aβ fibrils, soluble oligomers and intracellular Aβ. Both fibrillar and soluble oligomeric Aβ has been identified within the cell. Aβ formation is precluded by the proteolysis of APP by α-secretase ([3] Lammich et al., 1999; [4]Parvathy et al., 1999), which results in the generation of secreted APPsα and C83, a membrane bound fragment. C83 undergoes cleavage by γ-secretase to form two smaller fragments, P3 and AICD.

The tenant of the original amyloid hypothesis was that the gradual extracellular accumulation of insoluble, fibrillar Aβ (Glenner and Wong, 1984; Masters et al., 1985) somehow triggers the complex pathological changes that ultimately lead to cognitive dysfunction. This hypothesis was based on a number of findings that strongly implicated plaques and particularly Aβ as the primary cause of neurodegeneration.

In the early 1990s mutations in the APP gene on chromosome 21 were linked to several families who suffered from early-onset familial AD (FAD; St. George-Hyslop et al., 1990; Goate et al., 1991). Furthermore, many families with FAD have mutations in the genes encoding presenilin proteins, PS1 and PS2 (Schellenberg et al., 1992; Levy-Lahad et al., 1995a, b), proteins crucial to the proteolytic function of the γ-secretase complex. Aβ is elevated in AD patients and all APP mutations result either in the elevation of total Aβ production, as is the case with the K670N/M671L substitution (the Swedish APP mutation; Mullan et al., 1992) or, as with the presenilin FAD mutations, increase the generation of the highly amyloidogenic Aβ42 specifically, as occurs with the I716V Florida mutation (Eckman et al., 1997). In addition, Down's Syndrome (DS) patients almost invariably develop AD plaque pathology as a result of the duplication of the part of the chromosome 21 that carries the APP gene. Importantly, Aβ42, the highly fibrillar and predominant plaque Aβ species, appears neurotoxic in vitro (reviewed in Selkoe, 2001a).

The amyloid hypothesis still dominates thinking about disease progression and therapeutic drug development today. However, advances in the understanding of AD pathogenesis now provide strong support for modification of this hypothesis.

Direct evidence that amyloid plaques are pathogenic in vivo has been difficult to obtain. Tg mice that overexpress FAD-mutated APP have elevated cerebral Aβ levels and develop amyloid deposits in an age-dependent manner (reviewed in Hsiao Ashe, 2001). While APP trangenics exhibit many neuropathological AD characteristics and exhibit memory deficits they do not develop NFTs nor do they have significant neuronal loss, both important features of AD.

Although the total amount of Aβ (Aβ load) directly correlates with dementia (Cummings and Cotman, 1995; Parvathy et al., 2001), plaque burden is a poor correlate with the degree of dementia in AD (Terry et al., 1999) and, together with the incomplete recapitulation of AD pathology in APP Tg mice, these facts call into question the role of amyloid plaques in AD pathogenesis. Indeed, recent evidence suggests that the presence or absence of plaques is insufficient to fully account for the deleterious role of elevated Aβ in AD, and significant cognitive abnormalities have been observed in a number of AD Tg mice models prior to the appearance of amyloid plaques (Oddo et al., 2003; Ohno et al., 2004; Billings et al., 2005; Ohno et al., 2006).

While mounting evidence still suggests that Aβ plays a critical, early role in AD pathogenesis, the location and form (or forms) of Aβ responsible for brain damage observed during disease progression is a strong focus for debate.

OLIGOMERIC Aβ

Recently research has begun to move away from the insoluble, fibrillar amyloid plaque and towards soluble, non-fibrillar oligomeric forms of Aβ as potential toxic agents in AD. Kuo and colleagues determined that soluble Aβ could be detected at high concentrations in AD brain, compared to control tissue (Kuo et al., 1996). Indeed, the accumulation of soluble Aβ oligomers in human AD frontal cortex was detailed in a later study, with levels reaching up to 70-fold over those found in control brains (Gong et al., 2003). Studies of postmortem human brain show that soluble Aβ correlates better than insoluble Aβ or Aβ plaques with cognitive function in AD patients (McLean et al., 1999). Thus given the concentration and the potential for long distance diffusion through the brain parenchyma, soluble Aβ may have great neurotoxic potential.

Aβ oligomers are non-fibrillar Aβ assemblies that are soluble in physiological solutions. Initial ultrastructural analytical studies indicated that spherical Aβ oligomers coalesce to form protofibrils that then form mature fibrils (Harper et al., 1999; Bitan et al., 2003) suggesting that oligomers are intermediates on the fibril assembly pathway. However, a very recent inhibitor-based study indicates that oligomers are not necessarily obligate intermediates in the fibril formation pathway (Necula et al., 2007). While further work is required to clarify this issue these findings may indicate that there may be more than one pathway leading to Aβ fibril formation. Oligomers may either form fibrils directly, as originally proposed, or they may represent an "off pathway" assembly state that buffers the concentration of monomer that ultimately assembles into fibrils rather than the oligomers directly converting to fibrils (Necula et al., 2007).

Many oligomeric species have been described from studies based largely on the use of synthetic Aβ. These include Aβ derived diffusible ligands (ADDLs; Lambert et al., 1998) prefibrillar aggregates (Necula et al., 2007) and protofibrils (Hartley et al., 1999). ADDLs were originally described as low molecular weight trimeric or tetrameric Aβ species, but a recent solution state characterization of ADDLs indicated that the native ADDL population is composed of a heterogenous oligomeric component along with a significant amount of monomeric Aβ (Hepler et al., 2006).

In vitro studies have shown ADDLs to be neurotoxic (Lambert et al., 1998; Hartley et al., 1999; Lacor et al., 2007). While plaque load correlates poorly with AD severity, synapse loss is likely the best correlate of clinical deterioration in AD patients. Using highly differentiated hippocampal cultures it has been recently demonstrated that following specific binding to neurons, ADDLs cause abnormal spine morphology and a significant decrease in spine density and synaptic deterioration (Lacor et al., 2007). Interestingly, Hepler and colleagues reported that the interaction between ADDLs and primary hippocampal neurons is mediated exclusively by the oligomeric component of the ADDL population (Hepler et al., 2006). Interestingly, ADDLs disrupt neuronal physiology including long-term potentiation (LTP), a cellular correlate of memory and learning, in hippocampal slices (Wang et al., 2004). High frequency, repetitive electrical stimulation of specific synaptic circuits such as the CA3-Schaefer collateral-CA1 pathway in the mammalian hippocampus can induce a prolonged potentiation of synapse firing (LTP), which is referred to as inducing synaptic plasticity.

Importantly, Walsh and colleagues defined a synaptotoxic function for naturally secreted oligomers in vivo (Walsh et al., 2002).

While most Aβ oligomeric species have only been observed in vitro following incubation of synthetic Aβ, a few small oligomeric Aβ forms have also been identified in vivo. Indications that some form of soluble Aβ, rather than the amyloid deposit, likely caused memory deficits in the APP Tg mouse and in AD has come from a variety of studies. APP Tg mice demonstrated rapid memory improvement following passive immunization with anti-Aβ monoclonal antibodies (Dodart et al., 2002; Kotilinek et al., 2002). Given the fact that amyloid burden was unchanged following immunization, it was speculated that antibody-mediated sequestration and clearance of soluble amyloid in the brain was responsible for the memory rescue. Tg2576 mice expressing APP harboring the Swedish mutation develop memory deficits at an early age prior to amyloid deposition (Hsiao Ashe 2001). The absence of memory deficits in bigenic BACE-/-.Tg2576 mice that lack Aβ compared to florid deficits observed in the Aβ producing monogenic Tg2576 mice indicated that, in these pre-plaque mice, soluble Aβ assemblies are responsible for at least some aspects of AD-related memory deficits (Ohno et al., 2004).

Indeed, ADDLs can induce cognitive defects when administered in vivo (Lesne et al., 2006) and it has been recently demonstrated that a specific soluble oligomer may be responsible for memory loss in Tg2576 mice. Using a subcellular fractionation procedure followed by immunoblotting, Lesne and colleagues proposed that a soluble 56KDa, putative Aβ dodecamer (Aβ*56) is responsible for memory loss in 6-month old Tg2576 mice. Intraventricular injection of purified Aβ*56 into healthy rats led to significant impairment of long-term memory, while initial acquisition of spatial memory remained unaltered.

Aβ Location

In addition to the form (insoluble Aβ fibrils verses soluble Aβ oligomers), the location (extracellular verses intracellular) of neurotoxic Aβ species has become a hot topic for discussion. In 1985, Masters and colleagues reported that amyloid is initially deposited in the neuron and only later, in the extracellular space (Masters et al., 1985), and today, it is widely acknowledged that the extracellular Aβ aggregates comprising plaques have a neuronal origin.

Expression of the Aβ precursor, APP, is ubiquitous and Aβ42 has been identified within neurons of cognitively normal mouse, rat and human brain (Gouras et al., 2000; Takahashi et al., 2002). Taken together, these data strongly suggest that Aβ has a normal biological function although surprisingly, such a function remains elusive. Importantly however, an increasingly large body of evidence indicates that intraneuronal Aβ is a potential neurotoxic agent that initiates pathogenic events early on in AD progression.

Intraneuronal Aβ and the Human Condition

The accumulation of intracellular Aβ has been observed in neurons of mild cognitive impairment (MCI), AD and DS brain. MCI refers to the transitional state between cognitive changes associated with normal aging and the fully developed clinical features of dementia (Petersen, 2007). Importantly, MCI brain displayed significant amounts of region-specific intraneuronal Aβ42 immunoreactivity that was especially evident in areas prone to developing early AD neuropathology including pyramidal neurons of the hippocampus and entorhinal cortex. Aβ42 staining was far less prominent in brain regions relatively resistant to AD, such as the basal ganglia. Similar findings have been shown for significantly cognitively-impaired AD brain (Gouras et al., 2000; D'Andrea et al., 2001). Human neurons in AD-vulnerable brain regions specifically accumulate Aβ42, rather than Aβ40, and this immunoreactivity appears to precede both NFT and Aβ plaque deposition (Gouras et al., 2000, D'Andrea et al., 2001, Fernandez-Vizarra et al., 2004). Using immunohistochemical methods, AD brains with varying degrees of severity were examined for Aβ- and paired helical filament (PHF)-specific immunoreactivity. Intraneuronal Aβ was detected prior to the appearance of PHF-positive structures, adding further support to the notion that intraneuronal Aβ accumulation is an early neurodegenerative alteration in AD (Fernandez-Vizarra et al., 2004).

The majority of DS patients develop characteristic AD neuropathology. In young DS patients, hippocampal and entorhinal cortical neurons exhibited intraneuronal Aβ accumulation that was detected in the absence of mature extracellular Aβ plaques (Gyure et al., 2001; Busciglio et al., 2002). In a further study of DS patients, all tested Aβ42-antibodies revealed strong intraneuronal immunoreactivity, whereas antibodies against Aβ40 only bound mature plaques (Mori et al., 2002).

Intraneuronal Aβ in Transgenic Brain

FAD accounts for approximately 1-5% of all AD cases, with the majority of cases being sporadic in nature. However, knowledge of these disease-causing mutations has proven highly valuable for AD research and the expression of mutant APP and mutant PS, either individually or in combination, in Tg mouse models of AD has greatly aided understanding of disease pathogenesis. A large number of Tg mouse models are now available and these models recapitulate some key features of AD including increased Aβ production and amyloid plaque deposition. In specific AD Tg models early pathological changes such as synaptic, physiological and behavioral functions begin to decline as Aβ levels increase, prior to the appearance of Aβ plaques (Holcomb et al., 1998; Hsia et al., 1999; Moechars et al., 1999).

It is known that specific FAD mutations increase both secreted and intracellular Aβ42 (Martin et al., 1995; Wild-Bode et al., 1997). Furthermore, the recently identified Arctic (E693G) FAD mutation, decreases, rather than increases Aβ42 secretion and increases protofibril formation, leading the authors to speculate that intracellular increases in Aβ may be important for AD pathogenesis (Nilsberth et al., 2001; Lord et al., 2006). Thus, the phenotypic changes observed in preplaque Tg mice may reflect early pathological changes likely related, in part at least, to the formation and/or accumulation of intraneuronal Aβ. Indeed, a large number of Tg models display significant intraneuronal Aβ immunoreactivity in brain areas specifically affected in AD. Importantly, recent studies have determined that intraneuronal Aβ may be oligomeric in nature (Takahashi et al., 2004; Oddo et al., 2006a; Wirths et al., 2006).

The Tg2576 mouse model of AD is well characterized. In these mice, brain Aβ levels rise dramatically at six to ten months of age, but plaques don't appear until months later (Takahashi et al., 2002). Using immuno-electron microscopy, Takahashi and colleagues demonstrated the presence of intraneuronal Aβ42 within neuronal processes and synaptic compartments in AD-sensitive regions of Tg2576 brain. Prior to plaque development, Aβ42 accumulated presynaptically within axon terminals and especially postsynaptically within distal dendrites. The accumulation of Aβ42 increased with age in pre-plaque Tg2576 mice (Takahashi et al., 2002).

Mutations in PS1 account for a large percentage of FAD cases and worldwide studies on FAD cases have uncovered 161 pathogenic mutations in the PS1 gene (http://www.molgen.ua.ac.be/ADMutations/). Interestingly, aged mice harboring mutated PS1 (L286V), in the absence of any APP mutations, accumulate significant amounts of intracytoplasmic Aβx-42 and Aβ1-28, but not Aβx-40 in cortical neurons. Interestingly, there was no evidence for Aβ plaque pathology in these PS1 Tgs, even in mice as old as 24 months (Chui et al., 1999).

FAD is also known as early-onset AD and an APP mutation (T714I) found in an Austrian family is associated with an aggressive form of AD with an approximate age of onset of 34 years (Kumar-Singh et al., 2000). Recently, a novel Tg model has been generated, the APP-Au Tg model, in which, despite low transgene expression levels, the mice progressively deposit intraneuronal Aβ in select brain regions including the subiculum and CA1 and CA2 hippocampal regions. This deposition initiates at around 6 months and increases with age. Interestingly, similar to the PS1 monogenic mouse, intraneuronal Aβ was observed in the absence of extracellular Aβ deposits in APP-Au mice (Van Broeck et al., 2006). The authors suggest that these findings further support the hypothesis that intraneuronal Aβ may play a role in AD pathogenesis.

Aβ42-elevating FAD mutations act in an additive manner to increase Aβ42 generation. Intramolecular combination of I716V and V717I mutations within APP doubled Aβ42 production compared to individual mutations (Eckman et al., 1997), as did the two PS1 mutations M146L and L286V when introduced together into PS1 (Citron et al., 1998). Furthermore, the intermolecular combination of Aβ42-elevating mutations in APP and PS1 also additively increased Aβ42 production (Citron et al., 1998). In addition to increased Aβ42 production, the intermolecular combination of FAD mutations facilitates enhanced amyloid deposition (reviewed in Spires and Hyman 2005). While no human AD cases are caused by multiple FAD mutations, and it is plausible that un-anticipated effects on APP processing could potentially occur as a consequence of the mutation combinations, Tg mice expressing several FAD mutations (in either or both APP or PS) have still provided invaluable insight into AD pathogenesis. In fact the combination of multiple FAD mutations provides AD models that rapidly develop multiple pathological features of human AD (Oddo et al., 2003; Casas et al., 2004; Billings et al., 2005; Oakley et al., 2006). Importantly, many of these models exhibit profound, early intraneuronal Aβ deposition, similar to the intraneuronal Aβ observed in human conditions, that represents one of the earliest neuropathological manifestations of AD (Wirths et al., 2001; Wirths et al., 2002; Blanchard et al., 2003; Oddo et al., 2003; Casas et al., 2004; Schmitz et al., 2004; Lord et al., 2006; Oakley et al., 2006; Wirths et al., 2006a; Wirths et al., 2006b). Consequently, these models provide an excellent platform in which the relationship between intraneuronal Aβ accumulation and neurodegeneration can be examined.

Intraneuronal Aβ accumulation precedes plaque formation in Tg mice expressing mutant APP_{695} with the Swedish, Dutch (E693Q) and London (V717I) mutations in combination with mutant PS1 (M146L) (PDGFβ-APP/PS1). The abundant immunoreactivity was observed in hippocampal and cortical pyramidal neurons (Wirths et al., 2001). Similar findings were observed in APP/PS1 Tg mice expressing human APP_{751} with the Swedish and London mutations and PS1 with the M146L mutation (APP_{751}^{SL}PS1M146L). The robust intraneuronal Aβ staining appeared strongest in brain areas with early plaque formation including the subiculum and deep cortical layers. On a cellular level, the Aβ was observed in somatodendritic and axonal compartments (Wirths et al., 2002; Blanchard et al., 2003; Langui et al., 2004; Schmitz et al., 2004). In a related study, the same Tg model was used to examine spinal cord related Aβ-pathology (Wirths et al., 2006a). Motor deficits have been reported in AD (O'Keeffe et al., 1996; Scarmeas et al., 2004), and in contrast to NFT pathology, which is constantly described in the spinal cord of AD patients, little is known about cord Aβ pathology. To investigate this, Wirths and colleagues examined the spinal cord of the APP_{751}^{SL}PS1M146L Tg mice. Interestingly, in spinal cord motor neurons, amyloid plaque pathology was preceded by notable intraneuronal Aβ accumulation (Wirths et al., 2006a). This intracellular accumulation was detectable at the same time as Aβ accumulation within hippocampal and cortical neurons (Wirths et al., 2002; Wirths et al., 2006a).

In contrast to other APP mutations linked to AD, which frame the Aβ sequence, the Arctic mutation is located within the Aβ domain (Lord et al., 2006). In vitro, Arctic Aβ peptides readily form soluble Aβ protofibrils (Nilsberth et al., 2001). Recently, comparisons of Tg mice expressing APP with the Swedish mutation (tg-APP_{Swe}) to a novel mouse model expressing APP with both the Swedish and Arctic mutations (tg-APP_{ArcSwe}) demonstrated that the Arctic mutation may cause AD by facilitating aggressive, amyloidosis through the early accumulation of intracellular Aβ aggregates (Lord et al., 2006). Early, prominent intraneuronal Aβ immunoreactivity was observed in the deep layers of the cortex in young tg-APP_{ArcSwe} mice. Furthermore, intraneuronal aggregates increased with age and pre-dated Aβ plaque deposition in both Tg mouse models. In CA1 pyramidal neurons, intraneuronal Aβ aggregates were initially observed at 4 months of age, and continued to increase with the appearance of Aβ plaques at around 6 months in tg-APP_{ArcSwe}. At 9 months, grain-like intraneuronal Aβ aggregates appeared to be widespread throughout the cerebral cortex, subiculum and CA1 hippocampal region in tg-APP_{ArcSwe} mice with modest Aβ plaque deposition. In contrast, at 7 months, intracellular Aβ aggregates were found in tg-APP_{Swe} mice, although the intensity and frequency of aggregates was reduced in the monogenic mice compared to tg-APP_{ArcSwe} mice. At this age, no Aβ plaques were apparent in the APP_{Swe} mice and only a few, diffuse plaques could be observed in 15-17 month old tg-APP_{Swe} mice (Lord et al., 2006).

As an alternative to over-expression of mutant PS1, the APP^{SL}PS1KI model co-expresses M233T/L235P knock-in mutations in PS1 together with APP$_{751}$ harboring the Swedish plus the London mutation. Aβ42 is the major Aβ species present, likely as a consequence of the specific combination of double PS1 and APP mutations, and strong accumulation of intraneuronal Aβ is observed in the CA1/2 hippocampal pyramidal cell layer (Casas et al., 2004). Interestingly, as with the APP$_{751}$^{SL}PS1M146L Tg model detailed previously, APP^{SL}PS1KI mice accumulate significant amounts of intraneuronal Aβ in spinal cord motor neurons (Wirths et al., 2006b).

In addition to mutations in APP and PS proteins, mutant tau has proved to be extremely useful in the analysis of AD pathophysiology. A triple Tg model (3xTg-AD) expressing PS1$_{M146L}$, APP$_{Swe}$ and tau$_{P301L}$ transgenes has been used to examine the role of intraneuronal Aβ in AD pathogenesis (Oddo et al., 2003; Oddo et al., 2004; Billings et al., 2005; Oddo et al., 2005; Oddo et al., 2006a; Oddo et al., 2006b). Unlike other models that lack tau pathology, 3xTg-AD mice progressively develop plaques and tangles in AD-relevant brain regions. Immunohistochemical analysis of 3xTg-AD brain demonstrated that intraneuronal Aβ was the earliest neuropathological manifestation, being apparent by 3 to 4 months of age in the neocortex and by 6 months in the CA1 hippocampal subfield (Oddo et al., 2003).

The majority of Tg models generate Aβ plaques relatively slowly, however the co-expression of five FAD mutations recently led to the generation of an AD APP/PS1 Tg mouse model exhibiting accelerated plaque development in which the effects of very high cerebral Aβ42 levels could be examined (Oakley et al., 2006). The so-called 5XFAD mice co-express human APP with the Swedish, Florida and London mutations together with mutant PS1 (M146L + L286V). These mice generate Aβ42 almost exclusively and amyloid burden initiates within two months of birth. Importantly, prior to Aβ deposition, intraneuronal Aβ42 accumulates within neuronal soma and neuritis of cortical layer five and the subiculum. This immunostaining first appeared at 1.5 months and coincided with the initial rise in cerebral Aβ42 levels as measured by ELISA, occurring immediately before the extracellular deposition of Aβ in plaques.

SUBCELLULAR LOCALIZATION OF INTRANEURONAL Aβ

Cell biological studies have emphasized the subcellular site of Aβ production. It is known that the endoplasmic reticulum and intermediate compartments (ER/IC), the trans Golgi network (TGN) and the endosomal-lysosomal system are all intracellular sites of Aβ generation. Aβ produced by these pathways may be secreted, as is the case for TGN-generated Aβ (Xu et al., 1997) or remain intracellular as observed for ER/IC generated Aβ (Cook et al., 1997). The ER appears to be more selective for Aβ42 than Aβ40 generation. Indeed this pool of Aβ42 is secreted less efficiently than that from the Golgi, and intraneuronal pools of Aβ42 have been observed in vitro (Skovronsky et al., 1998).

At the subcellular level, various studies of both human and Tg mouse brain have localized abnormally accumulated intracellular Aβ to neuronal endosomal/lysosomal compartments in AD-sensitive brain regions. Neuronal endosome enlargement, possibly reflecting altered endocytic function, is a disease specific response that occurs years before the earliest stage of AD and DS (Cataldo et al., 2004). Analysis of both AD and DS brain at the ultrastructural level indicated that intracellular Aβ localized principally to Rab-5 positive endosomes and was prominent in enlarged endosomes in pyramidal neurons within at risk brain regions (Cataldo et al., 2004). In APP-Au mice, the majority of Aβ inclusions were co-localized with Rab7, a marker of late endosomes, although some inclusions were also observed in the lysosomal and Golgi systems (Van Broek et al., 2006). Co-localization of intraneuronal Aβ with lysosomal markers has also been observed in the $APP_{751}{}^{SL}PS1M146L$ mouse model (Langui et al., 2004). In a separate study, using cathespin-D, a marker of lysosomal structures, for co-localization analysis, it was shown that Aβ42 selectively accumulates in the perikaryon of pyramidal neurons of the entorhinal cortex and hippocampus in AD brain as discrete cathespin-D positive granules, indicating that they may be lysosome or lysosome-derived structures (D'Andrea et al., 2001).

To determine more precisely the subcellular localization sites of Aβ42, Takahashi and colleagues used immuno-gold electron microscopy (EM) to show that Aβ42 predominantly localizes to multivesicular bodies (MVBs) within pre- and post-synaptic compartments in human AD and Tg2576 mouse brain (Takahashi et al., 2002). MVBs are defined by their ultrastructural appearance in electron microscopic imaging and are thought to be part of the endosomal/lysosomal system, although detailed characterization of their cellular and molecular properties remains to be performed. However, the lumen of these ovoid or spherical organelles contains membrane bound vesicles and MVBs are known to be highly conserved compartments (Langui et al., 2004). Langui and colleagues demonstrated the accumulation of Aβ in granules within the lumen of MVBs and that the granules were also labeled with lysosomal markers including cathepsin D (Langui et al., 2004).

Pre-embedding immuno-gold EM demonstrated that Aβ42 normally resides in the outer limiting membrane of MVBs and smaller tubulo-vesicular organelles in mouse and human neurons. In human AD and Tg2576 mouse brain, Aβ42 localized to MVBs increases in an age-dependent manner. The increase in intraneuronal Aβ42 immunoreactivity with age has also been observed in DS brain (Gouras et al., 2000; Gyure et al., 2001; Busciglio et al., 2002). The Aβ42 increases were most obvious on MVBs localized to distal processes and pre- and post-synaptic compartments in nerve terminals.

FORM OF INTRANEURONAL Aβ

A century since Oskar Fischer and Fransesco Bonfiglio first suggested that intraneuronal material may play a role in AD pathogenesis, technical issues have prevented intraneuronal Aβ accumulation from being a central focus in AD research until the last few years. It is only relatively recently that C-terminal end specific Aβ40 and Aβ42 antibodies have been available to unequivocally detect intraneuronal Aβ. Prior to their development, antibodies directed against the Aβ domain of APP were used which could not differentiate Aβ from APP and other Aβ-containing APP fragments (Masters et al., 1985). Additionally, the use of specific protocols is required in order to consistently detect intraneuronal Aβ42, whereas a variety of protocols enable visualization of amyloid plaques (D'Andrea et al., 2002). Furthermore issues such as the tendency to inhibit the immunohistochemical reaction when plaques are observed, in order to prevent what is thought to be non-specific staining, may have previously prevented intraneuronal Aβ visualization.

As discussed earlier, it is now well-established that Aβ exists as soluble monomers, oligomers and insoluble fibrils. While several studies that identified the presence of intraneuronal Aβ did not deal in detail with its aggregation state (Wirths et al., 2001; Wirths et al., 2002; Blanchard et al., 2003), the data from studies that did, have generated a varied body of literature that reports both the detection of insoluble, fibrillogenic Aβ and soluble oligomeric Aβ within specific neuronal populations (Casas et al., 2004; Takahashi et al., 2004; Oakley et al., 2006; Oddo et al., 2006; Wirths et al., 2006b).

In some investigations, analysis was based on the absence or presence of thioflavin-S (thio-S) staining, known to be indicative of material in β-pleated sheet conformation, to determine if the intraneuronal Aβ was fibrillogenic (Gouras et al., 2000; Casas et al., 2004; Oakley et al., 2006). In a study of human tissue, the lack of thio-S staining, along with a lack of Bielschowsky silver staining and the absence of congo red birefringence under polarized light, indicated that intraneuronal amyloid in pyramidal neurons of the hippocampus and entorhinal cortex was non-fibrillogenic in nature (Gouras et al., 2000). Similar findings have been observed in certain Tg mouse models. Despite the proposed protofibrillogenic characteristics of the Arctic Aβ peptides (Nilsberth et al., 2001; Lord et al., 2006), the intracellular Aβ aggregates in tg-APP$_{ArcSwe}$ mice were thio-S-negative (Lord et al., 2006). Similar findings were observed in two other Tg models, the APP$_{751}$^{SL}PS1M146L mouse (Langui et al., 2004) and the APP-Au model (Van Broeck et al., 2006). Despite these data being somewhat consistent with findings from human brain tissue, it remains a possibility that the Aβ inclusions are too small to sequester enough of the β-pleated sheet binding dyes to be visible. Indeed, thio-S-immunoreactivity has been observed within neuronal populations in two other Tg mouse models of AD. Casas reported strong accumulation of intraneuronal Aβ42 and thio-S positive material in the CA1/2 hippocampal pyramidal neurons in APP^{SL}PS1KI mouse brain (Casas et al., 2004). Analysis of 5XFAD mouse brain using thio-S revealed a punctate, subcellular pattern within cell some of large pyramidal neurons (Oakley et al., 2006). The thio-S positive puncta were similar in number to the intraneuronal Aβ42-positive puncta and were absent in the negative control brain. The approximate 1:1 ratio of thio-S-positive and Aβ42-positive puncta suggested that much of the intraneuronal Aβ42 was in an aggregated state. In addition to the cell soma, thio-S positive neurites were apparent in 5XFAD cortex. It is well established that Aβ42 becomes aggregated more readily than Aβ40, especially under acidic conditions such as those of the endosomal environment. In both of these models, it is plausible that the high Aβ42 concentrations within acidic intracellular compartments could lead to enhanced Aβ42 aggregation. It is conceivable that such conditions may occur in AD with Aβ42-elevating FAD mutations, although it is unclear whether Aβ42 levels in sporadic AD cases are high enough to facilitate Aβ aggregation. However, it is interesting to note that in contrast to the findings of Gouras, thio-S-reactive deposits were detected within cells with intracellular Aβ immunoreactivity in AD brain (LaFerla et al., 1997). Obviously, further studies are required before firm conclusions regarding fibrillogenic Aβ within the cell can be made.

Soluble, potentially oligomeric, Aβ correlates better than insoluble, fibrillar, extracellular Aβ plaques with cognitive decline in AD patients (McLean et al., 1999). As described previously, soluble oligomeric Aβ assemblies appear neurotoxic and thus a critical issue with respect to Aβ toxicity is its aggregation state. Certainly, the origin of soluble Aβ oligomers and where and how they cause toxicity is of crucial interest. Until recently, the origin of Aβ oligomers was unclear. However, the development of oligomeric-specific antibodies has greatly facilitated understanding of the role Aβ oligomers play in pathogenesis. In contrast to the more common assumption that Aβ aggregation is initiated in the extracellular space and oligomers are derived from secreted Aβ monomers, data derived from human and Tg mouse brain tissue indicates that Aβ oligomerization begins within neurons (Walsh et al., 2000; Takahashi et al., 2004) and that the resultant Aβ oligomers accumulate intraneuronally (Kokubo et al., 2005; Oddo et al., 2006a; Gillardon et al., 2007).

Using immunoprecipitation and immunoblot analysis, the presence of SDS-stable oligomers in primary human neurons was demonstrated (Walsh et al., 2000). Intracellular Aβ oligomers were detected in neural cells that have no detectable oligomers in the growth media, further signifying that Aβ oligomers must have arisen intracellularly. Furthermore, Aβ oligomers could not be induced to form extracellularly in either the culture media or cerebral spinal fluid even though there are substantial levels of Aβ monomer present (Walsh et al., 2000). The authors concluded that the pathogenically critical process of Aβ oligomerization begins intraneuronally. These initial findings were supported by data from several other studies. Indeed, data from several of the mouse models described earlier suggests that the intraneuronal accumulation of Aβ oligomers might be involved in the very earliest stages of AD pathogenesis .

In both Tg2576 brain and also Tg2576 neurons in culture, Aβ42 localizes to and accumulates with time to MVBs in neuronal processes and synaptic compartments (Takahashi et al., 2002; Takahashi et al., 2004). Using aggregation state-specific antibodies the authors determined that in cultured Tg2576 neurons, Aβ42 aggregates into oligomers within endosomal vesicles and along microtubules (Takahashi et al., 2004). As determined by immuno gold EM analysis of Tg2576 neurons in vitro, as Aβ42 aggregates from monomer to oligomer a re-distribution of Aβ42 is observed, from the outer MVB membrane to the inner membranes of endosomal organelles and microtubules (Takahashi et al., 2004).

In Tg2576 mouse brain, in the absence of neuritic plaques, Aβ42 oligomer immunoreactivity could be detected in elongated structures, thought to be degenerating neuronal processes. Immunogold EM showed that Aβ42 oligomer containing neurites could be observed, with Aβ42 oligomer aggregations being observed close to synaptic active zones. Interestingly, by use of dot-blot analysis using an oligomer-specific antibody, Aβ oligomers have been detected in synaptosomal fractions, but not the mitochondrial fractions, of Tg2576 mouse brains, becoming first detectable at 6 months (Gillardon et al., 2007). Kokubo and colleagues used immuno EM to analyze old 18 to 20 month Tg2576 mouse brain. In agreement with other findings, Aβ oligomers localized to cell processes and were found with higher density at the axon terminal in Tg compared to non-Tg mouse brains. The distribution of immuno-gold particles indicated that while Aβ oligomers may not enter mitochondria they may contact these organelles (Kokubo et al., 2005).

In addition to the Tg2576 mouse model, SDS-resistant Aβ oligomers have also been shown to accumulate in an age-dependent manner in the 3xTg-AD model (Oddo et al., 2006a). Indeed, Aβ oligomerization in 3xTg-AD mice appears to initially occur within the neuron. The temporal profile of Aβ oligomers in the brain was observed using a panel of antibodies including two oligomeric-specific antibodies known not to cross-react with either natively folded APP or monomeric Aβ. Interestingly, in young 4 month old mice the majority of intracellular Aβ within hippocampal neurons was in a soluble, monomeric state. By 6 months old, specific oligomeric Aβ was also observed in this neuronal population. Oligomeric Aβ immunoreactivity and Aβ42 immunoreactivity were similar, showing a punctate staining pattern in the soma, consistent with labeling of an intracellular compartment. The Aβ42 antibody stained both monomeric and oligomeric forms of the peptide and so, unsurprisingly only a portion of Aβ42-positive deposits were recognized by the oligomer-specific antibody. However, a proportion of the oligomeric material appeared to be negative for Aβ42. The authors speculated that this staining pattern may indicate that intraneuronal oligomers exist in different combinations, some not recognized by the particular Aβ42 antibody used in the study. While this finding requires further analysis, it was hypothesized that these different conformations represent different stages of Aβ aggregation within the neuron (Oddo et al., 2006a).

It is important to note that while fibrillogenic intraneuronal Aβ in the APP[SL]PS1KI (Casas et al., 2004) and the 5XFAD (Oakley et al., 2006) mouse brain has been observed, Aβ42 oligomers are also highly abundant in these mouse models. While localization studies for Aβ42 oligomers have not yet been performed on 5XFAD mouse brain, Wirths and colleagues have demonstrated significant accumulation of both fibrillogenic and oligomeric Aβ in the somatodendritic compartment of spinal cord motor neurons in the APP[SL]PS1KI mouse (Wirths et al., 2006b).

Data regarding characterization of intraneuronal Aβ found in human brain is sparse. In human non-AD cortex, Aβ42 oligomers were not observed. In contrast, human AD cortex showed Aβ42 oligomer accumulations within dystrophic appearing processes and synaptic compartments. Aβ42 oligomers appeared to localize to tubulovesicular-like structures, although the authors were unable to classify these as being related to endosomes, ER or other organelles (Takahashi et al., 2004).

Intraneuronal Aβ Accumulation Correlates With Cognitive Deficits

It is increasingly evident that intraneuronal Aβ is associated with AD pathogenesis, being detectable in MCI brain, DS, and brains from patients with frank AD, and in the brains of several Tg models of AD. Importantly, as detailed previously, a number of studies have demonstrated that intraneuronal Aβ accumulation precedes the deposition of amyloid plaques and the appearance of NFTs and occurs as an early event in AD pathophysiology (Gouras et al., 2000; D'Andrea et al., 2001; Busciglio et al., 2002; Takahashi et al., 2002; Wirths et al., 2002; Blanchard et al., 2003; Oddo et al., 2004; Takahashi et al., 2004; Oakley et al., 2006). Recent attempts to characterize this form of Aβ have demonstrated that aggregated intraneuronal Aβ may be oligomeric and/or fibrillogenic in nature (Takahashi et al., 2004; Kokubo et al., 2005; Oakley et al., 2006; Oddo et al., 2006a; Gillardon et al., 2007).

An early study based on the use of Tg mice expressing a single APP mutation (the Indiana mutation; V717F) indicated that synaptic transmission can be impacted independently of plaque formation (Hsia et al., 1999). Indeed, it is now known that memory deficits arise in a number of Tg mouse models prior to the appearance of overt plaque pathology, including Tg2576, 3xTg-AD and 5XFAD mice (Oddo et al., 2004; Ohno et al., 2004, Billings et al., 2005; Ohno et al., 2006; Ohno et al., 2007). Importantly, recent studies demonstrate that the appearance of intraneuronal Aβ correlates with early indications of cognitive deficits (Oddo et al., 2004; Billings et al., 2005) and that the form of Aβ causing some of these deficits may be oligomeric (Takahashi et al., 2004; Oddo et al., 2006a).

Previously, we reported that young, preplaque Tg2576 mice exhibited memory deficits as shown by the Y-maze test (Ohno et al., 2004). Ablation of Aβ by targeted BACE1 gene deletion rescued the Y-maze deficit of these mice. Given the apparent Aβ-specific nature of the memory deficit in the absence of Aβ plaque pathology, it was hypothesized that soluble Aβ, rather than Aβ plaques may be responsible for poor memory performance of Tg2576 mice (Ohno et al., 2004). Indeed, soluble oligomers interfere with many critical neuronal activities including inhibition of LTP in both brain slices and in vivo (Walsh et al., 2002; Wang et al., 2004). While we did not determine the localization of oligomeric Aβ in this study, other reports demonstrate that in the absence of overt neuritic plaques, intense Aβ42 oligomeric immunoreactivity is present in elongated processes in young Tg2576 mouse brain (Takahashi et al., 2004; Gillardon et al., 2007).

Notably, synaptic loss/pathology is a better correlate with memory and cognitive decline than either plaques or NFTs and this is the likely most significant factor contributing to the initial stages of memory loss (Oddo et al., 2003). In both Tg2576 and human AD brain the accumulation of intraneuronal, oligomeric Aβ42 to MVBs within pre- and post-synaptic compartments is associated with abnormal synaptic morphology (Takahashi et al., 2002; Takahashi et al., 2004). In Tg2576, the accumulation of oligomeric intraneuronal Aβ42 preceded Aβ deposition in plaques. Aβ42-containing dendrites displayed features consistent with degenerating processes such as collapsed dark membranes. In older mice, increased intraneuronal Aβ42 was associated with swollen processes, in regions lacking organelles of normal appearance. In other regions intraneuronal Aβ42 was associated with MVBs displaying disrupted morphology (Takahashi et al., 2002). Indeed, the presence of the Aβ oligomer on the inner membrane of the MVB was intimately associated with the abnormal morphology of the endosomal organelle and microtubules. Interestingly, only Aβ42 monomers, but not oligomers, could be observed on endosomal vesicles with normal appearance. Normal synaptic functioning requires these subcellular structures, and it is unlikely that accumulation of Aβ42 at these sites allows for functional synapses. Thus, the accumulation of Aβ42 at synapses with associated cellular pathology in both Tg2576 and human AD brain provides a molecular basis for the clinical observation correlating dementia severity with markers of synaptic loss.

Interestingly, morphological signs of neurodegeneration associated with intraneuronal Aβ accumulation have been observed in another monogenic AD model, the PS1 Tg. It was observed that in aged mice, in which Aβ plaque pathology was absent, intraneuronal Aβ accumulation was associated with significantly accelerated neurodegeneration compared to wild type controls (Chui et al., 1999). Neurons exhibited a substantial increase in argyrophilia, considerable shrinkage of the soma, pyknosis of the nucleus and corkscrew-like deformation of dendritic segments.

The majority of Tg mouse models of AD do not exhibit NFT pathology, a key feature of the human disease. However, the 3xTg-AD mouse model is an exception, with the expression of mutant tau, in addition to mutant PS and APP transgenes, facilitating both plaque and tangle pathology in AD-relevant brain regions (Oddo et al., 2003). Prior to the appearance of such overt neuropathology, intraneuronal Aβ accumulates in the hippocampus and amygdala in 3xTg-AD mouse brain. Importantly, intrahippocampal administration of an anti-Aβ antibody effectively removes Aβ-associated pathology, including that linked to the intracellular accumulation of Aβ (Oddo et al., 2004). Several 3xTg-AD-based studies complement the findings from Tg2576 studies, and have demonstrated that deficits in synaptic plasticity, learning and memory appear to be induced by accumulation of intraneuronal Aβ (Oddo et al., 2003; Billings et al., 2005; Oddo et al., 2006a; Oddo et al., 2006b).

3xTg-AD mice were specifically examined for learning and memory deficits in spatial reference (Morris water maze; MWM) and contextual learning tasks (inhibitory avoidance), which involve the hippocampus and amygdala respectively. 2 month old, prepathologic mice were shown to be cognitively normal. However, in correlation with intraneuronal Aβ accumulation at 4 months, Tg mice showed deficits in long-term retention, where the 3xTg-AD mice learnt both tasks effectively but failed to retain the information. The retention deficits became apparent only when the acquisition of the spatial MWM task was analyzed on a per trial basis. In probe trials, 3xTg-AD mice demonstrated in tact short-term but impaired long-term memory. Interestingly, recent data has indicated that in very young 3xTg-AD mice, intraneuronal Aβ is predominantly in the form of soluble monomers (Oddo et al., 2006a).

Data indicating a causative role for intraneuronal Aβ42 accumulation in specific memory deficits was demonstrated by the intracerebroventricular (ICV) administration of anti-Aβ antibody to 3xTg-AD mice. Compared to PBS-injected control mice, levels of intraneuronal Aβ42 pathology in the hippocampus were reduced by 86%, 7 days post-injection. It was demonstrated that attention deficits were obliterated in the treated 3xTg-AD mice and that removal of intraneuronal Aβ pathology is sufficient to reverse early retention deficits. Furthermore, both intraneuronal Aβ42 pathology and the cognitive defects re-emerged a month after ICV injection (Billings et al., 2005). Thus the first cognitive impairment to emerge manifests as subtle impairment in long-term memory, the cause of which appears to be accumulated, soluble intraneuronal Aβ42 (Billings et al., 2005; Oddo et al., 2006a).

Memory deterioration appears to be time-dependent and short-term memory impairment was observed in 6 month old 3xTg-AD mice, along with a profound deficit in LTP and paired-pulse facilitation (Oddo et al., 2003). Synaptic deficits measured by deficits in LTP manifested prior to plaque and NFT formation. By 6 months of age, numerous pyramidal cells of the CA1 hippocampal subfield were strongly Aβ42 immunoreactive, although no Aβ plaques were detected in this brain region at this time. Immunohistochemical data indicates that a fraction of intraneuronal Aβ is oligomeric in nature in 3xTg-AD mice of this age.

Importantly, while LTP was significantly impaired in these mice (Oddo et al., 2003), mice expressing the mutant tau and PS1 transgenes in 2xTg-AD mice did not exhibit any LTP deficits. In addition, Oddo and colleagues previously indicated that 3xTg-AD mice have a selective loss of α7 nicotinic acetylcholine receptors (nAChR) in brain regions that accumulate intraneuronal Aβ (Oddo et al., 2005). Taken together, with the apparent profound LTP and cognitive deficits caused by intraneuronal Aβ in this mouse model, these data indicate that soluble oligomers may be responsible for these early pathological alterations.

5XFAD mice exhibit robust intraneuronal Aβ42 immunoreactivity at 1.5 months of age, prior to plaque deposition. Indeed, in a variety of behavioral paradigms, 5XFAD mice display hippocampus-dependent memory deficits similar to those of other Tg AD models (Oakley et al., 2006). Although very young 5XFAD mice were not examined, 4-6 month old mice exhibited memory impairments in both trace and contextual fear conditioning tests and the MWM, similar to the observations made in 3xTg-AD mice, where intraneuronal Aβ accumulation was linked to long-term retention deficits (Billings et al., 2005; Ohno et al., 2006). By examining spontaneous alteration in the Y-maze, the spatial working memory can be assessed. At 4-5 months of age, 5XFAD mice also exhibited deficits in spatial working memory. However, despite the accumulation of intraneuronal Aβ42 at 1.5 months, 2 month old 5XFAD mice did not exhibit a Y-maze deficit. In contrast to the MWM test, the Y-maze does not assay long-term memory retention, so testing 2 month old 5XFAD mice in the MWM may reveal retention impairments that correlate with intraneuronal Aβ.

In 4-5 month old 5XFAD mice, multiple forms of Aβ are present in AD-sensitive regions, including amyloid plaques, intraneuronal Aβ aggregates and Aβ oligomers (Ohno et al., 2006), and the subcellular presence and localization of the latter form in 5XFAD mice remains to be elucidated. Consequently, it is technically challenging to determine the exact form or forms of Aβ responsible for the poor performance of 5XFAD mice in the Y-maze. However, given the correlative association between synaptic pathology and memory dysfunction, it is interesting to note that in 5XFAD brain, intraneuronal Aβ42 has been associated with a subsequent decrease in synaptic marker proteins, syntaxin, synaptophysin and psd-95 (Oakley et al., 2006).

In addition to synaptic alterations and putative degeneration, intraneuronal Aβ has been linked to axonal degeneration (axonopathy) in APP[SL]PS1KI (Wirths et al., 2006b) and APP[SL]PS1M146L mice (Wirths et al., 2006a). In AD brain, axonal alterations manifest in the form of dystrophic neurites littering amyloid plaques. These neurites correspond to axonal swellings or spheroids that correspond to enlargements of the axon and abnormal accumulation of axonal cargoes, lipids and cytoskeletal proteins. The authors hypothesize that motor deficits observed in AD patients (O'Keeffe et al., 1996; Scarmeas et al., 2004) are likely due to disturbed axonal transport in the spinal cord. Interestingly, in both APP[SL]PS1KI and APP[SL]PS1M146L mice, abundant intraneuronal Aβ accumulation preceded plaque pathology in both brain regions and the spinal cord. Aβ-positive plaques in cervical, thoracic and lumbar regions of the spinal cord were preceded by the intraneuronal accumulation of a number of Aβ species including oligomeric Aβ forms in motor neurons of the spinal cord. In addition, there was also evidence for fibrillogenic Aβ in this neuronal population (Wirths et al, 2006b). The APP[SL]PS1M146L mice showed characteristic axonal spheroids, swellings, axonal demyelination and ovoids, which are myelin remnants of degenerated nerve fibers, which developed in an age-dependent manner. The authors propose that the accumulation of intracellular Aβ peptides leads to axonal degeneration in cerebral hemispheres, brain stem and spinal cord, with accumulation preceding Aβ plaque pathology and age-dependent axonopathy (Wirths et al., 2006a).

INTRANEURONAL Aβ AND CELLULAR ALTERATIONS CONSISTENT WITH NEURODEGENERATION

Intraneuronal Aβ accumulation precedes the deposition of amyloid plaques and the appearance of NFTs and correlates with the first indications of cognitive deficits. During early stages of the disease, intraneuronal Aβ accumulation appears to compromise synaptic functioning and has been associated with synaptic and axonal morphologies that are consistent with degeneration. However, why intraneuronal Aβ accumulates in the first place remains to be conclusively determined and the molecular mechanisms underlying the apparently deleterious effects of intraneuronal Aβ42 are only just being examined.

Conceivably, accumulated Aβ within the cell may arise from one or more of the following: Intraneuronal Aβ may represent an endogenously accumulated pool of Aβ that has remained in situ since synthesis. It may accumulate as a result of a compromised clearance and/or disruptions in the ubiquitin-proteasome system. Indeed, insulin degrading enzyme (IDE) and neprilysin (NEP) have been shown to degrade Aβ in vivo (Iwata et al., 2001; Selkoe, 2001b; Leissring et al., 2003). In addition to the generation of Aβ following internalization of APP from the plasma membrane (Koo and Squazzo, 1994), it has also been shown that neurons can readily internalize Aβ (Nagele et al., 2002) and therefore it cannot be ruled out that intraneuronal Aβ reflects endocytic uptake of extracellular Aβ. However, the fact that intracellular Aβ is most prominent before extracellular Aβ deposition argues against this possibility. In addition to internalized extracellular Aβ forming the intraneuronal Aβ pool, recent studies have also demonstrated a prion-like effect of exogenous Aβ, where exposure of human neuroblastoma NT2N cells to Aβ40 induced the formation of intraneuronal Aβ42 oligomers that were then released into the culture medium (Valerio et al., 2006), thus Aβ40 may sustain and amplify the pathological cascade triggered by Aβ42 in AD.

Consistent with clinical observations on the importance of intracellular accumulation, several reports have indicated the toxic effect of intraneuronal Aβ accumulation in model systems (LaFerla et al., 1995; Zhang et al., 2002; Magrane et al., 2004; Magrane et al., 2005). Indeed, in vitro models have proved useful for the examination of intraneuronal Aβ toxicity at the molecular level. Microinjection of Aβ42, but not Aβ40 into cultured primary human neurons is far more toxic than extracellular application of the peptide (Zhang et al., 2002). The significant neurotoxicity of accumulated intraneuronal Aβ42 was further demonstrated by use of a doxycycline-inducible adenoviral-based system that directs regulated intracellular Aβ42 expression (Magrane et al., 2004; Magrane et al., 2005).

It is now clear that oligomeric Aβ can be generated within, and accumulates inside, the neuron (Walsh et al., 2000; Takahashi et al., 2004; Oddo et al., 2006a). As detailed previously, in vitro studies have clearly demonstrated the synaptotoxicity of ADDL preparations, where the application of ADDL preparations to primary hippocampal cultures facilitated a significant loss is spine density and synaptic deterioration (Lacor et al., 2007). Importantly, there is considerable evidence indicating that Aβ oligomers can inhibit the maintenance of LTP (Walsh et al., 2002; Wang et al., 2004).

How soluble Aβ oligomers elicit these effects on synaptic plasticity is being intensively studied. It appears possible that, via initial binding to specific plasma membrane receptors, such as the α7 nAChR, soluble Aβ promotes the endocytosis of some NMDA receptors and thus Aβ oligomers may interfere with signaling pathways downstream of such receptors at synaptic plasma membranes in a way that facilitates an initial LTP response but not its persistence (Snyder et al., 2005; reviewed in Haas and Selkoe, 2007). In addition, there is also evidence that oligomers can physically permeabilize the membrane (reviewed in Glabe and Kayed, 2006). Membrane alteration likely leads to multiple changes within the cell including altered signaling pathways, mitochondrial dysfunction and perturbed calcium homeostasis. Thus it is possible that two types of event involving the activities of oligomeric Aβ may occur: an outside-in mechanism whereby Aβ oligomers act as extracellular ligands at synapses; and an inside-out mechanism where bioactive intracellular Aβ oligomers interfere with normal cell functionality.

Given the complex nature of AD pathogenesis combined with the presence of multiple forms of Aβ, the molecular mechanisms underlying pathogenic changes are difficult to analyze. Nevertheless, a number of studies have attempted to mechanistically link the accumulation of intraneuronal Aβ species to neurodegenerative events. Intraneuronal Aβ accumulation has been associated with i) Cellular stress and mitochondrial dysfunction ii) abnormalities in the endosomal/lysosomal and proteasomal systems.

Intraneuronal Aβ and Cellular Stress and Mitochondrial Dysfunction

Mitochondria are crucial in controlling cell life and death. They not only exert oxidative phosphorylation functions, generate ATP and free radicals but they also sequester calcium and serve as repositories for regulatory proteins of the intrinsic apoptotic pathway. Oxidative stress is increased in damaged mitochondria and mitochondrial dysfunction inevitably disturbs cell function, sensitizes cells to neurotoxic insults and may initiate cell death.

Studies on AD brain have provided evidence for increased levels of oxidative stress, mitochondrial dysfunction and impaired glucose uptake in vulnerable neuronal populations (Rapoport et al., 1991; Kish et al., 1992; Mutisya et al., 1994; MacGibbon et al., 1997; Kitamura et al., 1998; reviewed in Yankner, 1996; Smith et al., 2002). Indeed, defects in glucose utilization suggest possible abnormalities in mitochondrial function in AD. It has also been demonstrated that energy depletion and oxidative stress enhance Aβ formation suggesting a potential link between mitochondrial dysfunction, oxidative stress and Aβ production (Gabuzda et al., 1994; Gasparini et al., 1997). Indeed, we have previously demonstrated that acute energy inhibition with pharmacological agents in Tg2576 mice increased cerebral levels of BACE1 and Aβ40, adding further support to the suggestion that impaired brain energy metabolism may be one of the earliest pro-amyloidogenic events in AD (Velliquette et al., 2005).

On a molecular level, mitochondrial dysfunction is evidenced by altered COX activity in AD brain and upregulation in AD plaques of mitochondrial apoptotic proteins including BAX and other members of the pro-apoptotic bcl-2 family (Kish et al., 1992; Mutisya et al., 1994; MacGibbon et al., 1997; Kitamura et al., 1998). Importantly, a thorough study of a number of Tg mouse models has demonstrated that in APP/PS1 double Tg lines, intraneuronal non-fibrillar $A\beta$ accumulation in the brain is occasionally associated with abnormal granular accumulation within the cytoplasm and the proximal dendrites of APP and key markers of neuronal stress including Cox1 and Bax (Blanchard et al., 2003).

Theoretically, mitochondrial dysfunction and expression of pro-apoptotic molecules may facilitate the major neuronal loss that is observed in the late pathological stages of AD. Indeed, increased apoptosis may occur in AD brain (Guo et al., 1998; reviewed in Cotman, 1998). The suggestion that intraneuronal $A\beta$ precedes neuronal degeneration is further supported by the observation that this $A\beta42$ accumulation can be observed in both TUNEL-positive and –negative neurons in the cortex of DS patients with AD pathology, as well as in sporadic and familial AD cases (Busciglio et al., 2002). Further, the TUNEL-positive cells exhibited features consistent with neuronal apoptosis including chromitin condensations and cell body shrinkage. The $A\beta42$ immunoreactivity was observed in cells exhibiting loss of cellular membrane integrity although whether $A\beta$ oligomers played a role in this loss was not specifically examined.

In many of these scenarios it is difficult to equivocally separate cause from consequence. Cellular damage or stress induced by reactive oxygen species often induces cell death. Ohyagi and colleagues have demonstrated that in vitro, the pharmacological induction of apoptosis, but not necrosis, elevates intracellular $A\beta42$ levels (Ohyagi et al., 2000). Interestingly, these $A\beta42$ containing cells were TUNEL-negative, indicating that early stage apoptosis may induce $A\beta42$ accumulation as TUNEL staining represents the final stages of cell death.

$A\beta42$ is generated in the ER. Because neuronal mitochondria are often found in close association with the ER (Perkins et al., 1997), it is possible that the local $A\beta$ concentration is relatively higher in their vicinity compared to other cellular locales. Thus, it is also possible that, rather than $A\beta42$ accumulating as a consequence of altered mitochondrial function and the initiation of apoptosis, the high local concentrations of intraneuronal $A\beta42$ could affect mitochondrial membrane stability and/or normal oxidative phosphorylative functions. Such effects could be associated with significant mitochondrial dysfunction and synaptic impairment, and may ultimately lead to induction of apoptosis and neuronal loss in late-stage AD.

In vitro, the microinjection of $A\beta$ peptides into cultured neurons proved to be cytotoxic through the pro-apoptotic p53-Bax pathway (Zhang et al., 2002). Interestingly, the nonfibrillized and fibrillized $A\beta42$ peptides appeared equally toxic. In further reference to the neurotoxicity of $A\beta$ species, a study using Tg2576 mouse brain has indicated that whilst $A\beta$ oligomers were not observed within axonal mitochondria, the distribution of immunogold particles indicated contact between the oligomers and the mitochondria. Whether such contact would be sufficient to facilitate oligomer-induced alterations in the mitochondrial membrane remains to be determined (Kokubo et al., 2005). In contrast to these findings, a recent study has indicated that intracellular, oligomeric Aβ is present in mitochondria in AD brain and in the brain of an APP Tg expressing APP695, 751 and 770 bearing the Indiana and Swedish mutations (Tg mAPP mice). Furthermore, in Tg mAPP mice Aβ42 progressively accumulates at this subcellular site and is associated with deficits in oxidative phosphorylation (Caspersen et al., 2005), leading to a reduction in ATP production. The reasons for the differences in the apparent mitochondrial localization of Aβ42 in these two studies remains to be examined, although they may be related to the use of Tg models expressing different APP transgenes.

Important mechanistic data has been recently generated from in vitro studies using the inducible adenoviral-based system, mentioned previously. Regulated expression and accumulation of Aβ42 in the ER of primary neuronal cultures prompted the rapid induction of stress-inducible molecular chaperone, heat shock protein (Hsp70) and the intraneuronal Aβ42 was toxic to cultures within 24hrs (Magrane et al., 2004). Thus, the cellular stress response is an important mediator of intraneuronal Aβ toxicity, at least in vitro (Magrane et al., 2004). In an extension of this study, it was shown that intracellular Aβ specifically impairs the function of complex IV of the electron transport chain, an effect that likely accounts for the observed depression of ATP production (Caspersen et al., 2005; Veereshwarayya et al., 2006). The data indicate that intracellular Aβ directly interferes with oxidative phosphorylation resulting in oxidative stress (Veereshwarayya et al., 2006). Indeed, these findings support the idea that intraneuronal Aβ compromises mitochondrial function and leads to cell death. It was shown that Hsp60, Hsp70 and Hsp90 either alone, or in combination, provide differential protection against intracellular Aβ stress through the maintenance of mitochondrial oxidative phosphorylation and the functionality of the tricarboxylic acid cycle enzymes (Veereshwarayya et al., 2006). Magrane and colleagues also demonstrated that early dysfunction associated with intraneuronal Aβ in AD involves impairments of Akt signaling and suppression of the stress response (Magrane et al., 2005). Induction of Aβ42 expression in primary neuronal cultures lead to a sequential decrease in the levels of active, phospho-Akt, alongside an increase in glycogen synthase kinase (GSK) 3β and apoptosis. Importantly, the downregulation of Akt paralleled the accumulation of intraneuronal Aβ in vivo in Tg2576 mice. Thus it appears as though the Akt pathway plays a role in intracellular Aβ toxicity and further, that Akt activation is required to induce the cellular stress response that is neuroprotective against Aβ42-mediated neurotoxicity (Magrane et al., 2005). Thus, it is clear from these studies that intracellular Aβ can induce significant neurotoxicity at the level of the mitochondria and in experimental systems these deleterious effects can be negated by the activities of specific molecular chaperones.

ATP depletion, as observed with the intracellular accumulation of Aβ42 (Caspersen et al., 2005; Veereshwarayya et al., 2006) can lead to partial membrane depolarization, release of the voltage dependent Mg^{2+} block of NMDA receptors and an increase in calcium influx (Mattson, 1998). Interestingly, increases in intracellular calcium can trigger several pathways that are linked to the intraneuronal accumulation of Aβ and associated cellular dysfunction and death (Pierrot et al., 2006; Oakley et al., 2006). Data indicates that increases in cytoplasmic calcium may be both causative in Aβ accumulation (Pierrot et al., 2006; Cruz et al., 2006) and required for downstream events associated with accumulated intraneuronal Aβ (Oakley et al., 2006).

In cultured rat cortical neurons, increases in cytosolic calcium induced modification of APP metabolism that led to intraneuronal Aβ accumulation. While Aβ associated and tau-associated pathologies represent major, defining hallmarks of AD pathology, cellular mechanisms linking the two have remained elusive. However, following membrane depolarization, increased calcium concentrations induced a transient phosphorylation of both tau and APP that was dependent on GSK3 and cyclin dependent kinase 5 (Cdk5) protein kinases. Importantly, phosphorylation of APP on Thr-668 facilitated the intraneuronal accumulation of Aβ42, which then exerted neurotoxic effects (Pierrot et al., 2006).

The catalytic activation of Cdk5 requires association with its neuron-specific regulatory subunit p35 (Tsai et al., 1994). A calcium-dependent proteolytic cleavage of p35 generates p25, often as a result of neurotoxic stress, leading to aberrant Cdk5 activation. Importantly, significant increases in p25 or cdk5 activity in human brain have been reported (Lee et al., 1999; Patrick et al., 1999; Swatton et al., 2004). Furthermore, an inducible p25 Tg mouse model displays progressive neurodegeneration (brain atrophy and tau phosphorylation) that results in significant neuronal loss and NFT pathology (Cruz et al., 2003). Importantly, induction of p25 in these mice results in enhanced forebrain Aβ levels, prior to significant neuropathology. Intracellular Aβ accumulated in perinuclear regions and distended axons within the mouse forebrain (Cruz et al., 2006). In addition, the p25 Tg model also exhibited increased BACE1 protein levels. At the ultrastructural level, intraneuronal Aβ appeared to resemble amyloid fibrils and was associated with neurons exhibiting signs of degeneration. Furthermore, the temporal accumulation of intraneuronal Aβ in these mice, prior to Aβ plaque formation, corresponded to significant impairments in learning and memory (Fischer et al., 2005).

Cruz and colleagues proposed that disruptions in Cdk5 activity may adversely affect axonal transport and that such alterations may underlie the p25-induced increase in intraneuronal Aβ accumulation (Cruz et al., 2006). Furthermore, p25-induction may also promote Aβ production via increased levels of BACE1. Taken together, these data support the role of p25/cdk5 deregulation in aberrant APP processing, tau pathology and neuronal loss.

Clearly, abnormal p25/cdk5 activity exerts an effect on intraneuronal Aβ levels. However, reciprocal findings have shown that Aβ can induce conversion of p35 to p25 (Lee et al., 2003). Thus a vicious feed forward loop may exist between p25/Cdk5 and Aβ that could lead to key pathological events associated with AD. Interestingly, in 5XFAD mice, we show that p25 elevation may be an early pathogenic event (Oakley et al., 2006). In 5XFAD brain increases in p25 appear by 3 months of age and temporally coincide with the accumulation of intraneuronal Aβ. In older mice, the p25 increase in 5XFAD brain is significant and correlates with marked synaptic degeneration, as determined by a significant loss of pre- (synaptophysin and syntaxin) and post- (psd-95) synaptic markers in 5XFAD mice (Oakley et al., 2005). These data certainly support the role of intraneuronal Aβ42 in neurodegeneration although it is currently unclear as to whether the intraneuronal Aβ42 accumulation observed in 5XFAD mice occurs as a cause or consequence of alterations in p25 levels.

Intraneuronal Aβ and Abnormalities of the Endosomal/Lysosomal and Proteasomal Systems

Abnormalities of neuronal endosomes are amongst the earliest known pathological changes in AD. Intraneuronal Aβ has been localized to endosomal/lysosomal compartments in AD and DS brain and appears prominent in enlarged endosomes (Cataldo et al., 2004).

MVBs can be regarded as a sorting compartment within the endocytic pathway, and are considered to be late endosomes, formed from early endosomes by membrane imaginations that generate inner vesicles, the pH of which is decreased. MVBs are involved in the regulated trafficking of several proteins and membrane receptors, including the epidermal growth factor receptor (EGFR). It is known that the ubiquitin-proteasome system (UPS) regulates trafficking of the EGFR through the MVB sorting pathway (Longva et al., 2002). Following ligand binding at the plasma membrane, the EGFR is activated by phosphorylation and is then ubiquinated and trafficked to early endosomes, followed by transport in the MVB sorting system for degradation. Ubiquitination machinery located both at the outer surfaces of the outer MVB membrane and the proteasome coordinates the translocation of the EGF-EGFR complex to the inner membranes of the MVB for subsequent dephosphorylation and later degradation in lysosomes. Inhibition of the UPS facilitates the accumulation of ubiquinated EGFR by blocking the translocation of EGF-EGFR into the inner vesicles of MVBs, and the degradation of this ligand-receptor complex is blocked (Longva et al., 2002). As discussed previously, Aβ42 accumulates abnormally within MVBs (Takahashi et al., 2002; Takahashi et al., 2004) in cultured Tg2576 mouse neurons. Interestingly, the accumulation of EGF-EGFR complexes was observed in MVBs of these mutant neurons, indicative of reduced EGFR degradation (Almeida et al., 2006). Consistent with altered trafficking of EGFR within MVBs, elevated levels of phosphorylated EGFR were found in these neuronal populations. It is known that before the EGFR is translocated across the MVB membranes, the receptor must be de-ubiquinated. Proteasome activity is necessary for the removal of the ubiquitin moiety (Alwan et al., 2003). Indeed, analysis of proteasome activity in cultured Tg2576 neurons, which abnormally accumulate both Aβ42 and EGF-EGFR complexes, showed that these mutant neurons exhibited a marked decrease in proteasome activity. Proteasome activity has been reported to be reduced in Tg2576 mouse brain (Oh et al., 2005) and human AD brain (Keller et al., 2000). Thus the authors proposed that it is reduced proteasome activity that is responsible for the altered trafficking of EGFR within MVBs. While Aβ42 was reported to inhibit proteasome function in vitro (Gregori et al., 1995; Gregori et al., 1997), the mechanism by which the intraneuronal Aβ42 in Tg2576 neurons affects proteasomal activity remains to be determined, as the proteasome is generally considered to be cytosolic, whereas Aβ42 accumulates on either the inner side of, or within, the MVB outer membrane. However, the fact that treatment with a γ-secretase inhibitor blocked the cellular alterations in mutant neurons, including impaired proteasome activity, indicates that Aβ is responsible for alterations in the MVB and UPS in cultured Tg2576 neurons. While monomeric Aβ42 is localized to the outer limiting membrane of MVBs, and oligomeric Aβ42 is found on the inner membrane, the form or forms of intraneuronal Aβ responsible for the decreased proteasomal activity remain to be determined. Importantly, in addition to receptor trafficking, the UPS system has also been linked to the regulation of synaptic plasticity. Thus, it is plausible that the aberrant accumulation of intraneuronal Aβ42 impairs the proteasome, thus inhibiting the endocytic trafficking of neuronal receptors that may be a cause of synaptic dysfunction in AD.

Interestingly, data generated from the 3xTg-AD mice also indicates that the accumulation of intraneuronal Aβ may affect proteasome activity (Oddo et al., 2004). 3xTg-AD mice exhibit both Aβ plaque and NFT pathologies that facilitates examination of how one pathology may affect the other. Intrahippocampal immunization with anti-Aβ antibody rapidly diminishes Aβ load, leading to both intraneuronal and extracellular Aβ clearance. However, following Aβ reduction, tau levels in the somatodendritic compartment were also diminished. Importantly, proteasomal inhibition prevented the Aβ-mediated clearance of tau and the authors suggested that intraneuronal Aβ accumulation impairs proteasome function, which facilitates the accumulation of toxic moieties such as Tau (Oddo et al., 2004).

While the consequence of Aβ accumulation is beginning to be analyzed, the cause of this aberrant accumulation in AD remains largely unexplored. However, in reference to subcellular protein trafficking, we recently demonstrated that interference with isoprenoid synthesis facilitated the intracellular accumulation of amyloidogenic fragments including Aβ, at least in vitro (Cole et al., 2005, reviewed in Cole and Vassar, 2006). The post-translational attachment of isoprenoid moieties to specific target proteins including small GTPases (in a process termed isoprenylation) is crucially important for protein trafficking and signaling. Indeed, inhibition of isoprenylation is associated with significant cytoskeletal alterations and a decrease in the efficiency of vesicular transport. The molecular mechanisms that link alterations in isoprenoid levels to intracellular Aβ accumulation remain to be determined, although previous studies have demonstrated that specific isoprenylated G-proteins play an important role in the subcellular trafficking and processing of APP (Dugan et al., 1995; McConlogue et al., 1996).

INTRANEURONAL Aβ AND GROSS NEURONAL LOSS

Clearly, cellular alterations associated with intraneuronal Aβ accumulation, such as changes in oxidative stress and mitochondrial abnormalities, are intimately tied to apoptosis and it is known that significant neuronal loss is a key pathological feature of AD. However, most Tg mouse models of AD that express human mutant APP and/or PS1 and/or tau and consequently overproduce Aβ lack significant cell loss. Undoubtedly, overt neuronal degeneration and loss is a late event in AD pathogenesis, being proceeded by loss of neuronal synaptic density and synapse number which represent another invariant feature of the disease (Dekosky and Scheff, 1990). Indeed, human studies corroborate Tg studies in which it appears that cognitive impairments emerge prior to overt neuropathology and thus understanding early pathological events is of crucial importance.

Nevertheless, several AD Tg models now exist that demonstrate significant, region specific neuronal loss, including the APP[SL]PS1M146L mouse (Schmitz et al., 2004), APP[SL]PS1KI mouse (Casas et al., 2004) and the 5XFAD (Tg6799) mouse model (Oakley et al., 2006; Ohno et al., 2006). Such Tg models are certainly beneficial in piecing together the temporal and spatial course of pathological events involved in this disease and have enhanced our understanding of how early events impact neuropathological changes observed late in disease course, such as gross neuronal loss.

It was originally proposed that given the increased sensitivity of older primates, compared to younger primates, to Aβ neurotoxicity, the lack of neuronal loss in Tg mice with high amyloid burden might be attributed to their short life span. It is now clear that amyloid plaque burden is not essential for neuronal loss and that other, possibly intraneuronal forms of amyloid contribute to the apparent decrease in neuronal numbers (Schmitz et al., 2004; Casas et al., 2004; Oakley et al., 2006). However, it should be noted that other transgenics display intraneuronal Aβ but do not have significant neuron death (Takahashi et al., 2002, Oddo et al., 2003; Takahashi et al., 2004; Oddo et al., 2004; Oddo et al., 2006a). Why intraneuronal Aβ does not always correlate with neuron loss in all APP transgenics is unclear, but it may be related to the different combinations of FAD mutants, expression levels and promoters used in each line.

Stereologic and image analysis comparisons of young and aged APP^{SL}PS1M146L mice revealed a substantial age-related loss of hippocampal pyramidal neurons. While neuronal loss was observed at sites of Aβ aggregation, significant neuronal loss was also observed in areas of the parenchyma distant from plaques indicative that more than one mechanism underlies neuronal loss in this mouse model (Schmitz et al., 2004). Previously it has been proposed that β-sheet-structured Aβ may be neurotoxic (Urbanc et al., 2002). Thus, it is interesting to note that in both the APP^{SL}PS1KI and 5XFAD mouse models, the neuronal loss is tightly correlated with previous appearance of thio-S-positive intraneuronal Aβ aggregates. Similar findings were observed in the p25 inducible Tg model (Cruz et al., 2006). Data from these models provide support for the critical role of intraneuronal Aβ42 in neuronal loss. In 10 month old APP^{SL}PS1KI mice there is more than a 50% loss of CA1/2 hippocampal pyramidal cells that correlates with thio-S positive intraneuronal accumulation, but not with extracellular amyloid plaques (Casas et al., 2004). In the 5XFAD mouse model, large pyramidal neurons of layer 5 cortex and the subiculum exhibit prominent intraneuronal Aβ staining and it is this cell population that undergoes significant loss in aging mice (Oakley et al., 2006). Given the association between p25/Cdk5 activity and neuronal loss (Cruz et al., 2006) it is interesting to note that the temporal induction of p25 correlated not only with loss of synaptic markers but also with the significant neuronal loss. While our work does not unequivocally prove that intraneuronal Aβ aggregates cause neuronal degeneration, it does provide initial insights into a potential molecular mechanism involving p25, that may link fibrillar intraneuronal Aβ and neurodegeneration.

EVIDENCE FOR A ROLE FOR INTRANEURONAL Aβ IN EXTRACELLULAR PLAQUE FORMATION

Historically, the involvement of Aβ plaques in AD pathology has been considered of central importance. However, a plethora of data now suggests that soluble oligomeric and intraneuronal Aβ species are likely the key neurotoxic players early on in the course of AD pathogenesis, and current thinking has begun to suggest that Aβ plaques are tombstones of the disease rather than being actively involved in disease pathogenesis. Indeed, the poor correlation between cognitive defects and plaque number supports this notion although it should be considered that counting spherical plaques in two-dimensional cross-section must provide an imprecise measure of Aβ load. Furthermore, it must also be remembered that fibrillar Aβ plaques in AD brain are typically littered with dystrophic neurites, an observation that still supports the argument that insoluble, extracellular Aβ aggregates may contribute to neuronal injury. However, it is difficult to determine whether these large aggregates are inducing local neuronal injury and dysfunction as it is highly likely that such formations are intimately surrounded by numerous soluble forms of Aβ such as oligomers. Therefore, at this stage it should not be concluded that either the insoluble extracellular Aβ plaques or the smaller soluble Aβ species are the sole neurotoxic entity.

There is no doubt that cognitive impairments continue to worsen as a function of age, both in the human condition and in Tg models of AD (Oakley et al., 2006; Oddo et al., 2006a). Data from the 3xTg-AD mouse model indicates a potential stepwise progression of memory deficits that maybe directly related to emerging neuropathology. It was proposed that in young, pre-plaque mice, specific cognitive deficits manifesting as impaired long-term memory, were associated with intraneuronal Aβ accumulation. By 6 months of age, intraneuronal Aβ pathology worsened, and hippocampal neuronal populations were shown to contain oligomeric Aβ (Oddo et al., 2006a). Furthermore, extracellular Aβ deposition had initiated, with a corresponding impairment in short-term memory. The exacerbation of cognitive deficits may be explained in part by the progression from solely intraneuronal Aβ to both intraneuronal and extracellular Aβ (Billings et al., 2005). In 12 month old 3xTg-AD mice, intraneuronal Aβ oligomers were no longer visible in the CA1 region but were present extracellularly, indicating that between 6-12 months there is an age-dependent shift from predominantly intracellular to predominantly extracellular Aβ. Furthermore, this study provided correlative evidence that oligomers represent an intermediate step leading to plaque formation as the presence of extracellular oligomers appeared to pre-date extracellular thio-S positive plaques in 3xTg-AD mice (Oddo et al., 2006a). Importantly, while intraneuronal Aβ may cause the onset of cognitive impairments in 3xTg-AD mice, the appearance of plaques and tangles may further exacerbate cognitive impairment.

How amyloid plaques form remains a centrally important question in AD and until recently there has been a paucity of studies that have addressed the steps leading up to extracellular Aβ deposition in the brain parenchyma. Undoubtedly, pathways leading to Aβ plaque formation are likely to be diverse and complex. Indeed, multiple pathways of Aβ plaque formation are likely to exist and it is possible that plaque genesis arises as a consequence of several distinct processes that occur in parallel in AD.

It has been previously demonstrated that unilateral knife lesions of the perforant pathway of plaque-bearing Tg mice caused a significant reduction in amyloid burden in the ipsilateral dentate gyrus (Lazarov et al; 2002; Sheng et al., 2002). These data are consistent with the notion that Aβ plaques can form from Aβ released at the synapse, considered to be a major site of Aβ synthesis and secretion. However, in addition, there is growing evidence to support the notion that intraneuronal Aβ may act as a nidus for extracellular Aβ deposition. Given that intraneuronal Aβ42 accumulation occurs with early AD pathology and prior to extracellular plaque deposition, it has been suggested that extracellular plaques may develop from this intracellular pool. It has been demonstrated that the earliest Aβ42 positive senile plaques develop along the projections and at the terminals of early Aβ42-positive neurons. Indeed, there is some data which indicates that Aβ42 appears to aggregate within the cytoplasm and that some Aβ plaques are neuronal in shape (Gouras et al., 2000). Early Aβ42 immunoreactivity was observed along the axonal projections of Aβ42-positive neurons of the entorhinal cortex and at their terminal fields in the outer molecular layer of the dentate gyrus (Gouras et al., 2000). Pyramidal cells with excessive Aβ42 accumulation are frequently observed in brain regions of high plaque density. Furthermore, with increasing cognitive dysfunction and Aβ plaque deposition, intraneuronal Aβ42 immunoreactivity become less apparent (Gouras et al., 2000). Indeed, a clear inverse relationship between local plaque density and local pyramidal cell density has been observed (D'Andrea et al., 2001).

Data from several Tg mouse models adds further support for a central role of intraneuronal Aβ in extracellular plaque genesis (Lord et al., 2006; Oakley et al., 2006; Oddo et al., 2006b). Importantly, an inverse relationship between plaque number and intraneuronal load has been observed in the 3xTg-AD model (Oddo et al., 2006b). As 3xTg-AD mice age, intraneuronal Aβ42 immunoreactivity decreases as the extracellular plaque load increases. By use of a single intrahippocampal injection of anti-Aβ antibody, there is a reduction of the extracellular Aβ pool, which is followed by a reduction in the intraneuronal Aβ pool. Indeed, following antibody dissipation, the intraneuronal Aβ pathology re-emerges prior to plaque appearance (Oddo et al., 2006b). Thorough experimental analysis of these events clearly demonstrated that, at least in 3xTg-AD mice, the apparent reduction in intraneuronal Aβ42 immunoreactivity was not due to either a decrease in cell number, a reduction in transgene expression or an overall decrease in total Aβ levels. Furthermore, analysis of key enzymes that have been previously shown to degrade Aβ in vivo argued against enhanced degradation/clearance of Aβ being responsible for the decrease in intraneuronal Aβ immunoreactivity and peptide competition was also ruled out as a possible cause of this reduction as the intraneuronal Aβ staining was observed following excessive use of staining antibodies. Indeed, the decrease in intraneuronal Aβ immunoreactivity with age was also demonstrated in Tg2576 indicating that it is a feature of AD pathogenesis rather than being specifically related to a single Tg model (Oddo et al., 2006b).

The molecular mechanism(s) underlying the shift from intraneuronal Aβ accumulation to the extracellular appearance of the peptide is yet to be established in 3xTg-AD mice. Interestingly, Aβ is associated with cathespin D in the extracellular space in Tg models and man (Cataldo et al., 1990a; Cataldo et al., 1990b). This together with the fact that both of these molecules co-localize to the lumen of the MBVs and there is an age-dependent decrease in intraneuronal Aβ42-positive MVB granules, and a corresponding increase in extracellular Aβ plaques in APP$_{751}$^{SL}PS1M146L Tg mice, prompted the authors to suggest that exocytosis of the lysosomal content into the extracellular space may occur under specific conditions (Langui et al., 2004). Such a mechanism clearly links intraneuronal Aβ with Aβ plaque formation in the absence of gross neuronal loss.

While we have not methodically examined whether there is a specific decrease in intraneuronal Aβ42 accumulation with time in the 5XFAD mice, these mice exhibit clear neuronal loss in brain regions exhibiting substantial amounts of intraneuronal Aβ42 (Oakley et al., 2006). As previously discussed, apoptosis is associated with AD pathology. Data from 5XFAD mice indicate that intraneuronal Aβ-containing neurons frequently exhibit weak

NeuN staining and abnormal morphologies (Oakley et al., 2006). Immuno EM studies are required to further examine the nature of these morphological alterations, but it seems likely that the accumulated intraneuronal Aβ42 in 5XFAD brain is exerting a similar effect to that observed in both Tg2576 and human AD brain, where it was linked to morphological abnormalities reminiscent of neurodegeneration (Takahashi et al., 2002, Takahashi et al., 2004). Given the temporal sequence of pathological events observed in 5XFAD mice, we speculated that the high concentrations of Aβ42 within acidic intracellular compartments could lead to Aβ42 aggregation, which is known to be neurotoxic and in turn may impair Aβ-degrading mechanisms or inhibit Aβ secretion from the soma. Consequently, Aβ42 aggregates may accumulate and damage intracellular membranes. Such disruption could theoretically lead to release of enough Aβ42 to induce neurotoxicity, cause apoptosis and/or cell lysis leading to release of cytoplasmic contents into the extracellular environment whereby previously intraneuronal Aβ42 can form plaque seeds (Oakley et al., 2006). Indeed, the idea that each plaque represents the end product of a degenerated neuron is strengthened by a study that demonstrated that in AD brain, nuclear remnants are found at the center of most plaques. Interestingly the authors also report that Aβ plaques contain a number of neuron-specific mRNAs (D'Andrea et al., 2001).

It is important to consider that behavioral deficits can occur in Tg mice with little or no intraneuronal Aβ. Given the complexity of cognition, this may be explained by the likelihood that distinct triggers can lead to similar impairments in different Tg mice. Indeed, it is clear from certain Tg models that at least some extracellular Aβ does not originate from the intracellular pool (Herzig, et al., 2004). In conclusion, it appears highly likely that Aβ plaques form as a result of multiple pathways including synaptically released Aβ (Lazarov et al; 2002; Sheng et al., 2002), and accumulated intraneuronal Aβ released from the cell via active transport (Langui et al., 2004; Oddo et al., 2006b) or as a result of apoptosis and/or cell lysis (Gouras et al., 2000; D'Andrea et al., 2001; Oakley et al., 2006).

CONCLUDING REMARKS

There is growing evidence to support the notion that the accumulation of intraneuronal Aβ is a significant, early neuropathological event in the course of AD progression. The accumulation of intraneuronal Aβ has been observed in MCI, DS and AD brain in addition to Tg mouse brain. Intraneuronal Aβ is observed prior to Aβ plaque and NFT formation and neuronal loss, implying a potential causal relationship between intraneuronal Aβ and subsequent neurodegeneration (Gouras et al., 2000; D'Andrea et al., 2001; Gyure et al., 2001; Wirths et al., 2001; Busciglio et al., 2002; Mori et al., 2002; Takahashi et al., 2002; Oddo et al., 2003; Casas et al., 2004; Fernandez-Vizarra et al., 2004; Takahashi et al., 2004; Billings et al., 2005; Oakley et al., 2006; Oddo et al., 2006a; Oddo et al., 2006b). Indeed, significant behavioral and cognitive deficits correlate with intraneuronal Aβ accumulation in some AD transgenics (Oddo et al., 2004; Ohno et al., 2004; Billings et al., 2005; Oddo et al., 2006a). Intracellular Aβ has also been observed in primary neurons and occurs primarily as the more neurotoxic and fibrillogenic Aβ42 species (Skovronsky et al., 1998; Takahashi et al., 2004).

On a cellular and molecular level, the intracellular accumulation of Aβ42 has been associated with abnormal synaptic pathology (Takahashi et al., 2004), in addition to mitochondrial dysfunction and proapoptotic stresses (Blanchard et al., 2003; Caspersen et al., 2006). Such findings provide a putative mechanistic basis connecting intraneuronal Aβ accumulation to neurodegeneration. Importantly, findings indicate that the factor that may initially cause the accumulation of Aβ within the cell, (for example, mitochondrial dysfunction, apoptosis), may also be caused by the aberrant intraneuronal Aβ accumulation, thus setting in place a vicious cycle of cell damage and death.

It is now widely acknowledged that soluble Aβ oligomers are synaptotoxic and such assemblies may represent a key neurotoxic entity early on in the disease course (Walsh et al., 2002; Lacor et al., 2007). Importantly, while fibrillogenic intraneuronal Aβ42 has been observed in certain AD Tg models (Casas et al., 2004; Oakley et al., 2006), there is increasing evidence supporting the existence of intraneuronal Aβ oligomers (Walsh et al., 2000; Takahashi et al., 2004; Oddo et al., 2006a). Given the apparent stepwise progression of memory deficits, it has been proposed that different Aβ assembly forms may mediate diverse toxic effects at different stages of the disease, with intracellular Aβ oligomers exerting early effects, while the effects mediated by Aβ plaques may appear later in the disease course. Interestingly, it has been demonstrated that the intraneuronal and extracellular Aβ pools are mechanistically linked, where changes in one can elicit corresponding changes in the other (Oddo et al., 2006b). Although it appears likely that multiple molecular pathways lead to Aβ plaque genesis, in some cases, intraneuronal Aβ may serve as a source for some extracellular plaques (Oakley et al., 2006; Oddo et al., 2006b).

Taken together, this sea of information strongly indicates that intraneuronal accumulation of Aβ (likely oligomeric Aβ) occurs early in AD pathogenesis and may have significant impact on later pathological events. Thus accumulated intraneuronal Aβ appears to be potential target for AD therapeutics. Indeed, a recent in vitro study has demonstrated possible therapeutic benefits from a cell permeable compound that specifically targets intraneuronal Aβ (Maezawa et al., 2006). Nevertheless, due largely to technical difficulties, research into intraneuronal Aβ and oligomeric Aβ has only been initiated over the last few years, Indeed, given the fact that intraneuronal Aβ may actually be oligomeric Aβ, we are really just beginning to decipher why aberrant Aβ accumulation occurs in the first place and what the molecular mechanisms underlying the apparent neurotoxicity caused by intraneuronal Aβ are. Conclusive answers to questions such as these should surely accelerate the development of therapeutics aimed at blocking the earliest pathological changes observed in AD.

ACKNOWLEDGEMENTS

This work was supported by a Fellowship from The John Douglas French Alzheimer's Foundation (awarded to Sarah L. Cole, 2006-2008).

REFERENCES

Almeida, G. C., Takahashi, R.H., Gouras, G.K. β-amyloid accumulation impairs multivesicular body sorting by inhibiting the ubiquitin-proteasome system. *J. Neurosci.* *26:* 4277-4288, 2006.

Alwan, H.A., van Zoelen, E.J., van Leeuwen, J.E. Ligand-induced lysosomal epidermal growth factor receptor (EGFR) degradation is preceded by proteasome-dependent EGFR de-ubiquitination. *J. Biol. Chem. 278:* 35781–35790, 2003.

Billings, L.M., Oddo, S., Green, K.N., McGaugh, J.L., LaFerla, F.M. Intraneuronal Aβ causes the onset of early Alzheimer's disease-related cognitive deficits in transgenic mice. *Neuron 45:* 675-688, 2005.

Bitan, G., Kirkitadze, M. D., Lomakin, A., Vollers, S. S., Benedek, G. B., and Teplow, D. B. Amyloid beta -protein (Abeta) assembly: Abeta 40 and Abeta 42 oligomerize through distinct pathways. *Proc. Natl. Acad. Sci. U. S. A 100:* 330-335, 2003.

Blanchard, V., Moussaoui, S., Czech, C., Touchet, N., Bonici, B., Planche, M., Canton, T., Jedidi, I., Gohin, M., Wirths, O., Bayer, T.A.., Langui, D., Duyckaerts, C., Tremp, G., Pradier, L. Time sequence of maturation of dystrophic neurites associated with Aβ deposits in APP/PS1 transgenic mice. *Exp. Neurology 184:* 247–263, 2003.

Busciglio, J., Pelsman, A., Wong, C., Pigino, G., Yuan, M., Mori, H., Yankner, B.A. Altered metabolism of the amyloid beta precursor protein is associated with mitochondrial dysfunction in Down's syndrome. *Neuron 33:* 677– 688, 2002.

Casas, C., Sergeant, N., Itier, J.-M., Blanchard, V., Wirths, O., Van de Steeg, E., Ile Ret, G., Canton, T., Drobecq, H., Clark, A., Bonici, B., Delacourte, A., Benavides, J., Schmitz, C., Tremp, G., Bayer, T.A., Benoit, P., Pradier, L. Massive CA1/2 neuronal loss with intraneuronal and N-terminal truncated Aβ42 accumulation in a novel Alzheimer transgenic model. *Am. J. Pathol. 165:* 1289-1300, 2004.

Caspersen. C., Wang, N., Yao, J., Sosunov, A., Chen, X., Lustbader, J.W., Xu, H.W., Stern, D., McKhann, G., Yan, S.D. Mitochondrial Aβ: a potential focal point for neuronal metabolic dysfunction in Alzheimer's disease. *Faseb J. 19:* 2040-2041, 2005.

Cataldo, A.M., Nixon, R.A. Enzymatically active lysosomal proteases are associated with amyloid deposits in Alzheimer brain. *Proc. Natl. Acad. Sci. USA 87:* 3861–3865, 1990a.

Cataldo, A.M., Petanceska, S., Terio, N.B., Peterhoff, C.M., Durham, R., Mercken, M., Mehta, P.D., Buxbaum, J., Haroutunian, V., Nixon, R.A. Aβ localization in abnormal endosomes: association with earliest Aβ elevations in AD and Down syndrome. *Neurobiol. Aging 25:* 1263-1272, 2004.

Cataldo, A.M., Thayer, C.Y., Bird, E.D., Wheelock, T.R., Nixon, R.A. Lysosomal proteinase antigens are prominently localized within senile plaques of Alzheimer's disease: evidence for a neuronal origin. *Brain Res. 513:* 181–192, 1990b.

Chui, D.-H., Tanahashi, H., Ozawa, K., Ikeda, S., Checler, F., Ueda, O., Suzuki, H., Araki, W., Inoue, H., Shirotani, K., Takahashi, K., Gallyas, F., Tabira, T. Transgenic mice with Alzheimer presenilin 1 mutations show accelerated neurodegeneration without amyloid plaque formation. *Nature Med. 5:* 560-564, 1999

Citron, M., Eckman, C.B., Diehl, T.S., Corcoran, C., Ostaszewski, B.L., Xia, W., Levesque, G., St. George Hyslop, P., Younkin, S.G., Selkoe, D.J. Additive effects of PS1 and APP mutations on secretion of the 42-residue amyloid beta-protein. *Neurobiol. Dis. 5:*107–116, 1998.

Cole, S.L., Grudzien, A., Manhart, I.O., Kelly, B.L., Oakley, H., Vassar, R. Statins cause intracellular accumulation of amyloid precursor protein, β-secretase-cleaved fragments, and amyloid β-peptide via an isoprenoid-dependent mechanism. *J. Biol. Chem. 290:* 18755-18770, 2005.

Cole, S.L., Vassar, R. Isoprenoids and Alzheimer's disease: A complex relationship. *Neurobiol. Disease 22:* 209-222, 2006.

Cook, D.G., Forman, M.S., Sung, J.C., Leight, S., Kolson, D.L., Iwatsubo, T., Lee, V.M., Doms, R.W. Alzheimer's Abeta (1-42) is generated in the endoplasmic reticulum/intermediate compartment of NT2N cells. *Nat. Med. 3:* 1021-1023, 1997.

Cotman, C.W. Apoptosis decision cascades and neuronal degeneration in Alzheimer's disease. *Neurobiol. Aging 19:* S29-S32, 1998.

Cruz, J.C., Kim, D., Moy, L.Y., Dobbin, M.M., Sun, X., Broson, R.T., Tsai, L.H. p25/cyclin-dependent kinase 5 induces production and intraneuronal accumulation of amyloid beta in vivo. *J. Neurosci. 26:* 10536-10541, 2006.

Cruz, J.C., Tseng, H.C., Goldman, J.A., Shih, H., Tsai, L.H. Aberrant Cdk5 activation by p25 triggers pathological events leading to neurodegeneration and neurofibrillary tangles. *Neuron 40:* 471–483, 2003.

Cummings, B.J. and Cotman, C.W. Image analysis of beta-amyloid load in Alzheimer's disease and relation to dementia severity. *Lancet 346:* 1524-1528, 1995.

D'Andrea M.R., Nagele, R.G., Wang, H.-Y., Lee, D.H.S. Consistent immunohistochemical detection of intracellular β-amyloid 42 in pyramidal neurons of Alzheimer's disease entorhinal cortex. *Neurosci. Letts. 333:* 163-166, 2002.

D'Andrea, M.R., Nagele, R.G., Wang, H.-Y., Peterson, P.A., Lee, D.H.S. Evidence that neurons accumulating amyloid can undergo lysis to form amyloid plaques in Alzheimer's disease. *Histopathol. 38:* 120-134, 2001.

DeKosky, S.T., Scheff, S.W. Synapse loss in frontal cortex biopsies in Alzheimer's disease: correlation with cognitive severity. *Ann. Neurol. 27:* 457-464, 1990.

Dodart, J.C., Bales, K.R., Gannon, K.S., Greene, S.J., DeMattos, R.B., Mathis, C., DeLong, C.A., Wu, S., Wu, X., Holtzman, D.M., Paul, S.M. Immunization reverses memory deficits without reducing brain Aβ burden in Alzheimer's disease model. *Nat. Neurosci. 5:* 452-457, 2002.

Dugan, J. M., deWit, C., McConlogue, L., and Maltese, W. A. The Ras-related GTP-binding protein, Rab1, regulates early steps in exocytic transport and processing of beta-amyloid precursor protein. *J. Biol. Chem. 270:* 10982–10989, 1995.

Eckman, C.B., Mehta, N.D., Crook, R., Perez-tur, J., Prihar, G., Pfeiffer, E., Graff-Radford, N., Hinder, P., Yager, D., Zenk, B., Refolo, L.M., Prada, C.M., Younkin, S.G., Hutton, M., Hardy, J. A new pathogenic mutation in the APP gene (I716V) increases the relative proportion of A beta 42(43). *Hum. Mol. Genet. 6:* 2087–2089, 1997.

Fernandez-Vizarra, P., Fernandez, A.P., Castro-Blanco, S., Serrano, J., Bentura, M.L., Martinez-Murillo, R., Martinez, A., Rodrigo, J. Intra- and extracellular Abeta and PHF in clinically evaluated cases of Alzheimer's disease. *Histol. Histopathol. 19:* 823-844, 2004.

Fischer, A., Sananbenesi, F., Pang, P.T., Lu, B., Tsai, L.H. Opposing roles of transient and prolonged expression of p25 in synaptic plasticity and hippocampus-dependent memory. *Neuron 48:* 825– 838, 2005.

Gabuzda, D., Busciglio, J., Chen, L.B., Matsudaira, P., and Yankner, B.A. Inhibition of energy metabolism alters the processing of amyloid precursor protein and induces a potentially amyloidogenic derivative. *J. Biol. Chem. 269:* 13623-13628, 1994.

Gasparini, L., Racchi, M., Benussi, L., Curti, D., Binetti, G., Bianchetti, A., Trabucchi, M., Govoni, S. Effect of energy shortage and oxidative stress on amyloid precursor protein metabolism in COS cells. *Neurosci. Lett. 231:* 113-117, 1997.

Gillardon, F., Rist, W., Kussmaul, L., Vogel, J., Berg, M., Danzer, K., Kraut, N., Hengerer, B. Proteomic and functional alterations in brain mitochondria from Tg2576 mice occur before amyloid plaque deposition. *Proteomics 7:* 605-616, 2007.

Glabe, C.G., Kayed, R. Common structure and toxic function of amyloid oligomers implies a common mechanism of pathogenesis. *Neurology 66:* S74-S78, 2006.

Glenner, G.G., Wong, C.W. Alzheimer's disease: initial report of the purification and characterization of a novel cerebrovascular amyloid protein. *Biochem. Biophys. Res. Commun.120:* 885– 890, 1984.

Goate, A., Chartier-Harlin, M-C., Mullan, M., Brown, J., Crawford, F., Fidani L., Giuffra, L., Haynes, A., Irving, N., James, L., Mant, R., Newton, P., Rooke, K., Roques, P., Talbot, C., Pericak-Vance, M., Roses, A., Williamson, R., Rossor, M., Owen, M., Hardy, J. Segregation of a missense mutation in the amyloid precursor protein gene with familial Alzheimer's disease. *Nature 349:* 704 – 706, 1991.

Gong, Y., Chang, L., Viola, K.L., Lacor, P.N., Lambert, M.P., Finch, C.E., Krafft, G.A., Klein, W.L. Alzheimer's disease-affected brain: presence of oligomeric A beta ligands (ADDLs) suggests a molecular basis for reversible memory loss. *Proc. Natl. Acad. Sci. USA 100:* 10417-10422, 2003.

Gouras, G.K., Tsai, J., Naslund, J., Vincent, B., Edgar, M., Checler, F., Greenfield, J.P., Haroutunian, V., Buxbaum, J.D., Xu, H., Greengard, P., Relkin, N.R. Intraneuronal Abeta42 accumulation in human brain. *Am. J. Pathol. 156:* 15–20, 2000.

Gregori, L., Fuchs, C., Figueiredo-Pereira, M.E., Van Nostrand, W.E., Goldgaber, D. Amyloid beta-protein inhibits ubiquitin-dependent protein degradation in vitro. *J. Biol. Chem. 270:*19702–19708, 1995.

Gregori, L., Hainfeld, J.F., Simon, M.N., Goldgaber, D. Binding of amyloid beta protein to the 20 S proteasome. *J. Biol. Chem. 272:* 58–62, 1997.

Guo, Q., Fu, W., Xie, J., Luo, H., Sells, S.F., Geddes, J.W., Bondad, V., Rangnekar, V.M., Mattson, M.P. Par-4 is a mediator of neuronal degeneration associated with the pathogenesis of Alzheimer disease. *Nature Med. 4:* 957-962, 1998.

Gyure, K.A., Durham, R., Stewart, W.F., Smialek, J.E., Troncoso, J.C. Intraneuronal abeta-amyloid precedes development of amyloid plaques in Down syndrome. *Arch. Pathol. Lab. Med. 125:* 489–492, 2001.

Haas, C., Selkoe, D.J., Soluble protein oligomers in neurodegeneration: lessons from the Alzheimer's amyloid β-peptide. *Nature Rev. 8:* 101-112; 2007.

Harper, J. D., Wong, S. S., Lieber, C. M., and Lansbury, P. T., Jr. Assembly of Abeta amyloid protofibrils: an in vitro model for a possible early event in Alzheimer's disease. *Biochem.* 38: 8972-8980, 1999.

Hartley, D.M., Walsh, D.M., Ye, C.P., Diehl, T., Vasquez, S., Vassilev, P.M., Teplow, D.B., Selkoe, D.J. Protofibrillar intermediates of amyloid beta-protein induce acute electrophysiological changes and progressive neurotoxicity in cortical neurons. *J. Neurosci.* 19: 8876-8884, 1999.

Hepler, R.W., Grimm, K.M., Nahas, D.D., Breese, R., Chen Dodson, E., Acton, P., Keller, P,M., Yeager, M., Wang, H., Shughrue, P., Kinney, G., Joyce, J. G. Solution State Characterization of Amyloid β-Derived Diffusible Ligands. *Biochem.* 45: 15157-15167, 2006.

Herzig, M.C., Winkler, D.T., Burgermeister, P., Pfeifer, M., Kohler, E., Schmidt, S.D., Danner, S., Abramowski, D., Sturchler-Pierrat, C., Burki, K., Van Duinen, S.G., Maat-Schieman, M.L., Staufenbiel, M., Mathews, P.M., Jucker, M. Abeta is targeted to the vasculature in a mouse model of hereditary cerebral hemorrhage with amyloidosis. *Nat. Neurosci.* 7: 954-960, 2004.

Holcomb, L., Gordon, M.N., McGowan, E., Yu, X., Benkovic, S., Jantzen, P., Wright, K., Saad, I., Mueller, R., Morgan, D., Sanders, S., Zehr, C., O'Campo, K., Hardy, J., Prada, C.M., Eckman, C., Younkin, S., Hsiao, K., Duff, K. Accelerated Alzheimer-type phenotype in transgenic mice carrying both mutant amyloid precursor protein and presenilin 1 transgenes. *Nat. Med.* 4: 97–100, 1998.

Hsia, A.Y., Masliah, E., McConlogue, L., Yu, G-Q., Tatsuno, G., Hu, K., Kholodenko, D., Malenka, R.C., Nicoll, R.A., Mucke, L. Plaque-independent disruption of neural circuits in Alzheimer's disease mouse models. *Proc. Natl. Acad. Sci. USA 96:* 3228-3233, 1999.

Hsiao Ashe, K. Learning and memory in transgenic mice modeling Alzheimer's Disease. *Learn. Mem.* 8: 301-308, 2001.

Iwata, N., Tsubuki, S., Takaki, Y., Shirotani, K., Lu, B., Gerard, N.P., Gerard, C., Hama, E., Lee, H.J., Saiso, T.C. Metabolic regulation of brain Abeta by neprilysin. *Science 292:* 1550-1552, 2001.

Kaether, C., Haass, C., Steiner, H. Assembly, trafficking and function of gamma-secretase. *Neurodegener. Dis. 3:* 275-283, 2006.

Keller, J.N., Hanni, K.B., Markesbery, W.R. Impaired proteasome function in Alzheimer's disease. *J. Neurochem.* 75: 436–439, 2000.

Kish, S.J., Bergeron, C., Rajput, A., Dozic, S., Mastrogiacomo, F., Chang, L.J., Wilson, J.M., DiStefano, L.M., Nobrega, J.N. Brain cytochrome oxidase in Alzheimer's disease. *J. Neurochem.* 59: 776–779, 1992.

Kitamura, Y., Shimohama, S., Kamoshima, W., Ota, T., Matsuoka, Y., Nomura, Y., Smith, M.A., Perry, G., Whitehouse, P.J., Taniguchi, T. Alteration of proteins regulating apoptosis, Bcl-2, Bcl-x, Bax, Bak, Bad, ICH-1 and CPP32, in Alzheimer's disease. *Brain Res. 780:* 260–269, 1998.

Kokubo, H., Kayed, R., Glabe, C.G., Saido, T.C., Iwata, N., Helms, J.B., Yamaguchi, H. Oligomeric proteins ultrastructurally localize to cell processes, especially to axon terminals with higher density, but not lipid rafts in Tg2576 mouse brain. *Brain Res. 1045:* 224-228, 2005.

Koo, E.H., Squazzo, S.L. Evidence that production and release of amyloid beta-protein involves the endocytic pathway. *J. Biol. Chem. 269:*17386-17389, 1994.

Kotilinek, L.A., Bacskai, B., Westerman, M., Kawarabayashi, T., Younkin, L., Hyman, B.T., Younkin, S., Ashe, K.H. Reversible memory loss in a mouse transgenic model of Alzheimer's disease. *J. Neurosci. 22:*6331-6335, 2002.

Kumar-Singh, S., De Jonghe, C., Cruts, M., Kleinert, R., Wang, R., Mercken, M., De Strooper, B., Vanderstichele, H., Lofgren, A., Vanderhoeven, I., Backhovens, H., Vanmechelen, E., Kroisel, P.M., Van Broeckhoven, C. Nonfibrillar diffuse amyloid deposition due to a gamma (42)-secretase site mutation points to an essential role for N-truncated abeta (42) in Alzheimer's disease. *Hum. Mol. Genet. 9:* 2589-2598, 2000.

Kuo, Y.M., Emmerling, M.R., Vigo-Pelfrey, C., Kasunic, T.C., Kirkpatrick, J.B., Murdoch, G.H., Ball, M.J., Roher, A.E. Water-soluble Ab (N-40, N-42) oligomers in normal and Alzheimer disease brains. *J. Biol. Chem. 271:* 4077-4081, 1996.

Lacor, P.N., Buniel, M.C., Furlow, P.W., Clemente, A.S., Velasco, P.T., Wood, M., Viola, K.L., Klein, W.L. Aβ Oligomer-Induced Aberrations in Synapse Composition, Shape, and Density Provide a Molecular Basis for Loss of Connectivity in Alzheimer's Disease. *J. Neurosci. 27:* 796-807, 2007.

LaFerla, F.M., Tinkle, B.T., Bieberich, C.J., Haudenschild, C.C., Jay, G. The Alzheimer's Abeta peptide induces neurodegeneration and apoptotic cell death in transgenic mice. *Nat. Genet. 9:*21–30, 1995.

LaFerla, F.M., Troncoso, J.C., Strickland, D.K., Kawas, C.H., Jay, G. Neuronal cell death in Alzheimer's disease correlates with apoE uptake and intracellular Aβ stabilization. *J. Clin. Invest. 100:* 310-320, 1997.

Lambert, M.P., Barlow, A.K., Chromy, B.A., Edwards, C., Freed, R., Liosatos, M., Morgan, T.E., Rozovsky, I., Trommer, B., Viola, K.L, Wals, P., Zhang, C., Finch, C.E., Krafft, G.A., Klein, W.L. Diffusible, nonfibrillar ligands derived from Abeta1-42 are potent central nervous system neurotoxins. *Proc. Natl. Acad. Sci. U.S.A. 95:*6448-6453, 1998.

Lammich, S., Kojro, E., Postina, R., Gilbert, S., Pfeiffer, R., Jasionowski, M., Haass, C., Fahrenholz, F. Constitutive and regulated alpha-secretase cleavage of Alzheimer's amyloid precursor protein by a disintegrin metalloprotease. *Proc. Natl. Acad. Sci. USA 96:* 3922-3927, 1999.

Langui, D., Girardot, N., El Hachimi, K.H., Allinquant, B., Blanchard, V., Pradier, L., Duyckaerts, C. Subcellular Topography of Neuronal Aβ Peptide in APPxPS1 Transgenic Mice. *Am. J. Pathol. 165:* 1465-1477, 2004.

Lazarov, O., Lee, M., Peterson, D.A., Sisodia, S.S. Evidence that synaptically released beta-amyloid accumulates as extracellular deposits in the hippocampus of transgenic mice. *J. Neurosci. 22:* 9785–9793, 2002.

Lee, K.Y., Clark, A.W., Rosales, J.L., Chapman, K., Fung, T., Johnston, R.N. Elevated neuronal Cdc2-like kinase activity in the Alzheimer disease brain. *Neurosci. Res. 34:* 21–29, 1999.

Lee, M.S., Kao, S.C., Lemere, C.A., Xia, W., Tseng, H.C., Zhou, Y., Neve, R., Ahlijanian, M.K., Tsai, L.H. APP processing is regulated by cytoplasmic phosphorylation. *J. Cell Biol. 163:* 83–95, 2003.

Leissring, M.A., Farris, W., Chang, A.Y., Walsh, D.M., Wu, X., Sun, X., Frosch, M.P., Selkoe, D.J. Enhanced proteolysis of beta-amyloid in APP transgenic mice prevents plaque formation, secondary pathology, and premature death. *Neuron 40:* 1087-1093, 2003.

Lesne, S., Koh, M.T., Kotilinek, L., Kayed, R., Glabe, C.G., Yang, A., Gallagher, M., Ashe, K.H. A specific amyloid-β protein assembly in the brain impairs memory. *Nature 440:* 352-357, 2006.

Levy-Lahad, E., Wasco, W., Poorkaj, P., Romano, D.M., Oshima, J., Pettingell, W.H., Yu, C.E., Jondro, P.D., Schmidt, S.D., Wang, K., Crowley, A.C., Fu, Y.H., Guenette, S.Y., Galas, D., Nemens, E., Wijsman, E.M., Bird, T.D., Schellenberg, G.D., Tanzi, R.E. Candidate gene for the chromosome 1 familial Alzheimer's disease locus. *Science 269:* 973–977, 1995b.

Levy-Lahad, E., Wisjman, E.M., Nemens, E., Anderson, L., Goddard, K.A.B., Weber, J.L., Bird, T.D., Schellenberg, G.D. A familial Alzheimer's disease locus on chromosome 1. *Science 269:* 970–973, 1995a.

Longva, K.E., Blystad, F.D., Stang, E., Larsen, A.M., Johannessen, L.E., Madshus, I.H. Ubiquitination and proteasomal activity is required for transport of the EGF receptor to inner membranes of multivesicular bodies. *J. Cell Biol. 156:* 843– 854, 2002.

Lord, A., Kalimo, H., Eckman, C., Zhang, X-Q., Lannfelt, L., Nilsson, L.N.G. The Arctic Alzheimer mutation facilitates early intraneuronal Aβ aggregation and senile plaque formation in transgenic mice. *Neurobiol. Aging 27:* 67-77, 2006.

MacGibbon, G.A., Lawlor, P.A., Sirimanne, E.S., Walton, M.R., Connor, B., Young, D., Williams, C., Gluckman, P., Faull, R.L., Hughes, P., Dragunow, M. Bax expression in mammalian neurons undergoing apoptosis, and in Alzheimer's disease hippocampus. *Brain Res. 750:* 223–234, 1997.

Maezawa, I., Hong, H.S., Wu, H.C., Battina, S.K., Rana, S., Iwamoto, T., Radke, G.A., Pettersson, E., Martin, G.M., Hua, D.H., Jin, L.W. A novel tricyclic pyrone compound ameliorates cell death associated with intracellular amyloid-beta oligomeric complexes. *J. Neurochem. 98:* 57-67, 2006.

Magrane, J., Rosen, K.M. Smith, R.C., Walsh, K., Gouras, G.K., Querfurth, H.W. Intraneuronal beta-amyloid expression downregulates the Akt survival pathway and blunts the stress response. *J. Neurosci. 25:* 10960-10969, 2005.

Magrane, J., Smith, R.C., Walsh, K., Querfurth, H.W. Heat shock protein 70 participates in the neuroprotective response to intracellularly expressed beta-amyloid in neurons. *J Neurosci. 24:*1700–1706, 2004.

Martin, B.L., Schrader-Fischer, G., Busciglio, J., Duke, M., Paganetti, P., Yankner, B.A. Intracellular accumulation of beta-amyloid in cells expressing the Swedish mutant amyloid precursor protein. *J. Biol. Chem. 270:* 26727-26730, 1995.

Masters, C.L., Multhaup, G., Simms, G., Pottigiesser, J., Martins, R.N., Beyreuther, K. Neuronal origin of a cerebral amyloid: neurofibrillary tangles of Alzheimer's disease contain the same protein as the amyloid of plaque cores and blood vessels. *EMBO J. 4:* 2757– 2763, 1985.

Mattson, M. P. Free radicals, calcium and the synaptic plasticity-cell death continuum: emerging roles of the transcription factor NF kappa B. *Int. Rev. Neurobiol. 42:* 103–108, 1998.

McConlogue, L., Castellano, F., deWit, C., Schenk, D., and Maltese, W. A. Differential effects of a Rab6 mutant on secretory verses amyloidogenic processing of Alzheimer's beta-amyloid precursor protein. *J. Biol. Chem. 271,* 1343–1348, 1996.

McLean, C.A., Cherny, R.A., Fraser, F.W., Fuller, S.J., Smith, M.J., Beyreuther, K., Bush, A.I., Masters, C.L. Soluble pool of Abeta amyloid as a determinant of severity of neurodegeneration in Alzheimer's disease. *Ann. Neurol. 46:* 860-866, 1999.

Moechars, D., Dewachter, I., Lorent, K., Reverse, D., Baekelandt, V., Naidu, A., Tesseur, I., Spittaels, K., Haute, C.V., Checler, F., Godaux, E., Cordell, B., Van Leuven, F. Early phenotypic changes in transgenic mice that overexpress different mutants of amyloid precursor protein in brain. *J. Biol. Chem. 274:* 6483– 6492, 1999.

Mori, C., Spooner, E.T., Wisniewsk, K.E., Wisniewski, T.M., Yamaguch, H., Saido, T.C., Tolan, D.R., Selkoe, D.J., Lemere, C.A. Intraneuronal Abeta42 accumulation in Down syndrome brain. *Amyloid 9:* 88 –102, 2002.

Mullan, M., Crawford, F., Axelman, K., Houlden, H., Lilius, L,. Winblad, B., Lannfelt, L. A pathogenic mutation for probable Alzheimer's disease in the APP gene at the N-terminus of beta-amyloid. *Nat Genet. 1:* 345-7, 1992.

Mutisya, E.M., Bowling, A.C., Beal, M.F. Cortical cytochrome oxidase activity is reduced in Alzheimer's disease. *J. Neurochem. 63:* 2179–2184, 1994.

Nagele, R.G., D'Andrea, M.R., Anderson, W.J., Wang, H.-Y. Accumulation of beta-amyloid$_{1-42}$ in neurons is facilitated by the alpha 7 nicotinic acetylcholine receptor in Alzheimer's disease. *Neurosci. 110:* 199–211, 2002.

Necula, M., Kayed, R., Milton, S., Glabe, C.G. Small-molecule inhibitors of aggregation indicate that amyloid beta oligomerization and fibrillization pathways are independent and distinct. JBC Papers in Press. Published on February 6, 2007 as Manuscript M608207200.

Nilsberth, C., Westlind-Danielsson, A., Eckman, C.B., Condron, M.M., Axelman, K., Forslee, C., Stenh, C., Luthman, J., Teplow, D.B., Younkin, S.G., Naslund, J., Lannfelt, L. The 'Arctic' APP mutation (E693G) causes Alzheimer's disease by enhanced Aβ protofibril formation. *Nat. Neurosci. 4:* 887-893, 2001.

O'Keeffe, S.T., Kazeem, H., Philpott, R.M., Playfer, J.R., Gosney, M., Lye, M. Gait disturbance in Alzheimer's disease: a clinical study. *Age Ageing 25:* 313–316, 1996

Oakley, H., Cole, S.L., Logan, S., Maus, E., Shao, P., Craft, J., Guillozet-Bongaarts, A., Ohno, M., Disterhoft, J., Van Eldik, L., Berry, R., Vassar, R. Intraneuronal β-amyloid aggregates, neurodegeneration, and neuron loss in transgenic mice with five familial Alzheimer's disease mutations: Potential factors in amyloid plaque formation. *J. Neurosci. 26:* 10129-10140, 2006.

Oddo, S., Billings, L., Kesslak, J.P., Cribbs, D.H., LaFerla, F.M. Aβ immunotherapy leads to clearance of early, but not later, hyperphosphorylated tau aggregates via the proteasome. *Neuron 43:* 321-332, 2004.

Oddo, S., Caccamo, A., Green, K.N., Liang, K., Tran, L., Chen, Y., Leslie, F.M., LaFerla, F.M. Chronic nicotine administration exacerbates tau pathology in a transgenic model of Alzheimer's disease. *Proc. Natl. Acad. Sci. U. S. A 102:* 3046-3051, 2005.

Oddo, S., Caccamo, A., Shepherd, J.D., Murphy, M.P., Golde, T.E., Kayed, R., Metherate, R., Mattsom, M.P., Akbari, Y., LaFerla, F.M. Triple-transgenic model of Alzheimer's disease with plaques and tangles: Intracellular Aβ and synaptic dysfunction. *Neuron 39:* 409-421, 2003.

Oddo, S., Caccamo, A., Smith, I.F., Green, K.N., LaFerla, F.M. A dynamic relationship between intracellular and extracellular pools of Aβ. *Am. J. Pathol. 168:* 184-194, 2006b.

Oddo, S., Caccamo, A., Tran, L., Lambert, M.P., Glabe, C.G., Klein, W.L., LaFerla, F.M. Temporal profile of amyloid-β (Aβ) oligomerization in an in vivo model of Alzheimer disease. *J. Biol. Chem. 281:* 1599-1604, 2006a

Oh, S., Hong, H.S., Hwang, E., Sim, H.J., Lee, W., Shin, S.J., Mook-Jung, I. Amyloid peptide attenuates the proteasome activity in neuronal cells. *Mech. Ageing Dev. 126:* 1292–1299, 2005.

Ohno, M., Chang, L., Tseng, W., Oakley, H., Citron, M., Klein, W.L., Vassar, R., Disterhoft, J.F. Temporal memory deficits in Alzheimer's mouse models: rescue by genetic deletion of BACE1. *Eur. J. Neurosci. 23:* 251–260, 2006.

Ohno, M., Cole, S.L., Yasvoina, M., Zhao, J., Citron, M., Berry, R., Disterhoft, J.F., Vassar, R. BACE1 gene deletion prevents neuron loss and memory deficits in 5XFAD APP/PS1 transgenic mice. *Neurobiol. Dis. 26:* 134-145, 2007.

Ohno, M., Sametsky, E.A., Younkin, L.H., Oakley, H., Younkin, S.G., Citron, M., Vassar, R., Disterhoft, J.F. BACE1 deficiency rescues memory deficits and cholinergic dysfunction in a mouse model of Alzheimer's disease. *Neuron 41:* 27–33, 2004.

Ohyagi, Y., Yamada, T., Nishioka, K., Clarke, N.J., Tomlinson, A.J., Naylor, S., Nakabeppu, Y., Kira, J., Younkin, S.G. Selective increase in cellular Aβ42 is related to apoptosis but not necrosis. *Neuroreport 11:* 167-171, 2000.

Parvathy, S., Davies, P., Haroutunian, V., Purohit, D.P., Davis, K.L., Mohs, R.C., Park, H., Moran, T.M., Chan, J.Y., Buxbaum, J.D. Correlation between Abeta x-40-, Abeta x-42-, and Abeta x-43-containing amyloid plaques and cognitive decline. *Arch. Neurol. 58:* 2025-32, 2001.

Parvathy, S., Hussain, I., Karran, E.H., Turner, A.J., Hooper, N.M. Cleavage of Alzheimer's amyloid precursor protein by alpha-secretase occurs at the surface of neuronal cells. *Biochem. 38:* 9728-9734, 1999.

Patrick, G.N., Zukerberg, L., Nikolic, M., de la Monte, S., Dikkes, P., Tsai, L.H. Conversion of p35 to p25 deregulates Cdk5 activity and promotes neurodegeneration. *Nature 402:*615– 622, 1999.

Perkins, G., Renken, C., Martone, M.E., Young, S.J., Ellisman, M., Frey, T. Electron tomography of neuronal mitochondria: three-dimensional structure and organization of cristae and membrane contacts. *J. Struct. Biol. 119:* 260-272, 1997.

Petersen, R.C. Mild cognitive impairment: current research and clinical implications. *Semin. Neurol. 27:* 22-31, 2007.

Pierrot, N., Santos, S.F., Feyt, C., Morel, M., Brion, J.P., Octave, J.N. Calcium-mediated transient phosphorylation of tau and amyloid precursor protein followed by intraneuronal amyloid-beta accumulation. *J. Biol. Chem. 281:* 39907-39914, 2006.

Rapoport, S.I., Horwitz, B., Grady, C.L., Haxby, J.V., DeCarli, C., Schapiro, M.B. Abnormal brain glucose metabolism in Alzheimer's disease, as measured by position emission tomography. *Adv. Exp. Med. Biol. 291:* 231–248, 1991.

Scarmeas, N., Hadjigeorgiou, G.M., Papadimitriou, A., Dubois, B., Sarazin, M., Brandt, J., Albert, M., Marder, K., Bell, K., Honig, L.S., Wegesin, D., Stern, Y. Motor signs during the course of Alzheimer disease. *Neurology 63:* 975–82, 2004.

Schellenberg, G.D., Bird, T.D., Wijsman, E.M., Orr, H.T., Anderson, L., Nemens, E., White, J.A., Bonnycastle, L., Weber, J.L., Alonso, M.E., Potter, H., Heston, L.L., Martin, G.M. Genetic linkage evidence for a familial Alzheimer's disease locus on chromosome 14. *Science 258:* 668–671, 1992.

Schmitz, C., Rutten, B.P.F., Peilen, A., Schaefer, S., Wirhts, O., Tremp, G., Czech, C., Blanchard, V., Multhaup, G., Rezaie, P., Korr, H., Steinbusch, H.W.M., Pradier, L., Bayer, T.A. Hippocampal Neuron Loss Exceeds Amyloid Plaque Load in a Transgenic Mouse Model of Alzheimer's Disease. *Am. J. Pathol. 164:* 1495-1502, 2004.

Selkoe, D.J. Alzheimer's disease: genes, proteins, and therapy. *Physiol. Rev. 81:* 741–766, 2001a.

Selkoe, D.J. Clearing the brain's amyloid cobwebs. *Neuron 32:* 177-180, 2001b.

Sheng, J.G., Price, D.L., Koliatsos, V.E. Disruption of corticocortical connections ameliorates amyloid burden in terminal fields in a transgenic model of Aβ amyloidosis. *J. Neurosci. 22:* 9794 –9799, 2002.

Sisodia, S. S., Kim, S. H., and Thinakaran, G. Function and dysfunction of the presenilins. *Am. J. Hum. Genet. 65:* 7–12, 1995.

Skovronsky, D.M., Doms, R.W., Lee, V.M. Detection of a novel intraneuronal pool of insoluble amyloid beta protein that accumulates with time in culture. *J. Cell Biol. 141:* 1031-1039, 1998.

Smith, M.A., Drew, K.L., Nunomura, A., Takeda, A., Hirai, K., Zhu, X., Atwood, C.S., Raina, A.K., Rottkamp, C.A., Sayre, L.M., Friedland, R.P., Perry, G. Amyloid-β , tau alterations and mitochondrial dysfunction in Alzheimer disease: the chickens or the eggs. *Neurochem. Int. 4:* 527–531, 2002.

Snyder, E. M., Nong, Y., Almeida, C.G., Paul, S., Moran, T., Choi, E.Y., Nairn, A.C., Salter, M.W., Lombroso, P.J., Gouras, G.K., Greengard, P. Regulation of NMDA receptor trafficking by amyloid-β. *Nature Neurosci.* 8:1051–1058, 2005.

Spires, T.L., Hyman, B.T. Transgenic models of Alzheimer's disease: learning from animals. *NeuroRx 2:* 423– 437, 2005.

St George-Hyslop, P.H., Haines, J.L., Farrer, L.A., Polinsky, R., Van Broeckhoven, C., Goate, A., Crapper McLachlan, D.R., Orr, H., Bruni, A.C., Sorbi, S., Rainero, I., Foncin, J.-F., Pollen, D., Cantu, J.-M., Tupler, T., Voskresenskaya, N., Mayeux, R., Growdon, J., Fried, V.A., Myers, R.H., Nee, L., Backhovens, H., Martin, J-J., Rossor, M., Owen, M.J., Mullan, M., Percy, M.E., Karlinsky, H., Rich, S., Heston, L., Montesi, M., Mortilla, M., Nacmias, N., Gusella, J.F., Hardy, J.A. Genetic linkage studies suggest that Alzheimer's disease is not a single homogeneous disorder. *Nature 347:* 194 – 197, 1990.

Swatton, J.E., Sellers, L.A., Faull, R.L., Holland, A., Iritani, S., Bahn, S. Increased MAP kinase activity in Alzheimer's and Down syndrome but not in schizophrenia human brain. *Eur. J. Neurosci. 19:* 2711–2719, 2004.

Takahashi, R.H., Almeida, C.G., Kearney, P.F., Yu, F., Lin, M.T., Milner, T.A., Gouras, G.K. Oligomerization of Alzheimer's β-amyloid within processes and synapses of cultured neurons and brain. *J. Neurosci. 24:* 3592–3599, 2004.

Takahashi, R.H., Milner, T.A., Li, F., Nam, E.E., Edgar, M.A., Yamaguchi, H., Beal, M.F., Xu, H., Greengard, P., Gouras, G.K. Intraneuronal Alzheimer Aβ42 accumulates in multivesicular bodies and is associated with synaptic pathology. *Am. J. Pathol. 161:* 1869-1879, 2002.

Takahashi, R.H., Milner, T.A., Li, F., Nam, E.E., Edgar, M.A., Yamaguchi, H., Beal, M.F., Xu, H., Greengard, P., Gouras, G.K. Intraneuronal Alzheimer Abeta42 accumulates in multivesicular bodies and is associated with synaptic pathology. *Am. J. Pathol. 161:* 1869 –1879, 2002.

Terry, R.D., Masliah, E., Hansen, L.A. The neuropathology of Alzheimer disease and the structural basis of its cognitive alterations. In: Terry, RD., Katzman, R., Bick, KL., Sisodia, SS. (Eds). *Alzheimer Disease.* Lippincott Williams and Wilkins, Philadelphia, Publisher, 1999, pp. 187-206.

Tsai, L.H., Delalle, I., Caviness, Jr. V.S., Chae, T., Harlow, E. p35 is a neural specific regulatory subunit of cyclin-dependent kinase 5. *Nature 371:* 419–423, 1994.

Urbanc, B., Cruz, L., Le, R., Sanders, J., Hsiao Ashe, K., Duff, K., Stanley, H.E., Irizarry, M.C., Hyman, B.T. Neurotoxic effects of thioflavin S-positive amyloid deposits in transgenic mice and Alzheimer's disease. *Proc. Natl. Acad. Sci. USA 99:* 13990-13995, 2002.

Valerio, A., Boroni, F., Benarese, M., Sarnico, I., Ghisi, V., Grazia Bresciani, L., Ferrario, M., Borsani, G., Spano, P., Pizzi, M. NF-kB pathway: a target for preventing β-amyloid (Aβ)-induced neuronal damage and Aβ42 production. *Eur. J. Neurosci. 23:* 1711-1720, 2006.

Van Broeck, B., Vanhoutte, G., Pirici, D., Van Dam, D., Wils, H., Cuijt, I., Vennekens, K., Zabielski, M., Michalik, A., Theuns, J., De Deyn, P.P., Van der Linden, A., Van Broeckhoven, C., Kumar-Singh, S. Intraneuronal amyloid beta and reduced brain volume in a novel APP T714I mouse model for Alzheimer's disease. *Neurobiol. Aging.* Epub ahead of print, 2006.

Vassar, R. BACE1: the beta-secretase enzyme in Alzheimer's disease. *J. Mol. Neurosci. 23:* 105–114, 2004.

Vassar, R., Bennett, B.D., Babu-Khan, S., Kahn, S., Mendiaz, E.A., Denis, P., Teplow, D.B., Ross, S., Amarante, P., Loeloff, R., Luo, Y., Fisher, S., Fuller, J., Edenson, S., Lile, J., Jarosinski, M.A., Biere, A.L., Curran, E., Burgess, T., Louis, J.-C., Collins, F., Treanor, J., Rogers, G., Citron, M. β-secretase cleavage of Alzheimer's amyloid precursor protein by the transmembrane aspartic protease BACE. *Science 286:* 735-741, 1999.

Veereshwarayya, V., Kumar, P., Rosen, K.M., Mestril, R., Querfurth, H.W. Differential effects of mitochondrial heat shock protein 60 and related molecular chaperones to prevent intracellular beta-amyloid-induced inhibition of complex IV and limit apoptosis. *J. Biol. Chem. 281:* 29468-29478, 2006.

Velliquette, R.A., O'Connor, T., Vassar, R. Energy inhibition elevates β-secretase levels and activity and is potentially amyloidogenic in APP transgenic mice: Possible early events in Alzheimer's disease pathogenesis. *J. Neurosci. 25:* 10874-10883, 2005.

Walsh, D. M., Tseng, B. P., Rydel, R. E., Podlisny, M. B. & Selkoe, D. J. Detection of intracellular oligomers of amyloid β-protein in cells derived from human brain. *Biochemistry 39:* 10831–10839, 2000.

Walsh, D.M., Klyubin, I., Fadeeva, J.V., Cullen, W.K., Anwyl, R., Wolfe, M.S., Rowan, M.J., Selkoe, D.J. Naturally secreted oligomers of amyloid β protein potently inhibit hippocampal long-term potentiation in vivo. *Nature 416:* 535-539, 2002.

Wang, Q., Walsh, D.M., Rowan, M.J., Selkoe, D.J., Anwyl, R. Block of Long-Term Potentiation by Naturally Secreted and Synthetic Amyloid -Peptide in Hippocampal Slices Is Mediated via Activation of the Kinases c-Jun N-Terminal Kinase, Cyclin-Dependent Kinase 5, and p38 Mitogen-Activated Protein Kinase as well as Metabotropic Glutamate Receptor Type 5. *J. Neurosci. 24:*3370 –3378, 2004.

Wild-Bode, C., Yamazaki, T., Capell, A., Leimer, U., Steiner, H., Ihara, Y., Haass, C. Intracellular generation and accumulation of amyloid beta-peptide terminating at amino acid 42. *J. Biol. Chem. 272:* 16085-16088, 1997.

Wirths, O., Multhaup, G., Czech, C., Blanchard, V., Moussaoui, S., Tremp, G., Pradier, L., Beyreuther, K., Bayer, T.A. Intraneuronal Aβ accumulation precedes plaque formation in β-amyloid precursor protein and presenilin-1 double-transgenic mice. *Neurosci. Letts. 306:*116-120, 2001.

Wirths, O., Multhaup, G., Czech, C., Feldmann, N., Blanchard, V., Tremp, G., Beyreuther, K., Pradier, L., Bayer, T.A. Intraneuronal APP/Aβ Trafficking and Plaque Formation in β-Amyloid Precursor Protein and Presenilin-1 Transgenic Mice. *Brain Pathol. 12:* 275-286, 2002.

Wirths, O., Weis, J., Kayed, R., Saido, T.C., Bayer, T.A. Age-dependent axonal degeneration in an Alzheimer mouse model. Neurobiology of Aging. doi:10.1016/j.neurobiolaging.2006.07.021 2006b

Wirths, O., Weiss, J., Szczygielski, J., Multhaup, G., Bayer, T.A. Axonopathy in an APP/PS1 transgenic mouse model of Alzheimer's disease. *Acta Neuropathol 111:* 312–319, 2006a.

Xu, H., Sweeney, D., Wang, R., Thinakaran, G., Lo, A., Sisodia, S.S., Greengard, P., Gandy, S. Generation of Alzheimer beta-amyloid protein in the trans-Golgi network in the apparent absence of vesicle formation. *Proc. Natl. Acad. Sci. USA 94:* 3748-3752, 1997.

Yankner, B.A. Mechanisms of neuronal degeneration in Alzheimer's disease. *Neuron 16:* 921–932, 1996.

Zhang, Y., McLaughlin, R., Goodyer, C., LeBlanc, A. Selective cytotoxicity of intracellular amyloid beta peptide 1-42 through p53 and Bax in cultured primary human neurons. *J. Cell Biol. 156:* 519-529, 2002.

In: Research Progress in Alzheimer's Disease and Dementia   ISBN 978-1-60021-960-3
Editor: Miao-Kun Sun, pp. 135-176   © 2008 Nova Science Publishers, Inc.

Chapter VI

LIPOPROTEIN RECEPTORS IN ALZHEIMER'S DISEASE

Olav M. Andersen[*] *and Thomas E. Willnow*

Max-Delbrueck-Center for Molecular Medicine, Department for Molecular and
Cardiovascular Research, D-13125 Berlin, Germany.

ABSTRACT

Lipoproteins are the main transport form of cholesterol in plasma and extracellular
body fluids. They are taken up into tissues by endocytic receptors expressed on the
surface of target cells. The major class of lipoprotein receptors is a group of proteins
known as the low-density lipoprotein receptor gene family. Previously, the relevance of
lipoproteins and their receptors has mainly been discussed in terms of regulation of
systemic cholesterol homeostasis and as major risk factor for cardiovascular diseases.
Now, substantial experimental evidence points towards novel and unexpected roles for
lipoprotein receptors in regulation of neuronal processes leading to Alzheimer's disease.
In this chapter, we review current data from epidemiological, biochemical, as well as
experimental animal studies that highlight some of the molecular mechanisms that
underlie the contribution of lipoprotein receptors to onset and progression of
neurodegeneration.

Keywords: apolipoprotein E, cholesterol, lipoprotein receptor, vacuolar protein sorting,
amyloid precursor protein, statins, protein processing, endocytosis.

---

[*] Correspondence concerning this article should be addressed to: Olav Andersen, Max-Delbrueck-Center for
Molecular Medicine, Department for Molecular and Cardiovascular Research, Robert-Roessle-Strasse 10, D-
13125 Berlin, Germany. Tel.: +49 (30) 9406 3749, Fax: +49 (30) 9406 3382. E-mail: o.andersen@mdc-
berlin.de.

1. Introduction

Lipoproteins are the main carriers for lipids such as cholesterol, triglycerides, and lipophilic vitamins in the circulation. They transport these essential metabolites from the side of origin to target tissues where they deliver their cargo via specific lipoprotein receptors. So far, the relevance of lipoprotein metabolism has mainly been discussed in terms of cardiovascular diseases. Disturbances in this process may result in dramatic increases in plasma cholesterol levels and, consequently, in atherosclerosis and premature death from coronary artery disease. As well as representing a major risk factor for cardiovascular morbidity, recent findings now point to an equally important role for lipoprotein metabolism in onset and progression of Alzheimer's disease (AD). Links between lipid homeostasis and neurodegenerative processes have been established at many levels. Systemic and neuronal cholesterol concentrations, apolipoprotein profile, and lipoprotein receptor activity all have been shown to modulate AD progression. In the following chapter, we will describe basic concepts of the systemic and neuronal lipoprotein metabolism, and we will discuss current hypotheses how its components are believed to affect onset and progression of neurodegeneration. Particular emphasis will be given to the role of lipoprotein receptors in this context.

2. Systemic Lipoprotein Metabolism

2.1. Cholesterol Biosynthesis

The significance of cholesterol for animal cells is well appreciated both as a component of cellular membranes and as precursor for formation of steroid hormones, vitamins, and bile acids. Cholesterol is synthesized by a pathway intrinsic to all cells of the human body. The precursor for cholesterol formation is acetyl CoA, which can be formed from glucose, fatty acids, or amino acids. Two molecules of acetyl CoA fuse to acetoacetyl CoA, that further condenses with another molecule of acetyl CoA to form hydroxymethylglutaryl CoA (HMG-CoA). Reduction of HMG-CoA produces mevalonate, a reaction catalyzed by HMG-CoA reductase. This enzyme performs a major rate-limiting step in cholesterol biosynthesis and represents an attractive target for therapeutic strategies aimed at lowering cholesterol levels in patients. The first step in the cholesterol biosynthestic pathway is completed by a series of condensation reactions that produce isopentenyl pyrophosphate, an activated isoprene unit that is the key building block of cholesterol. In subsequent steps, six molecules of isopentenyl pyrophosphate react to form squalene. Squalene transforms into a tetracyclic product, squalene epoxide, which is finally converted into cholesterol.

2.2. Systemic Lipoprotein Metabolism

All cholesterol is transported in plasma and extracellular body fluids embedded in lipoprotein particles. Lipoproteins are macromolecular structures composed of a core of neutral lipids (mostly cholesterol esters and triglycerides) surrounded by an amphipathic shell of polar phospholipids and cholesterol. Also inserted in the shell are apolipoproteins (apo), such as apoB-100 and apoE that play important roles in the metabolism of lipoproteins. Some act as a scaffold for assembly of lipoproteins in cells that produce and secrete these particles. Others regulate the activity of enzymes (e.g. lipases) that modify lipoproteins in the circulation. Finally, apolipoproteins determine the cellular uptake of lipoproteins by interaction with specific cell surface receptors.

Most lipoproteins are formed in the Endoplasmic Reticulum (ER) involving the activity of the microsomal triglyceride transfer protein that loads lipids onto the apoprotein scaffold in the lumen of the ER. Subsequently, the nascent lipoprotein is secreted via the constitutive secretory pathway of the cell. Following enzymatic modification in the blood stream, lipoproteins traffic through the circulatory system to target tissues. There, they interact with lipoprotein receptors that recognize their apoprotein moiety. The apoprotein profile provides a unique signature of individual lipoprotein classes specifying the origin and types of lipids transported, as well as their destiny. For example, it defines sterols to be transported to the adrenal gland for steroid hormone production, it specifies lipophilic vitamins absorbed in the intestine to be sent to the liver for storage, or it marks cholesterol from glia cells required for membrane synthesis in neurons (see (Brown and Goldstein, 1986; Russell, 1992) for review).

2.3. Lipoprotein Metabolism and Cardiovascular Disease

The metabolism of lipoproteins is tightly regulated at the level of biosynthesis, enzymatic modification, and plasma clearance. Regulatory mechanisms are in place to ensure proper distribution of lipids to peripheral tissues but at the same time to prevent build up abnormal high levels of circulating lipids that are detrimental to the vasculature. Excess levels of circulating lipoproteins, such as low-density lipoproteins (LDL), result in faulty deposition of lipids in the vessel wall, causing narrowing of the arterial lumen and eventual complete block of blood flow. Pathologies of systemic lipoprotein metabolism are among the most important risk factors of cardiovascular complications, the major cause of morbidity and mortality in Western societies.

3. LIPOPROTEIN METABOLISM IN THE BRAIN

3.1. Lipoproteins and AD

Besides the liver, the brain is a major side of cholesterol biosynthesis and deposition. Cholesterol is required for embryonic development of the brain as judged from inborn errors in cholesterol biosynthesis in patients that result in severe developmental defects of this organ. In the adult brain, cholesterol is essential for normal function including membrane synthesis (Beffert et al., 1998).

Since the blood-brain-barrier (BBB) prevents passage of entire lipoprotein particles from the circulation into the brain, lipoprotein metabolism has to proceed locally in the nervous system using components individually imported from plasma or originating from local synthesis. Several apolipoproteins can be detected in brain parenchyma including apoE, apoJ, and apoD. Most prominent expression is seen for apoE, a polypeptide of 299 amino acid residues that is produced and secreted from glial cells, particularly from astrocytes. Three commonly occurring isoforms of the protein are found in the human population that differ by single nucleotide polymorphisms (SNPs) of the *apoe* gene on chromosome 19. The apoE3 isoform (Cys112, Arg158) prevails in populations, followed by apoE4 (Arg112, Arg158) and apoE2 (Cys112, Cys158). ApoE serves as ligand for receptor-mediated uptake of lipoproteins into neurons via neuronal apoE receptors of the LDL receptor gene family (to be discussed below). Substantial evidence suggests an important role of apoE in the (patho)physiology of the nervous system. ApoE synthesis increases dramatically after injury of the central or the peripheral nervous system (Mahley, 1988), while apoE deficiency in animal models significantly increases neurodegeneration during aging (Masliah et al., 1995). Most importantly for discussions in this chapter, a contribution of apoE to AD was revealed in 1993 by association studies of the apolipoprotein E ε4 allele with late-onset forms of the disorder (Rebeck et al., 1993; Strittmatter et al., 1993a; Strittmatter et al., 1993b).

3.2. Cholesterol Metabolism and Risk of AD

High levels of cholesterol are recognized as a significant risk factor for developing sporadic AD (reviewed in (Puglielli et al., 2003; Shobab et al., 2005; Wolozin, 2004). Amyloid β-peptide (Aβ), apoE and cholesterol oxidase have all been found in the core of fibrillar deposits in murine models with senile plaque formation pointing towards a functional link between cholesterol metabolism and plaque development.

Alterations in cholesterol homeostasis in AD patients support the notion that this pathway contributes to the disease entity. Conversion of cholesterol to 24S-hydroxycholesterol by 24-hydroxylase (*aka* CYP46) represents a major mechanism of brain specific cholesterol turnover (Lund et al., 2003). 24S-hydroxycholesterol is more soluble than cholesterol and, therefore, more easily exported from brain parenchyma. Accordingly, the amount of this metabolite in CSF is thought to reflect the rate of brain cholesterol synthesis in individuals. CSF levels of 24S-hydroxycholesterol are significantly higher in some patients suffering from AD compared to healthy controls (Lutjohann et al., 1996; Lutjohann et al., 2000; Papassotiropoulos et al., 2002; Papassotiropoulos et al., 2000; Schonknecht et al., 2002). Furthermore, polymorphisms in the gene encoding 24-hydroxylase have been associated with AD pathologies (Borroni et al., 2004; Kolsch et al., 2002). However, other studies failed to reproduce these findings (Desai et al., 2002; Ingelsson et al., 2004; Johansson et al., 2004).

Another critical step in regulation of cellular cholesterol homeostasis is performed by the family of ATP-binding cassette (ABC) transporters, sterol pumps that transport cholesterol and other lipids across membrane bilayers. ABC transporters have central functions in reverse cholesterol transport whereby excess cholesterol leaves peripheral tissues (such as the vessel wall) to be transported back to the liver. A similar beneficial function for ABC transporters in cholesterol efflux from the CNS has been suggested (Mauch et al., 2001). A protective role for ABC transporter activity in the brain is underscored by findings in mice with targeted disruption of ABCA1, an ABC family member expressed in neurons (Koldamova et al., 2003). Loss of ABCA1 function accelerates amyloid deposition in murine models of AD (Hirsch-Reinshagen et al., 2005; Koldamova et al., 2005; Wahrle et al., 2005).

3.3. Cholesterol Esterification and AD

In cells, excessive cholesterol is stored in cytoplasmic lipid droplets as cholesteryl esters. Esterification is performed by acyl-coenzyme A: cholesterol acyltransferase (ACAT), an enyme activity that determines the equilibrium of free versus esterified forms of cholesterol in cells. Cellular cholesteryl ester concentrations appear to have a profound effect on $A\beta$ generation, as ACAT inhibitors (such as CP113,818) reduce $A\beta$ levels. In cells lacking ACAT activity, the production of $A\beta$ is completely abolished (Miyazaki et al., 2003; Puglielli et al., 2004; Puglielli et al., 2001). Also, improvement of amyloid pathology and cognitive functions was achieved in mouse models of AD by application of ACAT inhibitors (Hutter-Paier et al., 2004).

3.4. Statins and AD

Statins are cholesterol-lowering drugs widely used to treat patients with hypercholesterolemia who are at risk of developing vascular disease. Statins competitively inhibit the conversion of HMG-CoA to melanovate by HMG-CoA reductase (Grimm et al., 2005). Statins also up-regulate the activity of LDL receptor, to further reduce blood cholesterol levels. Last but not least, statins increase the activity of lipoprotein lipase (LpL) leading to excellerated lipolysis of triglycerides in circulating lipoprotein particles. LpL has been identified in amyloid plaques of AD patients, while mutations in the encoding gene have been associated with clinically diagnosed AD, suggesting that inadequate levels of this enzyme may present an additonal risk factor for neurodegeneration (Baum et al., 1999).

As well as prevent cardiovascular disease, recent studies in patients suggest that such cholesterol lowering strategies may also help in prevention of AD (Jick et al., 2000; Wolozin et al., 2000). Experiments in transgenic mouse models report similar findings inasmuch as statins such as simvastatin (Fassbender et al., 2001), lovastatin (Kojro et al., 2001), and BM15.766 (Refolo et al., 2001) reduce amyloid deposition. It is noteworthy that $A\beta$ has been suggested to reduce cholesterol synthesis via a negative feedback mechanism, providing yet another link between cholesterol homeostasis and AD progression. Whether or not statins will become a major element in the therapeutic repertoire to combat AD is, however, still a matter of intense debate (Hoglund et al., 2004; Park et al., 2003).

3.5. High fat Diet, Obesity and AD

Epidemiological studies have shown that caloric intake significantly affects development of AD. For example, it has been reported that the more fat is consumed in daily meals, the greater the risk of developing senile dementia in populations may be (Grant, 1999). In contrast, diets rich in n-3 unsaturated fatty acids seem to protect against this condition (Huang et al., 2005; Morris et al., 2003b). Although other epidemiological studies in human cohorts have produced conflicting results (Freund-Levi et al., 2006), a significant correlation between dietary fat intake and extend of Aβ pathology has convincingly been documented in experimental animal models. Thus, it was shown that transgenic mice develop Aβ deposits more rapidly if fed a high fat/ high cholesterol diet and that levels of brain Aβ in these mice strongly correlate with both plasma and CNS cholesterol levels (Oksman et al., 2006; Refolo et al., 2000). Caloric restriction, on the other hand, decreases Aβ production and deposition in the brains of these animals. In line with these data, several clinical studies have reported that obesity is a risk factor for development of AD in women (Gustafson et al., 2003), and that dietary intake of saturated fatty acids increases AD risk (Morris et al., 2003a).

4. NEURONAL LIPOPROTEIN RECEPTORS

The main class of lipoprotein receptors is a group of structurally related proteins referred to as the LDL receptor gene family or LRPs (LDL receptor-related proteins) (Figure 1). Members of this gene family can be found in diverse phyla, including nematodes, insects, and vertebrates, suggesting evolutionary conservation of receptor functions. Ten receptor species exist in mammalian cell types. There, they carry out a multitude of diverse functions that includes endocytosis of lipoproteins and other macromolecules, but also regulation of signal transduction, cell migration, and antigen presentation. Common to all receptors is their ability to act as cellular uptake pathway for lipoproteins containing apoE or apoB-100.

Structural elements common to all gene family members are clusters of cysteine-rich complement-type repeats that form the ligand-binding domain (Figure 1). In addition, the receptors contain epidermal growth factor-like domains and six-bladed β-propellers with YWTD motifs involved in pH-dependent release of ligands in endosomes (Fass et al., 1997; Herz, 2001a; Jeon et al., 2001; Rudenko et al., 2002). Their short cytoplasmic domains carry interaction sites for intracellular adaptor proteins that are essential for proper trafficking and signal transduction by the receptors.

In the following, we will provide a brief description of LRPs expressed in the central and peripheral nervous system, and we discuss possible functions in these tissues. For detailed description of other gene family members or activities, readers are referred to recent excellent reviews on this subject (Herz, 2001b; Herz and Beffert, 2000; Herz and Bock, 2002; Nykjær and Willnow, 2002; Willnow et al., 1999).

LDLR

The LDL receptor is the prototypic founder of the gene family and best known for its role in clearance of cholesterol-rich lipoproteins from the circulation. The significance of this receptor for systemic lipoprotein metabolism is underscored by defects observed in patients suffering from Familial Hypercholesterolemia, inheritable LDL receptor gene defects. Loss of receptor activity in affected individuals results in an inability to clear LDL particles from the blood stream and in fulminate hypercholesterolemia. The LDL receptor is ubiquitously expressed including in neurons and astrocytes.

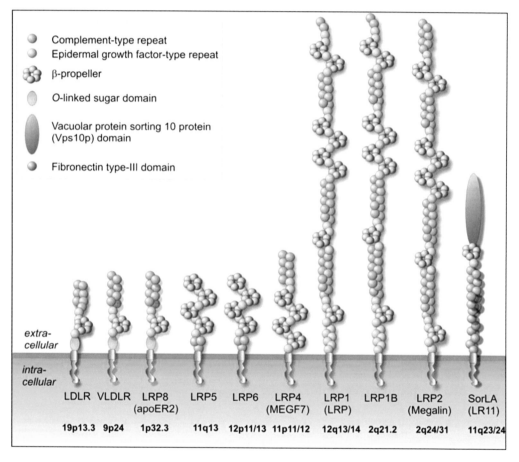

Figure 1. Structural organization of mammalian members of the LDL receptor gene family. Complement-type repeat (CR)-domains represent the main ligand-binding region. β-propellers contain a limited number of ligand recognition sites but are mainly involved in pH dependent release of ligands in endocytic vesicles. Other protein modules present in LDL receptor-related receptors (LRPs) are epidermal growth factor (EGF) repeats, O-linked glycosylation sites, as well as vacuolar protein sorting 10 protein (Vps10p) and fibronectin type III (FNIII) domains. The cytoplasmic domains contain sequence elements important for binding intracellular adaptor proteins, the most common one being the NPXY motif for fast coated-pit internalization. The chromosomal localization of the respective human genes is indicated under each receptor.

LRP1

LRP1 was the second member of the LDL receptor gene family to be identified, and originally proposed to act as substitute endocytic receptor for uptake of dietary lipoproteins in the liver. This function was confirmed in a number of studies in cultured cells and in genetically modified mouse models. However, subsequent studies also revealed a much broader ligand repertoire for this promiscuous clearance receptor that included proteases and protease inhibitors, coagulation factors, growth factors, virus proteins, and matrix proteins (see e.g. (Gliemann, 1998) for review). In the CNS, LRP1 is mainly found in granule cells of the dentate gyrus, pyramidal neurons of the hippocampus, and in neurons of the entorhinal cortex. Initial attempts to study the role of the receptor in the central nervous system were hampered by the early embryonic lethality encountered in the receptor-deficient mouse model (Herz et al., 1992). More recently, novel mouse lines with tissue-specific gene defects including loss of expression in neurons have been generated. These mice develop severe behavioral and motor abnormalities, including hyperactivity, tremor, and dystonia. These phenotypes are caused by abnormal neurotransmission, likely due to disruption of LRP1-containing protein complexes at the synapse (May et al., 2004).

LRP1B

This receptor is also known as LRP-DIT (for "*deleted-in-tumors*") because of its initial description as a gene frequently inactivated in lung cancer cell lines (Liu et al., 2000). An important role for the receptor in regulation of smooth muscle cells migration via control of cell-associated proteolytic activity has been suggested as the molecular mechanism underlying tumor growth control (Tanaga et al., 2004). In the central nervous system, LRP1B is expressed in the dentate gyrus. The role of the receptor in this tissue remains unclear, as LRP1B-deficient mice seem neurologically normal (Marschang et al., 2004).

LRP2

Also known as Megalin or GP330, this receptor represents the largest member of the LDL receptor gene family. The protein is typically expressed in absorptive epithelia including proximal tubules of the kidney, endometrium of the uterus, and ependyma, the epithelial cell layer that covers the luminal surface of brain ventricles and spinal canal. Inactivation of the receptor in gene targeted mice results in developmental defects of the forebrain, suggesting an important contribution of the receptor to formation of the brain. Rather than acting as endocytic receptor for lipoproteins, LRP2 mediates the cellular uptake of lipophilic vitamins and steroid hormones transported by plasma carrier proteins (Hammes et al., 2005; Nykjær et al., 1999).

VLDLR

The VLDL receptor exhibits the highest level of expression in heart and skeletal muscle. In the adult nervous system, the receptor is found in microglia in the dentate gyrus, in pyramidal neurons of the hippocampus, as well as in neurons of entorhinal cortex and temporal lobe of neocortex. While the function of the receptor in the adult CNS still remains elusive, an important contribution of receptor activity to embryonic development of this tissue has been uncovered. In the developing brain, the receptor serves as binding site for Reelin (D'Arcangelo et al., 1999; Hiesberger et al., 1999), a secreted factor that provides positional cues to migrating neurons in the embryonic brain. Consequently, loss of VLDL receptor activity in humans (Boycott et al., 2005) and in mouse models (Trommsdorff et al., 1999), results in abnormal layering of neurons in cortex and cerebellum, and in distinct neuroanatomical and behavioral deficits.

ApoER2

The apoE receptor-2 (or LRP8) is the second member of the gene family involved in regulation of neuronal migration via the Reelin signaling pathway (Trommsdorff et al., 1999). Its activity parallels the one described for VLDL receptor above. In the adult CNS, expression of the protein is most prominent in granule cells of the dentate gyrus, in pyramidal neurons of the hippocampus, and in cerebellar Purkinje cells (Kim et al., 1996).

SorLA

Sorting protein-related receptor with LDLR class A repeats (sorLA, *aka* LR11 or SORL1) is a chimeric receptor that harbors domains typically found in LRPs such as complement-type repeats and β-propellers (Jacobsen et al., 1996; Yamazaki et al., 1996a). In addition, the receptor polypeptide includes protein modules not present in the other lipoprotein receptors (Figure 1). In particular, the amino terminal region of the receptor contains a ~700 amino acid sequence homologous to a motif found in two copies in the vacuolar protein sorting 10 protein (Vps10p), an intracellular sorting receptor in yeast that directs proteins from the Golgi to the vacule (Marcusson et al., 1994). In the mammalian brain, sorLA is widely expressed in neurons throughout cortex, hippocampus and cerebellum (Hermans-Borgmeyer et al., 1998; Motoi et al., 1999). A possible function for sorLA in intracellular protein transport in neurons was suggested based on its structural similarity to Vps10p (Jacobsen et al., 1996), and recently confirmed in a sorLA-deficient mouse model (Andersen et al., 2005).

5. ROLE OF LIPOPROTEIN RECEPTORS IN APOE FUNCTION

Since the seminal finding that the *apoE* gene locus represents the most important risk factor for LOAD identified to date, intense research activities have been focused on the question how allelic variations of the gene may affect neurodegeneration. It is generally agreed that the type ε2 allele is protective whereas the type ε4 confers increased risk for LOAD (Corder et al., 1994; Corder et al., 1993) - exactly how these opposing activities come about are not fully understood. Among other hypotheses, distinct affects of apoE isoforms on APP processing (Hoe et al., 2005a; Hoe et al., 2006c; Irizarry et al., 2004), Aβ metabolism and aggregation (Bales et al., 2002), or neuronal survival have been advanced (Martins et al., 2006; Poirier, 2000) (see details below).

Regardless of the exact mechanism of apoE action in AD progression, the activity of neuronal apoE receptors are sure to play an important part in any such processes as they provide the main mechanism for cellular uptake und turnover of the apoprotein. Mice genetically deficient for LDL receptors exhibit significantly higher levels of apoE in the CSF compared to control animals, demonstrating a direct role for lipoprotein receptors in regulation of brain apoE levels. On the one hand, loss of LDL receptor function aggravates amyloid deposition and learning deficits in the Tg2576 mouse model of AD (Cao et al., 2006). On the other hand, breeding of LDLR-deficient mice with the PDAPP transgenic line does not significantly increase amyloid deposition (Fryer et al., 2005). Thus, it is still under debate whether the LDL receptor itself plays a causal role in AD pathology.

5.1. ApoE and Neuronal Cholesterol Homeostasis

Given its role in directing uptake of cholesterol-rich lipoproteins into neurons, distinct effects of apoE isoforms on cholesterol homeostasis in AD have been suggested. Consistent with this hypothesis, apoE receptors are expressed in brain regions particularly vulnerable to AD pathology. Being components of the cellular machinery that supplies cholesterol to neurons, functional interaction of apoE with its cognate receptors is crucial for control of cellular cholesterol homeostasis. Imbalances in this pathway may lead to quantitative changes in the amyloid precursor protein (APP) processing and Aβ generation (Figure 2). A number of recent studies provide evidence that cholesterol levels directly affect Aβ production rates (Abad-Rodriguez et al., 2004; Simons et al., 1998). Confusingly, both stimulatory and inhibitory effects of cholesterol concentrations on amyloidogenesis have been described, adding to the debate whether cholesterol lowering therapies may be beneficial for treatment of AD patients or not (Abad-Rodriguez et al., 2004).

5.2. ApoE and Aβ Interaction

An alternative hypothesis to explain how interaction of apoE with apoE receptors may affect AD progression has been advanced. Stable complex formation of Aβ with apoE has been reported, suggesting a pathway for catabolism of the peptide via apoE receptors

(Strittmatter et al., 1993a; Strittmatter et al., 1993b). In this model, Aβ internalized in complex with apoE would be subject to lysosomal degradation, effectively reducing the amount of molecules that could serve as building blocks for senile plaque formation (Figure 2). Intriguingly, Aβ clearance rates have been reported to vary with apoE species, being higher with ε2 and ε3, than ε4. These kinetics correlate well with the distinct binding affinities of the various apoE/Aβ complexes to LRP1, implicating this receptor in Aβ turnover (Jordan et al., 1998; Yang et al., 1999). As well as binding to apoE, Aβ also forms complexes with α$_2$-macroglobulin (Narita et al., 1997; Qiu et al., 1999; Van Uden et al., 2000) and lactoferrin (Qiu et al., 1999), two other LRP1 ligands that may serve as alternative clearance mechanisms for the peptide.

Besides facilitating Aβ clearance via lipoprotein receptors, apoE has also been suggested to alter conformation of Aβ upon binding, acting as chaperone that promotes amyloid plaque deposition. In this model, endocytic uptake and lysosomal degradation of the pro-amyloidogenic apolipoprotein may protect against senile plaque formation (Figure 2). This working model may also explain the isoform specific effects of apoE on LOAD inasmuch as ε4 promotes Aβ fibrillogenesis to a greater extent than ε2 and ε3 (Holtzman et al., 2000). In support of this concept, apoE-deficient mice show a dramatically reduced plaque load when crossed with transgenic models of AD (Bales et al., 1999; Bales et al., 1997). A similar role for apolipoprotein J (a ligand of LRP2 and apoER2) as facilitator of Aβ aggregation has been documented both alone (DeMattos et al., 2002) and in combination with apoE (DeMattos et al., 2004).

Finally, apoE promotes recruitment of astrocytes to regions in the brain with senile plaque burden inducing degradation of Aβ deposits (Koistinaho et al., 2004). This activity may provide yet another mechanism of apoE (and its receptors) contribution to AD.

5.3. Aβ Transport Across the Blood-Brain-Barrier

A key role of lipoprotein receptors in the export of Aβ from brain has been substantiated in a number of studies. Specific antagonists of LRP1 have been found to reduce the efflux of Aβ from brain by up to 90% in mice injected with labeled Aβ (Shibata et al., 2000). Rather than promoting the local uptake of Aβ into neurons, LRP1 expressed in brain capillaries might mediate the efflux across the BBB. This effect has been shown not only to occur for Aβ in complex with LRP1 ligands, but also by direct interaction between Aβ and LRP1 (Deane et al., 2004). Efficient shunt of Aβ across the BBB into plasma has been positively correlated with the ability of specific Aβ variants to bind LRP1, with more amyloidogenic species less likely to exit the brain. A similar mode of action has also been suggested for LRP2 expressed in ependyma and choroid plexus. This receptor is implicated in the transcytosis of complexes of Aβ with apoJ from brain parenchyma into CSF (Bell et al., 2006; Hammad et al., 1997; Zlokovic et al., 1996). Consistent with lipoprotein receptor-mediated Aβ transport across the BBB, reduced clearance of the peptide in animals lacking apoE has been documented (Shibata et al., 2000).

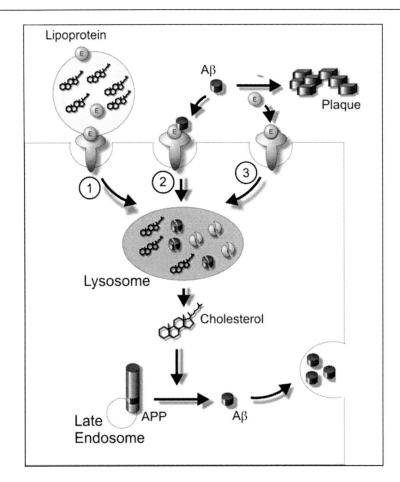

Figure 2. Roles for LRPs in neuronal apoE metabolism. Receptor-mediated uptake of apoE-containing lipoproteins increases the neuronal cholesterol pool affecting the rate of APP processing (1). Since high levels of intraneuronal cholesterol correlate with enhanced Aβ production, this lipoprotein receptor activity is amyloidogenic. Alternatively, lipoprotein receptors perform clearance of Aβ molecules in complex with receptor ligands, such as apoE, α₂M, and lactoferrin, depleting the substrate for plaque formation (2). Finally, apoE has a distinct function as chaperone for Aβ, promoting fibrillogenesis. This process is blocked by receptor-mediated uptake and catabolism of apoE (3). Lipoprotein receptor functions in (2) and (3) act anti-amyloidogenic.

6. LIPOPROTEIN RECEPTORS IN APP TRAFFICKING AND PROCESSING

The role of lipoprotein receptors in apoE-dependent activities in neurodegenerative processes may have been anticipated. However, recent findings point towards a different and unexpected contribution of these receptors to amyloidogenesis – the regulation of neuronal transport and processing of APP. In the following, we will discuss recent concepts that suggest a causal role for lipoprotein receptors in regulation of neuronal trafficking processes leading to Aβ production and senile plaque formation. While we briefly touch upon some of the basic concepts of APP processing, and the proteases involved, the reader is referred to more detailed description of these topics elsewhere in this textbook.

6.1. Trafficking and Proteolytic Processing of Amyloid Precursor Protein

The Aβ peptide is derived from the amyloid precursor, a 110-130 kDa type-1 membrane glycoprotein found in most cell types (Selkoe et al., 1988). APP is mainly expressed in three isoforms with 695, 751 or 770 amino acid residues, respectively. APP_{751} and APP_{770} variants harbor a Kunitz-type proteinase inhibitor domain in their extracellular regions, but the neuronal variant APP_{695} does not. Homologous APP-like proteins 1 and 2 (APLP1/2) have been identified, completing a family of three related polypeptides that is well conserved throughout evolution (Coulson et al., 2000).

APP can undergo two alternative proteolysis pathways that are decisive for onset and progression of neurodegenerative processes. In one pathway, APP is first cleaved within the Aβ peptide sequence by α-secretase, producing soluble APPα (sAPPα) and a membrane anchored carboxyl terminal fragment of 83 amino acid residues (C83). Subsequent processing by γ-secretase activity cleaves C83 further into the P3 peptide and the APP intracellular domain (AICD). Because initial cleavage by α-secretase destroys Aβ peptide, this processing step acts non-amyloidogenic. In contrast, the amyloidogenic pathway is initiated by β-secretase-mediated cleavage of APP at the amino terminus of the Aβ peptide releasing a soluble APP fragment known as sAPPβ. The remaining membrane bound peptide of 99 amino acid residues (C99) is also substrate to γ-secretase, releasing Aβ and the AICD.

The intracellular trafficking of APP represents a major determinant of amyloidogenic versus non-amyloidogenic processing (reviewed in (Kins et al., 2006; Selkoe, 1994; Small and Gandy, 2006; Suzuki et al., 2006; Walter, 2006). Non-amyloidogenic cleavage of APP by α-secretase mainly occurs in the trans-Golgi network (TGN) and at the plasma membrane (Haass et al., 1992b). It is limited by the residence time of the precursor protein at the cell surface (Haass et al., 1993; Koo and Squazzo, 1994). In contrast, radiolabeling of APP at the cell surface mainly produces labeled Aβ in a process that is dependent on endocytosis (Koo and Squazzo, 1994). Support for amyloidogenic processing of APP in the endocytic pathway stems from the predominant localization of the enzyme responsible for β-secretase cleavage, BACE1, in *late*-Golgi and endosomal compartments (Huse et al., 2000; Walter et al., 2001), and from its dependence on acidic pH present in endosomes for optimal enzymatic activity (Kinoshita et al., 2003a).

Whereas subcellular localization of α- and β-secretases correlates reasonably well with the observed proteolytic activities in secretory and endocytic pathways, respectively, γ-secretase activity does not. Presenilins (PS) are located in the ER to cis-Golgi compartments (Annaert et al., 1999; Culvenor et al., 1997; Cupers et al., 2001). However, γ-secretase cleavage of APP does not take place where most PS proteins are located. Rather, it requires the assembly of a multisubunit complex from several components that are located in more distal cell compartments. This obvious discrepancy is commonly referred to as the spatial paradox (Cupers et al., 2001; De Strooper, 2005).

Given its crucial role in determining APP processing fates, major attention has been focused on elucidating the intracellular trafficking routes of APP, and the regulatory mechanisms involved. Following co-translational transport into the ER, nascent APP molecules exit this organelle to move to early Golgi compartments. In route, APP is subject to N-glycosylation in ER and extensive O-glycosylation in Golgi (Dyrks et al., 1988; Weidemann et al., 1989). From Golgi compartments, most APP molecules seem to be targeted for fast lysosomal degradation resulting in a short half-life of precursor protein of ~20 min (Haass et al., 1992a). However, some APP molecules are retained in the Golgi for an extended period of time before moving through the secretory pathway to the neuronal cell surface (Caporaso et al., 1994; Palacios et al., 1992). Surface localized APP may then follow several fates. It may stay at the neuronal cell surface, but move along the axonal cell surface to change its localization from mainly axonal to dendrite membranes. (Koo et al., 1990; Simons et al., 1995; Yamazaki et al., 1995). Alternatively, it may internalize via coated pit regions to end up in lysosomes for degradation, or it may recycle from endosomes back to the cell surface (Koo et al., 1996; Marquez-Sterling et al., 1997; Yamazaki et al., 1996b). In general, APP sorting strongly depends on the particular cell type investigated and differs significantly between, for example, neurons and epithelial cells (De Strooper et al., 1995; Haass et al., 1994).

Molecular determinants of APP sorting are not completely understood, but clearly include intracellular sorting motifs present in the polypeptide sequence of APP (Lai et al., 1995). For example, basolateral sorting in polarized epithelia requires a combination of signals residing in the amino terminal protein domain and in tyrosine residue 653 in the AICD (Haass et al., 1995). Elements responsible for axonal sorting were identified in a region within the luminal APP fragment known as the carbohydrate domain (Tienari et al., 1996).

6.2. sorLA

Compelling evidence has established sorLA as an intracellular sorting factor for APP (Andersen et al., 2005; Offe et al., 2006; Rogaeva et al., 2007; Scherzer et al., 2004). Initially, gene expression profiling uncovered specific loss of the sorLA mRNA in lymphoblasts from AD patients (Scherzer et al., 2004). Subsequently, almost complete absence of receptor expression in individuals with AD was confirmed by Western blot and immunohistological analyses of brain biopsies (Andersen et al., 2005; Dodson et al., 2006; Scherzer et al., 2004). Finally, reduction of sorLA levels was specifically documented in patients suffering from LOAD but not in individuals with familial forms of this disease (Dodson et al., 2006). Taken together, these observations indicated low levels of sorLA activity as a primary cause rather than a secondary consequence of the neuronal cell loss in AD patients.

Given its structural homology to sorting receptors, a similar function for sorLA in neuronal transport of proteins such as APP was proposed (Andersen et al., 2005). This hypothesis was confirmed in a number of studies that demonstrated direct interaction between the carbohydrate-linked domain of APP with the CR-cluster of sorLA (Andersen et al., 2006).

Interaction of the proteins mainly occurs in *late*-Golgi and early endocytic compartments as shown by confocal immunocytochemistry and fluorescence lifetime imaging microscopy (Figure 3) (Andersen et al., 2005; Andersen et al., 2006; Spoelgen et al., 2006). Functional interaction results in impaired transition of APP to the neuronal plasma membrane, effectively reducing the extent of precursor processing in post-Golgi and endocytic compartments. In line with a presumed function for sorLA as intracellular transport factor for APP, internalization of the precursor from the cell surface was not affected by the receptor (Spoelgen et al., 2006). The significance of sorLA for APP processing *in vivo* was proven by targeted deletion of the *sorla* gene in mice, resulting in significantly higher levels of Aβ in the brain compared to control mice (Andersen et al., 2005). Taken together, these findings suggested a model whereby sorLA acts as an APP sorting factor that determines transport of the precursor into pathways less favorable for processing (Figure 3), likely by confining APP to the Golgi and impairing its transition to late secretory and endocytic compartments enriched in secretase activities (Andersen and Willnow, 2006; Marx, 2007; Shah and Yu, 2006).

Recent studies shed some light on possible determinants of sorLA trafficking through neuronal cell compartments. Firstly, the cytoplasmic tail of the protein was shown to bind members of the Golgi-localized, Gamma-ear-containing, Arf-binding (GGA) family of adaptor proteins (Jacobsen et al., 2002). GGAs are known to facilitate vesicular transport of target proteins between TGN and endosomes (reviewed in (Bonifacino, 2004)). Reducing expression of GGA1 in cells results in increased Aβ production, whereas overexpression of the adaptor decreases formation of the amyloid peptide (von Arnim et al., 2006; Wahle et al., 2006). Intriguingly, these effects are independent of a direct interaction between APP and GGA, suggesting the presence of a missing factor (such as sorLA) that may link both components (Wahle et al., 2006). A role for sorLA in GGA-dependent APP transport was further supported by confinement of APP to the Golgi in the presence of excess GGA1, similar to the situation seen with overexpression of the sorting receptor sorLA (Andersen et al., 2005; von Arnim et al., 2006).

A second regulatory mechanism in sorLA trafficking may involve the retromer, a multimeric protein complex responsible for retrograde trafficking of proteins from lysosomes to the Golgi (reviewed in (Seaman, 2004; Seaman, 2005)). Vps35 is the main component of the retromer known to bind Vps10p, the yeast homologue of sorLA (Nothwehr et al., 1999). This observation lead to the suggestion that a similar direct interaction between retromer and sorLA takes place in mammalian cells (Small and Gandy, 2006). Reducing retromer activity by selective depletion of individual protein components from cells (e.g. Vps35) leads to an increase in Aβ secretion, while overexpression of Vps35 reduces Aβ levels (Small et al., 2005), similar to the effects of sorLA on APP processing (Andersen et al., 2005).

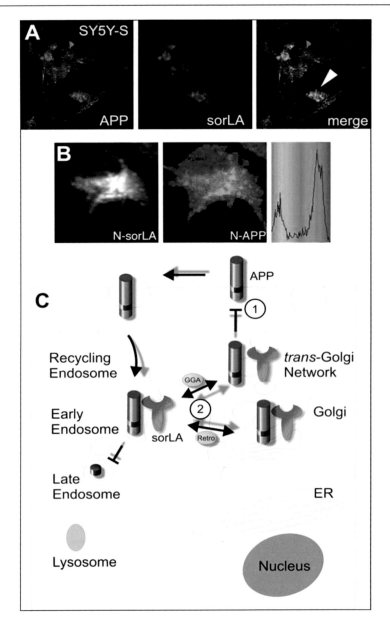

Figure 3. SorLA acts as intraneuronal sorting receptor for APP. (A) Co-localization of APP (green) and sorLA (red) in the perinuclear region (arrow head) in human neuroblastoma SH-SY5Y cells using immunofluorescence microscopy. (B) Fluorescence lifetime imaging microscopy (FLIM) of APP and sorLA in murine neuronal N2a cells using fluorophor-labeled antibodies against the amino terminal region of both proteins. Close proximity of the proteins is illustrated by the pseudo-colored image indicating shortening in lifetime of the donor fluorophore on sorLA (N-sorLA) from blue in the absence of proximity to orange/red in the presence of acceptor fluorophor on APP (N-APP). (C) SorLA functions as sorting receptor that prevents exit of APP from the Golgi to the cell surface, thereby reducing the number of precursor molecules that can be processed by secretases in post-Golgi compartments (1). In addition, sorLA may assist in retrograde transport of APP from early endosomes to the Golgi, further reducing the extent of Aβ production in endosomal compartments. The latter activity likely involves cytosolic adaptor proteins, such as members of the GGA family and the retromer complex (2).

6.3. LRP1

LRP1 is another member of the LDL receptor gene family implicated in regulation of cellular transport of APP (reviewed in (Bu et al., 2006; Waldron et al., 2006; Zerbinatti and Bu, 2005)).

The first hint that LRP1 may be involved in the metabolism of APP came from reports of Strickland and colleagues and Knauer et al. that LRP1 acts as receptor for secreted (Kounnas et al., 1995) or membrane-bound forms of the protein (Knauer et al., 1996). Because interaction between APP and LRP1 involved the KPI domain of APP not present in the neuronal variant of APP, the relevance of this association for AD-related processes has been questioned. However, further investigations uncovered a second mode of binding between LRP1 and APP via their cytoplasmic domains that applied to all isoforms including APP_{695}. Association does not involve direct protein-protein contacts of APP and LRP1 tail regions but requires linkage of the two proteins via cytoplasmic adaptor protein Fe65 (Gotthardt et al., 2000; Kinoshita et al., 2001; Pietrzik et al., 2004; Trommsdorff et al., 1998).

A model how interaction of APP with LRP1 may affect precursor protein transport and processing is given in Figure 4. In this model, LRP1 mainly regulates the retention time of APP on the cell surface, causing accelerated internalization and amyloidogenic processing in endocytic pathways (Cam et al., 2005; Pietrzik et al., 2002; Ulery et al., 2000; Yoon et al., 2005). Support for this model was provided by studies in a transgenic mouse model in which overexpression of LRP1 minireceptors in neurons resulted in increased Aβ levels in the brain, and in deficits in spatial learning and memory (Zerbinatti et al., 2004). Interestingly, in LRP1-transgenic mice a distinct fraction of Aβ was associated with the plasma membrane, indicating that LRP1 also facilitates intraneuronal amyloid accumulation (Zerbinatti et al., 2006). Thus, changes in LRP1 expression levels may affect AD progression both by altering trafficking of APP and by clearance of Aβ.

Assuming that increased LRP1 activity *in vivo* likely acts amyloidogenic, the outcome of studies in mice with targeted disruption of the receptor-associated protein (RAP) gene was surprising (Van Uden et al., 2002). RAP is an ER-resident chaperone required for efficient biosynthesis of LRP1 and other members of the LDL receptor gene family (Willnow et al., 1995; Willnow et al., 1996). Loss of RAP expression in gene-targeted mice resulted in impaired LRP1 expression in a hypomorphic mouse model of LRP1 deficiency. Surprisingly, breeding RAP-deficient mice with AD transgenic animals increased Aβ production. The opposite finding may have been anticipated if RAP deficiency would act via reducing the activity of the pro-amyloidogenic receptor LRP1. An alternative hypothesis to explain these observations may be that RAP deficiency primarily affects functional expression of anti-amyloidogenic LRPs such as sorLA or LRP1B (see below).

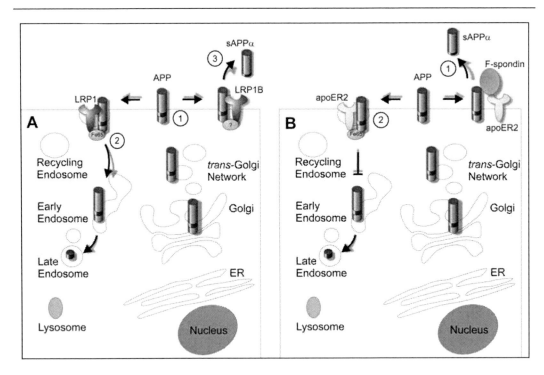

Figure 4. Role of lipoprotein receptors in APP trafficking. (A) LRP1 and LRP1B exhibit opposing effects on APP trafficking and processing into Aβ. Nascent APP molecules traverse the Golgi in route to the plasma membrane where they interact with LRP1 or LRP1B (1). Binding to LRP1 accelerates endocytosis of the precursor and delivery to endosomal compartments for cleavage by β-secretase (and subsequent γ-secretase) to generate Aβ. Interaction is likely facilitated by binding of Fe65 (2). In contrast, interaction of APP with LRP1B inhibits internalization and promotes α-secretase cleavage at the cell surface. This interaction also requires cytosolic adaptor proteins yet to be identified (3). (B) ApoE receptor-2 may modulate APP transport and processing in two ways. It may sequester APP at the cell surface promoting sAPPα production. This protein complex may include F-spondin (1). Alternatively, apoER2 may block endocytic uptake from the cell surface leading to anti-amyloidogenic processing. Similar to the situation with LRP1, this interaction requires adaptor protein Fe65 (2).

6.4. LRP1B

LRP1B is a lipoprotein receptor closely related to LRP1 that also forms immunoprecipitable complexes with APP. However, its influence on APP processing is opposite to that of LRP1 inasmuch as LRP1B retains APP molecules at the cell surface, impairing Aβ production (Cam et al., 2004). This specific effect on APP trafficking may be explained by much slower rates of endocytosis for LRP1B ($t_{1/2} > 10$min) as compared to LRP1 ($t_{1/2} < 0.5$min) (Li et al., 2001). Accordingly, LRP1B may be considered another APP-binding lipoprotein receptor that acts in a non-amyloidogenic fashion (Figure 4B) (Bu et al., 2006).

6.5. ApoER2

The forth member of the LDL receptor gene family implicated in APP transport and processing is ApoE receptor-2. It associates with APP both through extracellular and intracellular interactions.

Interaction of apoER2 with the extracellular domain of APP is modulated by F-spondin, a secreted protein that functions in axonal path finding, cell-cell interactions, and neural regeneration (Hoe et al., 2005b). F-spondin has been implicated in AD previously because it affects amyloidogenic processing by decreasing β-secretase activity (Ho and Südhof, 2004). New data now indicate that F-spondin leads to retention of APP at the cell surface in association with apoER2, similar to the situation seen for LRP1B (Hoe et al., 2005b). At the cytoplasmic site of the membrane, adaptors Dab1 and Fe65 have been reported to physically link APP and apoER2 leading to a decrease in Aβ production (Hoe et al., 2006a; Hoe et al., 2006d). Intriguingly, the adaptor X11α/β was recently reported to work pro-endocytic and increase amyloid production by accelerating apoER2-dependent APP internalization in the presence of apoE (He et al., 2007).

6.6. Physiological Relevance of APP Interaction with Lipoprotein Receptors

While interaction of APP with lipoprotein receptors bares particular relevance for amyloidogenic processing and amyloid plaque formation, one wonders what the physiological relevance of these interactions for neuronal function may be? Clearly, understanding the true meaning of these interactions requires a better appreciation of the physiological function of APP and its processing products. In the following, we will provide a brief discussion of the current state of the art concerning the physiological relevance of APP metabolism and action, and we speculate how lipoprotein receptors may come into play. Again, the reader is referred to more specialized sections in this textbook for in-depth discussions of the structure and function of APP.

Holo-APP

So far, the physiological function of APP has not been established with certainty. Previously, characterization of APP functions was hampered by redundancy between APP and related gene family members (reviewed in (Anliker and Müller, 2006). Now, generation of mouse models with combined gene deficiencies for all APPs have started to uncover some of the *in vivo* roles of these proteins, including functions in cell adhesion and neuronal migration (Heber et al., 2000; Herms et al., 2004; Soba et al., 2005; von Koch et al., 1997). Mice that lack all three APPs show cranial abnormalities displaying ectopic clusters of neuroblasts that migrates through the basal lamina and pial membrane resembling human type II lissencephaly (Herms et al., 2004). Phenocopy of such features (e.i. disruption of the basal membrane) by gene deletion of the Fe65 family of adaptor proteins in mouse supports the function of APP and mammalian homologues APLP1 and APLP2 in neuronal migration (Guénette et al., 2006). Because Fe65 links lipoprotein receptors LRP1 and apoER2 to the precursor protein, abovementioned activities of APP are likely modulated by LDL receptor-related proteins.

Secreted APP

As well as holo-APP, its proteolytic processing products also exert distinct neuronal activities – activities that may be governed by LRPs (Mattson, 1997; Turner et al., 2003). Likely members of the LDL receptor gene family that may partake in neuronal functions of secreted APPs are those that interact with the extracellular domain of the mature protein, namely LRP1, LPR1B, apoER2 and sorLA. Potentially, all of these receptors could act as cell surface receptors for sAPP, working as endocytic clearance or signal transducing receptors. For example, sAPP fragments that include the KPI-domain are more potent stimulators of neurite outgrowth than those without, implicating the KPI-domain receptor LRP1 in these processes (Qiu et al., 1995). In support of a novel role of LRP1-dependent signaling mechanisms, sAPP was specifically shown to activate the ERK-signaling pathway in neurons (Wallace et al., 1997), as also seen for other growth factors that signals via LRP1 (Lutz et al., 2002; Yang et al., 2004).

Aβ

Aβ is normally produced in healthy tissues. Here, it may carry out physiological activities that differ distinctly from its neurotoxic effects in a state of elevated production in AD (Haass et al., 1992b). Proposed physiological functions of the peptide include regulation of cell excitability, synaptic transmission and plasticity, as well as modulation of learning and memory (reviewed in (Mattson, 1997; Turner et al., 2003)). Not the least, such activities may be affected by lipoprotein receptors regulating the extent of Aβ formation.

APP Intracellular Domain (AICD)

The cleavage of APP by γ-secretase is similar to Notch, whose intracellular domain activates transcription by interaction with nuclear transcription factors. The physiological function of AICD was unknown until Südhof and colleagues demonstrated the presence of a transcriptional active complex of the AICD with Fe65 and the histone acetyltransferase Tip60 (Cao and Südhof, 2001). LRP1 has been found to undergo a similar γ-secretase-dependent intramembranous proteolysis (May et al., 2002) leading to the release of the cytoplasmic fragment of the receptor from the membrane (Kinoshita et al., 2003b). These data suggest a further mechanism how the family of lipoprotein receptors might influence the function of APP and its processing products.

7. LIPOPROTEIN RECEPTORS AND SECRETASES

7.1. Receptors as Secretase Substrates

Soluble variants of most neuronal lipoprotein receptors have been observed *in vitro* and *in vivo* (reviewed in (Rebeck et al., 2006)). They are generated by cleavage of the membrane-anchored mature proteins in a process known as ectodomain shedding. Intriguingly, ectodomain shedding involves the very same secretase activities that perform APP processing.

Ectodomain shedding by secretases has been reported for sorLA (Hampe et al., 2000; Hermey et al., 2006) (Böhm et al., 2006; Nyborg et al., 2006), LRP1 (May et al., 2002; Quinn et al., 1997; Quinn et al., 1999), LRP1B (Liu et al., 2007), and apoER2 (Koch et al., 2002; May et al., 2003). In case of the latter receptor, alternative splicing has been identified as a regulatory process to control shedding with some splice variants containing an O-linked glycosylation region (May et al., 2003) or a furin cleavage site (Brandes et al., 2001; Koch et al., 2002) that affects processing rates.

The relevance of ectodomain shedding of lipoprotein receptors remains unclear at present. Although not proven experimentally, high amounts of lipoprotein receptors expressed in neurons may compete with APP for access to the very same proteases, negatively affecting the extent of APP processing and Aβ production. In addition, the generation of the soluble intracellular domain of LRP1 has been shown to modulate the transcriptional activity of AICD (Kinoshita et al., 2003b), whereas processing of LRP1B by γ-secretase cleavage stimulates neuronal growth (Liu et al., 2007).

7.2. Lipoprotein Receptors and Transport of Secretase

Besides their role as substrates for secretase cleavage, members of the LDL receptor gene family have been proposed to control secretase activity via intracellular trafficking of the enzymes. For example, LRP1 has been shown to directly interact with BACE1 at the cell surface and to affect it's trafficking from the cell surface into early endosomes (von Arnim et al., 2005). Close interaction of BACE1 with sorLA has also been documented in neurons (Spoelgen et al., 2006), an interaction that likely involves the recruitment of GGA adaptors that bind the tails of both proteins (He et al., 2005; Jacobsen et al., 2002; Shiba et al., 2004; Wahle et al., 2005). Whether interaction of BACE1 with LRP1 and/or sorLA bares any relevance for amyloidogenic processing *in vivo* remains to be shown.

8. LIPOPROTEIN RECEPTORS IN REGULATION OF NEURONAL PLASTICITY

The loss of synapses in AD is substantially greater than can be explained by the extent of neuronal cell death, suggesting that synaptic deficiency may be a primary event in the early phases of the disease. One implication of this observation may be that molecular targets of Aβ-induced neurotoxicity could be of lesser importance than those that cause synaptic dysfunction when contemplating about intervention therapies (Small et al., 2001). Synaptic failure as disease-causing mechanism has gained significant momentum from a number of studies demonstrating that cognitive deficits in AD are better correlated with lack of synapses than with numbers of plaques and tangles in individuals with AD (Terry et al., 1991). Also, subtle alterations in hippocampal synaptic transmission have been shown to precede neuronal death (Selkoe, 2002). At the molecular level, assembly of oligomeric forms of Aβ has been demonstrated to induce synaptic dysfunction (Kim et al., 2006; Tanzi, 2005).

Several receptors of the LDL receptor gene family are present in high concentrations in synaptic membranes. As discussed in detail above, the ability of LRPs to regulate amyloid-β peptide production and catabolism suggests one mechanism how these receptors may modulate formation of oligomeric Aβ that is deleterious to synapses. However, the ability of some members to directly affect signal transduction and synaptic transmission in neurons suggests an alternative mode of action in AD progression. Particularly, VLDLR and apoER2 affect synaptic transmission and N-methyl-D-aspartate (NMDA) receptor activity (Herz and Chen, 2006). Both proteins synergize to enhance synaptic plasticity in response to Reelin (Petit-Turcotte et al., 2005; Sinagra et al., 2005; Weeber et al., 2002)). This function is dependent on binding of postsynaptic density protein 95 (PSD95) and JNK-interaction proteins (JIPs) to a region in the cytoplasmic tail that is alternatively spliced in neuronal receptor variants and that possess the ability to affect NMDA receptor phosphorylation (Beffert et al., 2005; Hoe et al., 2006b).

Additional evidence that links lipoprotein receptor activity to synaptic transmission in the adult brain is provided by studies on tissue-type plasminogen activator (tPA), a protease that enhances LTP and promotes synaptic plasticity (Baranes et al., 1998), and that is a ligand for LRP1 (Bu et al., 1992). Blocking tPA binding to LRP1 in neuronal slice cultures results in a reduced late-phase LTP (Zhuo et al., 2000). A regulatory role for LRP1 in NMDA receptor function and synaptic transmission is further supported by close association of LRP1 and NMDA receptors (May et al., 2004), likely caused by physical interaction of the cytoplasmic domains of both proteins via PSD95 (Gotthardt et al., 2000; May et al., 2004) (Figure 5). A fraction of neuronal LRP1 is located in the postsynaptic density, and is able to reduce the calcium response to NMDA treatment (Qiu et al., 2002). Ligand-induced dimerization of LRP1 is required for neuronal calcium influx, likely via NMDA receptors channeling (Bacskai et al., 2000).

9. GENETIC LINKAGE OF LIPOPROTEIN RECEPTORS TO AD

Approximately one hundred genes have so far been genetically linked to sporadic AD, even though findings have often been contested by conflicting data in different populations. Of particular interest to the readers of this chapter, several candidate genes seem to cluster in the field of brain cholesterol and lipoprotein metabolism (reviewed in (Carter, 2007)). In the following, we will discuss epidemiological studies concerned with lipoprotein receptors of the LDL receptor gene family. A more comprehensive collection of data can be found at the AlzGene database (http://www.alzgene.org) (Bertram et al., 2007).

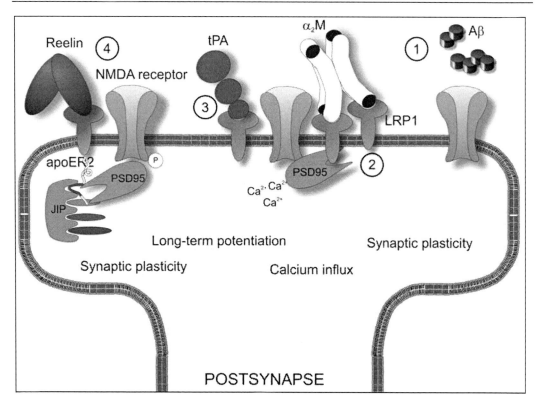

Figure 5. Lipoprotein receptors regulate NMDA receptor activity at the synapse. Lipoprotein receptors affect catabolism of Aβ at the synapse, thereby influencing the levels of oligomeric Aβ that is responsible for synaptic disfunction (1). Ligand-induced oligomerization of LRP1 (e.g., by α2-macroglobulin) regulates NMDA receptor activity and calcium influx, a function that requires functional association with PSD95 (2). LRP1 may also bind tissue-type plasminogen activator (tPA), a key regulator of synaptic plasticity (3). Finally, Reelin modulates NMDA receptor activity through binding to lipoprotein receptors apoER2 (and VLDLR), inducing complex formation with PSD95 and JIP that are important for synaptic plasticity (4).

The genetic profiles of lipoprotein receptors have been carefully examined. Particular focus has been on a possible association of SNPs in the gene encoding LRP1 on chromosome 12 with LOAD. While some studies found such association (Beffert et al., 1999; Kamboh et al., 1998), others failed to replicate these findings (Hatanaka et al., 2000; Kang et al., 1997; Lambert et al., 1999; Lambert et al., 1998; Lendon et al., 1997; Wavrant-DeVrieze et al., 1999; Wavrant-DeVrieze et al., 1997). Thus, despite overwhelming biochemical evidence implicating LRP1 activity in AD progression, *Lrp1* has not been confirmed as prognostic marker for sporadic AD. This conclusion is also reflected by meta-analysis of the exon 3 allele (*rs1799986*) with an overall non-significant odds ratio of 0.94 (95% CI, 0.83, 1.06). Similarly, no diagnostic SNPs have been identified with certainty in genes for LDL receptor, apoER2, and VLDL receptor (Lendon et al., 1997; Ma et al., 2002).

The situation is different for sorLA, the proposed APP trafficking receptor. In recent studies, several groups provided convincing evidence that SNPs in the gene for sorLA are strongly associated with sporadic AD (Lee et al., 2007; Rogaeva et al., 2007). Several polymorphisms distributed along the *sorla* gene were associated with AD in independent cohorts involving approximately 6,000 individual samples (Rogaeva et al., 2007). Unlike apoE, the analysis did not identify one SNP or haplotype that associates with all data sets, supporting the notion that there may be a high degree of allelic heterogeneity, with disease-associated variants occurring on multiple different haplotype backgrounds. The mapped *sorla* genotypes is likely to increase risk for AD by more than 20%, suggesting that sorLA is perhaps the most important genetic risk after apoE.

10. CONCLUSION

Because the prevalence of AD significantly increases with life expectancy, it is certain to reach epidemic proportions in aging populations of industrialized nations. Onset and progression of AD have a strong genetic component with estimates as high as 8 out of 10 cases being genetically associated (Gatz et al., 2006). The early-onset familial form of the disease is rare and is caused by single gene defects that follow an autosomal-dominant pattern of inheritance. However, most individuals suffer from the common, so called "sporadic" form of the disease that is influenced by multiple genetic and environmental factors. Surprisingly, systemic and cellular lipoprotein metabolism has emerged as one of the central physiological pathways that affects onset and progression of sporadic AD. Thus, regulatory processes in lipid homeostasis bare relevance both for cardiovascular and neurodegenerative diseases, the most common degenerative disorders affecting Western societies. Although the underlying pathological concepts of lipoprotein metabolism in AD are far from being understood in detail, future research into these mechanisms is certain to uncover major disease causing mechanisms, and to suggest scenarios how to treat this devastating disorder.

ACKNOWLEDGMENTS

The authors want to thank their collaborators for helpful discussions. Work in the authors' laboratory was supported by grants from the Danish Medical Research Foundation, The Lundbeck Foundation, The American Health Assistance Foundation, Alzheimer Forschung Initiative e.V., and The German Research Foundation (DFG).

REFERENCES

Abad-Rodriguez, J., Ledesma, M.D., Craessaerts, K., Perga, S., Medina, M., Delacourte, A., Dingwall, C., De Strooper, B. and Dotti, C.G. (2004) Neuronal membrane cholesterol loss enhances amyloid peptide generation. *J. Cell Biol.*, *167*, 953-960.

Andersen, O.M., Reiche, R., Schmidt, V., Gotthardt, M., Spoelgen, R., Behlke, J., Von Arnim, C.A., Breiderhoff, T., Jansen, P., Wu, X., Bales, K.R., Cappai, R., Masters, C.,

Gliemann, J., Mufson, E.J., Hyman, B.T., Paul, S.M., Nykjaer, A. and Willnow, T.E. (2005) SorLA/LR11, a neuronal sorting receptor that regulates processing of the amyloid precursor protein. *Proc. Natl. Acad. Sci. U. S. A.*, *102*, 13461-13466.

Andersen, O.M., Schmidt, V., Spoelgen, R., Gliemann, J., Behlke, J., Galatis, D., McKinstry, W.J., Parker, M.W., Masters, C.L., Hyman, B.T., Cappai, R. and Willnow, T.E. (2006) Molecular dissection of the interaction between APP and its neuronal trafficking receptor SorLA/LR11. *Biochemistry*, *45*, 2618-2628.

Andersen, O.M. and Willnow, T.E. (2006) Lipoprotein receptors in Alzheimer's disease. *Trends Neurosci.*, *29*, 687-694.

Anliker, B. and Müller, U. (2006) The functions of mammalian amyloid precursor protein and related amyloid precursor-like proteins. *Neurodegener. Dis.*, *3*, 239-246.

Annaert, W.G., Levesque, L., Craessaerts, K., Dierinck, I., Snellings, G., Westaway, D., George-Hyslop, P.S., Cordell, B., Fraser, P. and De Strooper, B. (1999) Presenilin 1 controls γ-secretase processing of amyloid precursor protein in pre-golgi compartments of hippocampal neurons. *J. Cell Biol.*, *147*, 277-294.

Bacskai, B.J., Xia, M.Q., Strickland, D.K., Rebeck, G.W. and Hyman, B.T. (2000) The endocytic receptor protein LRP also mediates neuronal calcium signaling via *N*-methyl-D-aspartate receptors. *Proc. Natl. Acad. Sci. U. S. A.*, *97*, 11551-11556.

Bales, K.R., Dodart, J.C., DeMattos, R.B., Holtzman, D.M. and Paul, S.M. (2002) Apolipoprotein E, amyloid, and Alzheimer disease. *Mol. Intervent.*, *2*, 363-375.

Bales, K.R., Verina, T., Cummins, D.J., Du, Y., Dodel, R.C., Saura, J., Fishman, C.E., DeLong, C.A., Piccardo, P., Petegnief, V., Ghetti, B. and Paul, S.M. (1999) Apolipoprotein E is essential for amyloid deposition in the APP(V717F) transgenic mouse model of Alzheimer's disease. *Proc. Natl. Acad. Sci. U. S. A.*, *96*, 15233-15238.

Bales, K.R., Verina, T., Dodel, R.C., Du, Y., Altstiel, L., Bender, M., Hyslop, P., Johnstone, E.M., Little, S.P., Cummins, D.J., Piccardo, P., Ghetti, B. and Paul, S.M. (1997) Lack of apolipoprotein E dramatically reduces amyloid β-peptide deposition. *Nat. Genet.*, *17*, 263-264.

Baranes, D., Lederfein, D., Huang, Y.Y., Chen, M., Bailey, C.H. and Kandel, E.R. (1998) Tissue plasminogen activator contributes to the late phase of LTP and to synaptic growth in the hippocampal mossy fiber pathway. *Neuron*, *21*, 813-825.

Baum, L., Chen, L., Masliah, E., Chan, Y.S., Ng, H.K. and Pang, C.P. (1999) Lipoprotein lipase mutations and Alzheimer's disease. *Am. J. Med. Genet.*, *88*, 136-139.

Beffert, U., Arguin, C. and Poirier, J. (1999) The polymorphism in exon 3 of the low density lipoprotein receptor-related protein gene is weakly associated with Alzheimer's disease. *Neurosci. Lett.*, *259*, 29-32.

Beffert, U., Danik, M., Krzywkowski, P., Ramassamy, C., Berrada, F. and Poirier, J. (1998) The neurobiology of apolipoproteins and their receptors in the CNS and Alzheimer's disease. *Brain Res. Brain Res. Rev.*, *27*, 119-142.

Beffert, U., Weeber, E.J., Durudas, A., Qiu, S., Masiulis, I., Sweatt, J.D., Li, W.P., Adelmann, G., Frotscher, M., Hammer, R.E. and Herz, J. (2005) Modulation of synaptic plasticity and memory by reelin involves differential splicing of the lipoprotein receptor apoer2. *Neuron*, *47*, 567-579.

Bell, R.D., Sagare, A.P., Friedman, A.E., Bedi, G.S., Holtzman, D.M., Deane, R. and Zlokovic, B.V. (2006) Transport pathways for clearance of human Alzheimer's amyloid β-peptide and apolipoproteins E and J in the mouse central nervous system. *J. Cereb. Blood Flow Metab.*

Bertram, L., McQueen, M.B., Mullin, K., Blacker, D. and Tanzi, R.E. (2007) Systematic meta-analyses of Alzheimer disease genetic association studies: the AlzGene database. *Nat. Genet.*, *39*, 17-23.

Böhm, C., Seibel, N., Henkel, B., Steiner, H., Haass, C. and Hampe, W. (2006) SorLA signaling by regulated intramembrane proteolysis. *J. Biol. Chem.*, *281*, 14547-14553.

Bonifacino, J.S. (2004) The GGA proteins: adaptors on the move. *Nat. Rev. Mol. Cell Biol.*, *5*, 23-32.

Borroni, B., Archetti, S., Agosti, C., Akkawi, N., Brambilla, C., Caimi, L., Caltagirone, C., Di Luca, M. and Padovani, A. (2004) Intronic CYP46 polymorphism along with ApoE genotype in sporadic Alzheimer Disease: from risk factors to disease modulators. *Neurobiol. Aging*, *25*, 747-751.

Boycott, K.M., Flavelle, S., Bureau, A., Glass, H.C., Fujiwara, T.M., Wirrell, E., Davey, K., Chudley, A.E., Scott, J.N., McLeod, D.R. and Parboosingh, J.S. (2005) Homozygous deletion of the very low density lipoprotein receptor gene causes autosomal recessive cerebellar hypoplasia with cerebral gyral simplification. *Am. J. Hum. Genet.*, *77*, 477-483.

Brandes, C., Kahr, L., Stockinger, W., Hiesberger, T., Schneider, W.J. and Nimpf, J. (2001) Alternative splicing in the ligand binding domain of mouse apoE receptor-2 produces receptor variants binding reelin but not α2-macroglobulin. *J. Biol. Chem.*, *276*, 22160-22169.

Brown, M.S. and Goldstein, J.L. (1986) A receptor-mediated pathway for cholesterol homeostasis. *Science*, *232*, 34-47.

Bu, G., Cam, J. and Zerbinatti, C. (2006) LRP in Amyloid-β Production and Metabolism. *Ann. N. Y. Acad. Sci.*, *1086*, 35-53.

Bu, G., Williams, S., Strickland, D.K. and Schwartz, A.L. (1992) Low density lipoprotein receptor-related protein/α2-macroglobulin receptor is an hepatic receptor for tissue-type plasminogen activator. *Proc. Natl. Acad. Sci. U. S. A.*, *89*, 7427-7431.

Cam, J.A., Zerbinatti, C.V., Knisely, J.M., Hecimovic, S., Li, Y. and Bu, G. (2004) The LDL receptor-related protein 1B retains β-APP at the cell surface and reduces amyloid-β peptide production. *J. Biol. Chem.*, *279*, 29639-29646.

Cam, J.A., Zerbinatti, C.V., Li, Y. and Bu, G. (2005) Rapid endocytosis of the low density lipoprotein receptor-related protein modulates cell surface distribution and processing of the β-amyloid precursor protein. *J. Biol. Chem.*, *280*, 15464-15470.

Cao, D., Fukuchi, K.I., Wan, H., Kim, H. and Li, L. (2006) Lack of LDL receptor aggravates learning deficits and amyloid deposits in Alzheimer transgenic mice. *Neurobiol. Aging*, *27*, 1632-1643.

Cao, X. and Südhof, T.C. (2001) A transcriptionally [correction of transcriptively] active complex of APP with Fe65 and histone acetyltransferase Tip60. *Science*, *293*, 115-120.

Caporaso, G.L., Takei, K., Gandy, S.E., Matteoli, M., Mundigl, O., Greengard, P. and De Camilli, P. (1994) Morphologic and biochemical analysis of the intracellular trafficking of the Alzheimer β/A4 amyloid precursor protein. *J. Neurosci.*, *14*, 3122-3138.

Carter, C.J. (2007) Convergence of genes implicated in Alzheimer's disease on the cerebral cholesterol shuttle: APP, cholesterol, lipoproteins, and atherosclerosis. *Neurochem. Int.*, *50*, 12-38.

Corder, E.H., Saunders, A.M., Risch, N.J., Strittmatter, W.J., Schmechel, D.E., Gaskell, P.C., Jr., Rimmler, J.B., Locke, P.A., Conneally, P.M., Schmader, K.E. and et al. (1994) Protective effect of apolipoprotein E type 2 allele for late onset Alzheimer disease. *Nat. Genet.*, *7*, 180-184.

Corder, E.H., Saunders, A.M., Strittmatter, W.J., Schmechel, D.E., Gaskell, P.C., Small, G.W., Roses, A.D., Haines, J.L. and Pericak-Vance, M.A. (1993) Gene dose of apolipoprotein E type 4 allele and the risk of Alzheimer's disease in late onset families. *Science*, *261*, 921-923.

Coulson, E.J., Paliga, K., Beyreuther, K. and Masters, C.L. (2000) What the evolution of the amyloid protein precursor supergene family tells us about its function. *Neurochem. Int.*, *36*, 175-184.

Culvenor, J.G., Maher, F., Evin, G., Malchiodi-Albedi, F., Cappai, R., Underwood, J.R., Davis, J.B., Karran, E.H., Roberts, G.W., Beyreuther, K. and Masters, C.L. (1997) Alzheimer's disease-associated presenilin 1 in neuronal cells: evidence for localization to the endoplasmic reticulum-Golgi intermediate compartment. *J. Neurosci. Res.*, *49*, 719-731.

Cupers, P., Bentahir, M., Craessaerts, K., Orlans, I., Vanderstichele, H., Saftig, P., De Strooper, B. and Annaert, W. (2001) The discrepancy between presenilin subcellular localization and γ-secretase processing of amyloid precursor protein. *J. Cell Biol.*, *154*, 731-740.

D'Arcangelo, G., Homayouni, R., Keshvara, L., Rice, D.S., Sheldon, M. and Curran, T. (1999) Reelin is a ligand for lipoprotein receptors. *Neuron*, *24*, 471-479.

De Strooper, B. (2005) Nicastrin: Gatekeeper of the γ-secretase complex. *Cell*, *122*, 318-320.

De Strooper, B., Craessaerts, K., Dewachter, I., Moechars, D., Greenberg, B., Van Leuven, F. and Van den Berghe, H. (1995) Basolateral secretion of amyloid precursor protein in Madin-Darby canine kidney cells is disturbed by alterations of intracellular pH and by introducing a mutation associated with familial Alzheimer's disease. *J. Biol. Chem.*, *270*, 4058-4065.

Deane, R., Wu, Z., Sagare, A., Davis, J., Du Yan, S., Hamm, K., Xu, F., Parisi, M., LaRue, B., Hu, H.W., Spijkers, P., Guo, H., Song, X., Lenting, P.J., Van Nostrand, W.E. and Zlokovic, B.V. (2004) LRP/amyloid beta-peptide interaction mediates differential brain efflux of Abeta isoforms. *Neuron*, *43*, 333-344.

DeMattos, R.B., Cirrito, J.R., Parsadanian, M., May, P.C., O'Dell, M.A., Taylor, J.W., Harmony, J.A., Aronow, B.J., Bales, K.R., Paul, S.M. and Holtzman, D.M. (2004) ApoE and Clusterin Cooperatively Suppress Aβ Levels and Deposition. Evidence that ApoE Regulates Extracellular Aβ Metabolism In Vivo. *Neuron*, *41*, 193-202.

DeMattos, R.B., O'Dell M, A., Parsadanian, M., Taylor, J.W., Harmony, J.A., Bales, K.R., Paul, S.M., Aronow, B.J. and Holtzman, D.M. (2002) Clusterin promotes amyloid plaque formation and is critical for neuritic toxicity in a mouse model of Alzheimer's disease. *Proc. Natl. Acad. Sci. U. S. A.*, *99*, 10843-10848.

Desai, P., DeKosky, S.T. and Kamboh, M.I. (2002) Genetic variation in the cholesterol 24-hydroxylase (CYP46) gene and the risk of Alzheimer's disease. *Neurosci. Lett.*, *328*, 9-12.

Dodson, S.E., Gearing, M., Lippa, C.F., Montine, T.J., Levey, A.I. and Lah, J.J. (2006) LR11/SorLA expression Is reduced in sporadic Alzheimer disease but not in familial Alzheimer disease. *J. Neuropathol. Exp. Neurol.*, *65*, 866-872.

Dyrks, T., Weidemann, A., Multhaup, G., Salbaum, J.M., Lemaire, H.G., Kang, J., Muller-Hill, B., Masters, C.L. and Beyreuther, K. (1988) Identification, transmembrane orientation and biogenesis of the amyloid A4 precursor of Alzheimer's disease. *EMBO J.*, *7*, 949-957.

Fass, D., Blacklow, S., Kim, P.S. and Berger, J.M. (1997) Molecular basis of familial hypercholesterolaemia from structure of LDL receptor module. *Nature*, *388*, 691-693.

Fassbender, K., Simons, M., Bergmann, C., Stroick, M., Lutjohann, D., Keller, P., Runz, H., Kuhl, S., Bertsch, T., von Bergmann, K., Hennerici, M., Beyreuther, K. and Hartmann, T. (2001) Simvastatin strongly reduces levels of Alzheimer's disease β-amyloid peptides Aβ42 and Aβ40 in vitro and in vivo. *Proc. Natl. Acad. Sci. U. S. A.*, *98*, 5856-5861.

Freund-Levi, Y., Eriksdotter-Jonhagen, M., Cederholm, T., Basun, H., Faxen-Irving, G., Garlind, A., Vedin, I., Vessby, B., Wahlund, L.O. and Palmblad, J. (2006) Omega-3 fatty acid treatment in 174 patients with mild to moderate Alzheimer disease: OmegAD study: a randomized double-blind trial. *Arch. Neurol.*, *63*, 1402-1408.

Fryer, J.D., Demattos, R.B., McCormick, L.M., O'Dell, M.A., Spinner, M.L., Bales, K.R., Paul, S.M., Sullivan, P.M., Parsadanian, M., Bu, G. and Holtzman, D.M. (2005) The low density lipoprotein receptor regulates the level of central nervous system human and murine apolipoprotein E but does not modify amyloid plaque pathology in PDAPP mice. *J. Biol. Chem.*, *280*, 25754-25759.

Gatz, M., Reynolds, C.A., Fratiglioni, L., Johansson, B., Mortimer, J.A., Berg, S., Fiske, A. and Pedersen, N.L. (2006) Role of genes and environments for explaining Alzheimer disease. *Arch. Gen. Psychiatry*, *63*, 168-174.

Gliemann, J. (1998) Receptors of the low density lipoprotein (LDL) receptor family in man. Multiple functions of the large family members via interaction with complex ligands. *Biol. Chem.*, *379*, 951-964.

Gotthardt, M., Trommsdorff, M., Nevitt, M.F., Shelton, J., Richardson, J.A., Stockinger, W., Nimpf, J. and Herz, J. (2000) Interactions of the low density lipoprotein receptor gene family with cytosolic adaptor and scaffold proteins suggest diverse biological functions in cellular communication and signal transduction. *J. Biol. Chem.*, *275*, 25616-25624.

Grant, W.B. (1999) Dietary links to Alzheimer's disease: 1999 update. *J. Alzheimer's Dis.*, *1*, 197-201.

Grimm, M.O., Grimm, H.S., Patzold, A.J., Zinser, E.G., Halonen, R., Duering, M., Tschape, J.A., De Strooper, B., Muller, U., Shen, J. and Hartmann, T. (2005) Regulation of cholesterol and sphingomyelin metabolism by amyloid-β and presenilin. *Nat. Cell Biol.*, *7*, 1118-1123.

Guénette, S., Chang, Y., Hiesberger, T., Richardson, J.A., Eckman, C.B., Eckman, E.A., Hammer, R.E. and Herz, J. (2006) Essential roles for the FE65 amyloid precursor protein-interacting proteins in brain development. *EMBO J.*, *25*, 420-431.

Gustafson, D., Rothenberg, E., Blennow, K., Steen, B. and Skoog, I. (2003) An 18-year follow-up of overweight and risk of Alzheimer disease. *Arch. Intern. Med.*, *163*, 1524-1528.

Haass, C., Hung, A.Y., Schlossmacher, M.G., Teplow, D.B. and Selkoe, D.J. (1993) β-Amyloid peptide and a 3-kDa fragment are derived by distinct cellular mechanisms. *J. Biol. Chem.*, *268*, 3021-3024.

Haass, C., Koo, E.H., Capell, A., Teplow, D.B. and Selkoe, D.J. (1995) Polarized sorting of beta-amyloid precursor protein and its proteolytic products in MDCK cells is regulated by two independent signals. *J. Cell Biol.*, *128*, 537-547.

Haass, C., Koo, E.H., Mellon, A., Hung, A.Y. and Selkoe, D.J. (1992a) Targeting of cell-surface β-amyloid precursor protein to lysosomes: alternative processing into amyloid-bearing fragments. *Nature*, *357*, 500-503.

Haass, C., Koo, E.H., Teplow, D.B. and Selkoe, D.J. (1994) Polarized secretion of beta-amyloid precursor protein and amyloid beta-peptide in MDCK cells. *Proc. Natl. Acad. Sci. U. S. A.*, *91*, 1564-1568.

Haass, C., Schlossmacher, M.G., Hung, A.Y., Vigo-Pelfrey, C., Mellon, A., Ostaszewski, B.L., Lieberburg, I., Koo, E.H., Schenk, D., Teplow, D.B. and Selkoe, D.J. (1992b) Amyloid β-peptide is produced by cultured cells during normal metabolism. *Nature*, *359*, 322-325.

Hammad, S.M., Ranganathan, S., Loukinova, E., Twal, W.O. and Argraves, W.S. (1997) Interaction of apolipoprotein J-amyloid β-peptide complex with low density lipoprotein receptor-related protein-2/megalin. A mechanism to prevent pathological accumulation of amyloid β-peptide. *J. Biol. Chem.*, *272*, 18644-18649.

Hammes, A., Andreassen, T.K., Spoelgen, R., Raila, J., Hubner, N., Schulz, H., Metzger, J., Schweigert, F.J., Luppa, P.B., Nykjaer, A. and Willnow, T.E. (2005) Role of endocytosis in cellular uptake of sex steroids. *Cell*, *122*, 751-762.

Hampe, W., Riedel, I.B., Lintzel, J., Bader, C.O., Franke, I. and Schaller, H.C. (2000) Ectodomain shedding, translocation and synthesis of SorLA are stimulated by its ligand head activator. *J. Cell Sci.*, *113*, 4475-4485.

Hatanaka, Y., Kamino, K., Fukuo, K., Mitsuda, N., Nishiwaki-Ueda, Y., Sato, N., Satoh, T., Yamamoto, H., Yoneda, H., Imagawa, M., Miki, T., Ohta, S. and Ogihara, T. (2000) Low density lipoprotein receptor-related protein gene polymorphisms and risk for late-onset Alzheimer's disease in a Japanese population. *Clin. Genet.*, *58*, 319-323.

He, X., Cooley, K., Chung, C.H., Dashti, N. and Tang, J. (2007) Apolipoprotein receptor 2 and X11α/β mediate apolipoprotein E-induced endocytosis of amyloid-β precursor protein and β-secretase, leading to amyloid-β production. *J. Neurosci.*, *27*, 4052-4060.

He, X., Li, F., Chang, W.P. and Tang, J. (2005) GGA proteins mediate the recycling pathway of memapsin 2 (BACE). *J. Biol. Chem.*, *280*, 11696-11703.

Heber, S., Herms, J., Gajic, V., Hainfellner, J., Aguzzi, A., Rülicke, T., Kretzschmar, H., von Koch, C., Sisodia, S.S., Tremml, P., Lipp, H.-P., Wolfer, D.P. and Müller, U. (2000)

Mice with combined gene knock-outs reveal essential and partially redundant functions of amyloid precursor protein family members. *J. Neurosci.*, *20*, 7951-7963.

Hermans-Borgmeyer, I., Hampe, W., Schinke, B., Methner, A., Nykjær, A., Süsens, U., Fenger, U., Herbarth, B. and Schaller, H.C. (1998) Unique expression pattern of a novel mosaic receptor in the developing cerebral cortex. *Mech. Dev.*, *70*, 65-76.

Hermey, G., Sjogaard, S.S., Petersen, C.M., Nykjær, A. and Gliemann, J. (2006) Tumour necrosis factor α-converting enzyme mediates ectodomain shedding of Vps10p-domain receptor family members. *Biochem. J.*, *395*, 285-293.

Herms, J., Anliker, B., Heber, S., Ring, S., Fuhrmann, M., Kretzschmar, H., Sisodia, S.S. and Müller, U. (2004) Cortical dysplasia resembling human type 2 lissencephaly in mice lacking all three APP family members. *EMBO J.*, *23*, 4106-4115.

Herz, J. (2001a) Deconstructing the LDL receptor - a rhapsody in pieces. *Nat. Struct. Biol.*, *8*, 476-478.

Herz, J. (2001b) The LDL receptor gene family: (un)expected signal transducers in the brain. *Neuron*, *29*, 571-581.

Herz, J. and Beffert, U. (2000) Apolipoprotein E receptors: Linking brain development and Alzheimer's disease. *Nat. Rev. Neurosci.*, *1*, 51-58.

Herz, J. and Bock, H.H. (2002) Lipoprotein receptors in the nervous system. *Annu. Rev. Biochem.*, *71*, 405-434.

Herz, J. and Chen, Y. (2006) Reelin, lipoprotein receptors and synaptic plasticity. *Nat Rev Neurosci*, *7*, 850-859.

Herz, J., Clouthier, D.E. and Hammer, R.E. (1992) LDL receptor-related protein internalizes and degrades uPA-PAI-1 complexes and is essential for embryo implantation. *Cell*, *71*, 411-421.

Hiesberger, T., Trommsdorff, M., Howell, B.W., Goffinet, A., Mumby, M.C., Cooper, J.A. and Herz, J. (1999) Direct binding of Reelin to VLDL receptor and ApoE receptor 2 induces tyrosine phosphorylation of disabled-1 and modulates tau phosphorylation. *Neuron*, *24*, 481-489.

Hirsch-Reinshagen, V., Maia, L.F., Burgess, B.L., Blain, J.F., Naus, K.E., McIsaac, S.A., Parkinson, P.F., Chan, J.Y., Tansley, G.H., Hayden, M.R., Poirier, J., Van Nostrand, W. and Wellington, C.L. (2005) The absence of ABCA1 decreases soluble ApoE levels but does not diminish amyloid deposition in two murine models of Alzheimer disease. *J. Biol. Chem.*, *280*, 43243-43256.

Ho, A. and Südhof, T.C. (2004) Binding of F-spondin to amyloid-β precursor protein: a candidate amyloid-β precursor protein ligand that modulates amyloid-β precursor protein cleavage. *Proc. Natl. Acad. Sci. U. S. A.*, *101*, 2548-2553.

Hoe, H.S., Harris, D.C. and Rebeck, G.W. (2005a) Multiple pathways of apolipoprotein E signaling in primary neurons. *J. Neurochem.*, *93*, 145-155.

Hoe, H.S., Magill, L.A., Guenette, S., Fu, Z., Vicini, S. and Rebeck, G.W. (2006a) FE65 interaction with the ApoE receptor ApoEr2. *J. Biol. Chem.*, *281*, 24521-24530.

Hoe, H.S., Pocivavsek, A., Chakraborty, G., Fu, Z., Vicini, S., Ehlers, M.D. and Rebeck, G.W. (2006b) Apolipoprotein E receptor 2 interactions with the N-methyl-D-aspartate receptor. *J. Biol. Chem.*, *281*, 3425-3431.

Hoe, H.S., Pocivavsek, A., Dai, H., Chakraborty, G., Harris, D.C. and Rebeck, G.W. (2006c) Effects of apoE on neuronal signaling and APP processing in rodent brain. *Brain Res.*, *1112*, 70-79.

Hoe, H.S., Tran, T.S., Matsuoka, Y., Howell, B.W. and Rebeck, G.W. (2006d) DAB1 and Reelin effects on amyloid precursor protein and ApoE receptor 2 trafficking and processing. *J. Biol. Chem.*, *281*, 35176-35185.

Hoe, H.S., Wessner, D., Beffert, U., Becker, A.G., Matsuoka, Y. and Rebeck, G.W. (2005b) F-spondin interaction with the apolipoprotein E receptor ApoEr2 affects processing of amyloid precursor protein. *Mol. Cell. Biol.*, *25*, 9259-9268.

Hoglund, K., Wiklund, O., Vanderstichele, H., Eikenberg, O., Vanmechelen, E. and Blennow, K. (2004) Plasma levels of β-amyloid(1-40), β-amyloid(1-42), and total β-amyloid remain unaffected in adult patients with hypercholesterolemia after treatment with statins. *Arch. Neurol.*, *61*, 333-337.

Holtzman, D.M., Bales, K.R., Tenkova, T., Fagan, A.M., Parsadanian, M., Sartorius, L.J., Mackey, B., Olney, J., McKeel, D., Wozniak, D. and Paul, S.M. (2000) Apolipoprotein E isoform-dependent amyloid deposition and neuritic degeneration in a mouse model of Alzheimer's disease. *Proc. Natl. Acad. Sci. U. S. A.*, *97*, 2892-2897.

Huang, T.L., Zandi, P.P., Tucker, K.L., Fitzpatrick, A.L., Kuller, L.H., Fried, L.P., Burke, G.L. and Carlson, M.C. (2005) Benefits of fatty fish on dementia risk are stronger for those without APOE epsilon4. *Neurology*, *65*, 1409-1414.

Huse, J.T., Pijak, D.S., Leslie, G.J., Lee, V.M. and Doms, R.W. (2000) Maturation and endosomal targeting of β-site amyloid precursor protein-cleaving enzyme. The Alzheimer's disease β-secretase. *J. Biol. Chem.*, *275*, 33729-33737.

Hutter-Paier, B., Huttunen, H.J., Puglielli, L., Eckman, C.B., Kim, D.Y., Hofmeister, A., Moir, R.D., Domnitz, S.B., Frosch, M.P., Windisch, M. and Kovacs, D.M. (2004) The ACAT inhibitor CP-113,818 markedly reduces amyloid pathology in a mouse model of Alzheimer's disease. *Neuron*, *44*, 227-238.

Ingelsson, M., Jesneck, J., Irizarry, M.C., Hyman, B.T. and Rebeck, G.W. (2004) Lack of association of the cholesterol 24-hydroxylase (CYP46) intron 2 polymorphism with Alzheimer's disease. *Neurosci. Lett.*, *367*, 228-231.

Irizarry, M.C., Deng, A., Lleo, A., Berezovska, O., Von Arnim, C.A., Martin-Rehrmann, M., Manelli, A., LaDu, M.J., Hyman, B.T. and Rebeck, G.W. (2004) Apolipoprotein E modulates γ-secretase cleavage of the amyloid precursor protein. *J. Neurochem.*, *90*, 1132-1143.

Jacobsen, L., Madsen, P., Moestrup, S.K., Lund, A.H., Tommerup, N., Nykjær, A., Sottrup-Jensen, L., Gliemann, J. and Petersen, C.M. (1996) Molecular characterization of a novel human hybrid-type receptor that binds the α_2-macroglobulin receptor-associated protein. *J. Biol. Chem.*, *271*, 31379-31383.

Jacobsen, L., Madsen, P., Nielsen, M.S., Geraerts, W.P.M., Gliemann, J., Smit, A.B. and Petersen, C.M. (2002) The sorLA cytoplasmic domain interacts with GGA1 and -2 and defines minimum requirements for GGA binding. *FEBS Lett.*, *511*, 155-158.

Jeon, H., Meng, W., Takagi, J., Eck, M.J., Springer, T.A. and Blacklow, S.C. (2001) Implications for familial hypercholesterolemia from the structure of the LDL receptor YWTD-EGF domain pair. *Nat. Struct. Biol.*, *8*, 499-504.

Jick, H., Zornberg, G.L., Jick, S.S., Seshadri, S. and Drachman, D.A. (2000) Statins and the risk of dementia. *Lancet, 356,* 1627-1631.

Johansson, A., Katzov, H., Zetterberg, H., Feuk, L., Johansson, B., Bogdanovic, N., Andreasen, N., Lenhard, B., Brookes, A.J., Pedersen, N.L., Blennow, K. and Prince, J.A. (2004) Variants of CYP46A1 may interact with age and APOE to influence CSF Abeta42 levels in Alzheimer's disease. *Hum. Genet., 114,* 581-587.

Jordan, J., Galindo, M.F., Miller, R.J., Reardon, C.A., Getz, G.S. and LaDu, M.J. (1998) Isoform-specific effect of apolipoprotein E on cell survival and β-amyloid-induced toxicity in rat hippocampal pyramidal neuronal cultures. *J. Neurosci., 18,* 195-204.

Kamboh, M.I., Ferrell, R.E. and DeKosky, S.T. (1998) Genetic association studies between Alzheimer's disease and two polymorphisms in the low density lipoprotein receptor-related protein gene. *Neurosci. Lett., 244,* 65-68.

Kang, D.E., Saitoh, T., Chen, X., Xia, Y., Masliah, E., Hansen, L.A., Thomas, R.G., Thal, L.J. and Katzman, R. (1997) Genetic association of the low-density lipoprotein receptor-related protein gene (LRP), an apolipoprotein E receptor, with late-onset Alzheimer's disease. *Neurology, 49,* 56-61.

Kim, D.-H., Iijima, H., Goto, K., Sakai, J., Ishii, H., Kim, H.-J., Suzuki, H., Kondo, H., Saeki, S. and Yamamoto, T. (1996) Human apolipoprotein E receptor 2. A novel lipoprotein receptor of the low density lipoprotein receptor family predominantly expressed in brain. *J. Biol. Chem., 271,* 8373-8380.

Kim, S.H., Tang, Y.P. and Sisodia, S.S. (2006) Aβ star: a light onto synaptic dysfunction? *Nat. Med., 12,* 760-761.

Kinoshita, A., Fukumoto, H., Shah, T., Whelan, C.M., Irizarry, M.C. and Hyman, B.T. (2003a) Demonstration by FRET of BACE interaction with the amyloid precursor protein at the cell surface and in early endosomes. *J. Cell Sci., 116,* 3339-3346.

Kinoshita, A., Shah, T., Tangredi, M.M., Strickland, D.K. and Hyman, B.T. (2003b) The intracellular domain of the low density lipoprotein receptor-related protein modulates transactivation mediated by amyloid precursor protein and Fe65. *J. Biol. Chem., 278,* 41182-41188.

Kinoshita, A., Whelan, C.M., Smith, C.J., Mikhailenko, I., Rebeck, G.W., Strickland, D.K. and Hyman, B.T. (2001) Demonstration by fluorescence resonance energy transfer of two sites of interaction between the low-density lipoprotein receptor-related protein and the amyloid precursor protein: role of the intracellular adapter protein Fe65. *J. Neurosci., 21,* 8354-8361.

Kins, S., Lauther, N., Szodorai, A. and Beyreuther, K. (2006) Subcellular trafficking of the amyloid precursor protein gene family and its pathogenic role in Alzheimer's disease. *Neurodegener. Dis., 3,* 218-226.

Knauer, M.F., Orlando, R.A. and Glabe, C.G. (1996) Cell surface APP751 forms complexes with protease nexin 2 ligands and is internalized via the low density lipoprotein receptor-related protein (LRP). *Brain Res., 740,* 6-14.

Koch, S., Strasser, V., Hauser, C., Fasching, D., Brandes, C., Bajari, T.M., Schneider, W.J. and Nimpf, J. (2002) A secreted soluble form of ApoE receptor 2 acts as a dominant-negative receptor and inhibits Reelin signaling. *EMBO J., 21,* 5996-6004.

Koistinaho, M., Lin, S., Wu, X., Esterman, M., Koger, D., Hanson, J., Higgs, R., Liu, F., Malkani, S., Bales, K.R. and Paul, S.M. (2004) Apolipoprotein E promotes astrocyte colocalization and degradation of deposited amyloid-beta peptides. *Nat Med*, *10*, 719-726.

Kojro, E., Gimpl, G., Lammich, S., Marz, W. and Fahrenholz, F. (2001) Low cholesterol stimulates the nonamyloidogenic pathway by its effect on the α-secretase ADAM 10. *Proc. Natl. Acad. Sci. U. S. A.*, *98*, 5815-5820.

Koldamova, R., Staufenbiel, M. and Lefterov, I. (2005) Lack of ABCA1 considerably decreases brain ApoE level and increases amyloid deposition in APP23 mice. *J. Biol. Chem.*, *280*, 43224-43235.

Koldamova, R.P., Lefterov, I.M., Ikonomovic, M.D., Skoko, J., Lefterov, P.I., Isanski, B.A., DeKosky, S.T. and Lazo, J.S. (2003) 22R-hydroxycholesterol and 9-cis-retinoic acid induce ATP-binding cassette transporter A1 expression and cholesterol efflux in brain cells and decrease amyloid beta secretion. *J. Biol. Chem.*, *278*, 13244-13256.

Kolsch, H., Lutjohann, D., Ludwig, M., Schulte, A., Ptok, U., Jessen, F., von Bergmann, K., Rao, M.L., Maier, W. and Heun, R. (2002) Polymorphism in the cholesterol 24S-hydroxylase gene is associated with Alzheimer's disease. *Mol. Psychiatry*, *7*, 899-902.

Koo, E.H., Sisodia, S.S., Archer, D.R., Martin, L.J., Weidemann, A., Beyreuther, K., Fischer, P., Masters, C.L. and Price, D.L. (1990) Precursor of amyloid protein in Alzheimer disease undergoes fast anterograde axonal transport. *Proc. Natl. Acad. Sci. U. S. A.*, *87*, 1561-1565.

Koo, E.H. and Squazzo, S.L. (1994) Evidence that production and release of amyloid β-protein involves the endocytic pathway. *J. Biol. Chem.*, *269*, 17386-17389.

Koo, E.H., Squazzo, S.L., Selkoe, D.J. and Koo, C.H. (1996) Trafficking of cell-surface amyloid β-protein precursor. I. Secretion, endocytosis and recycling as detected by labeled monoclonal antibody. *J. Cell Sci.*, *109*, 991-998.

Kounnas, M.Z., Moir, R.D., Rebeck, G.W., Bush, A.I., Argraves, W.S., Tanzi, R.E., Hyman, B.T. and Strickland, D.K. (1995) LDL receptor-related protein, a multifunctional ApoE receptor, binds secreted β-amyloid precursor protein and mediates its degradation. *Cell*, *82*, 331-340.

Lai, A., Sisodia, S.S. and Trowbridge, I.S. (1995) Characterization of sorting signals in the β-amyloid precursor protein cytoplasmic domain. *J. Biol. Chem.*, *270*, 3565-3573.

Lambert, J.C., Chartier-Harlin, M.C., Cottel, D., Richard, F., Neuman, E., Guez, D., Legrain, S., Berr, C., Amouyel, P. and Helbecque, N. (1999) Is the LDL receptor-related protein involved in Alzheimer's disease? *Neurogenetics*, *2*, 109-113.

Lambert, J.C., Wavrant-De Vrieze, F., Amouyel, P. and Chartier-Harlin, M.C. (1998) Association at LRP gene locus with sporadic late-onset Alzheimer's disease. *Lancet*, *351*, 1787-1788.

Lee, J.H., Cheng, R., Schupf, N., Manly, J., Lantigua, R., Stern, Y., Rogaeva, E., Wakutani, Y., Farrer, L., St George-Hyslop, P. and Mayeux, R. (2007) The association between genetic variants in SORL1 and Alzheimer disease in an urban, multiethnic, community-based cohort. *Arch. Neurol.*, *64*, 501-506.

Lendon, C.L., Talbot, C.J., Craddock, N.J., Han, S.W., Wragg, M., Morris, J.C. and Goate, A.M. (1997) Genetic association studies between dementia of the Alzheimer's type and three receptors for apolipoprotein E in a Caucasian population. *Neurosci. Lett.*, *222*, 187-190.

Li, Y., Lu, W., Marzolo, M.P. and Bu, G. (2001) Differential functions of members of the LDL receptor family suggested by their distinct endocytosis rates. *J. Biol. Chem.*, *21*, 18000-18006.

Liu, C.-X., Musco, S., Lisitsina, N.M., Forgacs, E., Minna, J.D. and Lisitsyn, N.A. (2000) *LRP-DIT*, a putative endocytic receptor gene, is frequently inactivated in non-small cell lung cancer cell lines. *Cancer Res.*, *60*, 1961-1967.

Liu, C.X., Ranganathan, S., Robinson, S. and Strickland, D.K. (2007) γ-Secretase-mediated Release of the Low Density Lipoprotein Receptor-related Protein 1B Intracellular Domain Suppresses Anchorage-independent Growth of Neuroglioma Cells. *J. Biol. Chem.*, *282*, 7504-7511.

Lund, E.G., Xie, C., Kotti, T., Turley, S.D., Dietschy, J.M. and Russell, D.W. (2003) Knockout of the cholesterol 24-hydroxylase gene in mice reveals a brain-specific mechanism of cholesterol turnover. *J. Biol. Chem.*, *278*, 22980-22988.

Lutjohann, D., Breuer, O., Ahlborg, G., Nennesmo, I., Siden, A., Diczfalusy, U. and Bjorkhem, I. (1996) Cholesterol homeostasis in human brain: evidence for an age-dependent flux of 24S-hydroxycholesterol from the brain into the circulation. *Proc. Natl. Acad. Sci. U. S. A.*, *93*, 9799-9804.

Lutjohann, D., Papassotiropoulos, A., Bjorkhem, I., Locatelli, S., Bagli, M., Oehring, R.D., Schlegel, U., Jessen, F., Rao, M.L., von Bergmann, K. and Heun, R. (2000) Plasma 24S-hydroxycholesterol (cerebrosterol) is increased in Alzheimer and vascular demented patients. *J. Lipid. Res.*, *41*, 195-198.

Lutz, C., Nimpf, J., Jenny, M., Boecklinger, K., Enzinger, C., Utermann, G., Baier-Bitterlich, G. and Baier, G. (2002) Evidence of functional modulation of the MEKK/JNK/cJun signaling cascade by the low density lipoprotein receptor-related protein (LRP). *J. Biol. Chem.*, *277*, 43143-43151.

Ma, S.L., Ng, H.K., Baum, L., Pang, J.C., Chiu, H.F., Woo, J., Tang, N.L. and Lam, L.C. (2002) Low-density lipoprotein receptor-related protein 8 (apolipoprotein E receptor 2) gene polymorphisms in Alzheimer's disease. *Neurosci. Lett.*, *332*, 216-218.

Mahley, R.W. (1988) Apolipoprotein E: cholesterol transport protein with expanding role in cell biology. *Science*, *240*, 622-630.

Marcusson, E.G., Horazdovsky, B.F., Cereghino, J.L., Gharakhanian, E. and Emr, S.D. (1994) The sorting receptor for yeast vacuolar carboxypeptidase Y is encoded by the *VPS10* gene. *Cell*, *77*, 579-586.

Marquez-Sterling, N.R., Lo, A.C., Sisodia, S.S. and Koo, E.H. (1997) Trafficking of cell-surface β-amyloid precursor protein: evidence that a sorting intermediate participates in synaptic vesicle recycling. *J. Neurosci.*, *17*, 140-151.

Marschang, P., Brich, J., Weeber, E.J., Sweatt, J.D., Shelton, J.M., Richardson, J.A., Hammer, R.E. and Herz, J. (2004) Normal development and fertility of knockout mice lacking the tumor suppressor gene LRP1b suggest functional compensation by LRP1. *Mol. Cell. Biol.*, *24*, 3782-3793.

Martins, I.J., Hone, E., Foster, J.K., Sünram-Lea, S.I., Gnjec, A., Fuller, S.J., Nolan, D., Gandy, S.E. and Martins, R.N. (2006) Apolipoprotein E, cholesterol metabolism, diabetes, and the convergence of risk factors for Alzheimer's disease and cardiovascular disease. *Mol. Psychiatry*, *11*, 721-736.

Marx, J. (2007) Molecular biology. Trafficking protein suspected in Alzheimer's disease. *Science*, *315*, 314.

Masliah, E., Mallory, M., Ge, N., Alford, M., Veinbergs, I. and Roses, A.D. (1995) Neurodegeneration in the central nervous system of apoE-deficient mice. *Exp Neurol*, *136*, 107-122.

Mattson, M.P. (1997) Cellular actions of β-amyloid precursor protein and its soluble and fibrillogenic derivatives. *Physiol. Rev.*, *77*, 1081-1132.

Mauch, D.H., Nagler, K., Schumacher, S., Goritz, C., Muller, E.C., Otto, A. and Pfrieger, F.W. (2001) CNS synaptogenesis promoted by glia-derived cholesterol. *Science*, *294*, 1354-1357.

May, P., Bock, H.H., Nimpf, J. and Herz, J. (2003) Differential glycosylation regulates processing of lipoprotein receptors by γ-secretase. *J. Biol. Chem.*, *278*, 37386-37392.

May, P., Reddy, Y.K. and Herz, J. (2002) Proteolytic processing of low density lipoprotein receptor-related protein mediates regulated release of its intracellular domain. *J. Biol. Chem.*, *277*, 18736-18743.

May, P., Rohlmann, A., Bock, H.H., Zurhove, K., Marth, J.D., Schomburg, E.D., Noebels, J.L., Beffert, U., Sweatt, J.D., Weeber, E.J. and Herz, J. (2004) Neuronal LRP1 Functionally Associates with Postsynaptic Proteins and Is Required for Normal Motor Function in Mice. *Mol. Cell. Biol.*, *24*, 8872-8883.

Miyazaki, A., Sakai, M., Sakamoto, Y. and Horiuchi, S. (2003) Acyl-coenzyme A:cholesterol acyltransferase inhibitors for controlling hypercholesterolemia and atherosclerosis. *Curr. Opin. Investig. Drugs*, *4*, 1095-1099.

Morris, M.C., Evans, D.A., Bienias, J.L., Tangney, C.C., Bennett, D.A., Aggarwal, N., Schneider, J. and Wilson, R.S. (2003a) Dietary fats and the risk of incident Alzheimer disease. *Arch. Neurol.*, *60*, 194-200.

Morris, M.C., Evans, D.A., Bienias, J.L., Tangney, C.C., Bennett, D.A., Wilson, R.S., Aggarwal, N. and Schneider, J. (2003b) Consumption of fish and n-3 fatty acids and risk of incident Alzheimer disease. *Arch. Neurol.*, *60*, 940-946.

Motoi, Y., Aizawa, T., Haga, S., Nakamura, S., Namba, Y. and Ikeda, K. (1999) Neuronal localization of a novel mosaic apolipoprotein E receptor, LR11, in rat and human brain. *Brain Res.*, *833*, 209-215.

Narita, M., Holtzman, D.M., Schwartz, A.L. and Bu, G. (1997) α_2-macroglobulin complexes with and mediates the endocytosis of β-amyloid peptide via cell surface low-density lipoprotein receptor- related protein. *J. Neurochem.*, *69*, 1904-1911.

Nothwehr, S.F., Bruinsma, P. and Strawn, L.A. (1999) Distinct domains within Vps35p mediate the retrieval of two different cargo proteins from the yeast prevacuolar/endosomal compartment. *Mol. Biol. Cell.*, *10*, 875-890.

Nyborg, A.C., Ladd, T.B., Zwizinski, C.W., Lah, J.J. and Golde, T.E. (2006) Sortilin, SorCS1b, and SorLA Vps10p sorting receptors, are novel γ-secretase substrates. *Mol. Neurodegener.*, *1*.

Nykjær, A., Dragun, D., Walther, D., Vorum, H., Jacobsen, C., Herz, J., Melsen, F., Christensen, E.I. and Willnow, T.E. (1999) An endocytic pathway essential for renal uptake and activation of the steroid 25-(OH) vitamin D_3. *Cell*, *96*, 507-515.

Nykjær, A. and Willnow, T.E. (2002) The low-density lipoprotein receptor gene family: a cellular Swiss army knife? *Trends Cell Biol.*, *12*, 273-280.

Offe, K., Dodson, S.E., Shoemaker, J.T., Fritz, J.J., Gearing, M., Levey, A.I. and Lah, J.J. (2006) The lipoprotein receptor LR11 regulates amyloid β production and amyloid precursor protein traffic in endosomal compartments. *J. Neurosci.*, *26*, 1596-1603.

Oksman, M., Iivonen, H., Hogyes, E., Amtul, Z., Penke, B., Leenders, I., Broersen, L., Lutjohann, D., Hartmann, T. and Tanila, H. (2006) Impact of different saturated fatty acid, polyunsaturated fatty acid and cholesterol containing diets on β-amyloid accumulation in APP/PS1 transgenic mice. *Neurobiol. Dis.*, *23*, 563-572.

Palacios, G., Palacios, J.M., Mengod, G. and Frey, P. (1992) β-amyloid precursor protein localization in the Golgi apparatus in neurons and oligodendrocytes. An immunocytochemical structural and ultrastructural study in normal and axotomized neurons. *Brain Res. Mol. Brain Res.*, *15*, 195-206.

Papassotiropoulos, A., Lutjohann, D., Bagli, M., Locatelli, S., Jessen, F., Buschfort, R., Ptok, U., Bjorkhem, I., von Bergmann, K. and Heun, R. (2002) 24S-hydroxycholesterol in cerebrospinal fluid is elevated in early stages of dementia. *J. Psychiatr. Res.*, *36*, 27-32.

Papassotiropoulos, A., Lutjohann, D., Bagli, M., Locatelli, S., Jessen, F., Rao, M.L., Maier, W., Bjorkhem, I., von Bergmann, K. and Heun, R. (2000) Plasma 24S-hydroxycholesterol: a peripheral indicator of neuronal degeneration and potential state marker for Alzheimer's disease. *Neuroreport*, *11*, 1959-1962.

Park, I.H., Hwang, E.M., Hong, H.S., Boo, J.H., Oh, S.S., Lee, J., Jung, M.W., Bang, O.Y., Kim, S.U. and Mook-Jung, I. (2003) Lovastatin enhances Aβ production and senile plaque deposition in female Tg2576 mice. *Neurobiol. Aging*, *24*, 637-643.

Petit-Turcotte, C., Aumont, N., Beffert, U., Dea, D., Herz, J. and Poirier, J. (2005) The apoE receptor apoER2 is involved in the maintenance of efficient synaptic plasticity. *Neurobiol. Aging*, *26*, 195-206.

Pietrzik, C.U., Busse, T., Merriam, D.E., Weggen, S. and Koo, E.H. (2002) The cytoplasmic domain of the LDL receptor-related protein regulates multiple steps in APP processing. *EMBO J.*, *21*, 5691-5700.

Pietrzik, C.U., Yoon, I.S., Jaeger, S., Busse, T., Weggen, S. and Koo, E.H. (2004) FE65 constitutes the functional link between the low-density lipoprotein receptor-related protein and the amyloid precursor protein. *J. Neurosci.*, *24*, 4259-4265.

Poirier, J. (2000) Apolipoprotein E and Alzheimer's disease. A role in amyloid catabolism. *Ann. N. Y. Acad. Sci.*, *924*, 81-90.

Puglielli, L., Ellis, B.C., Ingano, L.A. and Kovacs, D.M. (2004) Role of acyl-coenzyme a: cholesterol acyltransferase activity in the processing of the amyloid precursor protein. *J. Mol. Neurosci.*, *24*, 93-96.

Puglielli, L., Konopka, G., Pack-Chung, E., Ingano, L.A., Berezovska, O., Hyman, B.T., Chang, T.Y., Tanzi, R.E. and Kovacs, D.M. (2001) Acyl-coenzyme A: cholesterol acyltransferase modulates the generation of the amyloid beta-peptide. *Nat Cell Biol*, *3*, 905-912.

Puglielli, L., Tanzi, R.E. and Kovacs, D.M. (2003) Alzheimer's disease: the cholesterol connection. *Nat. Neurosci.*, *6*, 345-351.

Qiu, W.Q., Ferreira, A., Miller, C., Koo, E.H. and Selkoe, D.J. (1995) Cell-surface β-amyloid precursor protein stimulates neurite outgrowth of hippocampal neurons in an isoform-dependent manner. *J. Neurosci.*, *15*, 2157-2167.

Qiu, Z., Strickland, D.K., Hyman, B.T. and Rebeck, G.W. (1999) α_2-macroglobulin enhances the clearance of endogenous soluble β-amyloid peptide via low-density lipoprotein receptor-related protein in cortical neurons. *J. Neurochem.*, *73*, 1393-1398.

Qiu, Z., Strickland, D.K., Hyman, B.T. and Rebeck, G.W. (2002) α_2-Macroglobulin exposure reduces calcium responses to *N*-methyl-*D*-aspartate via low density lipoprotein receptor-related protein in cultured hippocampal neurons. *J. Biol. Chem.*, *277*, 14458-14466.

Quinn, K.A., Grimsley, P.G., Dai, Y.-P., Tapner, M., Chesterman, C.N. and Owensby, D.A. (1997) Soluble low density lipoprotein receptor-related protein (LRP) circulates in human plasma. *J. Biol. Chem.*, *272*, 23946-23951.

Quinn, K.A., Pye, V.J., Dai, Y.-P., Chesterman, C.N. and Owensby, D.A. (1999) Characterization of the soluble form of the low density lipoprotein receptor-related protein (LRP). *Exp. Cell Res.*, *251*, 433-441.

Rebeck, G.W., LaDu, M.J., Estus, S., Bu, G. and Weeber, E.J. (2006) The generation and function of soluble apoE receptors in the CNS. *Mol. Neurodegener.*, *1*, 15.

Rebeck, G.W., Reiter, J.S., Strickland, D.K. and Hyman, B.T. (1993) Apolipoprotein E in sporadic Alzheimer's disease: allelic variation and receptor interactions. *Neuron*, *11*, 575-580.

Refolo, L.M., Malester, B., LaFrancois, J., Bryant-Thomas, T., Wang, R., Tint, G.S., Sambamurti, K., Duff, K. and Pappolla, M.A. (2000) Hypercholesterolemia accelerates the Alzheimer's amyloid pathology in a transgenic mouse model. *Neurobiol. Dis.*, *7*, 321-331.

Refolo, L.M., Pappolla, M.A., LaFrancois, J., Malester, B., Schmidt, S.D., Thomas-Bryant, T., Tint, G.S., Wang, R., Mercken, M., Petanceska, S.S. and Duff, K.E. (2001) A cholesterol-lowering drug reduces β-amyloid pathology in a transgenic mouse model of Alzheimer's disease. *Neurobiol. Dis.*, *8*, 890-899.

Rogaeva, E., Meng, Y., Lee, J.H., Gu, Y., Kawarai, T., Zou, F., Katayama, T., Baldwin, C.T., Cheng, R., Hasegawa, H., Chen, F., Shibata, N., Lunetta, K.L., Pardossi-Piquard, R., Bohm, C., Wakutani, Y., Cupples, L.A., Cuenco, K.T., Green, R.C., Pinessi, L., Rainero, I., Sorbi, S., Bruni, A., Duara, R., Friedland, R.P., Inzelberg, R., Hampe, W., Bujo, H., Song, Y.Q., Andersen, O.M., Willnow, T.E., Graff-Radford, N., Petersen, R.C., Dickson, D., Der, S.D., Fraser, P.E., Schmitt-Ulms, G., Younkin, S., Mayeux, R., Farrer, L.A. and St George-Hyslop, P. (2007) The neuronal sortilin-related receptor SORL1 is genetically associated with Alzheimer disease. *Nat. Genet.*, *39*, 168-177.

Rudenko, G., Henry, L., Henderson, K., Ichtchenko, K., Brown, M.S., Goldstein, J.L. and Deisenhofer, J. (2002) Structure of the LDL receptor extracellular domain at endosomal pH. *Science*, *298*, 2353-2358.

Russell, D.W. (1992) Cholesterol biosynthesis and metabolism. *Cardiovasc. Drugs Ther.*, *6*, 103-110.

Scherzer, C.R., Offe, K., Gearing, M., Rees, H.D., Fang, G., Heilman, C.J., Schaller, H.C., Levey, A.I. and Lah, J.J. (2004) ApoE receptor LR11 in Alzheimer's disease: Gene profiling of lymphoblasts mirrors changes in the brain. *Arch. Neurol.*, *61*, 1200-1205.

Schonknecht, P., Lutjohann, D., Pantel, J., Bardenheuer, H., Hartmann, T., von Bergmann, K., Beyreuther, K. and Schroder, J. (2002) Cerebrospinal fluid 24S-hydroxycholesterol is increased in patients with Alzheimer's disease compared to healthy controls. *Neurosci. Lett.*, *324*, 83-85.

Seaman, M.N. (2004) Cargo-selective endosomal sorting for retrieval to the Golgi requires retromer. *J. Cell Biol.*, *165*, 111-122.

Seaman, M.N. (2005) Recycle your receptors with retromer. *Trends Cell Biol.*, *15*, 68-75.

Selkoe, D.J. (1994) Cell biology of the amyloid beta-protein precursor and the mechanism of Alzheimer's disease. *Annu. Rev. Cell Biol.*, *10*, 373-403.

Selkoe, D.J. (2002) Alzheimer's disease is a synaptic failure. *Science*, *298*, 789-791.

Selkoe, D.J., Podlisny, M.B., Joachim, C.L., Vickers, E.A., Lee, G., Fritz, L.C. and Oltersdorf, T. (1988) β-amyloid precursor protein of Alzheimer disease occurs as 110- to 135-kilodalton membrane-associated proteins in neural and nonneural tissues. *Proc. Natl. Acad. Sci. U. S. A.*, *85*, 7341-7345.

Shah, S. and Yu, G. (2006) sorLA: sorting out APP. *Mol. Interv.*, *6*, 74-76.

Shiba, T., Kametaka, S., Kawasaki, M., Shibata, M., Waguri, S., Uchiyama, Y. and Wakatsuki, S. (2004) Insights into the phosphoregulation of β-secretase sorting signal by the VHS domain of GGA1. *Traffic*, *5*, 437-448.

Shibata, M., Yamada, S., Kumar, S.R., Calero, M., Bading, J., Frangione, B., Holtzman, D.M., Miller, C.A., Strickland, D.K., Ghiso, J. and Zlokovic, B.V. (2000) Clearance of Alzheimer's amyloid-ss(1-40) peptide from brain by LDL receptor-related protein-1 at the blood-brain barrier. *J. Clin. Invest.*, *106*, 1489-1499.

Shobab, L.A., Hsiung, G.Y. and Feldman, H.H. (2005) Cholesterol in Alzheimer's disease. *Lancet Neurol.*, *4*, 841-852.

Simons, M., Ikonen, E., Tienari, P.J., Cid-Arregui, A., Monning, U., Beyreuther, K. and Dotti, C.G. (1995) Intracellular routing of human amyloid protein precursor: axonal delivery followed by transport to the dendrites. *J. Neurosci. Res.*, *41*, 121-128.

Simons, M., Keller, P., De Strooper, B., Beyreuther, K., Dotti, C.G. and Simons, K. (1998) Cholesterol depletion inhibits the generation of β-amyloid in hippocampal neurons. *Proc. Natl. Acad. Sci. U. S. A.*, *95*, 6460-6464.

Sinagra, M., Verrier, D., Frankova, D., Korwek, K.M., Blahos, J., Weeber, E.J., Manzoni, O.J. and Chavis, P. (2005) Reelin, very-low-density lipoprotein receptor, and apolipoprotein E receptor 2 control somatic NMDA receptor composition during hippocampal maturation in vitro. *J. Neurosci.*, *25*, 6127-6136.

Small, D.H., Mok, S.S. and Bornstein, J.C. (2001) Alzheimer's disease and Aβ toxicity: from top to bottom. *Nat. Rev. Neurosci.*, *2*, 595-598.

Small, S.A. and Gandy, S. (2006) Sorting through the cell biology of Alzheimer's disease: intracellular pathways to pathogenesis. *Neuron*, *52*, 15-31.

Small, S.A., Kent, K., Pierce, A., Leung, C., Kang, M.S., Okada, H., Honig, L., Vonsattel, J.P. and Kim, T.W. (2005) Model-guided microarray implicates the retromer complex in Alzheimer's disease. *Ann. Neurol.*, *58*, 909-919.

Soba, P., Eggert, S., Wagner, K., Zentgraf, H., Siehl, K., Kreger, S., Lower, A., Langer, A., Merdes, G., Paro, R., Masters, C.L., Müller, U., Kins, S. and Beyreuther, K. (2005) Homo- and heterodimerization of APP family members promotes intercellular adhesion. *EMBO J.*, *24*, 3624-3634.

Spoelgen, R., von Arnim, C.A., Thomas, A.V., Peltan, I.D., Koker, M., Deng, A., Irizarry, M.C., Andersen, O.M., Willnow, T.E. and Hyman, B.T. (2006) Interaction of the cytosolic domains of sorLA/LR11 with the amyloid precursor protein (APP) and β-secretase β-site APP-cleaving enzyme. *J. Neurosci.*, *26*, 418-428.

Strittmatter, W.J., Saunders, A.M., Schmechel, D., Pericak-Vance, M., Enghild, J., Salvesen, G.S. and Roses, A.D. (1993a) Apolipoprotein E: High-avidity binding to β-amyloid and increased frequency of type 4 allele in late-onset familial Alzheimer disease. *Proc. Natl. Acad. Sci. U. S. A.*, *90*, 1977-1981.

Strittmatter, W.J., Weisgraber, K.H., Huang, D.Y., Dong, L.-M., Salvesen, G.S., Pericak-Vance, M., Schmechel, D., Saunders, A.M., Goldgaber, D. and Roses, A.D. (1993b) Binding of human apolipoprotein E to synthetic amyloid β peptide: Isoform-specific effects and implications for late-onset Alzheimer disease. *Proc. Natl. Acad. Sci. U. S. A.*, *90*, 8098-8102.

Suzuki, T., Araki, Y., Yamamoto, T. and Nakaya, T. (2006) Trafficking of Alzheimer's disease-related membrane proteins and its participation in disease pathogenesis. *J. Biochem. (Tokyo)*, *139*, 949-955.

Tanaga, K., Bujo, H., Zhu, Y., Kanaki, T., Hirayama, S., Takahashi, K., Inoue, M., Mikami, K., Schneider, W.J. and Saito, Y. (2004) LRP1B attenuates the migration of smooth muscle cells by reducing membrane localization of urokinase and PDGF receptors. *Arterioscler. Thromb. Vasc. Biol.*, *24*, 1422-1428.

Tanzi, R.E. (2005) The synaptic Aβ hypothesis of Alzheimer disease. *Nat. Neurosci.*, *8*, 977-979.

Terry, R.D., Masliah, E., Salmon, D.P., Butters, N., DeTeresa, R., Hill, R., Hansen, L.A. and Katzman, R. (1991) Physical basis of cognitive alterations in Alzheimer's disease: synapse loss is the major correlate of cognitive impairment. *Ann. Neurol.*, *30*, 572-580.

Tienari, P.J., De Strooper, B., Ikonen, E., Simons, M., Weidemann, A., Czech, C., Hartmann, T., Ida, N., Multhaup, G., Masters, C.L., Van Leuven, F., Beyreuther, K. and Dotti, C.G. (1996) The β-amyloid domain is essential for axonal sorting of amyloid precursor protein. *EMBO J.*, *15*, 5218-5229.

Trommsdorff, M., Borg, J.-P., Margolis, B. and Herz, J. (1998) Interaction of cytosolic adaptor proteins with neuronal apolipoprotein E receptors and the amyloid precursor protein. *J. Biol. Chem.*, *273*, 33556-33560.

Trommsdorff, M., Gotthardt, M., Hiesberger, T., Shelton, J., Stockinger, W., Nimpf, J., Hammer, R.E., Richardson, J.A. and Herz, J. (1999) Reeler/Disabled-like disruption of neuronal migration in knockout mice lacking the VLDL receptor and ApoE receptor 2. *Cell*, *97*, 689-701.

Turner, P.R., O'Connor, K., Tate, W.P. and Abraham, W.C. (2003) Roles of amyloid precursor protein and its fragments in regulating neural activity, plasticity and memory. *Prog. Neurobiol.*, *70*, 1-32.

Ulery, P.G., Beers, J., Mikhailenko, I., Tanzi, R.E., Rebeck, G.W., Hyman, B.T. and Strickland, D.K. (2000) Modulation of β-amyloid precursor protein processing by the low density lipoprotein receptor-related protein (LRP). Evidence that LRP contributes to the pathogenesis of Alzheimer's disease. *J. Biol. Chem.*, *275*, 7410-7415.

Van Uden, E., Mallory, M., Veinbergs, I., Alford, M., Rockenstein, E. and Masliah, E. (2002) Increased extracellular amyloid deposition and neurodegeneration in human amyloid precursor protein transgenic mice deficient in receptor- associated protein. *J. Neurosci.*, *22*, 9298-9304.

Van Uden, E., Sagara, Y., Van Uden, J., Orlando, R., Mallory, M., Rockenstein, E. and Masliah, E. (2000) A protective role of the low density lipoprotein receptor-related protein against amyloid β-protein toxicity. *J. Biol. Chem.*, *275*, 30525-30530.

von Arnim, C.A., Kinoshita, A., Peltan, I.D., Tangredi, M.M., Herl, L., Lee, B.M., Spoelgen, R., Hshieh, T.T., Ranganathan, S., Battey, F.D., Liu, C.X., Bacskai, B.J., Sever, S., Irizarry, M.C., Strickland, D.K. and Hyman, B.T. (2005) The low density lipoprotein receptor-related protein (LRP) is a novel β-secretase (BACE1) substrate. *J. Biol. Chem.*, *280*, 17777-17785.

von Arnim, C.A., Spoelgen, R., Peltan, I.D., Deng, M., Courchesne, S., Koker, M., Matsui, T., Kowa, H., Lichtenthaler, S.F., Irizarry, M.C. and Hyman, B.T. (2006) GGA1 acts as a spatial switch altering amyloid precursor protein trafficking and processing. *J. Neurosci.*, *26*, 9913-9922.

von Koch, C.S., Zheng, H., Chen, H., Trumbauer, M., Thinakaran, G., van der Ploeg, L.H.T., Price, D.L. and Sisodia, S.S. (1997) Generation of APLP2 KO mice and early postnatal lethality in APLP2/APP double KO mice. *Neurobiol. Aging*, *18*, 661-669.

Wahle, T., Prager, K., Raffler, N., Haass, C., Famulok, M. and Walter, J. (2005) GGA proteins regulate retrograde transport of BACE1 from endosomes to the trans-Golgi network. *Mol. Cell. Neurosci.*, *29*, 453-461.

Wahle, T., Thal, D.R., Sastre, M., Rentmeister, A., Bogdanovic, N., Famulok, M., Heneka, M.T. and Walter, J. (2006) GGA1 is expressed in the human brain and affects the generation of amyloid β-peptide. *J. Neurosci.*, *26*, 12838-12846.

Wahrle, S.E., Jiang, H., Parsadanian, M., Hartman, R.E., Bales, K.R., Paul, S.M. and Holtzman, D.M. (2005) Deletion of Abca1 increases Aβ deposition in the PDAPP transgenic mouse model of Alzheimer disease. *J. Biol. Chem.*, *280*, 43236-43242.

Waldron, E., Jaeger, S. and Pietrzik, C.U. (2006) Functional role of the low-density lipoprotein receptor-related protein in Alzheimer's disease. *Neurodegener. Dis.*, *3*, 233-238.

Wallace, W.C., Akar, C.A., Lyons, W.E., Kole, H.K., Egan, J.M. and Wolozin, B. (1997) Amyloid precursor protein requires the insulin signaling pathway for neurotrophic activity. *Brain Res. Mol. Brain Res.*, *52*, 213-227.

Walter, J. (2006) Control of amyloid-β-peptide generation by subcellular trafficking of the β-amyloid precursor protein and β-secretase. *Neurodegener. Dis.*, *3*, 247-254.

Walter, J., Fluhrer, R., Hartung, B., Willem, M., Kaether, C., Capell, A., Lammich, S., Multhaup, G. and Haass, C. (2001) Phosphorylation regulates intracellular trafficking of β-secretase. *J. Biol. Chem.*, *276*, 14634-14641.

Wavrant-DeVrieze, F., Lambert, J.C., Stas, L., Crook, R., Cottel, D., Pasquier, F., Frigard, B., Lambrechts, M., Thiry, E., Amouyel, P., Tur, J.P., Chartier-Harlin, M.C., Hardy, J. and Van Leuven, F. (1999) Association between coding variability in the LRP gene and the risk of late-onset Alzheimer's disease. *Hum. Genet., 104*, 432-434.

Wavrant-DeVrieze, F., Perez-Tur, J., Lambert, J.C., Frigard, B., Pasquier, F., Delacourte, A., Amouyel, P., Hardy, J. and Chartier-Harlin, M.C. (1997) Association between the low density lipoprotein receptor-related protein (LRP) and Alzheimer's disease. *Neurosci. Lett., 227*, 68-70.

Weeber, E.J., Beffert, U., Jones, C., Christian, J.M., Förster, E., Sweatt, J.D. and Herz, J. (2002) Reelin and ApoE receptors cooperate to enhance hippocampal synaptic plasticity and learning. *J. Biol. Chem., 277*, 39944-39952.

Weidemann, A., Konig, G., Bunke, D., Fischer, P., Salbaum, J.M., Masters, C.L. and Beyreuther, K. (1989) Identification, biogenesis, and localization of precursors of Alzheimer's disease A4 amyloid protein. *Cell, 57*, 115-126.

Willnow, T.E., Armstrong, S.A., Hammer, R.E. and Herz, J. (1995) Functional expression of low density lipoprotein receptor-related protein is controlled by receptor-associated protein *in vivo*. *Proc. Natl. Acad. Sci. U. S. A., 92*, 4537-4541.

Willnow, T.E., Nykjær, A. and Herz, J. (1999) Lipoprotein receptors: new roles for ancient proteins. *Nat. Cell Biol., 1*, E157-E162.

Willnow, T.E., Rohlmann, A., Horton, J., Otani, H., Braun, J.R., Hammer, R.E. and Herz, J. (1996) RAP, a specialized chaperone, prevents ligand-induced ER retention and degradation of LDL receptor-related endocytic receptors. *EMBO J., 15*, 2632-2639.

Wolozin, B. (2004) Cholesterol and the biology of Alzheimer's disease. *Neuron, 41*, 7-10.

Wolozin, B., Kellman, W., Ruosseau, P., Celesia, G.G. and Siegel, G. (2000) Decreased prevalence of Alzheimer disease associated with 3-hydroxy-3-methyglutaryl coenzyme A reductase inhibitors. *Arch. Neurol., 57*, 1439-1443.

Yamazaki, H., Bujo, H., Kusunoki, J., Seimiya, K., Kanaki, T., Morisaki, N., Schneider, W.J. and Saito, Y. (1996a) Elements of neural adhesion molecules and a yeast vacuolar protein sorting receptor are present in a novel mammalian low density lipoprotein receptor family member. *J. Biol. Chem., 271*, 24761-24768.

Yamazaki, T., Koo, E.H. and Selkoe, D.J. (1996b) Trafficking of cell-surface amyloid β-protein precursor. II. Endocytosis, recycling and lysosomal targeting detected by immunolocalization. *J. Cell Sci., 109*, 999-1008.

Yamazaki, T., Selkoe, D.J. and Koo, E.H. (1995) Trafficking of cell surface β-amyloid precursor protein: retrograde and transcytotic transport in cultured neurons. *J. Cell. Biol., 129*, 431-442.

Yang, D.S., Small, D.H., Seydel, U., Smith, J.D., Hallmayer, J., Gandy, S.E. and Martins, R.N. (1999) Apolipoprotein E promotes the binding and uptake of β-amyloid into Chinese hamster ovary cells in an isoform-specific manner. *Neuroscience, 90*, 1217-1226.

Yang, M., Huang, H., Li, J., Li, D. and Wang, H. (2004) Tyrosine phosphorylation of the LDL receptor-related protein (LRP) and activation of the ERK pathway are required for connective tissue growth factor to potentiate myofibroblast differentiation. *FASEB J., 18*, 1920-1921.

Yoon, I.S., Pietrzik, C.U., Kang, D.E. and Koo, E.H. (2005) Sequences from the low density lipoprotein receptor-related protein (LRP) cytoplasmic domain enhance amyloid β protein production via the β-secretase pathway without altering amyloid precursor protein/LRP nuclear signaling. *J. Biol. Chem.*, *280*, 20140-20147.

Zerbinatti, C.V. and Bu, G. (2005) LRP and Alzheimer's disease. *Rev. Neurosci.*, *16*, 123-135.

Zerbinatti, C.V., Wahrle, S.E., Kim, H., Cam, J.A., Bales, K., Paul, S.M., Holtzman, D.M. and Bu, G. (2006) Apolipoprotein E and low density lipoprotein receptor-related protein facilitate intraneuronal Aβ42 accumulation in amyloid model mice. *J. Biol. Chem.*, *281*, 36180-36186.

Zerbinatti, C.V., Wozniak, D.F., Cirrito, J., Cam, J.A., Osaka, H., Bales, K.R., Zhuo, M., Paul, S.M., Holtzman, D.M. and Bu, G. (2004) Increased soluble amyloid-β peptide and memory deficits in amyloid model mice overexpressing the low-density lipoprotein receptor-related protein. *Proc. Natl. Acad. Sci. U. S. A.*, *101*, 1075-1080.

Zhuo, M., Holtzman, D.M., Li, Y., Osaka, H., DeMaro, J., Jacquin, M. and Bu, G. (2000) Role of tissue plasminogen activator receptor LRP in hippocampal long- term potentiation. *J. Neurosci.*, *20*, 542-549.

Zlokovic, B.V., Martel, C.L., Matsubara, E., McComb, J.G., Zheng, G., McCluskey, R.T., Frangione, B. and Ghiso, J. (1996) Glycoprotein 330/megalin: probable role in receptor-mediated transport of apolipoprotein J alone and in a complex with Alzheimer disease amyloid β at the blood-brain and blood-cerebrospinal fluid barriers. *Proc. Natl. Acad. Sci. U. S. A.*, *93*, 4229-4234.

In: Research Progress in Alzheimer's Disease and Dementia   ISBN 978-1-60021-960-3
Editor: Miao-Kun Sun, pp. 177-191   © 2008 Nova Science Publishers, Inc.

Chapter VII

CHOLESTEROL AND TAU HYPERPHOSPHORYLATION IN ALZHEIMER'S DISEASE

Thomas G. Ohm and Volker Meske

Institute of Integrative Neuroanatomy, Department of Clinical Cell- and Neurobiology,
D-10117 Berlin, Germany

ABSTRACT

Hyperphosphorylated protein tau is a major component of tangles, one of the two histological signs hallmarking Alzheimer's disease. Among the currently known risk factors, increased midlife plasma cholesterol and cholesterol-related genetic variants, such as the possession of the epsilon-4 allele, represent the most common ones. Interestingly, among all tauopathies, it is a juvenile hereditary dementia, Niemann Pick type C, which seems to share many features with Alzheimer's disease, including those that are ultrastructurally and immunologically indistinguishable. The current article reviews the literature on tau and cholesterol, statin and tau phosphorylation, and non-sterol isoprenoids and tau.

The longevity and wealth of the developed modern industrial societies contribute to the increase in the number of the patients with cardiovascular and neurodegenerative disorders in the elderly. Among the latter, Alzheimer's disease (AD) accounts for 60-70 percent, equalling to 4.5 million in the USA or 900.000 in Germany. In 2050, this number may have shown an increase by three-fold and over 80 million patients are estimated to suffer from this disorder worldwide. Given that only 100-140 families are known to bear a single gene mutation predictive for a future AD event (Bertram et al., 2005), the understanding of the complexity and contributing factors is eminent for deciphering the pathogenesis of AD. Among the identified risk factors, the cholesterol transporting molecule apolipoprotein E4 (apoE4) is considered to be of great importance (Crutcher, 2004). In 1993 and subsequently, Roses and co-workers reported that the apoE4-encoding allelic variant epsilon-4 of the genetic apoE-polymorphism significantly increased the risk for developing AD and was correlated with an earlier on-set of the disorder, both clinically (Corder et al., 1993, 1995) and histopathologically (Ohm et al., 1995,1999). Homozygous individuals may develop AD up to two decades earlier than non-possessors of the risky allelic variant. With a prevalence of 18-25% in a Caucasian population, the epsilon-4 allele represents by far the most important genetic risk factor and is – apart from an older age – the most common among all the identified risk factors. The ultimate way how this risk factor contributes to the (earlier) development of AD, however, is far from being understood.

Interestingly, the diagnostic histological hallmarks of AD, Aß-containing plaques and tangles formed by hyperphosphorylated and aggregated protein tau, are both promoted by the possession of the epsilon-4 allele (Ohm et al., 1995, 1999, Nagy et al., 1995, Ghebremedhin et al., 2001), suggesting that the risk factor may act upstream of both. Thus, and because apoE is the major cholesterol transporter in the brain (Weisgräber, 1994), required for the proper composition of the synaptic protein machinery (Mitter et al., 2003), function (Koudinov and Koudinova, 2003) and development (Göritz et al., 2002), it is tempting to speculate that the level of neuronal cholesterol may play a role in the pathogenesis of AD (Shobab et al., 2005).

This notion was also suggested by several other findings. Apart from the epsilon-4 allele, other cholesterol-related genetic risk factors have been reported. Some apolipoprotein E promotor variants may contribute independently from the apoE isoform to the development of AD (Bullido et al., 1998; Lambert et al., 2002), suggesting that the amount may also contribute to the risk. For instance, Cyp46 and ABC-A1 were found associated with AD (Katzov et al., 2004; Papassotiropoulos et al., 2005; Wollmer et al., 2003). However, the reported association was much less consistent than that with the apoE polymorphism because several other groups did not find the association (Shobab et al., 2005). Probably, it is a gene cluster or other genes that modulate the cholesterol related risk in AD (Papassotiropoulos et al., 2005). Together, the much weaker or even questionable association of other cholesterol-related genes with AD suggests that what modulates the risk may be more complex than just a simple relationship to cholesterol levels. This is in line with the ambiguity of the epidemiological studies dealing with cholesterol and/or lipid levels in blood and an association with AD. After the pioneering reports by Wolozin and co-workers and Jick and colleagues (Jick et al., 2000; Wolozin et al., 2000) a treatment for AD seemed to come into reach of clinical practice. Both groups reported a significantly reduced prevalence and incidence in a group of subjects taking statins. Statins are among the most commonly prescribed drugs for the treatment of hyper-cholesterolemia. Subsequently, many studies were performed and in conjunction with a strongly attenuated enthusiasm a much more nuanced picture has emerged. Obviously, serum cholesterol does not directly reflect brain cholesterol as both were regulated independently. Furthermore, age at onset of hyper-cholesterolemia and/or treatment, apoE genotype or other co-factors may play an important role (Kivipelto and Solomon, 2006; Rockwood, 20006; Wolozin et al., 2006). Moreover, pharmacological and epidemiological studies indicate an apparent paradox. On one hand, cholesterol in the brain is independently regulated from the rest of the body that is separated by the blood brain barrier, including the blood. On the other hand, both types blood brain barrier permeant (such as Simvastatin) and non-permeant statins (such as pravastatin) were reported to produce beneficial effects with respect to AD. Unfortunately, although the brain is the most cholesterol-rich organ, containing about 25% of whole body cholesterol, very little is known on the regulation and role of the mevalonate pathway in brain, i.e. the starting point of the lengthy (> 20 intermediates) and energy consuming cholesterol biosynthethic pathway (>100 ATP equivalents/1 cholesterol). Mevalonate is the precursor for sterol isoprenoids (e.g. cholesterol) and non-sterol isoprenoids (e.g. Geranylgeranylpyrophosphate (GGPP) (Figure 1). Thus, the mechanism by which statins may act favourably in the pathogenesis of AD does not seem to be direct on the cholesterol biosynthesis but may be the result of a multifaceted process.

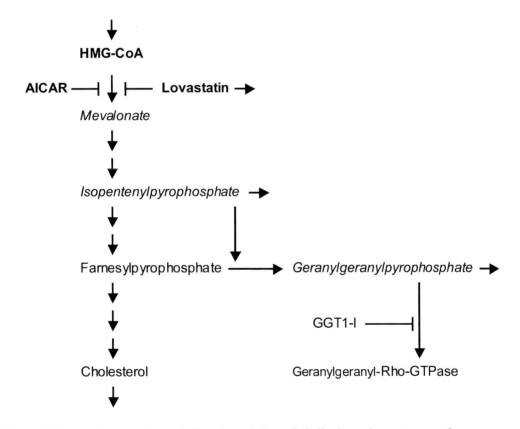

Figure 1. The mevalonate pathway (selected steps). Items in italics have shown to rescue from Lovastatin effects but not from AICAR. For details refer to text.

The prevailing and popular concept on how statins may act in AD is related to the cholesterol-dependency of Aß formation (Höglund et al., 2006) and the hypothesis that abnormal amounts of Aß amyloid is either causing AD (Hardy and Higgins, 1992) or boosting the development of AD (Schönheit et al., 2004a,b). No matter which way the latter - cause or booster - plays out, level of Aß should be regulated by cholesterol and statins should decrease the Aß level. Interestingly, Simvastatin, a blood brain barrier transgressing stain, produced (at a typically prescribed dose and after a treatment period of 36 weeks and also of

12 months) no significant effects on the CSF levels of Aß1-42, other Aß-subspecies (1-37,38,39,40) or apoE, in contrast to a significant reduction of cholesterol in the plasma (Höglund et al., 2006). This is partially in line with others' report (Simons et al., 2002), failing to show a reduction in Aß1-40 and 1-42 in the CSF but pointing post hoc to a significant reduction in Aß1-40 of the patients with mild cognitive decline (MMSE 21-26). Also in the study of Riekse and co-workers (Riekse et al., 2006), no effect on the CSF levels of Aß1-40, Aß1-42 or sAPP was found. Notably, however, a significant reduction in phosphorylated tau but not of total was found after treatment with a brain permeant statin. In contrast to the pioneering epidemiological studies cited above, the studies analyzing the CSF of the AD biomarkers Aß and tau (including their subspecies) were limited by a relative small number of examined cases. However, the possibility has been raised that statins may act beneficially not because of an impact on Aß-processing but 'directly' on tau.

A direct effect of different neuronal cholesterol levels on tau is unlikely, because cholesterol is a lipid and tau a highly soluble (mainly cytosolic) protein. Thus, as in the case of apoE, tau may not interact directly with cholesterol under physiological circumstances. Cholesterol may, however, signal to tau, i.e. cholesterol may act on tau independent from any effect on Aß processing. Our current knowledge on the effects of cholesterol changes or the role of the mevalonate pathway on tau is only starting to emerge. One reason for this lack of the knowledge is due to experimental difficulties. Two ways to study the impact of cholesterol on tau in neurons are easily proposed. On one hand, one may increase the level of free neuronal cholesterol, on the other, one may lower it. The problem, however, is that these conditions are not easy to achieve because of a well orchestrated homeostatic regulation under normal physiological conditions (Sato and Takano, 1995). Normally, neurons store excess free cholesterol in form of cholesterol esters which, under conditions of a higher demand, are then saponified and free cholesterol subsequently liberated. In addition, the endogenous neuronal biosynthesis is up- or down-regulated, for example, by acting on the rate-limiting enzyme of the mevalonate pathway, the HMG-CoA-reductase. Also, appropriate changes in the export and import of free cholesterol are performed, e.g., by modulating the numbers of the LDL-receptor that binds and internalizes cholesterol-rich apoE particles. These particles appear to be formed in astrocytes. In mature brain, neurons have down-regulated their endogenous cholesterol synthesis and use cholesterol delivered from astrocytes.

One way to overcome these regulatory mechanisms at least partially and for some time, is to load cholesterol directly into neuronal plasma membranes using the carrier ß-methylcyclodextrine (ßmcd). Primary neuronal cultures treated this way resulted in a mild dose- and time-dependent increase in tau phosphorylation. The loading is transient and thereby also not in a magnitude necessary to provoke a statistically relevant effect because of homeostatic reactions. Repeated applications in an attempt to cope with the homeostatic reactions has led to cell death and tau hypo-phosphorylation before tau degradation products are seen (Ohm and Meske, 2006). No effect is seen with ßmcd alone in various concentrations, ranging from 50-500 µg/ml, i.e., in a range usually used to load neurons with cholesterol. This suggests that the effect was due to cholesterol and not the carrier. Cholesterol added directly (without ßmcd) to the culture medium showed at a concentration of 1 µg/ml a growth promoting tendency, whereas 10 µg/ml is accompanied by an almost

60% loss of neurons. In all the cases of studies, tau was hypophosphorylated before apoptosis had been executed. This may indicate an protective effect of tau phosphorylation with respect to neuronal apoptosis. The changes of tau during apoptosis is reviewed elsewhere (Ohm and Meske, 2006). In other studies, mevalonate, the product of the HMG CoA-reductase reaction, and thus the starting precursor in cholesterol biosynthesis, was added to primary cortical neurons of rat, cultured in normal or cholesterol-free medium, and tau phosphorylation and survival were monitored. No changes in both parameters have been observed. This suggests that mevalonate was either not metabolized to cholesterol (for instance because of feedback regulatory loops), or cholesterol had been formed but failed to result in changes in viability or tau phosphorylation.

In other experiments, it was attempted to lower cholesterol experimentally. When cultured primary cortical neurons were given ßmcd at 5000 µg/ml, corresponding to concentrations used in order to remove free cholesterol from membranes, neurons died within a few hours, probably from a massively disturbed calcium homeostasis rather than the cholesterol loss itself (Ohm and Meske, 2006). Interestingly, however, blockade of HMG-CoA reductase by Lovastatin resulted in a biphasic response on tau. The study was done in the primary neurons that had been cultured in cholesterol-free medium in order to stimulate endogenous cholesterol formation but also in the presence of Lovastatin in order to block exactly this regulatory loop. After two days in vitro, the neurons showed a reduction in total cholesterol levels by ~15% and another 15% on day three but virtually no change in free cholesterol. This suggests that neuronal cholesterol is undergoing a relatively fast metabolic turnover which demands for an adequate supply. Because endogenous cholesterol biosynthesis was blocked by the statin, and other cells were lacking (e.g. astrocytes), it is conceivable to presume that the endogenous stores (i.e. esterified cholesterol) had been used to satisfy the need. This also suggests that the decrease rate (equalling on average 0.625% per hour) mainly reflects neuronal cholesterol turn-over. Interestingly, this turn-over is much faster than that of the whole brain (Lütjohann, 2006). In the rodent brain, the mean turn-over has been calculated from metabolisation of $^{18}O_2$ to be 0.02 - 0.05% per hour, corresponding to a half-life of 2-6 months. A conceivable explanation is that whole brain consists of a mixture of faster metabolising compartments (e.g. neurons and especially their synapses) and very slow ones (e.g. myelin). Whole brain determinations may thus underestimate the fast metabolising compartments because the vast majority of cholesterol is found in myelin.

Interestingly, a blockade of endogenous mevalonate biosynthesis resulted in a biphasic response of tau phosphorylation (Meske et al., 2003). In an earlier phase, i.e., within the first 48-72 hours, cultured primary cortical neurons became hyperphosphorylated at various epitopes. Among the tau epitopes studied was Serin199/202 which offered additional insights: This epitope highlights with the monoclonal antibody AT8 only when it is phosphorylated, whereas the monoclonal antibody Tau-1 binds only in the non-phosphorylated state. In the dose-response studies, a Lovastatin induced doubling of AT8 positive tau has been calculated, i.e. ~12% in controls but ~25% of tau was found phosphorylated at Serin199/202 after Lovastatin treatment. Another epitope is S262 and 356 labelled with the monoclonal antibody 12E8. This epitope is known to influence phosphorylation-dependent binding of tau to microtubules (Seubert et al., 1995). The phosphorylated tau has a reduced binding and thus probably also a lower ability to stabilize microtubules (Singh et al., 1996). Ocadaic acid-mediated inactivation of phosphatases is known to have the capability to dephosphorylate the examined epitopes. The fact that the time course of Lovastatin-induced tau hyperphosphorylation remained fairly the same under ocadaic acid treatment suggests that tau hyperphosphorylation was probably not due to an increased kinase activity (Meske et al., 2003). In a later phase, however, tau became dephosphorylated, i.e., when the Lovastatin treatment lasted about 72 hours. This hypophosphorylation apparently marked the beginning of the execution phase of neuronal apoptosis. Subsequently, tau became cleaved and neurons disintegrated (Meske et al., 2003). Because no tau fragmentation products have been seen before, phosphorylation seemed to protect from proteolytic cleavage of tau.

Because the Lovastatin inhibits the rate-limiting enzyme HMG CoA reductase, the effect is on top of the complete mevalonate-dependent biosynthetic pathways and not only of cholesterol (Holstein and Hohl, 2004). Thus, the observed effects might have been the result of any of the mevalonate-dependent metabolites, i.e. one of the sterol or non-sterol isoprenoids. A further dissection of the pathway revealed, indeed, that it is not the lack of sterol isoprenoid cholesterol that causes both hyperphosphorylation in the early phase, hypophosphorylation in the later phase, and subsequently neuronal apoptosis, but instead it is the lack of the non-sterol isoprenoid geranylgeranylpyrophosphate (GGPP; Garcia-Roman et al., 2001; Meske et al., 2003; Tanaka et al., 2000). This is indicated by several observations. Physiologically, mevalonate runs preferentially into the non-sterol branch to form, for instance, GGPP (Brown and Goldstein, 1980). Thus, low doses of Lovastatin will inhibit only the sterol branch with cholesterol at the end. Indeed, low concentrations of Lovastatin (< 1μM) did not associate with either changes in tau phosphorylation or neuronal apoptosis. In addition, the observed changes associated with the higher doses of Lovastatin could not be blocked by adding to the neurons cholesterol in various forms. The effects, however, were avoided if the Lovastatin treatment was accompanied by co-application of either mevalonate or GGPP within the first two days of treatment (i.e. the early phase). In turn, inhibition of the transfer of the geranylgeranyl residues onto target proteins by specifically blocking the geranylgeranyl transferase I (via the geranylgeranyltransferase I inhibitor, GGTI-287) mimicked the phenotype exactly. In contrast, neither the farnesyl transferase inhibition (in order to mimic the phenotype) nor the addition of farnesylpyrophosphate (FPP) (in an attempt to rescue the cells) showed any effects within the examined time frame of three days. Together, this clearly suggests that both the early and late phase effects critically depend on GGPP. It further supports the notion that Lovastatin is neurotoxic if its cortical concentrations are high enough to block the HMG CoA reductase, to the extent high enough for inhibition of not only cholesterol biosynthesis but also the formation of GGPP. Non-toxic concentration of a statin may also be toxic if the cell was already impaired, i.e. HMG CoA reductase was pre-inhibited (Feussner, 1994). Interestingly in this context, a slight but significant reduction in phosphorylated tau but not of total was found in demented patients after treatment with a brain-permeant statin (Riekse et al., 2006). AD patients might be more susceptible against adverse effects of statins than controls (Algottson and Winblad, 2004; Sparks et al., 2002), giving the effects of statins in AD a Janus-like face.

In accordance with a deficit in geranylgeranylation, the movement of the small GTPase RhoA from the inactive cytosolic form to the active membrane-bound geranylgeranylated form, was impaired in Lovastatin-treated neurons (Meske et al., 2003). This is of interest because, on one hand, RhoA participates in the regulation of the actin-associated cytoskeletal organisation and the control of cell viability. On the other hand, RhoA is also coupled to the microtubule systems by p190RhoGEF (van Horck et al., 2001). From cell culture experiments, it has been suggested that after Lovastatin treatment the microfilament system might be impaired before the microtubule system (Meske et al., 2003). Changes in the microfilament system occurred already after 12 hours whereas disturbances of the microtubule system were seen after 24 hours. In the control cells, tau was stained with the Tau-1 antibody mainly in the distal cell processes, whereas AT-8 labelled moderately the cell somata and only proximal parts of the cell processes. Under Lovastatin, Tau-1 staining became predominant over degenerating parts and the forming cellular debris. AT-8 staining was intensity and markedly increased in the soma and the axon before a drastic loss of immunoreaction occurred in the execution phase of apoptosis. Similar but accelerated changes were seen under GTI-287 treatment. In line with an altered RhoA signalling, a significant reduction in membrane-bound RhoA was found after Lovastatin treatment (Meske et al., 2003). GGPP, however, may play a role not only in the RhoA but also in cdc42 or Rac signalling. Further analysis is required to elucidate the mechanisms by which a statin causes the biphasic response in tau phosphorylation. It is also to note that GGPP and FPP may play a role in the formation of Aß-peptide and/or plaques and not the cholesterol (Pedrini et al., 2005). In AD pathogenesis, however, several other GGPP-dependent processes may play a role (Table 1).

Table 1. Effects of GGPP-deficiency or reduced geranylgeranylation

Reduced synaptic function/formation/lifetime
Increased microglial activation
Increased interleukin1-ß and nitric oxide production/levels
Biphasic changes in tau phosphorylation
Decrease of Aß42 secretion
Decrease of apoE secretion
Reduced cell division

(Details see: (Koudinov and Koudinova, 2001; Cordle and Landreth, 2005; Cordle et al., 2005; Meske et al., 2003; Zhou et al., 2003; Naidu et al., 2002; Fuse et al., 2004; Terano et al., 1998)).

Coupling of low GGPP to cell death (and in case of neurons the subsequent liberating of tau into the cerebrospinal fluid CSF where it may serve as a diagnostic marker) seems to be closured. Despite of several genetic disorders associated with impaired sterol isoprenoid synthesis, no cases of GGPP synthase deficiency have been reported. HMG-CoA reductase knockout mice are embryonic lethal and mutations in the mevalonate kinase gene leads to premature death and are accompanied with a higher sensitivity to statins (Houten et al., 2003).

A higher susceptibility of neurons to statins may be the result of several metabolic conditions. For instance, the level of mevalonate depends on the activity and amount of HMG-CoA reductase. With regards to AD, no data, neither on activity measures nor on HMG-CoA reductase levels, are available, probably because of a fast post mortal degradation of the protein (Meske V, Ohm TG; unpublished observations) due to a short half-life (2-3 hours in non-neuronal cells). It is, however, known that mevalonate biosynthesis is strongly regulated by the transcriptional level of the HMG-CoA reductase gene and the degree of phosphorylation (Panda and Devi, 2004). One published study so far, using brain homogenate, did not detect differences in the mRNA levels of HMG-CoA reductase between controls and AD tissues (Yasojima et al., 2001). The phosphorylation state of HMG-CoA reductase in AD is not known for the time being. Experimental data analyzing the relationship of phosphorylation-dependent HMG-CoA reductase activity and tau phosphorylation, however, start to evolve. Under physiological conditions, activity of HMG-CoA reductase is regulated by the AMP-dependent kinase (AMPK), i.e., the level of AMP. AMPK is central in the concerted regulation of energy supply and energy consumption (Hardie, 2004). Its activity is high when energy supply, for instance via glucose, is low, and subsequently levels of AMP increases while those of ATP decreases. The increase in AMP can be mimicked by the application of 5-aminoimidazole-4-carboxamide-1-ß-ribofuranoside (AICAR), eventually leading to the activation of AMPK and subsequently the inactivation of HMG-CoA reductase. Thereby, the achieved down-regulation of the cholesterol biosynthesis is high (>100 ATP equivalents/1 cholesterol). The effect of AICAR has been studied using primary cortical neurons cultured in cholesterol free medium in order to stimulate the endogenous cholesterol biosynthesis and cutting the neurons off from exogenous sources. AICAR applied at sub-millimolar concentrations has resulted in a decrease of free cholesterol almost of the magnitude observed with Lovastatin given in a micromolar range. Interestingly, the effect on tau phosphorylation and neuronal viability differed. AICAR induced a more than 50% reduction in the ratio of AT-8/Tau-1 signal after one day compared to the control cultures. After two days, only a faint AT-8 signal was detectable and virtually no AT-8 signal was seen after three days (Ohm and Meske, 2006). A minute analysis of AICAR-induced effects on tau phosphorylation revealed that they are independent from the mevalonate pathway and GGPP (Meske V, Albert F and Ohm TG, manuscript submitted).

A higher sensitivity to the toxic effects of statins was also found in the juvenile dementia Niemann Pick type C (NPC). Fibroblasts, as well as neurons, are more sensitive to inhibition of HMG-CoA reducase inhibition (Ohno et al., 1993). They die at significantly lower concentrations of statins than normal control cells (~ -50%; Meske V, Albert F and Ohm TG, unpublished observations). As it is of the normal rat (Meske et al, 2003) or mice neurons, cultured NPC neurons from a well-acknowledged NPC1 mouse model can be rescued from the statin challenge by either mevalonate or GGPP, but not by cholesterol or farnesylpyrophosphate (Meske V, Albert F and Ohm TG, unpublished observations). The higher sensitivity against a statin challenge may be the result of a loss of HMG-CoA reductase mRNA. Lovastatin was shown to kill cholesterol-loaden neurons preferentially (Ohm and Meske, 2006). NPC neurons have similar amounts of actin mRNA but about 50% less HMG-CoA reductase mRNA than the control neurons (Ohm et al., 2003). The more intraneuronal cholesterol, the less HMG-CoA reductase message has been detectable in cortical slices of NPC mice (Meske et al., 2002).

Quite interestingly, NPC is histopathologically characterised by the presence of numerous tangles (Suzuki et al., 1995; Love et al., 1995). These tangles are ultrastructurally (Auer et al., 1995; Love et al., 1995) and immunologically indistinguishable from those seen in AD several decades later (Table 2). It is also to note the absence of Aß-plaques, indicating that AD-like tangles are not downstream of Aß plaques as hypothesized in the amyloid cascade concept (Hardy and Higgins, 1992). In contrast to AD, NPC is mainly caused by mutations. In ~95% of cases a mutation in the NPC1 gene (Carstea et al., 1997) is responsible, in another ~5% it is a mutation in NPC2 also known as HE1 (Naureckiene et al., 2000). As it is with the risk factor apoE4, onset of tangle formation occurs many years earlier than in sporadic AD without these gene variants (up to 20 years earlier in epsilon-4 homozygous individuals [Ohm et al., 1995; 1997], and 30-40 earlier in NPC mutations [Love et al., 1995; Suzuki et al., 1995]).

Table 2. Immunoreactions of tangles in Alzheimer's disease (AD) and Niemann Pick type C disease (NPC)

Stain	Epitope	NPC	AD
T14	141-178	+	+
AT270	Thr181	+	+
PHF-1	Ser396/404	+	+
AT-8	Ser199,202/205	+	+
AT-180	Thr231, Ser235	+	+
AT-100	Ser214/Thr217/212	+	+
TG3	Thr231	+	+
12E8	Ser262/356	+	+
MC-1	5-15+312-322	+	+
ALZ-50	5-15+312-322	+	+
BR133	N-terminus	+	+
BR134	C-terminus	+	+

Data compiled from (Spillantini et al., 1999) and own stainings.

The functions of the respective proteins, NPC1 and NPC2, are still not elucidated. However, none of them seems to relate to tau, a tau kinase or tau phosphatase. The NPC1 and NPC2 defects seem not to be additive or supra-additive as indicated by genetically engineered mice models (Sleat et al., 2004). Thus, the cellular phenotype of NPC1 and NPC2 is quite similar with an intracellular misrouting of endocytosed lipids including cholesterol. The misrouted cargo such as cholesterol is deposited in a late-endosomal/lysosomal-like compartment. An endosomal/lysosomal abnormality was found as one of the earliest cell pathobiological signs in AD (Cataldo et al., 1996) and strengthens the notion of common pathophysiological pathways in AD and NPC (Nixon, 2005). Using the fluorescent compound filipin, the accumulated cholesterol can be visualized on a subcellular level. Co-localisation of filipin-stained cholesterol and AT-8-marked tangles showed that tangle-bearing neurons had significantly higher levels (3.5 fold) of intrasomal cholesterol than adjacent tangle-free neurons of the same nerve cell type (Distl et al., 2003). Interestingly, similar examinations of AD brain showed the same principal difference, although the ratio is much lower (Distl et al., 2001; Ohm et al., 2003). It is tempting to speculate that both NPC and AD share some metabolic alterations eventually leading to tangles. Unfortunately, the failure of NPC1 function alone mimics, in a well-acknowledged NPC1 mouse model, the human NPC phenotype – but not the tangle formation. Several AD-associated tau epitopes, however, were found hyperphosphorylated (Bu et al., 2002; Treiber-Held et al., 2003). A tempting explanation for this imperfect phenotype is that mouse tau may not form tangles. Another explanation was that the human brain harbours a co-factor required for tangle formation which is lacking in the mouse brain.

ACKNOWLEDGMENTS:

Own work cited in the review was supported by various grants of the Deutsche Forschungsgemeinschaft (DFG), the Hirnliga, the Alzheimer Forschungsinitiative International (AFI), and the Forschungskommission der Charité.

REFERENCES

Algotsson, A. and.Winblad B. Patients with Alzheimer's disease may be particularly susceptible to adverse effects of statins. *Dement. Geriatr. Cogn Disord. 17*:109-116, 2004.

Auer, I.A., Schmidt, M.L., Lee, V.M., Curry, B., Suzuki, K., Shin, R.W., Pentchev, P.G., Carstea, E.D. and Trojanowski, J.Q. Paired helical filament tau (PHFtau) in Niemann-Pick type C disease is similar to PHFtau in Alzheimer's disease. *Acta Neuropathol. Berl. 90*:547-551, 1995.

Bertram, L. and Tanzi, R.E. The genetic epidemiology of neurodegenerative disease. *J Clin. Invest 115*:1449-1457, 2005.

Brown, M.S. and Goldstein, J.L. Multivalent feedback regulation of HMG-CoA reductase, a control mechanism coordinating isoprenoid synthesis and cell growth. *J. Lipid Res. 21*:935-940, 1980.

Bu, B., Li, J., Davies, P. and and Vincent, I. Deregulation of cdk5, hyperphosphorylation, and cytoskeletal pathology in the Niemann-Pick type C murine model. *J Neurosci 22*:6515-6525, 2002.

Bullido, M.J., Artiga, M.J., Recuero, M., Sastre, I., Garcia, M.A., Aldudo, J., Lendon, C., Han, S.W., Morris, J.C., Frank, A., Vazquez, J., Goate, A. and Valdivieso, F. A Polymorphism in the regulatory region of APOE associated with risk for Alzheimer's dementia. *Nat. Genet. 18*:69-71, 1998.

Carstea, E.D., Morris, J.A., Coleman, K.G., Loftus, S.K., Zhang, D., Cummings, C., Gu, J., Rosenfeld, M.A., Pavan, W.J., Krizman, D.B., Nagle, J., Polymeropoulos, M.H., Sturley, S.L., Ioannou, Y.A., Higgins, M.E., Comly, M., Cooney, A., Brown, A., Kaneski, C.R., Blanchette Mackie, E.J., Dwyer, N.K., Neufeld, E.B., Chang, T.Y., Liscum, L., Tagle, D.A., and et al. Niemann-Pick C1 disease gene: homology to mediators of cholesterol homeostasis [see comments]. *Science 277*:228-231, 1997.

Cataldo, A.M., Hamilton, D.J., Barnett, J.L., Paskevich, P.A. and R.A.Nixon. Properties of the endosomal-lysosomal system in the human central nervous system: Disturbances mark most neurons in populations at risk to degenerate in Alzheimer's disease. *J. Neurosci.-199)*, 1996.

Corder, E.H., Saunders, A.M., Strittmatter, W.J., Schmechel, D.E., Gaskell, P., Small, G.W., Roses, A.D., Haines, J.L. and Pericak Vance, M.A. Gene dose of apolipoprotein E type 4 allele and the risk of Alzheimer's disease in late onset families [see comments]. *Science* *261*:921-923, 1993.

Corder, E.H., Saunders, A.M., Strittmatter, W.J., Schmechel, D.E., Gaskell, P.C., Rimmler, J.B., Locke, P.A., Conneally, P.M., Schmader, K.E., Tanzi, R.E., Gusella, J.F., Small, G.W., Roses, A.D., Pericak Vance, M.A. and Haines, J.L. Apolipoprotein E, survival in Alzheimer's disease patients, and the competing risks of death and Alzheimer's disease. *Neurology 45*:1323-1328, 1995.

Cordle, A., Koenigsknecht-Talboo, J., Wilkinson, B., Limpert, A. and Landreth, G. Mechanisms of statin-mediated inhibition of small G-protein function. *J Biol Chem* *280*:34202-34209, 2005.

Cordle, A. and Landreth, G. 3-hydroxy-3-methylglutaryl-coenzyme A reductase inhibitors attenuate beta-amyloid-induced microglial inflammatory responses. *J Neurosci 25*:299-307, 2005.

Crutcher, K.A. Apolipoprotein E is a prime suspect, not just an accomplice, in Alzheimer's disease. *J. Mol. Neurosci. 23*:181-188, 2004

Distl, R., Meske, V. and Ohm, T.G. Tangle-bearing neurons contain more free cholesterol than adjacent tangle-free neurons. *Acta Neuropathol 101*:547-554, 2001.

Distl, R., Treiber-Held, S., Albert, F., Meske, V., Harzer, K. and Ohm, T.G. Cholesterol storage and tau-pathology in Niemann-Pick type C disease brain. *J Pathol 200*:104-111, 2003.

Feussner, G. HMG CoA reductase inhibitors. *Curr Opin Lipidol 5*:59-68, 1994.

Fuse, M., Tanaka, T., Shibata, T., Yoshida, T., Noguchi, Y., Misawa, N., Yasuda, T., Saito, Y., Kohn, L.D., and Tatsuno, I. Regulation of geranylgeranyl pyrophosphate synthase in the proliferation of rat FRTL-5 cells: involvement of both cAMP-PKA and PI3-AKT pathways. *Biochem Biophys. Res Commun. 315*:1147-1153, 2004.

Garcia-Roman, N., Alvarez, A.M., Toro, M.J., Montes, A. and Lorenzo, M.J.. Lovastatin induces apoptosis of spontaneously immortalized rat brain neuroblasts: involvement of nonsterol isoprenoid biosynthesis inhibition. *Mol. Cell Neurosci 17*:329-341, 2001

Ghebremedhin, E., Schultz, C., Thal, D.R., Rüb, U., Ohm, T.G., Braak, E. and Braak, H. Gender and age modify the association between ApoE and AD-related neuropathology. *Neurology 56*:1696-1701, 2001.

Göritz, C., Mauch, D.H. and. Nägler, K.P.F W. Role of glia-derived cholesterol in synaptogenesis: new revelations in the synapse-glia affair. *J Physiol Paris 96*:257-263, 2002.

Hardie, D.G. AMP-activated protein kinase: a master switch in glucose and lipid metabolism. *Rev Endocr. Metab Disord. 5*:119-125, 2004.

Hardy, J.A. and Higgins, G.A. Alzheimer's disease: the amyloid cascade hypothesis. *Science* *256*:184-185, 1992.

Holstein, S.A. and Hohl, R.J. Isoprenoids: remarkable diversity of form and function. *Lipids* *39*:293-309, 2004.

Houten, S.M., Schneiders, M.S., Wanders, R.J. and Waterham, H.R. Regulation of isoprenoid/cholesterol biosynthesis in cells from mevalonate kinase-deficient patients. *J Biol. Chem. 278*:5736-5743, 2003.

Höglund, K., Wallin, A. and Blennow, K. Effect of statins on beta-amyloid metabolism in humans: potential importance for the development of senile plaques in Alzheimer's disease. *Acta Neurol Scand Suppl 185*:87-92, 2006.

Jick, H., Zornberg, G.L., Jick, S.S., Seshadri, S. and Drachman, D.A. Statins and the risk of dementia. *Lancet 356*:1627-1631, 2000.

Katzov, H., Chalmers, K. Palmgren, J., Andreasen, N., Johansson, B., Cairns, N.J., Gatz, M., Wilcock, G.K., Love, S., Pedersen, N.L., Brookes, A.J., Blennow, K., Kehoe, P.G. and Prince, J.A. Genetic variants of ABCA1 modify Alzheimer disease risk and quantitative traits related to beta-amyloid metabolism. *Hum. Mutat. 23*:358-367, 2004.

Kivipelto, M. and Solomon, A. Cholesterol as a risk factor for Alzheimer's disease - epidemiological evidence. *Acta Neurol Scand Suppl 185*:50-57, 2006.

Koudinov, A.R. and Koudinova, N.V. Essential role for cholesterol in synaptic plasticity and neuronal degeneration. *FASEB J 15*:1858-1860, 2001.

Koudinov, A.R. and Koudinova, N.V. Amyloid beta protein restores hippocampal long term potentiation: A central role for cholesterol? *Neurobiol Lipids 1*:45-56, 2003.

Lambert, J.C., Araria-Goumidi, L., Myllykangas, L., Ellis, C., Wang, J.C., Bullido, M.J., Harris, J.M., Artiga, M.J., Hernandez, D., Kwon, J.M., Frigard, B., Petersen, R.C., Cumming, A.M. Pasquier, F., Sastre, I., Tienari, P.J., Frank, A., Sulkava, R., Morris, J.C., Clair, D.St., Mann, D.M., Wavrant-DeVrieze, F., Ezquerra-Trabalon, M., Amouyel, P., Hardy, J., Haltia, M., Valdivieso, F., Goate, A.M., Perez-Tur, J., Lendon, C.L. and Chartier-Harlin, M.C. Contribution of APOE promoter polymorphisms to Alzheimer's disease risk. *Neurology 59*:59-66, 2002.

Love, S., Bridges, L.R. and Case, C.P. Neurofibrillary tangles in Niemann-Pick disease type C. *Brain 118*:119-129, 1995.

Lütjohann, D. Cholesterol metabolism in the brain: importance of 24S-hydroxylation. *Acta Neurol Scand Suppl 185*:33-42, 2006.

Meske,V., Treiber-Held, S., Tamannai, M. and Ohm T.G. Increased intraneuronal free cholesterol is associated with reduced HMG-COA-reducase and increased AT-8 epitope of tau-protein. *Neurobiol Aging 23[1S]*, S502. 2002.

Meske, V., Albert, F., Richter, D., Schwarze, J. and Ohm T.G. Blockade of HMG-CoA reductase activity causes changes in microtubule-stabilizing protein tau via suppression of geranylgeranylpyrophosphate formation. Implications for Alzheimer's disease. *Eur J Neurosci 17*:93-102, 2003.

Mitter, D., Reisinger, C., Hinz, H., Hollmann, S., Yelamanchili, S.V., Treiber-Held, S., Ohm, T.G., Herrmann, A. and Ahnert-Hilger, G. The synaptophysin/synaptobrevin interaction critically depends on the cholesterol content. *J Neurochem 84*:35-42, 2003.

Nagy, Z., Esiri, M.M., Jobst, K.A., Johnston, C., Litchfield, S., Sim, E., and Smith, A.D. Influence of the apolipoprotein E genotype on amyloid deposition and neurofibrillary tangle formation in Alzheimer's disease. *Neuroscience 69*:757-761, 1995.

Naidu, A., Xu, Q., Catalano, R. and Cordell, B. Secretion of apolipoprotein E by brain glia requires protein prenylation and is suppressed by statins. *Brain Res 958*:100-111, 2002.

Naureckiene, S., Sleat, D.E., Lackland, H., Fensom, A., Vanier, M.T., Wattiaux, R., Jadot, M. and Lobel P. Identification of HE1 as the second gene of Niemann-Pick C disease. *Science* 290:2298-2301, 2000.

Nixon, R.A. Endosome function and dysfunction in Alzheimer's disease and other neurodegenerative diseases. *Neurobiol. Aging* 26:373-382, 2005.

Ohm, T.G., Kirca, M., Bohl, J., Scharnagl, H., Gross, W. and März W. Apolipoprotein E polymorphism influences not only cerebral senile plaque load but also Alzheimer-type neurofibrillary tangle formation. *Neuroscience* 66:583-587, 1995.

Ohm, T.G., Scharnagl, H., März, W. and Bohl J. Apolipoprotein E isoforms and the development of low and high Braak stages of Alzheimer's disease-related lesions. *Acta Neuropathol. Berl.* 98:273-280, 1999.

Ohm, T.G., Treiber-Held, S., Distl, R., Glöckner, F., Schönheit, B., Tamannai, M. and Meske, V. Cholesterol and tau-protein - Findings in Alzheimer's and Niemann Pick C's disease. *Pharmacopsych* 36:S120-S126, 2003.

Ohm, T.G. and Meske V. Cholesterol, statins and tau. *Acta Neurol Scand Suppl* 114:93-101, 2006.

Ohno, K., Nanba, E., Nakano, T., Inui, K., Okada, S. and Takeshita, K. Altered sensitivities to potential inhibitors of cholesterol biosynthesis in Niemann-Pick type C fibroblasts. *Cell Struct. Funct.* 18:231-240, 1993.

Panda, T. and Devi, V.A. Regulation and degradation of HMGCo-A reductase. *Appl. Microbiol. Biotechnol.* 66:143-152, 2004.

Papassotiropoulos, A., Wollmer, M.A., Tsolaki, M., Brunner, F., Molyva, D., Lütjohann, D., Nitsch, R.M. and Hock, C. A cluster of cholesterol-related genes confers susceptibility for Alzheimer's disease. *J Clin. Psychiatry* 66:940-947, 2005.

Pedrini, S., Carter, T.L., Prendergast, G., Petanceska, S., Ehrlich, M.E. and Gandy, S. Modulation of statin-activated shedding of Alzheimner APP ectodomain by ROCK. *PLoS Med* 2:0069-0078, 2005.

Riekse, R.G., Li, G., Petrie, E.C., Leverenz, J.B., Vavrek, D., Vuletic, S., Albers, J.J., Montine, T.J., Lee, V.M., Lee, M., Seubert, P., Galasko, D., Schellenberg, G.D., Hazzard, W.R. and Peskind, E.R. Effect of statins on Alzheimer's disease biomarkers in cerebrospinal fluid. *J Alzheimers Dis* 10:399-406, 2006.

Rockwood, K. Epidemiological and clinical trials evidence about a preventive role for statins in Alzheimer's disease. *Acta Neurol Scand Suppl* 185:71-77,2006.

Sato, R. and Takano, T. Regulation of intracellular cholesterol metabolism. *Cell Struct. Funct.* 20:421-427, 1995.

Schönheit, B., Döscher, R. and Ohm, T.G. Scientific progress and a hardy paradigm - the 'amyloid cascade hypothesis' revisited. *Neurobiol Aging* 25:743-746, 2004.

Schönheit, B., Zarski, R. and Ohm, T.G. Spatial and temporal relationships between plaques and tangles in Alzheimer-pathology. *Neurobiol Aging* 25:697-711, 2004.

Seubert, P., Mawal Dewan, M., Barbour, R., Jakes, R., Goedert, M., Johnson, G., Litersky, J.M., Schenk, D., Lieberburg, I., Trojanowski, J.Q. and et al. Detection of phosphorylated Ser262 in fetal tau, adult tau, and paired helical filament tau. *J. Biol. Chem.* 270:18917-18922, 1995.

Shobab, L.A., Hsiung, G.Y. and Feldman, H.H. Cholesterol in Alzheimer's disease. *Lancet Neurol 4*:841-852, 2005.

Simons, M., Schwarzler, F., Lütjohann, D., von Bergmann, K., Beyreuther, K., Dichgans, J., Wormstall, H., Hartmann, T., Schulz, J.B. Treatment with simvastatin in normocholesterolemic patients with Alzheimer's disease: a 26-week randomized, placebo-controlled, double-blind trial. *Ann. Neurol. 52*:346-350, 2002.

Singh, T.J., Wang, J.Z., Novak, M., Kontzekova, E., Grundke Iqbal, I. and Iqbal K. Calcium/calmodulin-dependent protein kinase II phosphorylates tau at Ser-262 but only partially inhibits its binding to microtubules. *FEBS Lett. 387*:145-148, 1996.

Sleat, D.E., Wiseman, J.A., El Banna, M., Price, S.M., Verot, L., Shen, M.M., Tint, G.S., Vanier, M.T., Walkley, S.U. and Lobel, PGenetic evidence for nonredundant functional cooperativity between NPC1 and NPC2 in lipid transport. *Proc. Natl. Acad. Sci U. S. A 101*:5886-5891, 2004.

Sparks, D.L., Connor, D.J., Browne, P.J., Lopez, J.E. and Sabbagh, M.N. HMG-COA reductase inhibitors (statins) in the treatment of Alzheimer's disease and why it would be ill-adivse to use one that crosses the blood-brain barrier. *J Nutr Health Aging 6*:324-331, 2002.

Spillantini, M.G., Tolnay, M., Love, S. and Goedert, M. Microtubule-associated protein tau, heparan sulphate and alpha-synuclein in several neurodegenerative diseases with dementia. *Acta Neuropathol (Berl) 97*:585-594, 1999.

Suzuki, K., Parker, C.C., Pentchev, P.G., Katz, D., Ghetti, B., D'Agostino, A. and Carstea, E.D. Neurofibrillary tangles in Niemann-Pick disease type C. *Acta Neuropathol. Berl. 89*:227-238, 1995.

Tanaka, T., Tatsuno, I., Uchida, D., Moroo, I., Morio, H., Nakamura, S., Noguchi, Y., Yasuda, T., Kitagawa, M., Saito, Y. and Hirai, A. Geranylgeranyl-pyrophosphate, an isoprenoid of mevalonate cascade, is a critical compound for rat primary cultured cortical neurons to protect the cell death induced by 3-hydroxy-3-methylglutaryl-CoA reductase inhibition. *J Neurosci 20*:2852-2859, 2000.

Terano, T., Shiina, T., Noguchi, Y., Tanaka, T., Tatsuno, I., Saito, Y., Yasuda, T., Kitagawa, M. and Hirai, A. Geranylgeranylpyrophosphate plays a key role for the G1 to S transition in vascular smooth muscle cells. *J. Atheroscler. Thromb. 5*:1-6, 1998.

Treiber-Held, S., Distl, R., Albert, F. and Ohm, T.G. Spatial and temporal distribution of free cholesterol on single cell level in brain of a Niemann Pick type C mouse model. *J Pathol 200*:95-103, 2003.

van Horck, F.P., Ahmadian, M.R., Haeusler, L.C., Moolenaar, W.H. and Kranenburg, O. Characterization of p190RhoGEF, a RhoA-specific guanine nucleotide exchange factor that interacts with microtubules. *J Biol. Chem. 276*:4948-4956, 2001.

Weisgraber, K.H., Roses, A.D. and Strittmatter, W.J. The role of apolipoprotein E in the nervous system. *Curr. Opin. Lipidol. 5*:110-116, 1994.

Wollmer, M.A., Streffer, J.R., Lutjohann, D., Tsolaki, M., Iakovidou, V., Hegi, T., Pasch, T., Jung, H.H., Bergmann, K., Nitsch, R.M., Hock, C. and Papassotiropoulos, A. ABCA1 modulates CSF cholesterol levels and influences the age at onset of Alzheimer's disease. *Neurobiol. Aging 24*:421-426, 2003.

Wolozin, B., Kellman, W., Ruosseau, P., Celesia, G.G. and Siegel, G. Decreased prevalence of Alzheimer disease associated with 3-hydroxy-3-methyglutaryl coenzyme A reductase inhibitors. *Arch. Neurol 57*:1439-1443, 2000.

Wolozin, B., Manger, J., Bryant, R., Cordy, J., Green, R.C. and Mckee, A. Re-assessing the relationship between cholesterol, statins and Alzheimer's disease. *Acta Neurol Scand Suppl 185*:63-70, 2006.

Yasojima, K., McGeer, E.G. and Mcgeer, P.L. 3-hydroxy-3-methylglutaryl-coenzyme A reductase mRNA in Alzheimer and control brain. *NeuroReport 12*:2935-2938, 2001.

Zhou, Y., Su, Y., Li, B., Liu.F., Ryder, J.W., Wu, X., Gonzales-DeWhitt, P.A., Gelfanova, V., Hale, J.E., May, P.C., Paul, S.M. and Ni, B. Nonsteroidal anti-inflammatory drugs can lower amyloidogenic abeta42 by inhibiting rho. *Science 302*:1215-1217, 2003.

In: Research Progress in Alzheimer's Disease and Dementia   ISBN 978-1-60021-960-3
Editor: Miao-Kun Sun, pp. 193-250   © 2008 Nova Science Publishers, Inc.

Chapter VIII

DEVELOPMENT IN DIAGNOSTIC AND THERAPEUTIC STRATEGIES FOR ALZHEIMER'S DISEASE

Akila Shanmugam[1], Bernhard Monien[1,†], and Gal Bitan[1,2,3,∗]

[1]Department of Neurology, David Geffen School of Medicine, [2]Brain Research Institute, [3]Molecular Biology Institute, University of California at Los Angeles, Los Angeles, CA 90095-7334, USA.

ABSTRACT

Alzheimer's disease (AD) is a progressive neurodegenerative disease for which, at present, there is no cure. Accurate diagnosis of AD is difficult because the symptoms overlap with those manifested in other forms of dementia. Acetylcholinesterase inhibitors and memantine, drugs that currently are approved by the Food and Drug Administration (FDA) for AD, treat symptoms but not the underlying cause of the disease. The neuropathology of AD begins with compromised synaptic transmission and impaired plasticity, predominantly in the entorhinal cortex and the hippocampus. These neuropathological processes may begin years or even decades before manifestation of the first symptoms. Thus, by the time the first signs of disease become apparent, the underlying neuropathology may be already fairly advanced. Therefore, development of disease-modifying therapeutic strategies and accurate diagnostic measures for AD must focus on the events that initiate the disease at the earliest stages. Substantial evidence indicates that the primary cause of AD is an age-related imbalance between production and clearance of amyloid β-protein (Aβ). Prevention of Aβ production, enhancement of Aβ clearance, and inhibition of Aβ assembly into neurotoxic aggregates, thus are

† Current address: Deutsches Institut für Ernährungsforschung Potsdam-Rehbrücke, Abt. Ernährungstoxikologie, 14558 Nuthetal, Germany.

∗ Correspondence concerning this article should be addressed to: Gal Bitan, University of California at Los Angeles, Neuroscience Research Building I, Room 451, 635 Charles E. Young Drive South, Los Angeles, CA 90095-7334, USA. Tel.: +1 310 206 2082; Fax: +1 310 206 1700; gbitan@mednet.ucla.edu.

principal focuses of current therapeutic approaches. Present diagnosis of AD is based on clinical, neurophysiologic and neuroimaging assessments. These approaches are relatively sensitive and specific at the middle or late stages of AD but early diagnosis is challenging. With the advent of new drugs now in clinical trials, there is an urgent need for early diagnosis, not only for prescribing the correct treatment and validating the efficiency of the drugs, but also for understanding the underlying disease process.

ABBREVIATIONS

AD,	Alzheimer's disease;
ADAM,	A disintegrin and metalloprotein;
ADDLs,	Aβ-derived diffusible ligands;
APLP,	APP-like protein;
APP,	amyloid β-protein precursor;
Aβ,	amyloid β-protein;
BACE-1,	β-site APP-cleaving enzyme 1;
BBB,	blood–brain barrier;
CDR,	clinical dementia rating;
CMRgl,	cerebral metabolic rate for glucose;
CNS,	central nervous system;
COX,	cyclooxygenase;
CSF,	cerebrospinal fluid;
chGly,	cyclohexylglycine;
dsRNA,	double-stranded RNA;
ECE,	endothelin-converting enzyme;
EGCG,	epigallocatechin-3-gallate;
ELISA,	enzyme-linked immunosorbent assay;
ErbB4,	erythroblastic leukemia viral oncogene homolog-4;
ERK,	extracellular signal-regulated kinase;
FAD,	familial AD;
FDA,	Food and Drug Administration;
FDG,	^{18}F-labeled fluoro-2-deoxy-D-glucose ;
^{18}F-FDDNP,	2-(1-{6-[2-[^{18}F]fluoroethylmethylamino]-2-naphthyl}ethylidene) malononitrile;
GAG,	glycosaminoglycan;
IAPP,	islet amyloid polypeptide;
IDE,	insulin degrading enzyme;
ISF,	interstitial fluid;
LRP,	low-density lipoprotein receptor-related protein;
MAO,	monoamine oxidase;
MCI,	mild cognitive impairment;
MCIa,	amnestic MCI;
mLeu,	*N*-methyl leucine;
MMSE,	mini-mental state examination;

MoCA,	Montreal cognitive assessment test;
MRI,	magnetic resonance imaging;
mRNA,	messenger RNA;
MTA,	medial temporal lobe atrophy;
NEP,	neprilysin;
NFT,	neurofibrillary tangles;
NGF,	nerve growth factor;
NMDA,	N-methyl-D-aspartate;
NSAID,	non-steroidal anti-inflammatory drug;
PET,	positron emission tomography;
PIB,	Pittsburgh compound B;
PKC,	protein kinase C;
RAGE,	receptor for advanced glycation-end products;
RNAi,	RNA interference;
ROS,	reactive oxygen species;
siRNA,	small interfering RNA;
SPECT,	single-photon emission computed tomography;
SREBP,	sterol regulatory element-binding protein;
TACE,	tumor necrosis factor α converting enzyme;
^{99}Tc-ECD,	^{99}Tc-ethylcysteinate dimer;
^{99}Tc-HMPAO,	^{99}Tc-hexamethylpropyleneamine oxime;
tPA,	tissue-type plasminogen activator;
TrkA,	tyrosine kinase receptor A;
uPA,	urokinase-type plasminogen activator;
VBM,	voxel-based morphometry.

INTRODUCTION

Alzheimer's disease (AD) initially manifests as episodic memory lapses and difficulty with daily tasks, and then gradually causes decline of mental faculties, dementia, and finally death (Selkoe 2001a; Cummings 2004). AD is a disease of old age, typically affecting people in the seventh or eighth decade of life with incidence numbers rising steeply after age 65. Currently, AD has no cure. Based on the year 2000 census in the United States, the prevalence of AD has been estimated at 3.9–4.5 million and predicted to triple by 2050 due to the rapid aging of the population, if no cure is found (Hebert et al. 2003; Grant 2004). A recent report by the Alzheimer Association has suggested that in 2007, the prevalence of AD in the US has exceeded 5 million and may increase up to 16 million by the middle of the century (AlzheimerAssociation 2007a). The life span of patients with AD is 8 years on average and may extend up to 20 years from the onset of symptoms (AlzheimerAssociation 2007b). During the years of illness, the patients, their families, and their caretakers suffer grave emotional and financial duress. Current cost estimates of care for patients with AD in the US are over $148 billion a year (AlzheimerAssociation 2007a). Numbers in other countries, including developing countries, also are highly alarming (Beeri et al. 2002; Leung et al. 2003; Zencir et al. 2005).

The neuropathology of AD begins with compromised synaptic transmission and plasticity, predominantly in the entorhinal cortex and the hippocampus (Monien et al. 2006; Scheff et al. 2006). As the disease progresses, other brain regions become affected and increasing injury leads to dysfunction and eventually death of susceptible neurons. At late stages of AD, massive degeneration of affected brain areas leads to severe atrophy. Upon postmortem examination of AD brain, two hallmark lesions are observed—extracellular amyloid plaques and intracellular neurofibrillary tangles (NFT) (Alzheimer 1906; Alzheimer 1907), both contributing to the neurodegenerative process. Dead or dying neurons and an active inflammatory process including dystrophic astrocytes, and activated microglia typically surround the amyloid plaques (Heneka and O'Banion 2007). These pathological findings represent advanced stages of AD pathology. However, the events that set off the disease process may occur 10–15 years before manifestation of the first symptoms (Kawas et al. 2003). Thus, to develop efficient therapy for AD and to accurately diagnose AD early enough for the treatment to be as effective as possible, the events that initiate the disease at the earliest stages need to be targeted.

Most researchers agree that the primary cause of AD is an age-related imbalance between production and clearance of the amyloid β-protein (Aβ) or of particular forms of Aβ (Hardy and Selkoe 2002). Aβ is a small protein that is produced as part of normal metabolism (Haass et al. 1992) and has an unknown function. A plausible explanation for the fact that young people do not develop AD is that this imbalance is subtle and develops very slowly with aging. When the rate of production exceeds that of clearance, Aβ accumulates to above-optimal concentrations, leading to its self-association into neurotoxic assemblies. The association process is complex, likely proceeds via multiple pathways, and involves substantial conformational changes in Aβ. The final products of this process are Aβ polymers in which monomers are associated with each other non-covalently. The polymers, which are the form of Aβ found in amyloid plaques, are rich in β-sheet conformation and have a fibrillar morphology (Serpell 2000).

The Amyloid Cascade Hypothesis (Hardy and Higgins 1992) stipulates that the harmful action of Aβ causes the brain inflammation that is a part of the pathology of AD, and leads to hyperphosphorylation of protein tau, a component of the microtubule structure. Upon hyperphosphorylation, tau aggregates into paired helical filaments that comprise the NFT. Aggregation of hyperphosphorylated tau is not unique to AD but exists in, and may be the cause of, other neurodegenerative diseases termed "tauopathies" (Churcher et al. 2006; Iwatsubo 2006). In AD, evidence has indicated that hyperphosphorylation of tau and formation of NFT are downstream events that follow Aβ-induced insults to neurons (Lemere et al. 1996; Morishima-Kawashima and Hara 2002; Roberson et al. 2007).

Despite the fact that Aβ fibrils are the main proteinaceous components of the amyloid plaques, substantial evidence suggests that the actual disease-causing forms of Aβ are pre-fibrillar, oligomeric assemblies (Kirkitadze et al. 2002; Klein et al. 2004; Walsh and Selkoe 2004; Glabe 2006; Terry 2006; Haass and Selkoe 2007). Aβ fibrils may contribute to the neuropathology at later stages of the disease but are thought to be the end product of the self-association process rather than the predominant pathogenic form. Aβ oligomers vary in size and structure. Despite this structural variability, the majority of the oligomeric species tested have been found to be neurotoxic. Neurotoxic Aβ oligomers may be as small as dimers and trimers (Walsh et al. 2002) and as large as protofibrils (Hartley et al. 1999; Walsh et al. 1999), which may comprise hundreds of monomers and are the latest precursor known on the pathway to fibril formation. Several types of oligomers that share a spherical morphology, but may vary in size from a few nanometers to several dozen nanometers, have been shown to be neurotoxic (Lambert et al. 1998; Hoshi et al. 2003; Barghorn et al. 2005; Fradinger et al. 2005). Direct comparison of activity has shown that spherical Aβ oligomers are 10-100 times more neurotoxic than Aβ fibrils (Dahlgren et al. 2002). Aβ oligomers have been found in brain and cerebrospinal fluid (CSF) from patients with AD in concentrations considerably higher than in age-matched healthy individuals (Pitschke et al. 1998; Gong et al. 2003; Kayed et al. 2003; Georganopoulou et al. 2005). Studies of animal models of AD have shown that decline in memory and learning ability are observed before the formation of amyloid plaques (Hsia et al. 1999; Mucke et al. 2000; Jacobsen et al. 2006) and that Aβ oligomer concentration correlates with the degree of cognitive decline (Lesné et al. 2006), strongly suggesting that oligomers are the primary neurotoxins *in vivo*.

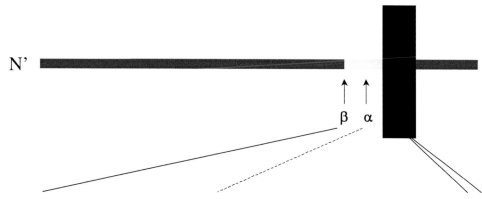

Figure 1. Proteolytic processing of APP by α-, β- and γ-secretases. Consecutive cleavage by β- and γ-secretases produces the amyloidogenic fragments Aβ40 and Aβ42, whereas cleavage by α-secretase precludes production of Aβ.

Aβ is produced from the amyloid β-protein precursor (APP), a large, type I membrane protein, through sequential proteolytic cleavage by β-secretase and γ-secretase, respectively (Nunan and Small 2000). Several forms of Aβ are produced, major among them are those comprising 40 (Aβ40) or 42 (Aβ42) amino acid residues, which differ only by the absence or presence of the two C-terminal residues, Ile[41] and Ala[42] (Figure 1). Despite this small difference in sequence, Aβ40 and Aβ42 display distinct behaviors clinically, biologically and biochemically. Aβ40 and Aβ42 exist *in vivo* at a concentration ratio of ~10:1, respectively (Wang et al. 1996). Aβ42 is deposited first during the development of AD (Suzuki et al.

1994) and is more neurotoxic than Aβ40 (Younkin 1995; El-Agnaf et al. 2000; Zhang et al. 2002). Aβ42 is the predominant component in parenchymal plaques whereas Aβ40 is the main component in vascular deposits (Roher et al. 1993; Gravina et al. 1995; Suo et al. 1998). An increase in the Aβ42/Aβ40 ratio is associated with early-onset familial AD (FAD) (Suzuki et al., 1994; Scheuner et al. 1996; De Jonghe et al. 2001), whereas treatments that decrease this ratio reduce the risk for AD (Weggen et al. 2001). Transgenic mice expressing high levels of Aβ40 in the absence of human APP do not develop overt amyloid pathology whereas mice expressing Aβ42 develop amyloid plaques and cerebral amyloid angiopathy (McGowan et al. 2005). In a drosophila model, each Aβ form expressed individually causes learning deficits, but expression of Aβ42 leads to extensive neurodegeneration, whereas expression of Aβ40 does not lead to the formation of amyloid deposits or neurodegeneration (Iijima et al. 2004). Aβ42 oligomers have been found to be substantially more neurotoxic than those of Aβ40 *in vitro* (Dahlgren et al., 2002; Fradinger et al., 2005). Aβ40 and Aβ42 oligomerize through distinct pathways (Bitan et al. 2003a; Bitan et al. 2003b) and give rise to distinct oligomers (Bitan et al., 2003a; Hoshi et al., 2003; Hepler et al. 2006). These assembly characteristics are thought to be related to formation of quasi-stable structures at the C-terminus of Aβ42 but not of Aβ40 (Urbanc et al. 2004; Lazo et al. 2005; Murakami et al. 2005; Krafft et al. 2006; Sgourakis et al. 2007). Thus, Aβ42 oligomers are believed to be the chief culprit in AD and are a major target for development of therapeutics for AD.

This chapter outlines the current status of therapy and the diagnosis in AD and discusses new, mechanism-based approaches pursued to develop disease-modifying agents that will treat the causes rather than the symptoms of AD, and to improve accuracy and sensitivity of AD diagnosis.

APPROVED THERAPY FOR AD

Cholinesterase Inhibitors

Current therapy for AD largely is restricted to symptomatic treatment. Early observations of a deficiency in cholingeric neurotransmission in AD have led to development of cholinesterase inhibitors as the first approved treatment (Bartus et al. 1982). Four of the five drugs approved in the USA for treatment of AD—Donepezil (Aricepts™, Eisai Co, Woodcliff Lake, NJ); Galantamine (Razadyne ER™, Ortho-McNeil Neurologics, Titusville, NJ); Rivastigmine (Exelon™, Novartis, Basel, Switzerland); and Tacrine (Cognex™, First Horizon Pharmaceutical, Roswell, GA), are acetylcholinesterase inhibitors, designed to compensate for the loss of cholinergic neurons by preventing the breakdown of the neurotransmitter acetylcholine by the enzyme acetylcholinesterase (Lleo et al. 2004). Tacrine, which was the first approved drug, causes considerable adverse side effects including nausea, diarrhea, urinary incontinence and liver toxicity and therefore today is prescribed rarely. The Cochrane dementia group has published three reviews on the evidence for the efficacy and safety of donepezil (Birks et al. 2000b), rivastigmine (Birks et al. 2000a), and galantamine (Olin and Schneider 2002). Although these drugs alleviate the symptoms of AD, they do so for a limited period and to a small extent. They do not resolve the underlying cause of the disease but treat one downstream process. TV3326 (Ladostigil™, Yissum Technology Transfer Company of the Hebrew University of Jerusalem, Israel), a second-generation cholinesterase inhibitor is under phase I/IIA clinical studies for the treatment of AD (Youdim and Bakhle 2006). TV3326 combines the neuroprotective effects of the anti-Parkinson's disease drug rasagiline, a selective monoamine oxidase (MAO)-B inhibitor, with the cholinesterase inhibitory activity of rivastigmine in a single molecule. It also exerts antidepressant activity by inhibition of MAO-A (Youdim 2006). Thus, TV3326 may be effective as a potential treatment for AD, Lewy body disease, and Parkinson's disease with dementia (Youdim et al. 2006).

NMDA Receptor Modulation

Another approach for symptomatic treatment of AD is attenuating glutamatergic excitotoxicity. Glutamate is the main excitatory neurotransmitter in the central nervous system (CNS). Under certain pathologic conditions, glutamate is involved in excitotoxicity—excessive activation of N-methyl-D-aspartate (NMDA) receptors with consequent intracellular accumulation of Ca^{2+}, leading to a cascade of events that results in neuronal death (Michaelis 1998). NMDA receptors recently have been reported to mediate synapse loss and oxidative stress caused by $A\beta$ oligomers (De Felice et al. 2007; Shankar et al. 2007). The fifth drug approved by the FDA and commonly prescribed to patients with AD is the non-competitive NMDA receptor antagonist memantine (Axura™ and Akatinol™, Merz, Frankfurt, Germany; Namenda™, Forest laboratories, New York, NY; Ebixa®™, Lundbeck, Copenhagen, Denmark). Memantine was shown to delay cognitive deterioration in patients with moderate to severe AD (Reisberg et al. 2003). Compared with donepezil monotherapy, combination therapy with donepezil and memantine resulted in modest cognitive improvement (Tariot et al. 2004). Despite a possible neuroprotective mode of action of memantine (Wenk et al. 1997; Miguel-Hidalgo et al. 2002), studies have shown that the drug relieves the symptoms of AD (Tariot et al., 2004) but there is no evidence supporting a disease-modifying role.

EXPERIMENTAL THERAPY

Approaches that interfere with the fundamental causative pathological processes in AD are a primary focus of current drug-development programs (Aisen 2005; Jacobsen et al. 2005; Golde 2006; Kennedy et al. 2007). Gradual accumulation of $A\beta$, particularly $A\beta42$, initiates a complex multistep cascade that includes disruption of synaptic transmission, oxidative stress, decline in neurotransmitter level, formation of NFT, gliosis, inflammatory processes, apoptosis, and neuronal death (Hardy and Selkoe 2002). Various stages of the amyloid cascade are being explored as targets for therapeutic intervention (Hardy and Selkoe 2002; Gandy et al. 2003; Golde 2003; Selkoe and Schenk 2003; Selkoe 2005; Moreira et al. 2006). Leading approaches include inhibition of $A\beta$ production, enhancement of $A\beta$ clearance, and inhibition of $A\beta$ assembly.

Inhibition of Aβ Production

Inhibiting Aβ production by targeting the secretases that cleave APP is an obvious therapeutic approach for AD. To generate Aβ, β-secretase first cleaves APP to produce a soluble N-terminal ectodomain, sAPPβ, and a membrane-anchored C-terminal stub. The latter then is cleaved within the membrane by γ-secretase to produce Aβ and a C-terminal fragment, which complexes with other proteins, relocates to the nucleus, and acts as a transcription regulator. Cleavage of APP within the Aβ domain by α-secretase is an alternative processing pathway that precludes Aβ formation (Figure 1) (Selkoe 2000). Strategies to reduce Aβ production, either through inhibition of β- or γ-secretases, or through activation of α-secretase, therefore are potential approaches for treatment and/or prevention of AD.

β-Secretase Inhibition

The membrane-anchored aspartic protease β-site APP-cleaving enzyme 1 (BACE-1) is the predominant β-secretase (Vassar 2004). Some β-secretase activity also has been assigned to the cysteine protease, cathepsin B (Hook et al. 2005). BACE-1 knockout mice are viable, show no major pathological abnormalities, and do not produce Aβ (Cai et al. 2001; Luo et al. 2001; Dominguez et al. 2005). The mice display subtle deficits in explorative activities and spatial learning and memory, suggesting that BACE-1 is important for the normal function of the brain (Laird et al. 2005). BACE-1 cleaves a variety of substrates in addition to APP, including the APP-like proteins APLP1 and APLP2, sialyltransferase, P-selectin glycoprotein ligand-1, low-density lipoprotein receptor-related protein (LRP) and the β-subunit of voltage-gated sodium channels (Hussain 2004; von Arnim et al. 2005; Wong et al. 2005). Therefore, the current approach in therapeutic inhibition of BACE-1 is to inhibit the enzyme only partially. Under partial inhibition conditions, other BACE-1 substrates may not be affected to levels that would cause damage, but Aβ production may be reduced to non-pathogenic levels.

Hopes for developing β-secretase inhibitors initially had been boosted by obtaining a high-resolution crystal structure of the BACE-1 protease domain complexed with a peptide inhibitor (Hong et al. 2000). However, the structure revealed that the active site of BACE-1 was unusually large and polar, characteristics that make obtaining potent small-molecule inhibitors difficult. Most of the inhibitors discovered initially were relatively large peptides, which did not cross cell membranes or the blood-brain barrier (BBB) and were metabolically unstable (Citron 2004; Cumming et al. 2004; Hussain 2004). Obtaining crystal structures of BACE-1 with smaller inhibitors (Patel et al. 2004) has given new insights into the way ligands bind to the active site and consequently has aided the development of more potent and selective cell-permeable compounds (Coburn et al. 2004; Stachel et al. 2004; Ghosh et al. 2005; John 2006; Stachel et al. 2006).

The first BACE-1 inhibitor shown to be effective *in vivo*, OM00-3, was a large peptide-based inhibitor that upon intraperitoneal injection into the brains of Tg2576 mice, which overexpress human APP containing the Swedish double mutation K670N and M671L, reduced soluble Aβ concentration (Chang et al. 2004). Subsequent progress in the development of BACE-1 inhibitors resulted in generation of smaller peptidomimetics (Kimura et al. 2005). Intrahippocampal injection of the peptidomimetic KMI-429 decreased the soluble pool of brain Aβ in both wild-type mice and Tg2576 mice (Asai et al. 2006). Recently, pharmacological inhibition of BACE-1 that leads to lowering of brain Aβ, has been achieved through oral administration of a non-peptidic compound, GSK188909 (GlaxoSmithKline, Essex, UK), in TASTPM mice, which overexpresses human APP containing the FAD-linked Swedish mutation and the presenilin-1 M146V mutation resulting in over production of Aβ (Hussain et al. 2007). These findings support the initiation of clinical trials using BACE-1 inhibitors.

γ-Secretase Inhibition

γ-Secretase is a membrane-bound aspartyl protease complex composed of presenilin-1 or presenilin-2, nicastrin, Aph1, and Pen2 (Chen et al. 2006; Wolfe 2006; Lundkvist and Näslund 2007). The complex composition of γ-secretase makes obtaining high-resolution structures of γ-secretase difficult. Potential safety concerns have been raised regarding the use of γ-secretase inhibitors because γ-secretase is known to cleave multiple substrates, including Notch, erythroblastic leukemia viral oncogene homolog-4 (ErbB4), and sterol regulatory element binding protein (SREBP) in addition to APP (De Strooper et al. 1999; Kimberly and Wolfe 2003; Wong et al. 2004; Fre et al. 2005; Yoon and Gaiano 2005; Barten et al. 2006). Despite the difficulty in obtaining a high-resolution structure of γ-secretase, several potent inhibitors have been discovered, both by academic laboratories and by pharmaceutical companies (Wolfe et al. 1998; Churcher and Beher 2005; Churcher et al., 2006; Tomita and Iwatsubo 2006; Asberom et al. 2007a; Asberom et al. 2007b; Best et al. 2007; Pissarnitski et al. 2007). A phase II clinical trial of one such compound, LY450139 (Eli Lilly, Indianapolis, IN) has been reported recently (Siemers et al. 2005; Siemers et al. 2006). Patients receiving LY450139 (30 mg daily for one week followed by 40 mg daily for five weeks) had reduced Aβ40 concentration levels in the plasma (average maximum reduction 38%) but no significant changes in the Aβ40 or Aβ42 concentration levels in the CSF, possibly because the dose used was not high enough (Siemers et al., 2006).

Modulation of γ-secretase to reduce specifically the generation of Aβ42 may be a safer approach than simple inhibition because under modulation conditions, γ-secretase cleavage of essential substrates is affected minimally. A number of modulators including non-steroidal anti-inflammatory drugs (NSAIDs) and NSAID-like molecules have been shown to increase the production of shorter Aβ species such as Aβ38, and decrease the production of Aβ42 without perturbing Notch signaling at therapeutic doses (Weggen et al., 2001; Takahashi et al. 2003; Czirr and Weggen 2006). A potential caveat of this approach is that NSAIDs also act as non-selective inhibitors of cyclooxygenases. Cyclooxygenase (COX)-1 protects the stomach lining from harsh acids and digestive chemicals and helps maintain kidney function. Therefore, the clinical merit of using NSAIDs as Aβ42-lowering drugs is limited by potentially significant gastrointestinal and renal toxicity. R-flurbiprofen (Flurizan™, Myriad Pharmaceuticals Inc., Salt Lake City, UT), the R-enantiomer of the NSAID S-flurbiprofen, which modulates γ-secretase activity with little or no COX-inhibitory activity (Eriksen et al. 2003; Geerts 2007) is now in phase III clinical trials for mild to moderate AD (Czirr and Weggen 2006). The drug was well tolerated in a phase II trial in patients with mild to moderate AD and showed retardation of cognitive decline in a subgroup of patients with mild dementia, suggesting that γ-secretase modulation is a viable disease-modifying approach (Wilcock et al. 2005).

α-Secretase Stimulation

α-Secretase cleaves APP within the Aβ sequence to produce a large N-terminal fragment, sAPPα and a small membrane-bound stub, CTFα, thereby precluding the formation of Aβ (Figure 1). sAPPα, may play a role in regulating neuronal excitability, plasticity, and survival, and has been reported to attenuate the neurotoxic effects of Aβ (Mattson et al. 1993; Furukawa and Mattson 1998; Small 1998; Kojro and Fahrenholz 2005). Several metalloprotease disintegrins, ADAM-9, ADAM-10, and TACE, have been identified as major α-secretases (Buxbaum et al. 1998; Lammich et al. 1999; Fahrenholz and Postina 2006). Neuronal overexpression of ADAM-10 in transgenic mice overexpressing human APP containing the FAD-linked London mutation, V717I, increases secretion of sAPPα, decreases Aβ production, delays plaque formation, and alleviates cognitive deficits (Postina et al. 2004). Protein kinase C (PKC) modulates the activity of α-secretase (Gandy and Greengard 1994a; Buxbaum et al., 1998) and therefore represents a possible target for drug development. Stimulation of α-secretase in Chinese hamster ovary (CHO) cells expressing human APP through activation of PKC by treatment with phorbol esters inhibits cellular production of Aβ (Zhu et al. 2001). Several groups have reported activation of α-secretase cleavage by muscarinic agonists, serotonin, glutamate, and estrogens (Vardy et al. 2005). Most of these compounds work by activating PKC-mediated signaling pathways, which alter the trafficking and subcellular distribution of APP and α-secretase (Hung et al. 1993; Gandy and Greengard 1994b; Koo 1997). Because PKC participates in many cellular processes, selective activation of α-secretase is challenging. This approach is still in development and has not yet advanced enough to support clinical trials.

Statins

Epidemiological studies have shown a link between using statins (3-hydroxy-3-methylglutaryl coenzyme A reductase inhibitors) to reduce blood cholesterol concentration and a decreased occurrence of AD (Wolozin et al. 2000). Cholesterol decreases α-secretase activity, and increases β- and γ-secretase activities (Golde and Eckman 2001). Thus cholesterol-lowering drugs may produce a net decrease in Aβ by increasing the α-secretase cleavage of APP and decreasing the β- and γ-secretase cleavage. However, two large trials using simvastatin (Zocor) (2002) and pravastatin (Shepherd et al. 2002) failed to find significant effects on the cognitive function of patients with mild to moderate AD. A pilot, proof-of-concept trial of atrovastatin (Lipitor) administered at 80 mg/day in 63 patients with mild to moderate AD showed some improvement in the cognitive functions (Sparks et al. 2006a; Sparks et al. 2006b) suggesting that larger trials with atrovastatin may be beneficial.

Enhancement of Aβ Clearance

Immunotherapy

Studies demonstrating that monoclonal antibodies could inhibit Aβ aggregation and Aβ-induced neurotoxicity *in vitro*, and that immunization with Aβ-derived antigens reduced plaque burden *in vivo* (Solomon et al. 1997; Solomon 2004), prompted major research efforts targeting Aβ clearance from the brain by the immune system. Exploration of Aβ immunotherapy in the PDAPP transgenic mouse model—a model that overexpresses the FAD-causing Indiana mutant form of human APP, V717F, has shown that either induction of humoral immune response against fibrillar Aβ42 or passive administration of anti-Aβ monoclonal antibodies (mAbs) can prevent amyloid plaque formation in young animals (Schenk et al. 1999) and reduce plaque burden with improvement in cognitive function in older mice (Morgan et al. 2000). Several hypotheses have been proposed for the mechanism of plaque clearance by Aβ immunotherapy: 1) Direct binding of antibodies to Aβ resulting in solubilization of Aβ fibrils or neutralization of Aβ oligomers (Solomon et al., 1997; Frenkel et al. 1999; Klyubin et al. 2005); 2) Fc-receptor-mediated phagocytosis of Aβ by microglial cells in the brain (Schenk et al., 1999; Wilcock et al. 2004a); and 3) "peripheral sink" action in which anti-Aβ antibodies bind Aβ in the plasma causing an efflux of Aβ from the brain by altering the equilibrium across the BBB (DeMattos et al. 2001; Matsuoka et al. 2003).

Despite initial encouraging results in animal models, a phase II clinical trial of active immunization therapy using aggregated Aβ42 with QS21 as an adjuvant (AN-1792; Elan Corporation, San Francisco, CA) was halted because approximately 6% of the patients participating in the trial developed severe meningoencephalitis (Schenk 2002). Postmortem study of brains from patients who had participated in the trial indicated that plaque densities were reduced in many areas of the neocortex, suggesting that the induced immune response was effective in clearing Aβ deposits (Nicoll et al. 2003; Ferrer et al. 2004; Masliah et al. 2005; Nicoll et al. 2006). Although a response to Aβ immunization could not be correlated with changes in cognitive and functional measures, in follow-up studies, a subgroup of patients who developed high levels of Aβ42-specific antibodies showed improvement in cognitive and functional tests compared to the control groups (Hock et al. 2003; Fox et al. 2005; Gilman et al. 2005). However, this correlation was lost when the sample size of evaluated patients was increased (Gilman et al., 2005). These data raise concerns that in contrast to data obtained with transgenic mice, clearance of brain deposits of Aβ in humans may not be a reliable proxy for cognitive improvement. Studies in a non-transgenic canine model, in which aged beagles have been actively immunized with fibrillar or oligomeric Aβ, find that although immunotherapy produces strong clearance of Aβ deposits in the brain of the animals (Pop et al. 2006), there is no significant improvement in their memory performance (Head et al. 2006). A relevant observation is that in transgenic mice, unlike humans or dogs, accumulation and deposition of Aβ in the brain does not cause neurodegeneration. Thus, removal of Aβ from the brains of the mice may be sufficient for reconstruction of synaptic networks. However, in the case of patients with AD, where massive neurodegeneration had been taking place for years, removal of Aβ deposits likely would be insufficient for resoration of cognitive abilities. It may be necessary to start immunizing humans prior to initial deposition of Aβ and/or to combine immunization with other therapeutic means, such as antioxidants and behavior enrichment to improve the function of existing neurons and cortical circuits.

Although the exact cause of the meningoencephalitis that occurred in the AN-1792 trial is unknown, it has been suggested that patients may have developed an autoimmune T-cell response to the immunogen because the adjuvant used, QS21, was a proinflammatory Th1 response-inducing adjuvant (Cribbs et al. 2003). In order to reduce the risk of a T-cell-mediated immune response, new Aβ peptide immunogens and adjuvants currently are tested (Agadjanyan et al. 2005; Ghochikyan et al. 2006; Seabrook et al. 2007). In humans, T-cells were shown to recognize an epitope in the region Aβ(16-33), whereas the majority of antibodies generated in mice, monkeys, and humans recognize epitopes in the N-terminal region Aβ(1-16) (Lemere et al. 2006). Vaccination with N-terminal Aβ fragments may lead to a predominantly humoral response, thereby avoiding the T-cell-associated reactions believed to have caused meningoencephalitis in the AN-1792 trial. Current research efforts aim at development of Th2-inducing adjuvants that promote humoral responses and limit Th1-type cellular immunogenicity (Schenk et al. 2005).

Another approach for anti-Aβ immunotherapy without generating a cellular immune response is passive immunization. Administration of exogenous anti-Aβ antibodies has been shown to mimic many of the effects of active immunization (Bard et al. 2000; DeMattos et al., 2001; Wilcock et al. 2004b; Hartman et al. 2005). In addition to avoiding the T-cell response, patient serum antibody titers can be monitored and controlled more precisely with passive immunization. Another advantage of passive immunization is that it offers the ability to choose antibodies that recognize and bind specific forms of Aβ. Such antibodies can be modified to control binding specificity, binding affinity, and BBB permeability, and if adverse reactions to the treatment develop, the treatment can be discontinued and the antibody can be cleared rapidly (Brendza and Holtzman 2006). Currently, Elan Corporation in collaboration with Wyeth Pharmaceuticals (Madison, NJ) is performing a phase II passive immunization clinical trial with a humanized monoclonal antibody, AAB-001, and a phase I clinical trial with an active Aβ immuno-conjugate, ACC-001 (Dasilva et al. 2006; Kennedy et al., 2007). Though passive immunization offers several advantages over active immunization, if better control can be gained over the parameters of actively immunizing humans to Aβ, active immunization is a preferred long-term solution. Active immunization leads to a continuous production of antibodies, alleviating the need for continuous treatment and precluding the peaks and troughs associated with infusion of antibodies, and thus, may be less invasive and more cost-effective than passive immunization (Maier et al. 2005; Brendza and Holtzman 2006).

Enhancement of Aβ Degradation

Studies of proteases that cleave Aβ and participate in Aβ clearance have revealed that the proteases neprilysin (NEP), insulin-degrading enzyme (IDE), endothelin-converting enzymes 1 and 2 (ECE-1, ECE-2), and plasmin, each may play a role in degradation of Aβ in the brain. Consequently, selective activation of these proteases has become a target for anti-amyloid therapy (Tanzi et al. 2004; Eckman and Eckman 2005; Wang et al. 2006).

NEP, a membrane-bound, extracellular metalloendopeptidase, has been identified as a major extracellular Aβ degrading enzyme in the brain (Iwata et al. 2000). NEP levels are reduced in normal human brains and transgenic mouse models of AD as a result of aging (Iwata et al. 2002; Apelt et al. 2003; Caccamo et al. 2005; Iwata et al. 2005). NEP levels are particularly low in vulnerable brain areas and correlate inversely with Aβ-related pathology in AD patients (Akiyama et al. 2001; Fukami et al. 2002). Intracerebral injection of a viral construct that leads to NEP expression in PDAPP mice reduced cortical amyloid deposits by ~50% (Marr et al. 2003; Marr et al. 2004). Overexpression of NEP also protects hippocampal neurons from Aβ toxicity *in vitro* (El-Amouri et al. 2007). These results suggest that overexpression of NEP by gene therapy approaches in vulnerable areas of AD brain may protect the neurons from the toxic effects of Aβ. Recent observations that the neurohormone somatostatin modulates brain Aβ levels through regulation of NEP activity suggests that increasing the brain concentration of somatostatin or using somatostatin receptor agonists is a potential therapeutic strategy for AD (Saito et al. 2005).

IDE is a large zinc-binding metalloprotease that cleaves multiple short polypeptides with little sequence specificity. Endogenous levels of both Aβ40 and Aβ42 are elevated in the brains of IDE-knockout mice (Farris et al. 2003; Miller et al. 2003a) and in primary cultured neurons derived from IDE-deficient mice (Farris et al., 2003). Overexpression of IDE or NEP reduces accumulation of Aβ in the brain of TgCRND8 transgenic mice, which expresses human APP bearing both the Swedish and Indiana FAD-linked mutations (Leissring et al. 2003; Marr et al., 2003; Iwata et al. 2004). IDE and NEP each have a number of substrates other than Aβ. Therefore, additional safety studies are needed to determine whether enhancing IDE/NEP activity may produce unwanted effects.

ECE is a membrane-bound zinc metallopeptidase homologous to NEP. Both Aβ40 and Aβ42 concentration levels are significantly higher in mice deficient of ECE-1 and the closely related ECE-2, when compared with age-matched wild-type littermate controls (Eckman et al. 2003), suggesting that ECE activity might be an important factor involved in Aβ clearance *in vivo*. Recently, Choi et al. have demonstrated that neuronal overexpression of the ε isozyme of PKC, PKCε increases ECE activity and reduces amyloid plaque pathology in transgenic mice expressing human APP bearing the Indiana mutation (Choi et al. 2006). Additional studies are needed to determine if ECE activation is a viable therapeutic strategy for AD.

Plasmin is a serine protease that plays an important role in the blood clotting system and degrades several proteins in the plasma, including fibrin clots (Henkin et al. 1991). Aβ can activate, and be degraded by, the plasmin system. Aggregated Aβ binds to and stimulates tissue-type plasminogen activator (tPA) (Kingston et al. 1995; Wnendt et al. 1997) and induces expression of tPA and urokinase-type plasminogen activator (uPA) both *in vitro* and *in vivo* (Tucker et al. 2000). Both tPA and uPA cleave plasminogen to generate active plasmin, which in turn degrades fibrin aggregates (Henkin et al., 1991). Several lines of evidence implicate the plasmin system in AD (Van Nostrand and Porter 1999; Tucker et al., 2000; Selkoe 2001b). Brain tissues from AD patients have low plasmin concentration levels and plasmin activity is reduced in serum of AD patients compared to healthy individuals (Ledesma et al. 2000; Dotti et al. 2004). Aβ injected into the hippocampus of plasmin-deficient mice is removed more slowly than in wild-type mice, providing additional evidence for the role of this enzyme in Aβ clearance (Melchor et al. 2003). However, unlike mice deficient in NEP, IDE, or ECE-1 and ECE-2, mice deficient in plasmin (plasminogen knockout mice) do not have elevated levels of endogenous Aβ (Tucker et al. 2004) suggesting that plasmin does not contribute to the regulation of steady-state Aβ levels under non-pathogenic conditions, but may play a more important role in Aβ clearance after aggregation is initiated (Eckman and Eckman 2005).

The activity of the Aβ-degrading enzymes that help regulating accumulation of Aβ in the brain decreases with aging. Upregulation of these enzymes can reduce Aβ accumulation significantly. Regulation of each of the Aβ-degrading enzymes is complex and their brain concentrations depend on multiple factors. Therefore, more pre-clinical studies are required to assess safety and effectiveness issues before these approaches can be used in human studies.

Promoting Receptor-Mediated Aβ Efflux from the Brain

Increased Aβ concentration in brain interstitial fluid (ISF) is one source for formation of neurovascular and cerebral neurotoxic Aβ assemblies (Ghiso and Frangione 2002). Accumulation of Aβ in the ISF might be a direct consequence of deficient efflux (Zlokovic et al. 2000) or increased influx of circulating Aβ across the BBB (Zlokovic 2004). Aβ influx and efflux across the BBB are mediated by the receptor for advanced glycation-end products (RAGE) and low-density lipoprotein receptor-related protein (LRP), respectively (Deane et al. 2003; Deane et al. 2004a; Deane et al. 2004b; Donahue et al. 2006; Deane and Zlokovic 2007). Significant upregulation of RAGE at the BBB is observed in AD patients and in transgenic mouse models of AD, including PDAPP and Tg2576 mice. Activation of RAGE by its interaction with Aβ may take place at an early stage of AD (Deane et al., 2003) and prevention of this interaction, therefore, is a potential strategy for early intervention (Arancio et al. 2004; Lue et al. 2005; Geroldi et al. 2006; Deane and Zlokovic 2007). Peripheral administration of a soluble form of RAGE reduces Aβ concentration in the brain of Tg2576 and PDAPP mice either by preventing influx of Aβ by RAGE-Aβ interaction or via the egress of Aβ from the CNS through a peripheral sink mechanism (Deane et al., 2003). TTP488 (TransTech Pharma, Inc., High point, NC), an orally bioavailable RAGE inhibitor currently is in phase II clinical trials (TransTechPharma 2005; ClinicalTrials.gov 2006).

LRP is linked to AD genetically (Kang et al. 2000) and may influence APP processing and metabolism (Herz and Strickland 2001). LRP also affects neuronal Aβ uptake through complexing of Aβ with the LRP ligands such as α2-macroglobulin (Du et al. 1997), apolipoprotein J (Matsubara et al. 1995), apolipoprotein E (Yang et al. 1997), transthyretin (Schwarzman et al. 1994), and albumin (Biere et al. 1996). LRP plays an opposing role to that of RAGE by transporting brain-derived Aβ out of the brain and into the blood (Shibata et al. 2000; Herz and Marschang 2003; Wang et al. 2003). Thus, enhancing LRP-mediated Aβ efflux may be a viable pharmacological approach for decreasing Aβ in the brain and facilitating Aβ clearance (Deane and Zlokovic 2007). The functional role of LRP in Aβ clearance is under active investigation but is not ready for clinical trials.

Inhibition of Aβ Assembly

Aβ toxicity is closely related to its self-assembly (Lansbury 1997; Teplow 1998; De Felice and Ferreira 2002). Because the physiological role of Aβ is unknown, inhibiting Aβ production or enhancing its clearance may lead to adverse side effects. In contrast, Aβ self-assembly is purely a pathogenic process. Therefore, preventing Aβ assembly may be an advantageous therapeutic approach for AD.

Small-Molecule Inhibitors

Interaction of Aβ with glycosaminoglycans (GAG) occurs at a particular binding site on Aβ, Aβ(13-16), and promotes Aβ assembly (McLaurin et al. 1999). Thus, this interaction may be viewed as a ligand–receptor system, in which GAG act as agonists, which upon binding to their specific binding site on the receptor, Aβ, promote a biological function—self assembly. If this is true, then putative antagonists may bind to the same binding site, inhibiting the interaction of GAG with Aβ and thereby preventing Aβ assembly. This rationale has led to the discovery of Tramiprosate (3-amino-1-propanesulfonic acid; Alzhemed[TM], Neurochem Inc., Quebec, Canada), a GAG-mimetic, which binds preferentially to soluble Aβ at the GAG-binding site and maintains Aβ in a random coil/α-helix-rich conformation. The compound reduces both soluble and fibrillar Aβ concentrations in the TgCRND8 transgenic mouse model (Gervais et al. 2006). A phase II clinical study with Alzhemed[TM] showed a ~33% decrease of CSF Aβ42 concentration after 3 months of treatment in patients with mild AD and a ~14% decrease of Aβ42 in patients with moderate AD (Aisen et al. 2006). Alzhemed[TM] currently is in phase III clinical studies (Neurochem 2007). Aisen et al. have hypothesized that the greater reduction of Aβ concentration in patients with mild AD suggests that the drug may be more effective during the early stages of AD, before extensive Aβ assembly into fibrils and plaques occurs (Aisen et al., 2006). Disappointingly, however, no significant differences were found in cognitive and clinical assessments between the Alzhemed[TM] and placebo groups after three months of treatment. These results, together with findings form the AN-1792 immunotherapy trial discussed above, increase the concerns that removal of Aβ deposits from the brain may not yield the expected improvement in cognitive abilities for patients with AD.

Metal Chelators

A body of evidence suggests that Aβ deposition in AD may be influenced by endogenous transition metal ions (Bush 2003). Copper and zinc ions propagate the formation of toxic Aβ aggregates through interaction with specific amino-acid residues, such as histidine and tyrosine, in Aβ (Atwood et al. 2004). Although Aβ–metal interactions may participate in normal metal-ion homeostasis, age-dependent increase in Cu^{2+}, Zn^{2+} and Fe^{3+} concentrations, leading to accelerated Aβ aggregation may be an etiologic neurochemical event in the generation and progression of AD (Bush et al. 1994; Atwood et al. 1998). In fact, zinc and copper ions are directly coordinated with Aβ in AD-affected brain (Opazo et al. 2002; Dong et al. 2003).

A therapeutic approach has been devised based on the observations that Cu/Zn chelators can dissolve Aβ deposits in AD-affected postmortem brain tissue (Cherny et al. 1999). Bush et al. have identified chelators that are capable of interfering selectively with pathologically relevant metal–protein interaction without depleting the metal necessary for normal physiologic function (Cherny et al. 2001; Bush 2003; Ritchie et al. 2003; Opazo et al. 2006). Among these tested chelators, clioquinol (PBT-1, Prana Biotechnology Ltd., Parkville,

Australia) showed promising effects in phase I and II clinical studies (Ritchie et al., 2003). However, due to a toxic impurity in the drug, phase III studies were not carried out (PranaBiotechnology 2005). A new drug, PBT-2 (Prana Biotechnology Ltd.), which inhibits Aβ aggregation by a similar mechanism is under phase II clinical studies (AlzForum 2007).

Polyphenols

Epidemiological studies have shown that moderate red wine intake reduces the risk of developing AD (Lindsay et al. 2002; Truelsen et al. 2002; Luchsinger et al. 2004). Resveratrol, a polyphenol abundant in grapes and red wine, attenuates Aβ-induced cytotoxicity (Jang and Surh 2003; Savaskan et al. 2003). Anti-amyloidogenic effects of several polyphenols, such as tannic acid (TA), myreticin, curcumin, and rosemarinic acid, on Aβ also have been investigated (Hamaguchi et al. 2006). TA dose-dependently inhibits the formation of Aβ fibrils from freshly prepared Aβ solutions and destabilizes preformed Aβ fibrils *in vitro* (Ono et al. 2004). Curcumin, a polyphenolic diketone from turmeric, inhibits the formation of Aβ oligomers and fibrils and reduces amyloid plaques *in vivo* (Yang et al. 2005). Tg2576 mice treated with curcumin show reduced oxidative damage and amyloid pathology when compared to untreated mice (Lim et al. 2001). Binding of curcumin with copper and iron ions is suggested as one of the possible mechanisms of its protective action in AD (Baum and Ng 2004). The polyphenol epigallocatechin-3-gallate (EGCG), an ingredient extracted from green tea, is a potent anti-inflammatory agent and antioxidant (Ahmed et al. 2002; Lee et al. 2003). EGCG protects cultured hippocampal neurons exposed to Aβ-induced oxidative stress (Choi et al. 2001). These beneficial effects suggest that polyphenols are a promising class of compounds for general neuroprotection and anti-amyloid activity.

Inositol Derivatives

Derivatives of phosphatidylinositol and inositol (cyclohexanehexol) sterioisomers, have been studied as potential inhibitors of Aβ assembly (McLaurin et al. 1998; McLaurin et al. 2000) based on the observation that phosphatidylinositol lipids facilitate Aβ oligomerization and fibrillation (McLaurin and Chakrabartty 1996; McLaurin and Chakrabartty 1997). Inositol stereoisomers inhibit Aβ fibrillogenesis, accelerate disassembly of preformed fibrils, stabilize Aβ in nontoxic, β-structured spherical micellar structures, and protect primary cultured neurons against Aβ oligomer-induced toxicity (McLaurin et al., 1998; McLaurin et al., 2000). This activity is dependent on the stereochemistry of the inositols. *Scyllo*-inositol and *epi*-inositol are more effective than the *myo*-inositol when given orally to TgCRND8 mice in ameliorating several AD-like phenotypes, including impaired cognition, altered synaptic physiology, cerebral Aβ pathology, and accelerated mortality (McLaurin et al. 2006). Alimentary administration of *scyllo*-inositol (AZD 103, Transition Therapeutics Inc., Toronto, Canada) to rats injected with soluble Aβ oligomers prevents reference memory errors and inhibition of long-term potentiation induced by soluble Aβ oligomers (Townsend et al. 2006). AZD 103 currently is in a phase I clinical trial (TransitionTherapeuticsInc. 2006).

β-Sheet Breaker Peptides

β-Sheet breaker peptides are short, synthetic peptides capable of binding Aβ and destabilizing amyloidogenic Aβ conformers, thereby precluding the formation of β-sheet rich amyloid (Soto et al. 1996; Tjernberg et al. 1996; Nakagami et al. 2002). β-Sheet breaker peptides typically are derived from amino acid sequences in the central hydrophobic core of Aβ, but have a low propensity to adopt β-sheet conformation themselves and therefore inhibit the transition of full-length Aβ to a β-sheet rich conformation. The five-residue peptide LPFFD (iAβ5) blocks the formation of amyloid fibrils in a rat model of amyloidosis in which freshly prepared Aβ42 is injected directly into the amygdala (Soto et al. 1998). A derivative of iAβ5, iAβ5p (acetyl-LPFFD-amide), modified for protection against proteolytic degradation by exopeptidases and to increase transport through the blood–brain barrier (Poduslo et al. 1999), was found to reduce amyloid load and cerebral damage in double-transgenic mice overexpressing human APP containing the London mutation and human presenilin-1 bearing the FAD-causing mutation A246E (Permanne et al. 2002). Another study on the neuroprotective effect of chronic intraperitoneal administration of iAβ5p in rats, in which behavioral deficits were induced by intrahippocampal injection of Aβ-fibrils, reports that after the injection, the animals showed partial reduction of the amyloid deposits formed and decreased astrocytic response around the injection site compared to animals treated with saline. In addition, the iAβ5p-treated animals showed a significant improvement in spatial learning (Chacon et al. 2004). These results suggest that β-sheet breaker peptides may be useful for treatment of AD. Gordon et al. have developed inhibitors for Aβ40 self-assembly from peptides that are homologous to the central core domain of Aβ (Aβ16-20), but contain N-methyl amino acids at alternate positions (Gordon et al. 2001; Gordon et al. 2002). When these inhibitor peptides are arrayed in an extended β-strand conformation, the alternating position of N-methyl amino groups gives the peptides two distinct faces, one exhibiting a normal pattern of peptide backbone hydrogen bonds allowing the binding to Aβ and the other face having limited hydrogen-bonding capabilities due to the replacement of the amide protons by N-methyl groups, thereby preventing further assembly. Kokkoni et al. have optimized the structure of N-methylated peptide inhibitors of Aβ aggregation derived from the region Aβ(16–20) by varying the peptide length, N-methylation sites, acetylation and amidation of the N- and C-termini, side-chain identity, and chirality, via five peptide/peptidomimetic libraries (Kokkoni et al. 2006). The peptide D-[(chGly)-(Tyr)-(chGly)-(chGly)-(mLeu)]-NH$_2$ (where chGly = cyclohexyl glycine and mLeu = N-methyl leucine) was the most active inhibitor of Aβ aggregation (Kokkoni et al., 2006).

A conformationally constrained islet amyloid polypeptide (IAPP) mimic, IAPP-GI, recently has been reported as one of the most potent inhibitors of Aβ40 self-assembly (Yan et al. 2007). IAPP-GI is generated by N-methylation of two amide bonds on the same side of a β-strand in the amyloid core sequence IAPP(22–27) (NFGAIL sequence) of full-length IAPP (Yan et al. 2006). This sequence is analogous to the sequence NKGAII in positions 28–32 of Aβ. IAPP is a 37-residue polypeptide that acts as a neuroendocrine regulator of glucose homeostasis. Self-assembly and aggregation of IAPP into fibrillar amyloid causes type II diabetes (T2D). IAPP-GI is the only known peptide-derived compound that binds with high affinity to both IAPP (Yan et al., 2006) and Aβ40 (Yan et al., 2007) and blocks and reverses cytotoxic self-assembly of both polypeptides. Because clinical studies suggest that persons suffering from T2D might be at risk of AD, and vice versa (Janson et al. 2004; Nicolls 2004), IAPP-GI could be a highly potent lead compound for designing novel therapeutic compounds targeting both AD and T2D.

Penke and co-workers designed β-sheet breaker peptides derived from sequences in the C-terminal region of Aβ (Hetenyi et al. 2002). The peptide RIIGLa inhibited aggregation and neurotoxicity of Aβ42 in cultured neuroblastoma cells (Fülöp et al. 2004). Based on β-sheet packing in fibril structures suggesting that Met[35] packs against Gly[33] in the C-terminus of Aβ40 and against Gly[37] in the C-terminus of Aβ42, Sato et al. designed peptides for interference with β-sheet packing with the general sequence Gly-x-Phe-x-Gly-x-Phe, where x represents any amino acid. The peptides were found to inhibit Aβ fibril maturation and Aβ42-induced toxicity in rat cortical neurons (Sato et al. 2006). Recently, we found that peptides derived from the C-terminus of Aβ42 inhibited the neurotoxicity of Aβ42 oligomers and rescued Aβ42-induced inhibition of mini excitatory postsynaptic currents in primary hippocampal neurons (Fradinger et al., manuscript in preparation). These data suggest that peptide inhibitors derived from the sequence of Aβ or of related amyloidogenic peptides provide useful lead compounds for development of Aβ assembly inhibitors as potential drugs for AD.

Alternative Disease Modification Strategies

RNA Interference for Treatment of FAD

RNA interference (RNAi) is the process of mRNA degradation induced by hydbridization with a short sequence of complementary RNA, thereby forming double-stranded RNA (dsRNA) (Agrawal et al. 2003). The RNAi pathway is thought to be an ancient mechanism for protecting cells against viruses and rogue genetic elements that use dsRNA in their life cycles. By activating a sequence-specific RNA degradation process, RNAi post-transcriptionally inhibits protein expression. Early-onset FAD is caused by mutations in the genes that encode APP or presenilins (Goate et al. 1991; Mullan et al. 1992; Scheuner et al., 1996; Selkoe 2001a; Higgins and Jacobsen 2003; Rocchi et al. 2003). The majority of these mutations cause increased concentrations of Aβ or increased Aβ42/Aβ40 ratio (Suzuki et al., 1994; Scheuner et al., 1996; De Jonghe et al., 2001). The hereditary pattern is autosomal dominant, thus patients with FAD-causing mutations also have one normal allele of the mutant protein. Selective silencing of the disease-causing mutant allele by RNAi, while leaving the normal allele fully expressed, is a novel approach that has been explored in recent years as a therapeutic strategy for dominantly inherited diseases (Ding et al. 2003; Miller et al. 2003b; Miller et al. 2004). This approach recently was applied successfully to silencing APP-encoding alleles bearing the London and Swedish mutations *in vitro* (Feng et al. 2006) and the Swedish mutation *in vivo* (Rodriguez-Lebron et al. 2006), suggesting that RNAi may be a useful strategy for treatment of FAD.

Nerve growth Factor Therapy

Nerve growth factor (NGF), a member of the neurotrophin gene family maintains the survival of cholinergic neurons of the basal forebrain nociceptive dorsal root ganglion neurons, and certain third-order sympathetic neurons (Huang and Reichardt 2001). The loss of basal forebrain cholinergic neurons, which release the majority of acetylcholine in the cerebral cortex and hippocampus (Mesulam and Geula 1988) enhancing synaptic efficacy and modulating active cortical circuits (Kilgard and Merzenich 1998; Conner et al. 2003), is at least partially responsible for the cognitive decline observed in AD patients (Perry et al. 1978; Bartus et al., 1982). NGF promotes survival of those neurons by activating its high-affinity tyrosine-kinase receptor TrkA. Downstream of TrkA, the small G-protein p21ras plays a pivotal role in controlling neuronal survival and differentiation (Hock et al. 1998; Hock et al. 2000a; Hock et al. 2000b). Therefore, treating AD patients with NGF to improve cholinergic function may ameliorate disease symptoms. NGF has been shown to improve memory functions in animal models of AD (Hagg et al. 1989; Fischer et al. 1991; Koliatsos et al. 1991; Frick et al. 1997). However, safe delivery of NGF to the brain is challenging because NGF does not cross the BBB due to its size and polarity. Gene delivery has made it possible to deliver sufficient amount of NGF specifically to sites of degenerating neurons, thereby circumventing the need to cross the BBB and avoiding adverse effects such as weight loss and pain observed during ventricular administration to the brain (Tuszynski 2002). A phase I trial of *ex vivo* NGF gene delivery using CERE-110 (Ceregene Inc., San Diego, CA), a preparation that carries the gene encoding NGF encased in a harmless viral coating that protects the gene and facilitates its delivery to brain cells, improved the rate of cognitive decline in 6 out of 8 patients with mild AD (Tuszynski et al. 2005).

Cerebrolysin is a low molecular weight peptide preparation produced by proteolytic breakdown of purified porcine brain proteins, which mimics the effects of NGF (Francis-Turner and Valouskova 1996). Intravenous infusion of Cerebrolysin, (Cere, Ebewe pharmaceuticals, Unterach, Austria) has shown promising results in several clinical trials (Ruther et al. 2000; Ruether et al. 2001; Alvarez et al. 2006). In a recent trial with Cere, a 10 ml dose per day for 24 weeks was found optimal for treatment of patients with mild to moderate AD and a 60 ml dose per day was suggested to be useful for patients with more severe stages of AD (Alvarez et al., 2006).

Antioxidants

One of the mechanisms by which Aβ causes neurotoxicity is generation of free radicals and reactive oxygen species (ROS) (Behl et al. 1994). By a vicious cycle, oxidative stress enhances the activity of β-secretase resulting in increased production and accumulation of Aβ (Tamagno et al. 2002), which increases mitochondrial dysfunction and oxidative stress (Casley et al. 2002). In fact, aging-related oxidative stress has been hypothesized to be the initial cause for increased Aβ production that leads to sporadic AD (Barger 2004; Lee et al. 2004; Lee et al. 2006). Hence, attenuation of oxidative stress by antioxidants has been explored as a potentially useful means of therapeutic intervention (Hajieva and Behl 2006). Several epidemiologic studies provide evidence supporting the concept that vitamin E and vitamin C may delay the onset of AD (Zandi et al. 2004). A retrospective review comparing patients treated with a donepezil together with vitamin E indicated that the combination treatment lowered the rate of cognitive decline significantly (Klatte et al. 2003). However, a clinical study that compared the effects of vitamin E to that of donepezil and placebo has concluded that vitamin E showed no beneficial effects in patients with mild cognitive impairment (MCI) (Petersen et al. 2005). Thus, the value of treating patients with AD with vitamin E remains unclear.

DIAGNOSIS OF AD

Current Clinical Diagnosis

Cognitive Assessment

In clinical practice, AD usually is diagnosed by application of cognitive assessment tools that detect symptoms, such as memory loss, disorientation, and problems with routine tasks. Two common diagnostic tools for AD are the Clinical Dementia Rating (CDR) (Morris 1993) and Mini Mental State Examination (MMSE) (Folstein et al. 1975). CDR scores for staging cognitive impairment range from 0 – no impairment, through 0.5 – very mild, 1 – mild, 2 – moderate, and 3 – severe dementia (Morris 1993). In the MMSE, a score of 20–24 out of a maximum of 30 points suggests a 'mild dementia', whereas lower scores indicate more advanced stages of cognitive decline (Folstein et al., 1975). The MMSE detects AD with a sensitivity of ~ 80% (Kalbe et al. 2004). The CDR and the MMSE tests are highly important in AD research because they are used to define patient groups and to monitor the disease progress in studies of diagnostic tools and medical treatments.

Recently, the importance of early diagnosis of AD for success of therapeutic intervention has been given increased recognition (Cummings 2004; Nestor et al. 2004; Monien et al., 2006). The symptoms observed in early AD often are described as MCI, an imprecise, yet clinically useful, term for distinguishing between normal cognitive aging and the beginning of dementia (Petersen 2004). The diagnostic criteria for MCI include the following key features: 1) the person is neither cognitively normal nor demented; 2) evidence of cognitive decline over time is observed or reported by the patient and/or informant; 3) general intellectual functions and activities of daily living are preserved; and 4) according to the CDR, individuals are diagnosed with 'questionable dementia' (score = 0.5) (Petersen et al. 2001). However, this definition of MCI was reported to be too vague to allow accurate distinction of MCI from normal, age-related cognitive decline on one hand, and from mild AD on the other hand (Winblad et al. 2004). Petersen notes that accurate division of subjects into healthy individuals, patients with MCI, and patients with AD based on cognitive assessment alone is impossible because the ranges of cognitive abilities observed for those three groups overlap (Petersen 2004). Two additional problems complicate the diagnosis of MCI based on cognitive assessment alone. First, the symptoms classified as MCI may precede not only AD, but also various other types of dementia, such as dementia associated with Parkinson's disease, Pick's disease, vascular dementia, and Lewy body dementia. In addition, certain medications, such as anticholinergic (Ancelin et al. 2006) and sedative (Sjogren et al. 2005) drugs, and conditions such as depression, cerebral injuries, and alcohol abuse may cause MCI symptoms. Under these transient circumstances, MCI may be non-progressive and/or reversible. Second, the classification of the patient is subjective, depending on the judgment of the clinician and is hindered by the heterogeneity of character and etiology among patients. The daily disposition of patients plays an important role in the result of psychometric tests, as do their levels of education, intelligence, and motivation.

Despite these difficulties with early detection of AD, cognitive tests are essential frontline tools for the assessment of cognitive (dys)function in individuals once they become present in clinical settings. Two main research approaches currently attempt to overcome the problems associated with the diagnosis of MCI by cognitive assessment. One approach to better characterize the heterogeneous nature of the symptomatic patterns of MCI and define tighter criteria for AD-specific MCI has led to the definition of four subtypes of MCI. Of these subtypes, amnestic MCI (MCIa), a variant characterized by memory loss as the predominant symptom, has been proposed as an important risk factor for AD (Petersen 2005). A different approach follows the design of novel cognitive assessment tools for detection of subtle differences between MCI and normal, age-related cognitive decline. An ideal cognitive test should be quick to administer, easy to score, well tolerated and accepted by patients, and should be relatively independent of culture, language, and education (Shulman 2000). To be effective not only for MCI and for AD but also for other forms of dementia, tests also should cover a broad range of cognitive domains. Longitudinal studies of individuals with MCIa have identified cognitive domains affected by the development of dementia, particularly episodic memory (story recall, word list learning), and semantic memory (recall of names). Attention processing, visuospatial skills, and mental speed also are affected (Nestor et al., 2004). Based on these findings, a variety of screening tools with moderate to high sensitivity and specificity capable of discerning patients with MCI from cognitively intact individuals have been developed (Flicker et al. 1991; Tierney et al. 1996; Devanand et al. 1997; Albert et al. 2001; Amieva et al. 2004). Two recent examples are the Montreal Cognitive Assessment test (MoCA) (Nasreddine et al. 2005) and the DemTect (Kalbe et al., 2004). Both psychometric tools showed high sensitivity in distinguishing MCI (90% and 80%, respectively) and AD (both 100%) from age-matched controls, in contrast to the lower sensitivity of the widely used MMSE for the detection of MCI (69% and 18% determined by Kalbe et al. (Kalbe et al., 2004) and Nasreddine et al. (Nasreddine et al., 2005), respectively). The specificity for the identification of healthy individuals in the control groups was determined to be 87% (MoCA), 92% (DemTect) and 100% (MMSE).

To enhance the predictive power of currently available cognitive assessment tools, tests may be optimized in the following ways: First, the results of psychological assessments may be improved by test repetition, following the cognitive impairment of an individual in intervals of three to six months. It has been shown that monitoring of incipient dementia progression to determine a specific rate of cognitive decline has a greater accuracy in diagnosis of MCI than a single cognitive assessment (Kurz et al. 2004). Second, knowledge of the time course in which brain regions are affected by AD and their participation in specific cognitive tasks, such as semantic memory and attention processing, may lead to a schedule that describes the loss of cognitive abilities during the progression of AD. For the establishment of such a time course, future development of tests that monitor the condition of specific cognitive domains or functions is needed. With the characteristic change of several cognitive parameters, the diagnosis of AD-specific MCI using three cognitive assessments over a period of six months is predicted to be improved substantially.

Neuroimaging

Quantitative high-resolution brain imaging techniques enable minimally invasive examination of alterations in brain anatomy and function, facilitating identification of affected regions in early stages of AD. Structural evaluation of brain damage allows differentiating among certain etiologies of cognitive decline, thereby separating patients with emerging AD from other subjects with MCI, e.g., those with brain tumors, subdural haematoma, or normal pressure hydrocephalus. In addition, neuroimaging provides diagnostic information complementary to psychometric tests, thereby improving the prediction of AD progression (Winblad et al., 2004).

Currently, standard clinical diagnostic procedures for AD include brain examination with magnetic resonance imaging (MRI), or less frequently, single-photon emission-computed tomography (SPECT). Structural imaging with MRI to find markers for AD progression has been focused on the medial temporal lobe. The medial temporal lobe consists of the hippocampal region (CA fields, dentate gyrus, and subicular complex) and the adjacent perirhinal, entorhinal, and parahippocampal cortices. These structures are essential for declarative memory (episodic and semantic memory) and are the areas primarily affected during memory impairment (Squire et al. 2004). Interestingly, NFT density in the medial temporal lobe correlates with performance in memory tests supporting the notion that NFT are a pathological substrate that causes memory loss in AD (Guillozet et al. 2003). MRI studies have confirmed that atrophy of the medial temporal lobe and volumetric decrease of the hippocampus and entorhinal cortex are sensitive markers for AD (Du et al. 2001; Scheltens et al. 2002; Du et al. 2003; Jack et al. 2004; Jack et al. 2005). However, AD progression varies widely among patients and a standardized scale, correlating specific levels of brain atrophy with stages of memory impairment applicable to all patients may not be attainable. It has been shown that the rate of atrophy in both the hippocampus and entorhinal cortex provide greater accuracy than a single-point assessment for the detection of MCI. Comparative longitudinal surveys suggest that using the rate of medial temporal lobe atrophy (MTA) may help distinguishing between healthy individuals and patients with MCI or mild AD, devising standards for prediction of the future course of dementia (Chong et al. 2006). Conversion of healthy persons to patients with MCI correlates well with reduction of hippocampal volume (Du et al., 2001), entorhinal cortex volume (Killiany et al. 2000; Killiany et al. 2002) or both (Dickerson et al. 2001; Jack et al., 2004), and MCI patients who convert to AD have greater rates of MTA than those who are cognitively stable (Jack et al. 1999; Dickerson et al., 2001; Du et al., 2001; Visser et al. 2002; deToledo-Morrell et al. 2004; Jack et al., 2004; Devanand et al. 2007). These data support the use of rates of volume loss observed in hippocampus and entorhinal cortex as surrogate markers for disease progression alongside with psychometric screening tools.

Despite encouraging results, the time-consuming analysis of MRI recordings, which includes determination of regions of interest and subsequent calculation of volumetric measures is an obstacle in clinical routine (Nestor et al., 2004). An interesting alternative to fully computerized processing of three-dimensional brain images is the 'visual rating scale assessment' of MTA (Scheltens et al. 1992). This method is quick, easily performed by untrained personnel, and is a more accurate evaluation system compared to semi-automatic region-of-interest analysis of hippocampus and entorhinal cortex (Wahlund et al. 2000;

Bresciani et al. 2005). MTA rates measured by visual assessment differentiate effectively patients with MCI from normal individuals and patients with AD, and therefore, yield good predictive accuracy for the conversion of MCI to AD (80–90%) (Visser et al., 2002; Rusinek et al. 2003; Schott et al. 2003; Korf et al. 2004). Voxel-based morphometry (VBM, voxel = volumetric pixel) is an automatic method for computational neuroanatomical evaluation of MRI data (Chetelat et al. 2002). VBM involves a voxel-wise comparison of the local concentration of gray matter between two groups of subjects (Ashburner and Friston 2000). The first VBM study of MCI patients showed marked gray matter loss predominantly affecting the hippocampal region and cingulate gyri, and extending into the temporal neocortex (Chetelat et al., 2002). Discussion of other methods of MRI evaluation is beyond the scope of the chapter. Further details can be found in a comprehensive review by Nestor et al. (Nestor et al., 2004).

As an alternative to MRI, SPECT may be used to support the diagnosis of AD based on neuropsychological tests. Detection of single γ-photons emitted from molecules containing the radioactive isotope ^{99}Tc, e.g., ^{99}Tc-hexamethylpropyleneamine oxime (^{99}Tc-HMPAO) and ^{99}Tc-ethylcysteinate dimer (^{99}Tc-ECD) (van Dyck et al. 1996) enables measurements of cerebral blood flow. SPECT is used to confirm the clinical diagnosis of AD by measuring bilateral parieto-temporal perfusion deficits (Vlasenko et al. 1997), enhancing the sensitivity of the diagnosis by cognitive assessment from ~ 75% to ~ 90% (Read et al. 1995). The progression of AD has been tracked upon serial SPECT examinations by showing a progressive reduction of cerebral blood flow in the left hippocampus, parahippocampus, and cerebral association cortex (Kogure et al. 2000). The value of SPECT in the diagnosis of questionable or early dementia cases recently has been studied. Decreased cerebral blood flow in individuals with MCI who subsequently converted to AD was most prominent in cingulate gyri (Johnson et al. 1998; Kogure et al., 2000; Huang et al. 2002; Borroni et al. 2006), the temporo-parietal lobes (Encinas et al. 2003; Hirao et al. 2005; Borroni et al., 2006), and the precunei (Kogure et al., 2000; Hirao et al., 2005; Borroni et al., 2006). Compared with data from stable MCI patients, these markers could predict the conversion of MCI to AD with a sensitivity of 70–80% at least 2 years before the patients were clinically diagnosed with AD (Kogure et al., 2000).

RECENT PROGRESS IN DIAGNOSIS OF EARLY AD

In recent years, development and fine-tuning of diagnostic techniques, which are essential for detection of AD at an early stage, and standardized monitoring of disease progress during clinical trials have advanced at a rapid pace. To diagnose early AD reliably, the techniques used should be reproducible, highly sensitive, and specific for AD relative to other forms of dementia. Ideally, they also would be inexpensive, easy to perform, and non-invasive. Recent promising advances in the fields of neuroimaging and biomarker assays that have not yet become part of routine clinical practice are presented here.

Brain Glucose Metabolism as an Imaging Marker for AD

Whereas structural imaging methods detect structural changes of the brain during the progress of AD, functional imaging techniques are directed towards understanding the molecular level of pathophysiological processes underlying the disease. A common method for imaging of resting cerebral activity is detection of changes in regional glucose metabolism by positron-emission tomography (PET) using ^{18}F-labeled fluoro-2-deoxy-D-glucose (FDG) as a tracer. The radioactive decay of the isotope results in emission of a positron. Subsequent annihilation on contact with an electron yields two γ-photons emitted with equal energy in opposite directions enabling highly sensitive detection (Hoffman and Phelps 1986). FDG PET studies reveal characteristic and progressive reduction in regional measurements of cerebral metabolic rate for glucose (CMRgl) in patients with AD (Minoshima et al. 1995; Moriearty et al. 1999; Silverman et al. 2001) and MCI (Berent et al. 1999; Arnaiz et al. 2001; Chetelat et al. 2003; Drzezga et al. 2003). In patients with AD, CMRgl reduction in the posterior cingulate, parietal, temporal, and prefrontal cortices are correlated with dementia severity (Minoshima et al., 1995) and progression (Alexander et al. 2002). In a retrospective study of patients with mild to moderate dementia, the pattern of hypometabolism offered a sensitivity and specificity of 94% and 73%, respectively, for the prediction of subsequent clinical decline and the histopathological diagnosis of AD (Silverman et al., 2001). In patients diagnosed with MCIa (Arnaiz et al., 2001; Drzezga et al., 2003), isolated memory impairment (Berent et al., 1999), or non-amnestic MCI (Chetelat et al., 2003), regional CMRgl reduction helped distinguish subsequent AD converters from non-converters. Some overlap between the groups was found (Berent et al., 1999; Arnaiz et al., 2001; Chetelat et al., 2003; Drzezga et al., 2003). In a longitudinal study of MCIa patients, the one-year rate of decline for CMRgl was greater in subsequent AD converters than in non-converters (Drzezga et al., 2003). These studies indicate that discrimination of various stages during progression of AD by neuroimaging and cautious prediction of progression to AD within the heterogeneous group of patients with MCI subjects may be feasible.

Molecular Probes as Imaging Markers for AD

Another promising area of brain imaging research focuses on developing tracer compounds that bind to abnormal brain deposits implicated in AD. Initial data indicate that one such tracer, Pittsburgh compound B (PIB), binds to amyloid plaques and reveals their presence and number in a PET scan (Klunk et al. 2004; Mathis et al. 2005). PIB is a thioflavin derivative that is selective for Aβ-containing plaques at the concentrations used for imaging studies. A number of clinical PIB PET studies have begun recently in order to accrue longitudinal data for the diagnostic value of PIB. Another imaging probe allowing visualizing brain pathology in living AD patients with PET is 2-(1-{6-[2-[^{18}F]fluoroethylmethylamino]-2-naphthyl}ethylidene)malononitrile (^{18}F-FDDNP). ^{18}F-FDDNP PET was used to discern AD patients and cognitively normal persons with high accuracy by labelling senile plaques and NFT in brain tissue (Shoghi-Jadid et al. 2002). More recently, ^{18}F-FDDNP PET was shown to track disease progression from MCIa to AD efficiently (Small et al. 2006). In the latter study, which included 25 patients with AD, 28 patients with MCI, and 30 normal individuals, the PET imaging showed a clear correlation between cognitive deterioration and FDDNP concentration in the temporal, parietal and frontal brain regions, where the abnormal protein deposits typically accumulate early in patients with MCI and advancing in those with AD. ^{18}F-FDDNP PET yielded excellent diagnostic accuracy with sensitivity values of 95 and 98% for the distinction between MCI patients and normal individuals, and between MCI patients and AD patients, respectively, and predicted disease progression and brain pathology precisely (Small et al., 2006).

Metabolic Markers for AD

Metabolic biomarkers for AD may be assessed in different body fluids, including CSF, blood, and urine (Thal et al. 2006). Thus far, the most encouraging results were obtained in studies of CSF biomarkers. The CSF is in direct contact with the brain and thus reflects biochemical changes due to pathological processes. Analyses of various biomolecules in the CSF by lumbar puncture was routine in neurological practice to diagnose infectious, inflammatory, and degenerative conditions of the CNS, such as meningitis, Guillain-Barré syndrome, and multiple sclerosis (Andreasen and Blennow 2005). With the advent of less invasive diagnostic modalities, currently this procedure is performed mostly in research settings.

Leading candidate biomarkers for early AD are the proteins that reflect key features of AD pathology, namely Aβ, tau, and hyperphosphorylated tau (p-tau). The clinical diagnosis of AD was shown to correlate with increased CSF levels of tau and p-tau, and with decreased levels of Aβ42 (Andreasen and Blennow 2005). The mean sensitivities of the assays are 85% for Aβ42, and 80% for tau and p-tau for the differentiation between patients with AD and non-demented individuals, whereas the overall specificity is ~ 90% (Blennow 2004b). The ratio of Aβ42/Aβ40 has a higher diagnostic accuracy for differentiating patients with AD from normal individuals than Aβ42 alone, with a sensitivity of 94% (Lewczuk et al. 2004).

To distinguish patients with MCI from normal individuals, low Aβ42, and high tau and p-tau CSF concentration levels are equally sensitive compared to the differentiation between healthy persons and AD patients at later stages of the disease (Andreasen et al. 1999; Arai et al. 2000; Andreasen et al. 2001; Gottfries et al. 2001; Lautenschlager et al. 2001; Maruyama et al. 2001; Riemenschneider et al. 2002; Andreasen et al. 2003). The prognostic value of CSF biomarkers for the conversion of patients with MCI to AD has been evaluated in a longitudinal study, showing that decreased levels of Aβ42 and increased levels of tau discriminate patients with MCI that progress to AD from those that do not progress with sensitivities (and specificities) of 59% (100%) and 83% (90%), respectively (Hampel et al. 2004). The data suggest that CSF markers are indicative of pathology very early in the disease process in AD, and may be of clinical value to differentiate MCI cases with incipient AD, which will progress to full-fledged AD, from incidents of non-progressive or reversible MCI.

Despite the high accuracy of the biomarker assays for distinction of MCI cases from healthy individuals, the data must be interpreted with caution. Current quantitative analyses of CSF or serum biomarkers for AD diagnosis use enzyme-linked immunosorbent assay (ELISA). The technical limitations and confounding factors of this technique have been discussed in detail by Andreasen and Blennow (Blennow 2004a; Andreasen and Blennow 2005). In addition, changes in levels of Aβ, tau, and p-tau are not necessarily specific for AD and do not allow differentiating AD accurately from other forms of dementia, such as Lewy body dementia or vascular dementia (Andreasen and Blennow 2005). Because the current average sensitivity for the discrimination between patients with AD and healthy individuals using CSF biomarker detection is ~ 85%, these assays do not offer a considerable increase in predictive value over existing algorithms comprising neuropsychological and imaging modalities (Andreasen and Blennow 2005).

New approaches in the field of AD biomarkers target the detection of soluble assemblies of Aβ. In contrast to the less toxic amyloid plaques and Aβ monomers, soluble Aβ oligomers play a key role in the early pathogenesis of AD. Aβ oligomers are believed to be the primary neurotoxins causing synaptic impairment and cognitive deterioration in early AD, several years before plaques are formed and brain atrophy is observed (Lue et al. 1999; McLean et al. 1999; Wang et al. 1999; Gong et al., 2003). Two novel approaches that do not rely on ELISA target the monitoring of soluble Aβ42 oligomers. Recently, a compound derived from a library of benzofurans was shown to bind selectively to Aβ oligomers but not to Aβ fibrils. The specificity of this compound may be used to detect and quantify soluble Aβ oligomers in CSF samples as a surrogate marker for the early detection of AD (Tan-Hehir et al. 2006). Another technique for specific detection of soluble Aβ assemblies that may offer increased sensitivity and specificity over ELISA used a 'bio-barcode' assay, in which Aβ-derived diffusible ligands (ADDLs) were detected with femtomolar sensitivity in CSF of patients with AD but not in age-matched healthy individuals (Georganopoulou et al., 2005). The bio-barcode assay is based on ADDL recognition with conformation-specific antibodies linked to oligonucleotide-modified nanoparticles. Several hundred copies of the bio-barcode DNA are released from the nanoparticle and amplified to provide a highly sensitive signal for antigen identification (Fradinger and Bitan 2005).

To avoid a lumbar puncture, detection of plasma levels of AD-related biomarkers has been studied. Unfortunately, the results of these studies have been disappointing. Plasma concentrations of Aβ42 do not correlate with those in CSF (Mehta et al. 2001). Longitudinal studies did not show consistent changes in plasma Aβ over time in patients with AD (Mayeux et al. 2003), and cross-sectional differences between patients with AD and healthy individuals that would allow plasma Aβ concentrations to be used as a diagnostic measure have not been identified (Blasko et al. 2006). Secondary pathophysiologic and metabolic alterations in AD, including those related to inflammation (interleukins), cholesterol metabolism (cholesterol, apolipoprotein E, and homocysteine), and oxidative stress (antioxidants and lipid peroxides) also have been studied as potential biomarkers (Thal et al., 2006). Although serum and plasma levels of these biomarkers are altered in AD relative to non-demented, age-matched individuals, they do not have sufficient discriminatory power to allow reliable diagnosis (Irizarry 2004).

Two promising alternatives for fast and non-invasive tests for AD currently are under development. One approach is based on the finding that Aβ aggregates can form deposits in the eye lens of patients with AD (Goldstein et al. 2003). Accumulation of Aβ causes scattering of a weak laser beam directed into the lens allowing detection of protein deposits. In laboratory experiments using transgenic mouse models of AD, this approach distinguished transgenic mice from healthy mice with a sensitivity of 100% (Moncaster et al. 2006). More research is needed to determine the applicability of this test in patients with AD and to correlate between the amount of protein deposit found in the eye and the level of dementia. Another test that may be applied at very early stages of AD is a skin test based on detection of AD-specific abnormalities related to an inflammatory response. Khan et al. have shown that the level of phosphorylation of extracellular signal-regulated kinases ERK1 and ERK2 in fibroblasts is significantly lower in patients with AD than in healthy individuals. This difference has been used to distinguish between the two groups with excellent accuracy in a cohort of 60 patients (Khan and Alkon 2006). Further work is directed at reproduction of the results in trials with greater numbers of patients to verify the sensitivity and reproducibility of these observations.

CONCLUSION

Currently, there are no disease-modifying therapies approved for AD. A number of promising targets and therapeutic strategies for the treatment of AD are under active investigation. At present, it is too early to determine if one strategy, and which strategy, will work best. Quite likely, a combination of treatments tailored for individual patients will be the most beneficial route. Inhibition of Aβ production, assembly, and toxicity has become a primary focus for contemporary drug development programs. Recent developments include identification and clinical assessment of β- and γ-secretase inhibitors and modulators, inhibitors of Aβ oligomerization, and safer active and passive anti-Aβ immunization strategies. NGF gene therapy and RNA interference for FAD are alternative promising approaches. These therapies are likely to have the best efficacy in the early or even preclinical phases of the disease, before cognitive deficits have become apparent because at these stages the main pathological process is synapse loss but not neuronal loss. If the pathologic molecular processes causing synapse impairment can be inhibited, the brain likely will have sufficient plasticity to repair injured neurons and regenerate affected synapses. At later stages of AD, when substantial neuronal loss has occurred, regeneration may be more difficult or impossible. Development of tools for early diagnosis of AD at preclinical stages is invaluable for evaluating the outcome of clinical trials and for successful application of these therapies.

Currently, unequivocal diagnosis of AD is not possible in living patients. It is still equally difficult to discriminate with certainty patients with MCI from healthy individuals and from patients with AD. Despite several confounding factors, cognitive assessment of patients is the most common tool in clinical routine. Imaging techniques, such as MRI and SPECT help support the initial diagnosis and to rule out other sources of cognitive decline. A combination of the rate of cognitive deterioration and the rate of MTA has superior diagnostic/prognostic value compared to a single assessment. Periodic repetition of examination is recommended. An important goal of current research in brain imaging and biomarker detection is to shift the limit of detection in the development of AD to an earlier stage when the future patient is still presymptomatic. New developments in brain imaging target visualization of Aβ lesions rather than brain atrophy using tracer compounds such as PIB and FDDNP. However, Aβ deposition occurs relatively late in the pathogenesis of AD and is preceded by soluble Aβ assemblies. Targeting the detection of non-fibrillar Aβ assemblies will be highly valuable for distinguishing effectively normal elderly people from those with MCIa at presymptomatic stages. These developments and future non-invasive diagnostic methods possibly using detection of Aβ aggregates in the eye or AD-specific inflammatory markers in the skin hold promise for fast and reliable early diagnosis of AD allowing initiation of immediate therapeutic interventions that would prevent and/or reverse the disease.

ACKNOWLEDGEMENTS

The authors would like to thank Dr. A. Farid Rahimi for his help in preparing the manuscript. This work was supported by grants AG027818 from the NIH/NIA and 2005/2E from the Larry L Hillblom Foundation, and by a generous gift from the Turken family.

REFERENCES

Agadjanyan, M.G., Ghochikyan, A., Petrushina, I., Vasilevko, V., Movsesyan, N., Mkrtichyan, M., Saing, T., Cribbs, D.H. Prototype Alzheimer's disease vaccine using the immunodominant B cell epitope from β-amyloid and promiscuous T cell epitope pan HLA DR-binding peptide. *J. Immunol. 174:* 1580-1586, 2005.

Agrawal, N., Dasaradhi, P.V., Mohmmed, A., Malhotra, P., Bhatnagar, R.K., Mukherjee, S.K. RNA interference: biology, mechanism, and applications. *Microbiol. Mol. Biol. Rev. 67:* 657-685, 2003.

Ahmed, I., John, A., Vijayasarathy, C., Robin, M.A., Raza, H. Differential modulation of growth and glutathione metabolism in cultured rat astrocytes by 4-hydroxynonenal and green tea polyphenol, epigallocatechin-3-gallate. *Neurotoxicology 23:* 289-300, 2002.

Aisen, P.S. The development of anti-amyloid therapy for Alzheimer's disease: from secretase modulators to polymerisation inhibitors. *CNS Drugs 19:* 989-996, 2005.

Aisen, P.S., Saumier, D., Briand, R., Laurin, J., Gervais, F., Tremblay, P., Garceau, D. A Phase II study targeting amyloid-β with 3APS in mild-to-moderate Alzheimer disease. *Neurology 67:* 1757-1763, 2006.

Akiyama, H., Kondo, H., Ikeda, K., Kato, M., McGeer, P.L. Immunohistochemical localization of neprilysin in the human cerebral cortex: inverse association with vulnerability to amyloid β-protein (Aβ) deposition. *Brain Res. 902:* 277-281, 2001.

Albert, M.S., Moss, M.B., Tanzi, R., Jones, K. Preclinical prediction of AD using neuropsychological tests. *J. Int. Neuropsychol. Soc. 7:* 631-639, 2001.

Alexander, G.E., Chen, K., Pietrini, P., Rapoport, S.I., Reiman, E.M. Longitudinal PET Evaluation of Cerebral Metabolic Decline in Dementia: A Potential Outcome Measure in Alzheimer's Disease Treatment Studies. *Am. J. Psychiatry 159:* 738-745, 2002.

Alvarez, X.A., Cacabelos, R., Laredo, M., Couceiro, V., Sampedro, C., Varela, M., Corzo, L., Fernandez-Novoa, L., Vargas, M., Aleixandre, M., Linares, C., Granizo, E., Muresanu, D., Moessler, H. A 24-week, double-blind, placebo-controlled study of three dosages of Cerebrolysin in patients with mild to moderate Alzheimer's disease. *Eur. J. Neurol. 13:* 43-54, 2006.

AlzForum. 2007, "Drugs in clinical trials." From http://www.alzforum.org/drg/drc/ detail.asp?id=110.

Alzheimer, A. Über einen eigenartigen schweren Erkrankungsprozeß der Hirnrinde. *Neurologisches Centralblatt 23:* 1129-1136, 1906.

Alzheimer, A. Üeber eine eigenartige Erkrankung der Hirnrinde. *Centralblatt für Nervenheilkunde und Psychiatrie 30:* 177-179, 1907.

AlzheimerAssociation. 2007a, "Every 72 seconds someone in America develops Alzheimer's." From http://www.alz.org/news_and_events_rates_rise.asp.

AlzheimerAssociation. 2007b, "Stages of Alzheimer's." From http://www.alz.org/alzheimers_disease_stages_of_alzheimers.asp.

Amieva, H., Rouch-Leroyer, I., Letenneur, L., Dartigues, J.F., Fabrigoule, C. Cognitive slowing and learning of target detection skills in pre-demented subjects. *Brain Cogn. 54:* 212-214, 2004.

Ancelin, M.L., Artero, S., Portet, F., Dupuy, A.M., Touchon, J., Ritchie, K. Non-degenerative mild cognitive impairment in elderly people and use of anticholinergic drugs: longitudinal cohort study. *BMJ J. 332:* 455-459, 2006.

Andreasen, N., Blennow, K. CSF biomarkers for mild cognitive impairment and early Alzheimer's disease. *Clin. Neurol. Neurosurg. 107:* 165-173, 2005.

Andreasen, N., Minthon, L., Davidsson, P., Vanmechelen, E., Vanderstichele, H., Winblad, B., Blennow, K. Evaluation of CSF-tau and CSF-Aβ42 as diagnostic markers for Alzheimer disease in clinical practice. *Arch. Neurol. 58:* 373-379, 2001.

Andreasen, N., Minthon, L., Vanmechelen, E., Vanderstichele, H., Davidsson, P., Winblad, B., Blennow, K. Cerebrospinal fluid tau and Aβ42 as predictors of development of Alzheimer's disease in patients with mild cognitive impairment. *Neurosci. Lett. 273:* 5-8, 1999.

Andreasen, N., Vanmechelen, E., Vanderstichele, H., Davidsson, P., Blennow, K. Cerebrospinal fluid levels of total-tau, phospho-tau and Aβ42 predicts development of Alzheimer's disease in patients with mild cognitive impairment. *Acta Neurol. Scand. Suppl. 179:* 47-51, 2003.

Apelt, J., Ach, K., Schliebs, R. Aging-related down-regulation of neprilysin, a putative β-amyloid-degrading enzyme, in transgenic Tg2576 Alzheimer-like mouse brain is accompanied by an astroglial upregulation in the vicinity of β-amyloid plaques. *Neurosci. Lett. 339:* 183-186, 2003.

Arai, H., Ishiguro, K., Ohno, H., Moriyama, M., Itoh, N., Okamura, N., Matsui, T., Morikawa, Y., Horikawa, E., Kohno, H., Sasaki, H., Imahori, K. CSF phosphorylated tau protein and mild cognitive impairment: a prospective study. *Exp. Neurol. 166:* 201-203, 2000.

Arancio, O., Zhang, H.P., Chen, X., Lin, C., Trinchese, F., Puzzo, D., Liu, S., Hegde, A., Yan, S.F., Stern, A., Luddy, J.S., Lue, L.F., Walker, D.G., Roher, A., Buttini, M., Mucke,

L., Li, W., Schmidt, A.M., Kindy, M., Hyslop, P.A., Stern, D.M., Du Yan, S.S. RAGE potentiates Aβ-induced perturbation of neuronal function in transgenic mice. *EMBO J.* *23:* 4096-4105, 2004.

Arnaiz, E., Jelic, V., Almkvist, O., Wahlund, L.O., Winblad, B., Valind, S., Nordberg, A. Impaired cerebral glucose metabolism and cognitive functioning predict deterioration in mild cognitive impairment. *Neuroreport 12:* 851-855, 2001.

Asai, M., Hattori, C., Iwata, N., Saido, T.C., Sasagawa, N., Szabo, B., Hashimoto, Y., Maruyama, K., Tanuma, S., Kiso, Y., Ishiura, S. The novel β-secretase inhibitor KMI-429 reduces amyloid β peptide production in amyloid precursor protein transgenic and wild-type mice. *J. Neurochem. 96:* 533-540, 2006.

Asberom, T., Bara, T.A., Clader, J.W., Greenlee, W.J., Guzik, H.S., Josien, H.B., Li, W., Parker, E.M., Pissarnitski, D.A., Song, L., Zhang, L., Zhao, Z. Tetrahydroquinoline sulfonamides as γ-secretase inhibitors. *Bioorg. Med. Chem. Lett. 17:* 205-207, 2007a.

Asberom, T., Zhao, Z., Bara, T.A., Clader, J.W., Greenlee, W.J., Hyde, L.A., Josien, H.B., Li, W., McPhail, A.T., Nomeir, A.A., Parker, E.M., Rajagopalan, M., Song, L., Wong, G.T., Zhang, L., Zhang, Q., Pissarnitski, D.A. Discovery of γ-secretase inhibitors efficacious in a transgenic animal model of Alzheimer's disease. *Bioorg. Med. Chem. Lett. 17:* 511-516, 2007b.

Ashburner, J., Friston, K.J. Voxel-based morphometry--the methods. *Neuroimage 11:* 805-821, 2000.

Atwood, C.S., Moir, R.D., Huang, X., Scarpa, R.C., Bacarra, N.M., Romano, D.M., Hartshorn, M.A., Tanzi, R.E., Bush, A.I. Dramatic aggregation of Alzheimer Aβ by Cu(II) is induced by conditions representing physiological acidosis. *J. Biol. Chem. 273:* 12817-12826, 1998.

Atwood, C.S., Perry, G., Zeng, H., Kato, Y., Jones, W.D., Ling, K.Q., Huang, X., Moir, R.D., Wang, D., Sayre, L.M., Smith, M.A., Chen, S.G., Bush, A.I. Copper mediates dityrosine cross-linking of Alzheimer's amyloid-β. *Biochemistry 43:* 560-568, 2004.

Bard, F., Cannon, C., Barbour, R., Burke, R.L., Games, D., Grajeda, H., Guido, T., Hu, K., Huang, J., Johnson-Wood, K., Khan, K., Kholodenko, D., Lee, M., Lieberburg, I., Motter, R., Nguyen, M., Soriano, F., Vasquez, N., Weiss, K., Welch, B., Seubert, P., Schenk, D., Yednock, T. Peripherally administered antibodies against amyloid β-peptide enter the central nervous system and reduce pathology in a mouse model of Alzheimer disease. *Nat. Med. 6:* 916-919, 2000.

Barger, S.W. An unconventional hypothesis of oxidation in Alzheimer's disease: intersections with excitotoxicity. *Front. Biosci. 9:* 3286-3295, 2004.

Barghorn, S., Nimmrich, V., Striebinger, A., Krantz, C., Keller, P., Janson, B., Bahr, M., Schmidt, M., Bitner, R.S., Harlan, J., Barlow, E., Ebert, U., Hillen, H. Globular amyloid β-peptide oligomer - a homogenous and stable neuropathological protein in Alzheimer's disease. *J. Neurochem. 95:* 834-847, 2005.

Barten, D.M., Meredith, J.E., Jr., Zaczek, R., Houston, J.G., Albright, C.F. γ-secretase inhibitors for Alzheimer's disease: balancing efficacy and toxicity. *Drugs R. D. 7:* 87-97, 2006.

Bartus, R.T., Dean, R.L., 3rd, Beer, B., Lippa, A.S. The cholinergic hypothesis of geriatric memory dysfunction. *Science 217:* 408-414, 1982.

Baum, L., Ng, A. Curcumin interaction with copper and iron suggests one possible mechanism of action in Alzheimer's disease animal models. *J. Alzheimers Dis. 6:* 367-377; discussion 443-449, 2004.

Beeri, M.S., Werner, P., Adar, Z., Davidson, M., Noy, S. Economic cost of Alzheimer disease in Israel. *Alzheimer Dis. Assoc. Disord. 16:* 73-80, 2002.

Behl, C., Davis, J.B., Lesley, R., Schubert, D. Hydrogen peroxide mediates amyloid β protein toxicity. *Cell 77:* 817-827, 1994.

Berent, S., Giordani, B., Foster, N., Minoshima, S., Lajiness-O'Neill, R., Koeppe, R., Kuhl, D.E. Neuropsychological function and cerebral glucose utilization in isolated memory impairment and Alzheimer's disease. *J. Psychiatr. Res. 33:* 7-16, 1999.

Best, J.D., Smith, D.W., Reilly, M.A., O'Donnell, R., Lewis, H.D., Ellis, S., Wilkie, N., Rosahl, T.W., Laroque, P.A., Boussiquet-Leroux, C., Churcher, I., Atack, J.R., Harrison, T., Shearman, M.S. The novel γ secretase inhibitor N-[cis-4-[(4-chlorophenyl)sulfonyl]-4-(2,5-difluorophenyl)cyclohexyl]-1,1,1-trifluoromethanesulfonamide (MRK-560) reduces amyloid plaque deposition without evidence of notch-related pathology in the Tg2576 mouse. *J. Pharmacol. Exp. Ther. 320:* 552-558, 2007.

Biere, A.L., Ostaszewski, B., Stimson, E.R., Hyman, B.T., Maggio, J.E., Selkoe, D.J. Amyloid β-peptide is transported on lipoproteins and albumin in human plasma. *J. Biol. Chem. 271:* 32916-32922, 1996.

Birks, J., Grimley Evans, J., Iakovidou, V., Tsolaki, M. Rivastigmine for Alzheimer's disease. *Cochrane Database Syst. Rev.:* CD001191, 2000a.

Birks, J.S., Melzer, D., Beppu, H. Donepezil for mild and moderate Alzheimer's disease. *Cochrane Database Syst. Rev.:* CD001190, 2000b.

Bitan, G., Kirkitadze, M.D., Lomakin, A., Vollers, S.S., Benedek, G.B., Teplow, D.B. Amyloid β-protein (Aβ) assembly: Aβ40 and Aβ42 oligomerize through distinct pathways. *Proc. Natl. Acad. Sci. USA 100:* 330-335, 2003a.

Bitan, G., Vollers, S.S., Teplow, D.B. Elucidation of primary structure elements controlling early amyloid β-protein oligomerization. *J. Biol. Chem. 278:* 34882-34889, 2003b.

Blasko, I., Jellinger, K., Kemmler, G., Krampla, W., Jungwirth, S., Wichart, I., Tragl, K.H., Fischer, P. Conversion from cognitive health to mild cognitive impairment and Alzheimer's disease: Prediction by plasma Aβ42, medial temporal lobe atrophy and homocysteine. *Neurobiol. Aging*, 2006.

Blennow, K. Cerebrospinal fluid protein biomarkers for Alzheimer's disease. *NeuroRx 1:* 213-225, 2004a.

Blennow, K. CSF biomarkers for mild cognitive impairment. *J. Intern. Med. 256:* 224-234, 2004b.

Borroni, B., Anchisi, D., Paghera, B., Vicini, B., Kerrouche, N., Garibotto, V., Terzi, A., Vignolo, L.A., Di Luca, M., Giubbini, R., Padovani, A., Perani, D. Combined 99mTc-ECD SPECT and neuropsychological studies in MCI for the assessment of conversion to AD. *Neurobiol. Aging 27:* 24-31, 2006.

Brendza, R.P., Holtzman, D.M. Aβ immunotherapies in mice and men. *Alzheimer Dis. Assoc. Disord. 20:* 118-123, 2006.

Bresciani, L., Rossi, R., Testa, C., Geroldi, C., Galluzzi, S., Laakso, M.P., Beltramello, A., Soininen, H., Frisoni, G.B. Visual assessment of medial temporal atrophy on MR films in Alzheimer's disease: comparison with volumetry. *Aging Clin. Exp. Res. 17:* 8-13, 2005.

Bush, A.I. The metallobiology of Alzheimer's disease. *Trends Neurosci. 26:* 207-214, 2003.

Bush, A.I., Pettingell, W.H., Multhaup, G., d Paradis, M., Vonsattel, J.P., Gusella, J.F., Beyreuther, K., Masters, C.L., Tanzi, R.E. Rapid induction of Alzheimer Aβ amyloid formation by zinc. *Science 265:* 1464-1467, 1994.

Buxbaum, J.D., Liu, K.N., Luo, Y., Slack, J.L., Stocking, K.L., Peschon, J.J., Johnson, R.S., Castner, B.J., Cerretti, D.P., Black, R.A. Evidence that tumor necrosis factor α converting enzyme is involved in regulated α-secretase cleavage of the Alzheimer amyloid protein precursor. *J. Biol. Chem. 273:* 27765-27767, 1998.

Caccamo, A., Oddo, S., Sugarman, M.C., Akbari, Y., LaFerla, F.M. Age- and region-dependent alterations in Aβ-degrading enzymes: implications for Aβ-induced disorders. *Neurobiol. Aging 26:* 645-654, 2005.

Cai, H., Wang, Y., McCarthy, D., Wen, H., Borchelt, D.R., Price, D.L., Wong, P.C. BACE1 is the major β-secretase for generation of Aβ peptides by neurons. *Nat. Neurosci. 4:* 233-234, 2001.

Casley, C.S., Canevari, L., Land, J.M., Clark, J.B., Sharpe, M.A. β-amyloid inhibits integrated mitochondrial respiration and key enzyme activities. *J. Neurochem. 80:* 91-100, 2002.

Chacon, M.A., Barria, M.I., Soto, C., Inestrosa, N.C. β-sheet breaker peptide prevents Aβ-induced spatial memory impairments with partial reduction of amyloid deposits. *Mol. Psychiatry. 9:* 953-961, 2004.

Chang, W.P., Koelsch, G., Wong, S., Downs, D., Da, H., Weerasena, V., Gordon, B., Devasamudram, T., Bilcer, G., Ghosh, A.K., Tang, J. *In vivo* inhibition of Aβ production by memapsin 2 (β-secretase) inhibitors. *J. Neurochem. 89:* 1409-1416, 2004.

Chen, F., Hasegawa, H., Schmitt-Ulms, G., Kawarai, T., Bohm, C., Katayama, T., Gu, Y., Sanjo, N., Glista, M., Rogaeva, E., Wakutani, Y., Pardossi-Piquard, R., Ruan, X., Tandon, A., Checler, F., Marambaud, P., Hansen, K., Westaway, D., St George-Hyslop, P., Fraser, P. TMP21 is a presenilin complex component that modulates γ-secretase but not ε-secretase activity. *Nature 440:* 1208-1212, 2006.

Cherny, R.A., Atwood, C.S., Xilinas, M.E., Gray, D.N., Jones, W.D., McLean, C.A., Barnham, K.J., Volitakis, I., Fraser, F.W., Kim, Y., Huang, X., Goldstein, L.E., Moir, R.D., Lim, J.T., Beyreuther, K., Zheng, H., Tanzi, R.E., Masters, C.L., Bush, A.I. Treatment with a copper-zinc chelator markedly and rapidly inhibits β-amyloid accumulation in Alzheimer's disease transgenic mice. *Neuron 30:* 665-676, 2001.

Cherny, R.A., Legg, J.T., McLean, C.A., Fairlie, D.P., Huang, X., Atwood, C.S., Beyreuther, K., Tanzi, R.E., Masters, C.L., Bush, A.I. Aqueous dissolution of Alzheimer's disease Aβ amyloid deposits by biometal depletion. *J. Biol. Chem. 274:* 23223-23228, 1999.

Chetelat, G., Desgranges, B., De La Sayette, V., Viader, F., Eustache, F., Baron, J.C. Mapping gray matter loss with voxel-based morphometry in mild cognitive impairment. *Neuroreport 13:* 1939-1943, 2002.

Chetelat, G., Desgranges, B., de la Sayette, V., Viader, F., Eustache, F., Baron, J.C. Mild cognitive impairment: Can FDG-PET predict who is to rapidly convert to Alzheimer's disease? *Neurology 60:* 1374-1377, 2003.

Choi, D.S., Wang, D., Yu, G.Q., Zhu, G., Kharazia, V.N., Paredes, J.P., Chang, W.S., Deitchman, J.K., Mucke, L., Messing, R.O. PKCε increases endothelin converting enzyme activity and reduces amyloid plaque pathology in transgenic mice. *Proc. Natl. Acad. Sci. USA 103:* 8215-8220, 2006.

Choi, Y.T., Jung, C.H., Lee, S.R., Bae, J.H., Baek, W.K., Suh, M.H., Park, J., Park, C.W., Suh, S.I. The green tea polyphenol (-)-epigallocatechin gallate attenuates β-amyloid-induced neurotoxicity in cultured hippocampal neurons. *Life Sci. 70:* 603-614, 2001.

Chong, M.S., Lim, W.S., Sahadevan, S. Biomarkers in preclinical Alzheimer's disease. *Curr. Opin. Investig. Drugs 7:* 600-607, 2006.

Churcher, I., Beher, D. γ-secretase as a therapeutic target for the treatment of Alzheimer's disease. *Curr. Pharm. Des. 11:* 3363-3382, 2005.

Churcher, I., Beher, D., Best, J.D., Castro, J.L., Clarke, E.E., Gentry, A., Harrison, T., Hitzel, L., Kay, E., Kerrad, S., Lewis, H.D., Morentin-Gutierrez, P., Mortishire-Smith, R., Oakley, P.J., Reilly, M., Shaw, D.E., Shearman, M.S., Teall, M.R., Williams, S., Wrigley, J.D. 4-substituted cyclohexyl sulfones as potent, orally active β-secretase inhibitors. *Bioorg. Med. Chem. Lett. 16:* 280-284, 2006.

Citron, M. β-secretase inhibition for the treatment of Alzheimer's disease--promise and challenge. *Trends Pharmacol. Sci. 25:* 92-97, 2004.

ClinicalTrials.gov. 2006, "Safety of TTP488 in Patients With Mild to Moderate Alzheimer's Disease." From http://clinicaltrials.gov/ct/show/NCT00141661.

Coburn, C.A., Stachel, S.J., Li, Y.M., Rush, D.M., Steele, T.G., Chen-Dodson, E., Holloway, M.K., Xu, M., Huang, Q., Lai, M.T., DiMuzio, J., Crouthamel, M.C., Shi, X.P., Sardana, V., Chen, Z., Munshi, S., Kuo, L., Makara, G.M., Annis, D.A., Tadikonda, P.K., Nash, H.M., Vacca, J.P., Wang, T. Identification of a small molecule nonpeptide active site β-secretase inhibitor that displays a nontraditional binding mode for aspartyl proteases. *J. Med. Chem. 47:* 6117-6119, 2004.

Conner, J.M., Culberson, A., Packowski, C., Chiba, A.A., Tuszynski, M.H. Lesions of the Basal forebrain cholinergic system impair task acquisition and abolish cortical plasticity associated with motor skill learning. *Neuron 38:* 819-829, 2003.

Cribbs, D.H., Ghochikyan, A., Vasilevko, V., Tran, M., Petrushina, I., Sadzikava, N., Babikyan, D., Kesslak, P., Kieber-Emmons, T., Cotman, C.W., Agadjanyan, M.G. Adjuvant-dependent modulation of Th1 and Th2 responses to immunization with β-amyloid. *Int. Immunol. 15:* 505-514, 2003.

Cumming, J.N., Iserloh, U., Kennedy, M.E. Design and development of BACE-1 inhibitors. *Curr. Opin. Drug Discov. Devel. 7:* 536-556, 2004.

Cummings, J.L. Alzheimer's disease. *N. Engl. J. Med. 351:* 56-67, 2004.

Czirr, E., Weggen, S. γ-secretase modulation with Aβ42-lowering nonsteroidal anti-inflammatory drugs and derived compounds. *Neurodegener. Dis. 3:* 298-304, 2006.

Dahlgren, K.N., Manelli, A.M., Stine, W.B., Jr., Baker, L.K., Krafft, G.A., LaDu, M.J. Oligomeric and fibrillar species of amyloid-β peptides differentially affect neuronal viability. *J. Biol. Chem. 277:* 32046-32053, 2002.

Dasilva, K.A., Aubert, I., McLaurin, J. Vaccine development for Alzheimer's disease. *Curr. Pharm. Des. 12:* 4283-4293, 2006.

De Felice, F.G., Ferreira, S.T. β-amyloid production, aggregation, and clearance as targets for therapy in Alzheimer's disease. *Cell Mol. Neurobiol. 22:* 545-563, 2002.

De Felice, F.G., Velasco, P.T., Lambert, M.P., Viola, K., Fernandez, S.J., Ferreira, S.T., Klein, W.L. Aβ oligomers induce neuronal oxidative stress through an *N*-methyl-D-aspartate receptor-dependent mechanism that is blocked by the Alzheimer drug memantine. *J. Biol. Chem. 282:* 11590-11601, 2007.

De Jonghe, C., Esselens, C., Kumar-Singh, S., Craessaerts, K., Serneels, S., Checler, F., Annaert, W., Van Broeckhoven, C., De Strooper, B. Pathogenic APP mutations near the γ-secretase cleavage site differentially affect Aβ secretion and APP C-terminal fragment stability. *Hum. Mol. Genet. 10:* 1665-1671, 2001.

De Strooper, B., Annaert, W., Cupers, P., Saftig, P., Craessaerts, K., Mumm, J.S., Schroeter, E.H., Schrijvers, V., Wolfe, M.S., Ray, W.J., Goate, A., Kopan, R. A presenilin-1-dependent γ-secretase-like protease mediates release of Notch intracellular domain. *Nature 398:* 518-522, 1999.

Deane, R., Du Yan, S., Submamaryan, R.K., LaRue, B., Jovanovic, S., Hogg, E., Welch, D., Manness, L., Lin, C., Yu, J., Zhu, H., Ghiso, J., Frangione, B., Stern, A., Schmidt, A.M., Armstrong, D.L., Arnold, B., Liliensiek, B., Nawroth, P., Hofman, F., Kindy, M., Stern, D., Zlokovic, B. RAGE mediates Aβ peptide transport across the blood-brain barrier and accumulation in brain. *Nat. Med. 9:* 907-913, 2003.

Deane, R., Wu, Z., Sagare, A., Davis, J., Du Yan, S., Hamm, K., Xu, F., Parisi, M., LaRue, B., Hu, H.W., Spijkers, P., Guo, H., Song, X., Lenting, P.J., Van Nostrand, W.E., Zlokovic, B.V. LRP/Aβ peptide interaction mediates differential brain efflux of Aβ isoforms. *Neuron 43:* 333-344, 2004a.

Deane, R., Wu, Z., Zlokovic, B.V. RAGE (yin) versus LRP (yang) balance regulates alzheimer Aβ-peptide clearance through transport across the blood-brain barrier. *Stroke 35:* 2628-2631, 2004b.

Deane, R., Zlokovic, B.V. Role of the blood-brain barrier in the pathogenesis of Alzheimer's disease. *Curr. Alzheimer Res. 4:* 191-197, 2007.

DeMattos, R.B., Bales, K.R., Cummins, D.J., Dodart, J.C., Paul, S.M., Holtzman, D.M. Peripheral anti-Aβ antibody alters CNS and plasma Aβ clearance and decreases brain Aβ burden in a mouse model of Alzheimer's disease. *Proc. Natl. Acad. Sci. USA 98:* 8850-8855, 2001.

deToledo-Morrell, L., Stoub, T.R., Bulgakova, M., Wilson, R.S., Bennett, D.A., Leurgans, S., Wuu, J., Turner, D.A. MRI-derived entorhinal volume is a good predictor of conversion from MCI to AD. *Neurobiol. Aging 25:* 1197-1203, 2004.

Devanand, D.P., Folz, M., Gorlyn, M., Moeller, J.R., Stern, Y. Questionable dementia: clinical course and predictors of outcome. *J. Am. Geriatr. Soc. 45:* 321-328, 1997.

Devanand, D.P., Pradhaban, G., Liu, X., Khandji, A., De Santi, S., Segal, S., Rusinek, H., Pelton, G.H., Honig, L.S., Mayeux, R., Stern, Y., Tabert, M.H., de Leon, M.J. Hippocampal and entorhinal atrophy in mild cognitive impairment: prediction of Alzheimer disease. *Neurology 68:* 828-836, 2007.

Dickerson, B.C., Goncharova, I., Sullivan, M.P., Forchetti, C., Wilson, R.S., Bennett, D.A., Beckett, L.A., deToledo-Morrell, L. MRI-derived entorhinal and hippocampal atrophy in incipient and very mild Alzheimer's disease. *Neurobiol. Aging 22:* 747-754, 2001.

Ding, H., Schwarz, D.S., Keene, A., Affar el, B., Fenton, L., Xia, X., Shi, Y., Zamore, P.D., Xu, Z. Selective silencing by RNAi of a dominant allele that causes amyotrophic lateral sclerosis. *Aging Cell 2:* 209-217, 2003.

Dominguez, D., Tournoy, J., Hartmann, D., Huth, T., Cryns, K., Deforce, S., Serneels, L., Camacho, I.E., Marjaux, E., Craessaerts, K., Roebroek, A.J., Schwake, M., D'Hooge, R., Bach, P., Kalinke, U., Moechars, D., Alzheimer, C., Reiss, K., Saftig, P., De Strooper, B. Phenotypic and biochemical analyses of BACE1- and BACE2-deficient mice. *J. Biol. Chem. 280:* 30797-30806, 2005.

Donahue, J.E., Flaherty, S.L., Johanson, C.E., Duncan, J.A., 3rd, Silverberg, G.D., Miller, M.C., Tavares, R., Yang, W., Wu, Q., Sabo, E., Hovanesian, V., Stopa, E.G. RAGE, LRP-1, and amyloid-β protein in Alzheimer's disease. *Acta Neuropathol. (Berl) 112:* 405-415, 2006.

Dong, J., Atwood, C.S., Anderson, V.E., Siedlak, S.L., Smith, M.A., Perry, G., Carey, P.R. Metal binding and oxidation of Aβ within isolated senile plaque cores: Raman microscopic evidence. *Biochemistry 42:* 2768-2773, 2003.

Dotti, C.G., Galvan, C., Ledesma, M.D. Plasmin deficiency in Alzheimer's disease brains: causal or casual? *Neurodegener. Dis. 1:* 205-212, 2004.

Drzezga, A., Lautenschlager, N., Siebner, H., Riemenschneider, M., Willoch, F., Minoshima, S., Schwaiger, M., Kurz, A. Cerebral metabolic changes accompanying conversion of mild cognitive impairment into Alzheimer's disease: a PET follow-up study. *Eur. J. Nucl. Med. Mol. Imaging 30:* 1104-1113, 2003.

Du, A.T., Schuff, N., Amend, D., Laakso, M.P., Hsu, Y.Y., Jagust, W.J., Yaffe, K., Kramer, J.H., Reed, B., Norman, D., Chui, H.C., Weiner, M.W. Magnetic resonance imaging of the entorhinal cortex and hippocampus in mild cognitive impairment and Alzheimer's disease. *J. Neurol. Neurosurg. Psychiatry 71:* 441-447, 2001.

Du, A.T., Schuff, N., Zhu, X.P., Jagust, W.J., Miller, B.L., Reed, B.R., Kramer, J.H., Mungas, D., Yaffe, K., Chui, H.C., Weiner, M.W. Atrophy rates of entorhinal cortex in AD and normal aging. *Neurology 60:* 481-486, 2003.

Du, Y., Ni, B., Glinn, M., Dodel, R.C., Bales, K.R., Zhang, Z., Hyslop, P.A., Paul, S.M. α2-Macroglobulin as a β-amyloid peptide-binding plasma protein. *J. Neurochem. 69:* 299-305, 1997.

Eckman, E.A., Eckman, C.B. Aβ-degrading enzymes: modulators of Alzheimer's disease pathogenesis and targets for therapeutic intervention. *Biochem. Soc. Trans. 33:* 1101-1105, 2005.

Eckman, E.A., Watson, M., Marlow, L., Sambamurti, K., Eckman, C.B. Alzheimer's disease β-amyloid peptide is increased in mice deficient in endothelin-converting enzyme. *J. Biol. Chem. 278:* 2081-2084, 2003.

El-Agnaf, O.M., Mahil, D.S., Patel, B.P., Austen, B.M. Oligomerization and toxicity of β-amyloid-42 implicated in Alzheimer's disease. *Biochem. Biophys. Res. Commun. 273:* 1003-1007, 2000.

El-Amouri, S.S., Zhu, H., Yu, J., Gage, F.H., Verma, I.M., Kindy, M.S. Neprilysin protects neurons against Aβ peptide toxicity. *Brain Res.*, 2007.

Encinas, M., De Juan, R., Marcos, A., Gil, P., Barabash, A., Fernandez, C., De Ugarte, C., Cabranes, J.A. Regional cerebral blood flow assessed with 99mTc-ECD SPET as a marker of progression of mild cognitive impairment to Alzheimer's disease. *Eur. J. Nucl. Med. Mol. Imaging 30:* 1473-1480, 2003.

Eriksen, J.L., Sagi, S.A., Smith, T.E., Weggen, S., Das, P., McLendon, D.C., Ozols, V.V., Jessing, K.W., Zavitz, K.H., Koo, E.H., Golde, T.E. NSAIDs and enantiomers of flurbiprofen target γ-secretase and lower Aβ42 *in vivo*. *J. Clin. Invest. 112:* 440-449, 2003.

Fahrenholz, F., Postina, R. α-secretase activation--an approach to Alzheimer's disease therapy. *Neurodegener. Dis. 3:* 255-261, 2006.

Farris, W., Mansourian, S., Chang, Y., Lindsley, L., Eckman, E.A., Frosch, M.P., Eckman, C.B., Tanzi, R.E., Selkoe, D.J., Guenette, S. Insulin-degrading enzyme regulates the levels of insulin, amyloid β-protein, and the β-amyloid precursor protein intracellular domain *in vivo*. *Proc. Natl. Acad. Sci. USA 100:* 4162-4167, 2003.

Feng, X., Zhao, P., He, Y., Zuo, Z. Allele-specific silencing of Alzheimer's disease genes: the amyloid precursor protein genes with Swedish or London mutations. *Gene 371:* 68-74, 2006.

Ferrer, I., Boada Rovira, M., Sanchez Guerra, M.L., Rey, M.J., Costa-Jussa, F. Neuropathology and pathogenesis of encephalitis following amyloid-β immunization in Alzheimer's disease. *Brain Pathol. 14:* 11-20, 2004.

Fischer, W., Bjorklund, A., Chen, K., Gage, F.H. NGF improves spatial memory in aged rodents as a function of age. *J. Neurosci. 11:* 1889-1906, 1991.

Flicker, C., Ferris, S.H., Reisberg, B. Mild cognitive impairment in the elderly: predictors of dementia. *Neurology 41:* 1006-1009, 1991.

Folstein, M.F., Folstein, S.E., McHugh, P.R. "Mini-mental state". A practical method for grading the cognitive state of patients for the clinician. *J. Psychiatr. Res. 12:* 189-198, 1975.

Fox, N.C., Black, R.S., Gilman, S., Rossor, M.N., Griffith, S.G., Jenkins, L., Koller, M. Effects of Aβ immunization (AN1792) on MRI measures of cerebral volume in Alzheimer disease. *Neurology 64:* 1563-1572, 2005.

Fradinger, E.A., Bitan, G. En route to early diagnosis of Alzheimer's disease--are we there yet? *Trends Biotechnol. 23:* 531-533, 2005.

Fradinger, E.A., Spring, S.M., Condron, M.M., Bitan, G., Teplow, D.B. Structural stabilization of oligomers increases neurotoxicity of the amyloid β-protein (Aβ). Program No. 587.14. 2005 Neuroscience Meeting Planner. Society for Neuroscience, 2005.

Fradinger, E.A., Spring, S.M., Tan, M., Condron, M.C., Monien, B.H., Xie, C.-W., Bitan, G. C-terminal fragments inhibit amyloid β-protein oligomerization and neurotoxicity. Manuscript in preparation.

Francis-Turner, L., Valouskova, V. Nerve growth factor and nootropic drug Cerebrolysin but not fibroblast growth factor can reduce spatial memory impairment elicited by fimbria-fornix transection: short-term study. *Neurosci. Lett. 202:* 193-196, 1996.

Fre, S., Huyghe, M., Mourikis, P., Robine, S., Louvard, D., Artavanis-Tsakonas, S. Notch signals control the fate of immature progenitor cells in the intestine. *Nature 435:* 964-968, 2005.

Frenkel, D., Balass, M., Katchalski-Katzir, E., Solomon, B. High affinity binding of monoclonal antibodies to the sequential epitope EFRH of β-amyloid peptide is essential for modulation of fibrillar aggregation. *J. Neuroimmunol. 95:* 136-142, 1999.

Frick, K.M., Price, D.L., Koliatsos, V.E., Markowska, A.L. The effects of nerve growth factor on spatial recent memory in aged rats persist after discontinuation of treatment. *J. Neurosci. 17:* 2543-2550, 1997.

Fukami, S., Watanabe, K., Iwata, N., Haraoka, J., Lu, B., Gerard, N.P., Gerard, C., Fraser, P., Westaway, D., St George-Hyslop, P., Saido, T.C. Aβ-degrading endopeptidase, neprilysin, in mouse brain: synaptic and axonal localization inversely correlating with Aβ pathology. *Neurosci. Res. 43:* 39-56, 2002.

Fülöp, L., Zarandi, M., Datki, Z., Soos, K., Penke, B. β-amyloid-derived pentapeptide RIIGLa inhibits Aβ(1-42) aggregation and toxicity. *Biochem. Biophys. Res. Commun. 324:* 64-69, 2004.

Furukawa, K., Mattson, M.P. Secreted amyloid precursor protein α selectively suppresses *N*-methyl-D-aspartate currents in hippocampal neurons: involvement of cyclic GMP. *Neuroscience 83:* 429-438, 1998.

Gandy, S., Greengard, P. Processing of Alzheimer Aβ-amyloid precursor protein: cell biology, regulation, and role in Alzheimer disease. *Int. Rev. Neurobiol. 36:* 29-50, 1994a.

Gandy, S., Greengard, P. Regulated cleavage of the Alzheimer amyloid precursor protein: molecular and cellular basis. *Biochimie 76:* 300-303, 1994b.

Gandy, S., Martins, R.N., Buxbaum, J. Molecular and cellular basis for anti-amyloid therapy in Alzheimer disease. *Alzheimer Dis. Assoc. Disord. 17:* 259-266, 2003.

Geerts, H. Drug evaluation: (R)-flurbiprofen--an enantiomer of flurbiprofen for the treatment of Alzheimer's disease. *IDrugs 10:* 121-133, 2007.

Georganopoulou, D.G., Chang, L., Nam, J.M., Thaxton, C.S., Mufson, E.J., Klein, W.L., Mirkin, C.A. Nanoparticle-based detection in cerebral spinal fluid of a soluble pathogenic biomarker for Alzheimer's disease. *Proc. Natl. Acad. Sci. USA 102:* 2273-2276, 2005.

Geroldi, D., Falcone, C., Emanuele, E. Soluble receptor for advanced glycation end products: from disease marker to potential therapeutic target. *Curr. Med. Chem. 13:* 1971-1978, 2006.

Gervais, F., Paquette, J., Morissette, C., Krzywkowski, P., Yu, M., Azzi, M., Lacombe, D., Kong, X., Aman, A., Laurin, J., Szarek, W.A., Tremblay, P. Targeting soluble Aβ peptide with Tramiprosate for the treatment of brain amyloidosis. *Neurobiol. Aging,* 2006.

Ghiso, J., Frangione, B. Amyloidosis and Alzheimer's disease. *Adv. Drug. Deliv. Rev. 54:* 1539-1551, 2002.

Ghochikyan, A., Mkrtichyan, M., Petrushina, I., Movsesyan, N., Karapetyan, A., Cribbs, D.H., Agadjanyan, M.G. Prototype Alzheimer's disease epitope vaccine induced strong Th2-type anti-Aβ antibody response with Alum to Quil A adjuvant switch. *Vaccine 24:* 2275-2282, 2006.

Ghosh, A.K., Kumaragurubaran, N., Tang, J. Recent developments of structure based β-secretase inhibitors for Alzheimer's disease. *Curr. Top. Med. Chem. 5:* 1609-1622, 2005.

Gilman, S., Koller, M., Black, R.S., Jenkins, L., Griffith, S.G., Fox, N.C., Eisner, L., Kirby, L., Rovira, M.B., Forette, F., Orgogozo, J.M. Clinical effects of Aβ immunization (AN1792) in patients with AD in an interrupted trial. *Neurology 64:* 1553-1562, 2005.

Glabe, C.G. Common mechanisms of amyloid oligomer pathogenesis in degenerative disease. *Neurobiol. Aging 27:* 570-575, 2006.

Goate, A., Chartier-Harlin, M.C., Mullan, M., Brown, J., Crawford, F., Fidani, L., Giuffra, L., Haynes, A., Irving, N., James, L., et al. Segregation of a missense mutation in the amyloid precursor protein gene with familial Alzheimer's disease. *Nature 349:* 704-706, 1991.

Golde, T.E. Alzheimer disease therapy: can the amyloid cascade be halted? *J. Clin. Invest. 111:* 11-18, 2003.

Golde, T.E. Disease modifying therapy for AD? *J. Neurochem. 99:* 689-707, 2006.

Golde, T.E., Eckman, C.B. Cholesterol modulation as an emerging strategy for the treatment of Alzheimer's disease. *Drug Discov. Today 6:* 1049-1055, 2001.

Goldstein, L.E., Muffat, J.A., Cherny, R.A., Moir, R.D., Ericsson, M.H., Huang, X., Mavros, C., Coccia, J.A., Faget, K.Y., Fitch, K.A., Masters, C.L., Tanzi, R.E., Chylack, L.T.J., Bush, A.I. Cytosolic β-amyloid deposition and supranuclear cataracts in lenses from people with Alzheimer's disease. *Lancet 361:* 1258-1265., 2003.

Gong, Y., Chang, L., Viola, K.L., Lacor, P.N., Lambert, M.P., Finch, C.E., Krafft, G.A., Klein, W.L. Alzheimer's disease-affected brain: presence of oligomeric Aβ ligands (ADDLs) suggests a molecular basis for reversible memory loss. *Proc. Natl. Acad. Sci. USA 100:* 10417-10422, 2003.

Gordon, D.J., Sciarretta, K.L., Meredith, S.C. Inhibition of β-amyloid(40) fibrillogenesis and disassembly of β-amyloid(40) fibrils by short β-amyloid congeners containing *N*-methyl amino acids at alternate residues. *Biochemistry 40:* 8237-8245, 2001.

Gordon, D.J., Tappe, R., Meredith, S.C. Design and characterization of a membrane permeable *N*-methyl amino acid-containing peptide that inhibits Aβ1-40 fibrillogenesis. *J. Pept. Res. 60:* 37-55, 2002.

Gottfries, J., Blennow, K., Lehmann, M.W., Regland, B., Gottfries, C.G. One-carbon metabolism and other biochemical correlates of cognitive impairment as visualized by principal component analysis. *J. Geriatr. Psychiatry Neurol. 14:* 109-114, 2001.

Grant, W.B. Year 2000 prevalence of Alzheimer disease in the United States. *Arch. Neurol. 61:* 802-803; author reply 803, 2004.

Gravina, S.A., Ho, L.B., Eckman, C.B., Long, K.E., Ötvös, L., Jr, Younkin, L.H., Suzuki, N., Younkin, S.G. Amyloid β protein (Aβ) in Alzheimer's disease brain- Biochemical and immunocytochemical analysis with antibodies specific for forms ending at Aβ40 or Aβ42(43). *J. Biol. Chem. 270:* 7013-7016, 1995.

Guillozet, A.L., Weintraub, S., Mash, D.C., Mesulam, M.M. Neurofibrillary tangles, amyloid, and memory in aging and mild cognitive impairment. *Arch. Neurol. 60:* 729-736, 2003.

Haass, C., Schlossmacher, M.G., Hung, A.Y., Vigo-Pelfrey, C., Mellon, A., Ostaszewski, B.L., Lieberburg, I., Koo, E.H., Schenk, D., Teplow, D.B., et al. Amyloid β-peptide is produced by cultured cells during normal metabolism [see comments]. *Nature 359:* 322-325, 1992.

Haass, C., Selkoe, D.J. Soluble protein oligomers in neurodegeneration: lessons from the Alzheimer's amyloid β-peptide. *Nat. Rev. Mol. Cell Biol. 8:* 101-112, 2007.

Hagg, T., Fass-Holmes, B., Vahlsing, H.L., Manthorpe, M., Conner, J.M., Varon, S. Nerve growth factor (NGF) reverses axotomy-induced decreases in choline acetyltransferase, NGF receptor and size of medial septum cholinergic neurons. *Brain Res. 505:* 29-38, 1989.

Hajieva, P., Behl, C. Antioxidants as a potential therapy against age-related neurodegenerative diseases: Aβ toxicity and Alzheimer's disease. *Curr. Pharm. Des. 12:* 699-704, 2006.

Hamaguchi, T., Ono, K., Yamada, M. Anti-amyloidogenic therapies: strategies for prevention and treatment of Alzheimer's disease. *Cell Mol. Life Sci. 63:* 1538-1552, 2006.

Hampel, H., Teipel, S.J., Fuchsberger, T., Andreasen, N., Wiltfang, J., Otto, M., Shen, Y., Dodel, R., Du, Y., Farlow, M., Moller, H.J., Blennow, K., Buerger, K. Value of CSF β-amyloid1-42 and tau as predictors of Alzheimer's disease in patients with mild cognitive impairment. *Mol. Psychiatry. 9:* 705-710, 2004.

Hardy, J., Selkoe, D.J. The amyloid hypothesis of Alzheimer's disease: progress and problems on the road to therapeutics. *Science 297:* 353-356, 2002.

Hardy, J.A., Higgins, G.A. Alzheimer's disease: the amyloid cascade hypothesis. *Science 256:* 184-185, 1992.

Hartley, D.M., Walsh, D.M., Ye, C.P.P., Diehl, T., Vasquez, S., Vassilev, P.M., Teplow, D.B., Selkoe, D.J. Protofibrillar intermediates of amyloid β-protein induce acute electrophysiological changes and progressive neurotoxicity in cortical neurons. *J. Neurosci. 19:* 8876-8884, 1999.

Hartman, R.E., Izumi, Y., Bales, K.R., Paul, S.M., Wozniak, D.F., Holtzman, D.M. Treatment with an amyloid-β antibody ameliorates plaque load, learning deficits, and hippocampal long-term potentiation in a mouse model of Alzheimer's disease. *J. Neurosci. 25:* 6213-6220, 2005.

Head, E., Pop, V., Barrett, E.G., Kraus, K., Segura, A., Murphy, M.P., Vasilevko, V., Glabe, C., Kayed, R., Milton, S., Cribbs, D.H., Cotman, C.W. Lack of cognitive improvement in aged canines actively immunized with fibrillar or oligomeric β-amyloid. Program No. 270.20. 2006 Neuroscience Meeting Planner. Society for Neuroscience, 2006.

HeartProtectionStudyCollaborativeGroup. MRC/BHF Heart Protection Study of cholesterol lowering with simvastatin in 20,536 high-risk individuals: a randomised placebo-controlled trial. *Lancet 360:* 7-22, 2002.

Hebert, L.E., Scherr, P.A., Bienias, J.L., Bennett, D.A., Evans, D.A. Alzheimer disease in the US population: prevalence estimates using the 2000 census. *Arch. Neurol. 60:* 1119-1122, 2003.

Heneka, M.T., O'Banion, M.K. Inflammatory processes in Alzheimer's disease. *J. Neuroimmunol. 184:* 69-91, 2007.

Henkin, J., Marcotte, P., Yang, H.C. The plasminogen-plasmin system. *Prog. Cardiovasc. Dis. 34:* 135-164, 1991.

Hepler, R.W., Grimm, K.M., Nahas, D.D., Breese, R., Dodson, E.C., Acton, P., Keller, P.M., Yeager, M., Wang, H., Shughrue, P., Kinney, G., Joyce, J.G. Solution State Characterization of Amyloid β-Derived Diffusible Ligands. *Biochemistry 45:* 15157-15167, 2006.

Herz, J., Marschang, P. Coaxing the LDL receptor family into the fold. *Cell 112:* 289-292, 2003.

Herz, J., Strickland, D.K. LRP: a multifunctional scavenger and signaling receptor. *J. Clin. Invest. 108:* 779-784, 2001.

Hetenyi, C., Szabo, Z., Klement, E., Datki, Z., Kortvelyesi, T., Zarandi, M., Penke, B. Pentapeptide amides interfere with the aggregation of β-amyloid peptide of Alzheimer's disease. *Biochem. Biophys. Res. Commun. 292:* 931-936, 2002.

Higgins, G.A., Jacobsen, H. Transgenic mouse models of Alzheimer's disease: phenotype and application. *Behav. Pharmacol. 14:* 419-438, 2003.

Hirao, K., Ohnishi, T., Hirata, Y., Yamashita, F., Mori, T., Moriguchi, Y., Matsuda, H., Nemoto, K., Imabayashi, E., Yamada, M., Iwamoto, T., Arima, K., Asada, T. The prediction of rapid conversion to Alzheimer's disease in mild cognitive impairment using regional cerebral blood flow SPECT. *Neuroimage 28:* 1014-1021, 2005.

Hock, C., Heese, K., Hulette, C., Rosenberg, C., Otten, U. Region-specific neurotrophin imbalances in Alzheimer disease: decreased levels of brain-derived neurotrophic factor and increased levels of nerve growth factor in hippocampus and cortical areas. *Arch. Neurol. 57:* 846-851, 2000a.

Hock, C., Heese, K., Muller-Spahn, F., Hulette, C., Rosenberg, C., Otten, U. Decreased trkA neurotrophin receptor expression in the parietal cortex of patients with Alzheimer's disease. *Neurosci. Lett. 241:* 151-154, 1998.

Hock, C., Konietzko, U., Streffer, J.R., Tracy, J., Signorell, A., Muller-Tillmanns, B., Lemke, U., Henke, K., Moritz, E., Garcia, E., Wollmer, M.A., Umbricht, D., de Quervain, D.J., Hofmann, M., Maddalena, A., Papassotiropoulos, A., Nitsch, R.M. Antibodies against β-amyloid slow cognitive decline in Alzheimer's disease. *Neuron 38:* 547-554, 2003.

Hock, C.H., Heese, K., Olivieri, G., Hulette, C.H., Rosenberg, C., Nitsch, R.M., Otten, U. Alterations in neurotrophins and neurotrophin receptors in Alzheimer's disease. *J. Neural Transm. Suppl. 59:* 171-174, 2000b.

Hoffman, E.J., Phelps, M.E. Positron emission tomography: principles and quantitation. In: Phelps, M.E., Mazziotta, J., Schelbert, H., (Eds.) *Positron emission tomography and autoradiography: principles and applications for the brain and heart.* Raven Press, 1986, pp. 237-286.

Hong, L., Koelsch, G., Lin, X., Wu, S., Terzyan, S., Ghosh, A.K., Zhang, X.C., Tang, J. Structure of the protease domain of memapsin 2 (β-secretase) complexed with inhibitor. *Science 290:* 150-153, 2000.

Hook, V., Toneff, T., Bogyo, M., Greenbaum, D., Medzihradszky, K.F., Neveu, J., Lane, W., Hook, G., Reisine, T. Inhibition of cathepsin B reduces β-amyloid production in regulated secretory vesicles of neuronal chromaffin cells: evidence for cathepsin B as a candidate β-secretase of Alzheimer's disease. *Biol. Chem. 386:* 931-940, 2005.

Hoshi, M., Sato, M., Matsumoto, S., Noguchi, A., Yasutake, K., Yoshida, N., Sato, K. Spherical aggregates of β-amyloid (amylospheroid) show high neurotoxicity and activate tau protein kinase I/glycogen synthase kinase-3β. *Proc. Natl. Acad. Sci. USA 100:* 6370-6375, 2003.

Hsia, A.Y., Masliah, E., McConlogue, L., Yu, G.Q., Tatsuno, G., Hu, K., Kholodenko, D., Malenka, R.C., Nicoll, R.A., Mucke, L. Plaque-independent disruption of neural circuits in Alzheimer's disease mouse models. *Proc. Natl. Acad. Sci. USA 96:* 3228-3233, 1999.

Huang, C., Wahlund, L.O., Svensson, L., Winblad, B., Julin, P. Cingulate cortex hypoperfusion predicts Alzheimer's disease in mild cognitive impairment. *BMC Neurol. 2:* 9, 2002.

Huang, E.J., Reichardt, L.F. Neurotrophins: roles in neuronal development and function. *Annu. Rev. Neurosci. 24:* 677-736, 2001.

Hung, A.Y., Haass, C., Nitsch, R.M., Qiu, W.Q., Citron, M., Wurtman, R.J., Growdon, J.H., Selkoe, D.J. Activation of protein kinase C inhibits cellular production of the Aβ-protein. *J. Biol. Chem. 268:* 22959-22962, 1993.

Hussain, I. The potential for BACE1 inhibitors in the treatment of Alzheimer's disease. *IDrugs 7:* 653-658, 2004.

Hussain, I., Hawkins, J., Harrison, D., Hille, C., Wayne, G., Cutler, L., Buck, T., Walter, D., Demont, E., Howes, C., Naylor, A., Jeffrey, P., Gonzalez, M.I., Dingwall, C., Michel, A., Redshaw, S., Davis, J.B. Oral administration of a potent and selective non-peptidic BACE-1 inhibitor decreases β-cleavage of amyloid precursor protein and amyloid-β production *in vivo. J. Neurochem. 100:* 802-809, 2007.

Iijima, K., Liu, H.P., Chiang, A.S., Hearn, S.A., Konsolaki, M., Zhong, Y. Dissecting the pathological effects of human Aβ40 and Aβ42 in Drosophila: a potential model for Alzheimer's disease. *Proc. Natl. Acad. Sci. USA 101:* 6623-6628, 2004.

Irizarry, M.C. Biomarkers of Alzheimer disease in plasma. *NeuroRx 1:* 226-234, 2004.

Iwata, N., Higuchi, M., Saido, T.C. Metabolism of amyloid-β peptide and Alzheimer's disease. *Pharmacol. Ther. 108:* 129-148, 2005.

Iwata, N., Mizukami, H., Shirotani, K., Takaki, Y., Muramatsu, S., Lu, B., Gerard, N.P., Gerard, C., Ozawa, K., Saido, T.C. Presynaptic localization of neprilysin contributes to efficient clearance of Aβ peptide in mouse brain. *J. Neurosci. 24:* 991-998, 2004.

Iwata, N., Takaki, Y., Fukami, S., Tsubuki, S., Saido, T.C. Region-specific reduction of Aβ-degrading endopeptidase, neprilysin, in mouse hippocampus upon aging. *J. Neurosci. Res. 70:* 493-500, 2002.

Iwata, N., Tsubuki, S., Takaki, Y., Watanabe, K., Sekiguchi, M., Hosoki, E., Kawashima-Morishima, M., Lee, H.J., Hama, E., Sekine-Aizawa, Y., Saido, T.C. Identification of the major Aβ1-42-degrading catabolic pathway in brain parenchyma: suppression leads to biochemical and pathological deposition. *Nat. Med. 6:* 143-150, 2000.

Iwatsubo, T. Tauopathy: an overview. *Neuropathology 26:* 455-456, 2006.

Jack, C.R., Jr., Petersen, R.C., Xu, Y.C., O'Brien, P.C., Smith, G.E., Ivnik, R.J., Boeve, B.F., Waring, S.C., Tangalos, E.G., Kokmen, E. Prediction of AD with MRI-based hippocampal volume in mild cognitive impairment. *Neurology 52:* 1397-1403, 1999.

Jack, C.R., Jr., Shiung, M.M., Gunter, J.L., O'Brien, P.C., Weigand, S.D., Knopman, D.S., Boeve, B.F., Ivnik, R.J., Smith, G.E., Cha, R.H., Tangalos, E.G., Petersen, R.C. Comparison of different MRI brain atrophy rate measures with clinical disease progression in AD. *Neurology 62:* 591-600, 2004.

Jack, C.R., Jr., Shiung, M.M., Weigand, S.D., O'Brien, P.C., Gunter, J.L., Boeve, B.F., Knopman, D.S., Smith, G.E., Ivnik, R.J., Tangalos, E.G., Petersen, R.C. Brain atrophy rates predict subsequent clinical conversion in normal elderly and amnestic MCI. *Neurology 65:* 1227-1231, 2005.

Jacobsen, J.S., Reinhart, P., Pangalos, M.N. Current concepts in therapeutic strategies targeting cognitive decline and disease modification in Alzheimer's disease. *NeuroRx 2:* 612-626, 2005.

Jacobsen, J.S., Wu, C.-C., Redwine, J.M., Comery, T.A., Arias, R., Bowlby, M., Martone, R., Morrison, J., Pangalos, M., Reinhart, P.H., Bloom, F.E. Early-onset behavioral and synaptic deficits in a mouse model of Alzheimer's disease. *Proc. Natl. Acad. Sci. USA 103:* 5161-5166, 2006.

Jang, J.H., Surh, Y.J. Protective effect of resveratrol on β-amyloid-induced oxidative PC12 cell death. *Free Radic. Biol. Med. 34:* 1100-1110, 2003.

Janson, J., Laedtke, T., Parisi, J.E., O'Brien, P., Petersen, R.C., Butler, P.C. Increased risk of type 2 diabetes in Alzheimer disease. *Diabetes 53:* 474-481, 2004.

John, V. Human β-secretase (BACE) and BACE inhibitors: progress report. *Curr. Top. Med. Chem. 6:* 569-578, 2006.

Johnson, K.A., Jones, K., Holman, B.L., Becker, J.A., Spiers, P.A., Satlin, A., Albert, M.S. Preclinical prediction of Alzheimer's disease using SPECT. *Neurology 50:* 1563-1571, 1998.

Kalbe, E., Kessler, J., Calabrese, P., Smith, R., Passmore, A.P., Brand, M., Bullock, R. DemTect: a new, sensitive cognitive screening test to support the diagnosis of mild cognitive impairment and early dementia. *Int. J. Geriatr. Psychiatry 19:* 136-143, 2004.

Kang, D.E., Pietrzik, C.U., Baum, L., Chevallier, N., Merriam, D.E., Kounnas, M.Z., Wagner, S.L., Troncoso, J.C., Kawas, C.H., Katzman, R., Koo, E.H. Modulation of amyloid β-protein clearance and Alzheimer's disease susceptibility by the LDL receptor-related protein pathway. *J. Clin. Invest. 106:* 1159-1166, 2000.

Kawas, C.H., Corrada, M.M., Brookmeyer, R., Morrison, A., Resnick, S.M., Zonderman, A.B., Arenberg, D. Visual memory predicts Alzheimer's disease more than a decade before diagnosis. *Neurology 60:* 1089-1093, 2003.

Kayed, R., Head, E., Thompson, J.L., McIntire, T.M., Milton, S.C., Cotman, C.W., Glabe, C.G. Common structure of soluble amyloid oligomers implies common mechanism of pathogenesis. *Science 300:* 486-489, 2003.

Kennedy, G.J., Golde, T.E., Tariot, P.N., Cummings, J.L. Amyloid-Based interventions in Alzheimer's disease. *CNS Spectr. 12:* 1-14, 2007.

Khan, T.K., Alkon, D.L. An internally controlled peripheral biomarker for Alzheimer's disease: Erk1 and Erk2 responses to the inflammatory signal bradykinin. *Proc. Natl. Acad. Sci. USA 103:* 13203-13207, 2006.

Kilgard, M.P., Merzenich, M.M. Cortical map reorganization enabled by nucleus basalis activity. *Science 279:* 1714-1718, 1998.

Killiany, R.J., Gomez-Isla, T., Moss, M., Kikinis, R., Sandor, T., Jolesz, F., Tanzi, R., Jones, K., Hyman, B.T., Albert, M.S. Use of structural magnetic resonance imaging to predict who will get Alzheimer's disease. *Ann. Neurol. 47:* 430-439, 2000.

Killiany, R.J., Hyman, B.T., Gomez-Isla, T., Moss, M.B., Kikinis, R., Jolesz, F., Tanzi, R., Jones, K., Albert, M.S. MRI measures of entorhinal cortex vs hippocampus in preclinical AD. *Neurology 58:* 1188-1196, 2002.

Kimberly, W.T., Wolfe, M.S. Identity and function of γ-secretase. *J. Neurosci. Res. 74:* 353-360, 2003.

Kimura, T., Shuto, D., Hamada, Y., Igawa, N., Kasai, S., Liu, P., Hidaka, K., Hamada, T., Hayashi, Y., Kiso, Y. Design and synthesis of highly active Alzheimer's β-secretase (BACE1) inhibitors, KMI-420 and KMI-429, with enhanced chemical stability. *Bioorg. Med. Chem. Lett. 15:* 211-215, 2005.

Kingston, I.B., Castro, M.J., Anderson, S. *In vitro* stimulation of tissue-type plasminogen activator by Alzheimer amyloid β-peptide analogues. *Nat. Med. 1:* 138-142, 1995.

Kirkitadze, M.D., Bitan, G., Teplow, D.B. Paradigm shifts in Alzheimer's disease and other neurodegenerative disorders: The emerging role of oligomeric assemblies. *J. Neurosci. Res. 69:* 567-577, 2002.

Klatte, E.T., Scharre, D.W., Nagaraja, H.N., Davis, R.A., Beversdorf, D.Q. Combination therapy of donepezil and vitamin E in Alzheimer disease. *Alzheimer Dis. Assoc. Disord. 17:* 113-116, 2003.

Klein, W.L., Stine, W.B., Jr., Teplow, D.B. Small assemblies of unmodified amyloid β-protein are the proximate neurotoxin in Alzheimer's disease. *Neurobiol. Aging 25:* 569-580, 2004.

Klunk, W.E., Engler, H., Nordberg, A., Wang, Y., Blomqvist, G., Holt, D.P., Bergstrom, M., Savitcheva, I., Huang, G.F., Estrada, S., Ausen, B., Debnath, M.L., Barletta, J., Price, J.C., Sandell, J., Lopresti, B.J., Wall, A., Koivisto, P., Antoni, G., Mathis, C.A., Langstrom, B. Imaging brain amyloid in Alzheimer's disease with Pittsburgh Compound-B. *Ann. Neurol. 55:* 306-319, 2004.

Klyubin, I., Walsh, D.M., Lemere, C.A., Cullen, W.K., Shankar, G.M., Betts, V., Spooner, E.T., Jiang, L., Anwyl, R., Selkoe, D.J., Rowan, M.J. Amyloid β-protein immunotherapy neutralizes Aβ oligomers that disrupt synaptic plasticity *in vivo. Nat. Med. 11:* 556-561, 2005.

Kogure, D., Matsuda, H., Ohnishi, T., Asada, T., Uno, M., Kunihiro, T., Nakano, S., Takasaki, M. Longitudinal evaluation of early Alzheimer's disease using brain perfusion SPECT. *J. Nucl. Med. 41:* 1155-1162, 2000.

Kojro, E., Fahrenholz, F. The non-amyloidogenic pathway: structure and function of α-secretases. *Sub-cell. Biochem. 38:* 105-127, 2005.

Kokkoni, N., Stott, K., Amijee, H., Mason, J.M., Doig, A.J. *N*-Methylated peptide inhibitors of β-amyloid aggregation and toxicity. Optimization of the inhibitor structure. *Biochemistry 45:* 9906-9918, 2006.

Koliatsos, V.E., Applegate, M.D., Knusel, B., Junard, E.O., Burton, L.E., Mobley, W.C., Hefti, F.F., Price, D.L. Recombinant human nerve growth factor prevents retrograde degeneration of axotomized basal forebrain cholinergic neurons in the rat. *Exp. Neurol. 112:* 161-173, 1991.

Koo, E.H. Phorbol esters affect multiple steps in β-amyloid precursor protein trafficking and amyloid β-protein production. *Mol. Med. 3:* 204-211, 1997.

Korf, E.S., Wahlund, L.O., Visser, P.J., Scheltens, P. Medial temporal lobe atrophy on MRI predicts dementia in patients with mild cognitive impairment. *Neurology 63:* 94-100, 2004.

Krafft, G.A., Joyce, J., Jerecic, J., Lowe, R., Hepler, R.W., Nahas, D.D., Kinney, G., Pray, T. Design of arrested-assembly Aβ1-42 peptide variants to elucidate the ADDL oligomerization pathway and conformational specificity of anti-ADDL antibodies. Program No. 509.5. 2006 Neuroscience Meeting Planner. Atlanta, GA: Society for Neuroscience, 2006.

Kurz, A., Diehl, J., Riemenschneider, M., Perneczky, R., Lautenschlager, N. Mild cognitive disorder. Questions of definition, diagnosis, prognosis and therapy. *Nervenarzt 75:* 6-15, 2004.

Laird, F.M., Cai, H., Savonenko, A.V., Farah, M.H., He, K., Melnikova, T., Wen, H., Chiang, H.C., Xu, G., Koliatsos, V.E., Borchelt, D.R., Price, D.L., Lee, H.K., Wong, P.C. BACE1, a major determinant of selective vulnerability of the brain to Aβ amyloidogenesis, is essential for cognitive, emotional, and synaptic functions. *J. Neurosci. 25:* 11693-11709, 2005.

Lambert, M.P., Barlow, A.K., Chromy, B.A., Edwards, C., Freed, R., Liosatos, M., Morgan, T.E., Rozovsky, I., Trommer, B., Viola, K.L., Wals, P., Zhang, C., Finch, C.E., Krafft, G.A., Klein, W.L. Diffusible, nonfibrillar ligands derived from Aβ1-42 are potent central nervous system neurotoxins. *Proc. Natl. Acad. Sci. USA 95:* 6448-6453, 1998.

Lammich, S., Kojro, E., Postina, R., Gilbert, S., Pfeiffer, R., Jasionowski, M., Haass, C., Fahrenholz, F. Constitutive and regulated α-secretase cleavage of Alzheimer's amyloid precursor protein by a disintegrin metalloprotease. *Proc. Natl. Acad. Sci. USA 96:* 3922-3927, 1999.

Lansbury, P.T. Inhibition of amyloid formation - a strategy to delay the onset of alzheimers-disease. *Curr. Opin. Chem. Biol. 1:* 260-267, 1997.

Lautenschlager, N.T., Riemenschneider, M., Drzezga, A., Kurz, A.F. Primary degenerative mild cognitive impairment: study population, clinical, brain imaging and biochemical findings. *Dement. Geriatr. Cogn. Disord. 12:* 379-386, 2001.

Lazo, N.D., Grant, M.A., Condron, M.C., Rigby, A.C., Teplow, D.B. On the nucleation of amyloid β-protein monomer folding. *Protein Sci. 14:* 1581-1596, 2005.

Ledesma, M.D., Da Silva, J.S., Crassaerts, K., Delacourte, A., De Strooper, B., Dotti, C.G. Brain plasmin enhances APP α-cleavage and Aβ degradation and is reduced in Alzheimer's disease brains. *EMBO reports 1:* 530-535, 2000.

Lee, H.G., Casadesus, G., Zhu, X., Takeda, A., Perry, G., Smith, M.A. Challenging the amyloid cascade hypothesis: senile plaques and Aβ as protective adaptations to Alzheimer disease. *Ann. N. Y. Acad. Sci. 1019:* 1-4, 2004.

Lee, H.G., Zhu, X., Nunomura, A., Perry, G., Smith, M.A. Amyloid β: the alternate hypothesis. *Curr. Alzheimer Res. 3:* 75-80, 2006.

Lee, S.R., Im, K.J., Suh, S.I., Jung, J.G. Protective effect of green tea polyphenol (-)-epigallocatechin gallate and other antioxidants on lipid peroxidation in gerbil brain homogenates. *Phytother. Res. 17:* 206-209, 2003.

Leissring, M.A., Farris, W., Chang, A.Y., Walsh, D.M., Wu, X., Sun, X., Frosch, M.P., Selkoe, D.J. Enhanced proteolysis of β-amyloid in APP transgenic mice prevents plaque formation, secondary pathology, and premature death. *Neuron 40:* 1087-1093, 2003.

Lemere, C.A., Blusztajn, J.K., Yamaguchi, H., Wisniewski, T., Saido, T.C., Selkoe, D.J. Sequence of deposition of heterogeneous amyloid β-peptides and Apo E in Down syndrome - Implications for initial events in amyloid plaque formation. *Neurobiol. Dis. 3:* 16-32, 1996.

Lemere, C.A., Maier, M., Jiang, L., Peng, Y., Seabrook, T.J. Aβ immunotherapy for the prevention and treatment of Alzheimer disease: lessons from mice, monkeys, and humans. *Rejuvenation Res. 9:* 77-84, 2006.

Lesné, S., Koh, M.T., Kotilinek, L., Kayed, R., Glabe, C.G., Yang, A., Gallagher, M., Ashe, K.H. A specific amyloid-β protein assembly in the brain impairs memory. *Nature 440:* 352-357, 2006.

Leung, G.M., Yeung, R.Y., Chi, I., Chu, L.W. The economics of Alzheimer disease. *Dement. Geriatr. Cogn. Disord. 15:* 34-43, 2003.

Lewczuk, P., Esselmann, H., Otto, M., Maler, J.M., Henkel, A.W., Henkel, M.K., Eikenberg, O., Antz, C., Krause, W.R., Reulbach, U., Kornhuber, J., Wiltfang, J. Neurochemical diagnosis of Alzheimer's dementia by CSF Aβ42, Aβ42/Aβ40 ratio and total tau. *Neurobiol. Aging 25:* 273-281, 2004.

Lim, G.P., Chu, T., Yang, F., Beech, W., Frautschy, S.A., Cole, G.M. The curry spice curcumin reduces oxidative damage and amyloid pathology in an Alzheimer transgenic mouse. *J. Neurosci. 21:* 8370-8377, 2001.

Lindsay, J., Laurin, D., Verreault, R., Hebert, R., Helliwell, B., Hill, G.B., McDowell, I. Risk factors for Alzheimer's disease: a prospective analysis from the Canadian Study of Health and Aging. *Am. J. Epidemiol. 156:* 445-453, 2002.

Lleo, A., Berezovska, O., Growdon, J.H., Hyman, B.T. Clinical, pathological, and biochemical spectrum of Alzheimer disease associated with PS-1 mutations. *Am. J. Geriatr. Psychiatry 12:* 146-156, 2004.

Luchsinger, J.A., Tang, M.X., Siddiqui, M., Shea, S., Mayeux, R. Alcohol intake and risk of dementia. *J. Am. Geriatr. Soc. 52:* 540-546, 2004.

Lue, L.F., Kuo, Y.M., Roher, A.E., Brachova, L., Shen, Y., Sue, L., Beach, T., Kurth, J.H., Rydel, R.E., Rogers, J. Soluble Aβ peptide concentration as a predictor of synaptic change in Alzheimer's disease. *Am. J. Pathol. 155:* 853-862, 1999.

Lue, L.F., Yan, S.D., Stern, D.M., Walker, D.G. Preventing activation of receptor for advanced glycation endproducts in Alzheimer's disease. *Curr. Drug Targets CNS Neurol. Disord. 4:* 249-266, 2005.

Lundkvist, J., Näslund, J. γ-secretase: a complex target for Alzheimer's disease. *Curr. Opin. Pharmacol. 7:* 112-118, 2007.

Luo, Y., Bolon, B., Kahn, S., Bennett, B.D., Babu-Khan, S., Denis, P., Fan, W., Kha, H., Zhang, J., Gong, Y., Martin, L., Louis, J.C., Yan, Q., Richards, W.G., Citron, M., Vassar, R. Mice deficient in BACE1, the Alzheimer's β-secretase, have normal phenotype and abolished β-amyloid generation. *Nat. Neurosci. 4:* 231-232, 2001.

Maier, M., Seabrook, T.J., Lemere, C.A. Developing novel immunogens for an effective, safe Alzheimer's disease vaccine. *Neurodegener. Dis. 2:* 267-272, 2005.

Marr, R.A., Guan, H., Rockenstein, E., Kindy, M., Gage, F.H., Verma, I., Masliah, E., Hersh, L.B. Neprilysin regulates Aβ peptide levels. *J. Mol. Neurosci. 22:* 5-11, 2004.

Marr, R.A., Rockenstein, E., Mukherjee, A., Kindy, M.S., Hersh, L.B., Gage, F.H., Verma, I.M., Masliah, E. Neprilysin gene transfer reduces human amyloid pathology in transgenic mice. *J. Neurosci. 23:* 1992-1996, 2003.

Maruyama, M., Arai, H., Sugita, M., Tanji, H., Higuchi, M., Okamura, N., Matsui, T., Higuchi, S., Matsushita, S., Yoshida, H., Sasaki, H. Cerebrospinal fluid Aβ(1-42) levels in the mild cognitive impairment stage of Alzheimer's disease. *Exp. Neurol. 172:* 433-436, 2001.

Masliah, E., Hansen, L., Adame, A., Crews, L., Bard, F., Lee, C., Seubert, P., Games, D., Kirby, L., Schenk, D. Aβ vaccination effects on plaque pathology in the absence of encephalitis in Alzheimer disease. *Neurology 64:* 129-131, 2005.

Mathis, C.A., Klunk, W.E., Price, J.C., DeKosky, S.T. Imaging technology for neurodegenerative diseases: progress toward detection of specific pathologies. *Arch. Neurol. 62:* 196-200, 2005.

Matsubara, E., Frangione, B., Ghiso, J. Characterization of apolipoprotein J-Alzheimer's Aβ interaction. *J. Biol. Chem. 270:* 7563-7567, 1995.

Matsuoka, Y., Saito, M., LaFrancois, J., Gaynor, K., Olm, V., Wang, L.L., Casey, E., Lu, Y.F., Shiratori, C., Lemere, C., Duff, K. Novel therapeutic approach for the treatment of Alzheimer's disease by peripheral administration of agents with an affinity to β-amyloid. *J. Neurosci. 23:* 29-33, 2003.

Mattson, M.P., Cheng, B., Culwell, A.R., Esch, F.S., Lieberburg, I., Rydel, R.E. Evidence for excitoprotective and intraneuronal calcium-regulating roles for secreted forms of the β-amyloid precursor protein. *Neuron 10:* 243-254, 1993.

Mayeux, R., Honig, L.S., Tang, M.X., Manly, J., Stern, Y., Schupf, N., Mehta, P.D. Plasma Aβ40 and Aβ42 and Alzheimer's disease: relation to age, mortality, and risk. *Neurology 61:* 1185-1190, 2003.

McGowan, E., Pickford, F., Kim, J., Onstead, L., Eriksen, J., Yu, C., Skipper, L., Murphy, M.P., Beard, J., Das, P., Jansen, K., Delucia, M., Lin, W.L., Dolios, G., Wang, R., Eckman, C.B., Dickson, D.W., Hutton, M., Hardy, J., Golde, T. Aβ42 is essential for parenchymal and vascular amyloid deposition in mice. *Neuron 47:* 191-199, 2005.

McLaurin, J., Chakrabartty, A. Membrane disruption by Alzheimer β-amyloid peptides mediated through specific binding to either phospholipids or gangliosides. Implications for neurotoxicity. *J. Biol. Chem. 271:* 26482-26489, 1996.

McLaurin, J., Chakrabartty, A. Characterization of the interactions of Alzheimer β-amyloid peptides with phospholipid membranes. *Eur. J. Biochem. 245:* 355-363, 1997.

McLaurin, J., Franklin, T., Chakrabartty, A., Fraser, P.E. Phosphatidylinositol and inositol involvement in Alzheimer Aβ fibril growth and arrest. *J. Mol. Biol. 278:* 183-194, 1998.

McLaurin, J., Franklin, T., Zhang, X., Deng, J., Fraser, P.E. Interactions of Alzheimer Aβ peptides with glycosaminoglycans effects on fibril nucleation and growth. *Eur. J. Biochem. 266:* 1101-1110, 1999.

McLaurin, J., Golomb, R., Jurewicz, A., Antel, J.P., Fraser, P.E. Inositol stereoisomers stabilize an oligomeric aggregate of Alzheimer Aβ peptide and inhibit Aβ-induced toxicity. *J. Biol. Chem. 275:* 18495-18502, 2000.

McLaurin, J., Kierstead, M.E., Brown, M.E., Hawkes, C.A., Lambermon, M.H., Phinney, A.L., Darabie, A.A., Cousins, J.E., French, J.E., Lan, M.F., Chen, F., Wong, S.S., Mount, H.T., Fraser, P.E., Westaway, D., St George-Hyslop, P. Cyclohexanehexol inhibitors of Aβ aggregation prevent and reverse Alzheimer phenotype in a mouse model. *Nat. Med.* *12:* 801-808, 2006.

McLean, C.A., Cherny, R.A., Fraser, F.W., Fuller, S.J., Smith, M.J., Beyreuther, K., Bush, A.I., Masters, C.L. Soluble pool of Aβ amyloid as a determinant of severity of neurodegeneration in Alzheimer's disease. *Ann. Neurol. 46:* 860-866, 1999.

Mehta, P.D., Pirttila, T., Patrick, B.A., Barshatzky, M., Mehta, S.P. Aβ protein 1-40 and 1-42 levels in matched cerebrospinal fluid and plasma from patients with Alzheimer disease. *Neurosci. Lett. 304:* 102-106, 2001.

Melchor, J.P., Pawlak, R., Strickland, S. The tissue plasminogen activator-plasminogen proteolytic cascade accelerates amyloid-β (Aβ) degradation and inhibits Aβ-induced neurodegeneration. *J. Neurosci. 23:* 8867-8871, 2003.

Mesulam, M.M., Geula, C. Nucleus basalis (Ch4) and cortical cholinergic innervation in the human brain: observations based on the distribution of acetylcholinesterase and choline acetyltransferase. *J. Comp. Neurol. 275:* 216-240, 1988.

Michaelis, E.K. Molecular biology of glutamate receptors in the central nervous system and their role in excitotoxicity, oxidative stress and aging. *Prog. Neurobiol. 54:* 369-415, 1998.

Miguel-Hidalgo, J.J., Alvarez, X.A., Cacabelos, R., Quack, G. Neuroprotection by memantine against neurodegeneration induced by β-amyloid(1-40). *Brain Res. 958:* 210-221, 2002.

Miller, B.C., Eckman, E.A., Sambamurti, K., Dobbs, N., Chow, K.M., Eckman, C.B., Hersh, L.B., Thiele, D.L. Amyloid-β peptide levels in brain are inversely correlated with insulysin activity levels *in vivo*. *Proc. Natl. Acad. Sci. USA 100:* 6221-6226, 2003a.

Miller, V.M., Gouvion, C.M., Davidson, B.L., Paulson, H.L. Targeting Alzheimer's disease genes with RNA interference: an efficient strategy for silencing mutant alleles. *Nucleic Acids Res. 32:* 661-668, 2004.

Miller, V.M., Xia, H., Marrs, G.L., Gouvion, C.M., Lee, G., Davidson, B.L., Paulson, H.L. Allele-specific silencing of dominant disease genes. *Proc. Natl. Acad. Sci. USA 100:* 7195-7200, 2003b.

Minoshima, S., Frey, K.A., Koeppe, R.A., Foster, N.L., Kuhl, D.E. A diagnostic approach in Alzheimer's disease using three-dimensional stereotactic surface projections of fluorine-18-FDG PET. *J. Nucl. Med. 36:* 1238-1248, 1995.

Moncaster, J., Moir, R., Lu, S., Fu, L., Chadwick, O., Arnett, E., Ericsson, M., Klunk, W., Mathis, C., Chylack, L., Clark, J., Tanzi, R., Goldstein, L.E. Early, premorbid detection of β-amyloid pathology by non-invasive *in vivo* quasi-elastic light scattering in the lens. 10th International Conference on Alzheimer's disease and related disorders, Madrid. 2006.

Monien, B.H., Apostolova, L.G., Bitan, G. Early diagnostics and therapeutics for Alzheimer's disease--how early can we get there? *Expert Rev. Neurother. 6:* 1293-1306, 2006.

Moreira, P.I., Zhu, X., Nunomura, A., Smith, M.A., Perry, G. Therapeutic options in Alzheimer's disease. *Expert Rev. Neurother. 6:* 897-910, 2006.

Morgan, D., Diamond, D.M., Gottschall, P.E., Ugen, K.E., Dickey, C., Hardy, J., Duff, K., Jantzen, P., DiCarlo, G., Wilcock, D., Connor, K., Hatcher, J., Hope, C., Gordon, M., Arendash, G.W. Aβ peptide vaccination prevents memory loss in an animal model of Alzheimer's disease. *Nature 408:* 982-985, 2000.

Moriearty, P.L., Seubert, P., Galasko, D., Markwell, S., Unni, L., Vicari, S., Becker, R.E. Effects of time and cholinesterase inhibitor treatment on multiple cerebrospinal fluid parameters in Alzheimer's disease. *Methods Find. Exp. Clin. Pharmacol. 21:* 549-554, 1999.

Morishima-Kawashima, M., Hara, Y. Alzheimer's disease: β-amyloid protein and tau. *J. Neurosci. Res. 70:* 392-401, 2002.

Morris, J.C. The Clinical Dementia Rating (CDR): current version and scoring rules. *Neurology 43:* 2412-2414, 1993.

Mucke, L., Masliah, E., Yu, G.Q., Mallory, M., Rockenstein, E.M., Tatsuno, G., Hu, K., Kholodenko, D., Johnson-Wood, K., McConlogue, L. High-level neuronal expression of Aβ(1-42) in wild-type human amyloid protein precursor transgenic mice: Synaptotoxicity without plaque formation. *J. Neurosci. 20:* 4050-4058, 2000.

Mullan, M., Crawford, F., Axelman, K., Houlden, H., Lilius, L., Winblad, B., Lannfelt, L. A pathogenic mutation for probable Alzheimer's disease in the APP gene at the N-terminus of β-amyloid. *Nat. Genet. 1:* 345-347, 1992.

Murakami, K., Irie, K., Ohigashi, H., Hara, H., Nagao, M., Shimizu, T., Shirasawa, T. Formation and stabilization model of the 42-mer Aβ radical: implications for the long-lasting oxidative stress in Alzheimer's disease. *J. Am. Chem. Soc. 127:* 15168-15174, 2005.

Nakagami, Y., Nishimura, S., Murasugi, T., Kaneko, I., Meguro, M., Marumoto, S., Kogen, H., Koyama, K., Oda, T. A novel β-sheet breaker, RS-0406, reverses amyloid β-induced cytotoxicity and impairment of long-term potentiation *in vitro*. *Br. J. Pharmacol. 137:* 676-682, 2002.

Nasreddine, Z.S., Phillips, N.A., Bedirian, V., Charbonneau, S., Whitehead, V., Collin, I., Cummings, J.L., Chertkow, H. The Montreal Cognitive Assessment, MoCA: a brief screening tool for mild cognitive impairment. *J. Am. Geriatr. Soc. 53:* 695-699, 2005.

Nestor, P.J., Scheltens, P., Hodges, J.R. Advances in the early detection of Alzheimer's disease. *Nat. Med. 10 Suppl:* 34-41, 2004.

Neurochem. 2007, "Neurochem receives second recommendation from European Data Safety Monitoring Board to continue Phase III for tramiprosate (ALZHEMED™)." From http://www.neurochem.com/PR197.htm.

Nicoll, J.A., Barton, E., Boche, D., Neal, J.W., Ferrer, I., Thompson, P., Vlachouli, C., Wilkinson, D., Bayer, A., Games, D., Seubert, P., Schenk, D., Holmes, C. Aβ species removal after Aβ42 immunization. *J. Neuropathol. Exp. Neurol. 65:* 1040-1048, 2006.

Nicoll, J.A., Wilkinson, D., Holmes, C., Steart, P., Markham, H., Weller, R.O. Neuropathology of human Alzheimer disease after immunization with Aβ peptide: a case report. *Nat. Med. 9:* 448-452, 2003.

Nicolls, M.R. The clinical and biological relationship between Type II diabetes mellitus and Alzheimer's disease. *Curr. Alzheimer Res. 1:* 47-54, 2004.

Nunan, J., Small, D.H. Regulation of APP cleavage by α-, β- and γ-secretases. *FEBS Lett. 483:* 6-10, 2000.

Olin, J., Schneider, L. Galantamine for Alzheimer's disease. *Cochrane Database Syst. Rev.:* CD001747, 2002.

Ono, K., Hasegawa, K., Naiki, H., Yamada, M. Anti-amyloidogenic activity of tannic acid and its activity to destabilize Alzheimer's β-amyloid fibrils *in vitro*. *Biochim. Biophys. Acta 1690:* 193-202, 2004.

Opazo, C., Huang, X., Cherny, R.A., Moir, R.D., Roher, A.E., White, A.R., Cappai, R., Masters, C.L., Tanzi, R.E., Inestrosa, N.C., Bush, A.I. Metalloenzyme-like activity of Alzheimer's disease β-amyloid. Cu-dependent catalytic conversion of dopamine, cholesterol, and biological reducing agents to neurotoxic $H(2)O(2)$. *J. Biol. Chem. 277:* 40302-40308, 2002.

Opazo, C., Luza, S., Villemagne, V.L., Volitakis, I., Rowe, C., Barnham, K.J., Strozyk, D., Masters, C.L., Cherny, R.A., Bush, A.I. Radioiodinated clioquinol as a biomarker for β-amyloid: Zn complexes in Alzheimer's disease. *Aging Cell 5:* 69-79, 2006.

Patel, S., Vuillard, L., Cleasby, A., Murray, C.W., Yon, J. Apo and inhibitor complex structures of BACE (β-secretase). *J. Mol. Biol. 343:* 407-416, 2004.

Permanne, B., Adessi, C., Saborio, G.P., Fraga, S., Frossard, M.J., Van Dorpe, J., Dewachter, I., Banks, W.A., Van Leuven, F., Soto, C. Reduction of amyloid load and cerebral damage in a transgenic mouse model of Alzheimer's disease by treatment with a β-sheet breaker peptide. *Faseb J. 16:* 860-862, 2002.

Perry, E.K., Tomlinson, B.E., Blessed, G., Bergmann, K., Gibson, P.H., Perry, R.H. Correlation of cholinergic abnormalities with senile plaques and mental test scores in senile dementia. *Br. Med. J. 2:* 1457-1459, 1978.

Petersen, R.C. Mild cognitive impairment as a diagnostic entity. *J. Intern. Med. 256:* 183-194, 2004.

Petersen, R.C. Mild cognitive impairment: where are we? *Alzheimer Dis. Assoc. Disord. 19:* 166-169, 2005.

Petersen, R.C., Doody, R., Kurz, A., Mohs, R.C., Morris, J.C., Rabins, P.V., Ritchie, K., Rossor, M., Thal, L., Winblad, B. Current concepts in mild cognitive impairment. *Arch. Neurol. 58:* 1985-1992, 2001.

Petersen, R.C., Thomas, R.G., Grundman, M., Bennett, D., Doody, R., Ferris, S., Galasko, D., Jin, S., Kaye, J., Levey, A., Pfeiffer, E., Sano, M., van Dyck, C.H., Thal, L.J. Vitamin E and donepezil for the treatment of mild cognitive impairment. *N. Engl. J. Med. 352:* 2379-2388, 2005.

Pissarnitski, D.A., Asberom, T., Bara, T.A., Buevich, A.V., Clader, J.W., Greenlee, W.J., Guzik, H.S., Josien, H.B., Li, W., McEwan, M., McKittrick, B.A., Nechuta, T.L., Parker, E.M., Sinning, L., Smith, E.M., Song, L., Vaccaro, H.A., Voigt, J.H., Zhang, L., Zhang, Q., Zhao, Z. 2,6-Disubstituted *N*-arylsulfonyl piperidines as γ-secretase inhibitors. *Bioorg. Med. Chem. Lett. 17:* 57-62, 2007.

Pitschke, M., Prior, R., Haupt, M., Riesner, D. Detection of single amyloid β-protein aggregates in the cerebrospinal fluid of Alzheimer's patients by fluorescence correlation spectroscopy. *Nat. Med. 4:* 832-834, 1998.

Poduslo, J.F., Curran, G.L., Kumar, A., Frangione, B., Soto, C. β-sheet breaker peptide inhibitor of Alzheimer's amyloidogenesis with increased blood-brain barrier permeability and resistance to proteolytic degradation in plasma. *J. Neurobiol. 39:* 371-382, 1999.

Pop, V., Head, E., Barrett, E.G., Murphy, M.P., Nistor, M., Patel, A.Y., Vasilevko, V., Glabe, C., Kayed, R., Milton, S., Cribbs, D.H., Cotman, C.W. Reduced cortical β-amyloid in aged canines actively immunized with fibrillar or oligomeric β-amyloid. Program No. 270.21. 2006 Neuroscience Meeting Planner. Society for Neuroscience, 2006.

Postina, R., Schroeder, A., Dewachter, I., Bohl, J., Schmitt, U., Kojro, E., Prinzen, C., Endres, K., Hiemke, C., Blessing, M., Flamez, P., Dequenne, A., Godaux, E., van Leuven, F., Fahrenholz, F. A disintegrin-metalloproteinase prevents amyloid plaque formation and hippocampal defects in an Alzheimer disease mouse model. *J. Clin. Invest. 113:* 1456-1464, 2004.

PranaBiotechnology. 2005, "Prana Biotechnology cancels plans for placque clinical study ", From http://www.pranabio.com/company_profile/press_releases_item.asp?id=90. .

Read, S.L., Miller, B.L., Mena, I., Kim, R., Itabashi, H., Darby, A. SPECT in dementia: clinical and pathological correlation. *J. Am. Geriatr. Soc. 43:* 1243-1247, 1995.

Reisberg, B., Doody, R., Stoffler, A., Schmitt, F., Ferris, S., Mobius, H.J. Memantine in moderate-to-severe Alzheimer's disease. *N. Engl. J. Med. 348:* 1333-1341, 2003.

Riemenschneider, M., Lautenschlager, N., Wagenpfeil, S., Diehl, J., Drzezga, A., Kurz, A. Cerebrospinal fluid tau and β-amyloid 42 proteins identify Alzheimer disease in subjects with mild cognitive impairment. *Arch. Neurol. 59:* 1729-1734, 2002.

Ritchie, C.W., Bush, A.I., Mackinnon, A., Macfarlane, S., Mastwyk, M., MacGregor, L., Kiers, L., Cherny, R., Li, Q.X., Tammer, A., Carrington, D., Mavros, C., Volitakis, I., Xilinas, M., Ames, D., Davis, S., Beyreuther, K., Tanzi, R.E., Masters, C.L. Metal-protein attenuation with iodochlorhydroxyquin (clioquinol) targeting Aβ amyloid deposition and toxicity in Alzheimer disease: a pilot phase 2 clinical trial. *Arch. Neurol. 60:* 1685-1691, 2003.

Roberson, E.D., Scearce-Levie, K., Palop, J.J., Yan, F., Cheng, I.H., Wu, T., Gerstein, H., Yu, G.Q., Mucke, L. Reducing endogenous tau ameliorates amyloid β-induced deficits in an Alzheimer's disease mouse model. *Science 316:* 750-754, 2007.

Rocchi, A., Pellegrini, S., Siciliano, G., Murri, L. Causative and susceptibility genes for Alzheimer's disease: a review. *Brain Res. Bull. 61:* 1-24, 2003.

Rodriguez-Lebron, E., Govion, C., Miller, V.M., Gonzalez-Alegre, P., Moore, S.A., Davidson, B.L., Paulson, H.L. *In vivo* allele-specific silencing of the Swedish APP mutant: Development of an RNAi strategy against familial forms of Alzheimer's disease. Program No. 412.7. 2006 Neuroscience Meeting Planner. Atlanta, GA: Society for Neuroscience, 2006.

Roher, A.E., Lowenson, J.D., Clarke, S., Woods, A.S., Cotter, R.J., Gowing, E., Ball, M.J. β-amyloid(1-42) is a major component of cerebrovascular amyloid deposits: Implications for the pathology of Alzheimer disease. *Proc. Natl. Acad. Sci. USA 90:* 10836-10840, 1993.

Ruether, E., Husmann, R., Kinzler, E., Diabl, E., Klingler, D., Spatt, J., Ritter, R., Schmidt, R., Taneri, Z., Winterer, W., Koper, D., Kasper, S., Rainer, M., Moessler, H. A 28-week, double-blind, placebo-controlled study with Cerebrolysin in patients with mild to moderate Alzheimer's disease. *Int. Clin. Psychopharmacol. 16:* 253-263, 2001.

Rusinek, H., De Santi, S., Frid, D., Tsui, W.H., Tarshish, C.Y., Convit, A., de Leon, M.J. Regional brain atrophy rate predicts future cognitive decline: 6-year longitudinal MR imaging study of normal aging. *Radiology 229:* 691-696, 2003.

Ruther, E., Ritter, R., Apecechea, M., Freytag, S., Gmeinbauer, R., Windisch, M. Sustained improvements in patients with dementia of Alzheimer's type (DAT) 6 months after termination of Cerebrolysin therapy. *J. Neural Transm. 107:* 815-829, 2000.

Saito, T., Iwata, N., Tsubuki, S., Takaki, Y., Takano, J., Huang, S.M., Suemoto, T., Higuchi, M., Saido, T.C. Somatostatin regulates brain Aβ peptide Aβ42 through modulation of proteolytic degradation. *Nat. Med. 11:* 434-439, 2005.

Sato, T., Kienlen-Campard, P., Ahmed, M., Liu, W., Li, H., Elliott, J.I., Aimoto, S., Constantinescu, S.N., Octave, J.N., Smith, S.O. Inhibitors of amyloid toxicity based on β-sheet packing of Aβ40 and Aβ42. *Biochemistry 45:* 5503-5516, 2006.

Savaskan, E., Olivieri, G., Meier, F., Seifritz, E., Wirz-Justice, A., Muller-Spahn, F. Red wine ingredient resveratrol protects from β-amyloid neurotoxicity. *Gerontology 49:* 380-383, 2003.

Scheff, S.W., Price, D.A., Schmitt, F.A., Mufson, E.J. Hippocampal synaptic loss in early Alzheimer's disease and mild cognitive impairment. *Neurobiol. Aging 27:* 1372-1384, 2006.

Scheltens, P., Fox, N., Barkhof, F., De Carli, C. Structural magnetic resonance imaging in the practical assessment of dementia: beyond exclusion. *Lancet Neurol. 1:* 13-21, 2002.

Scheltens, P., Leys, D., Barkhof, F., Huglo, D., Weinstein, H.C., Vermersch, P., Kuiper, M., Steinling, M., Wolters, E.C., Valk, J. Atrophy of medial temporal lobes on MRI in "probable" Alzheimer's disease and normal ageing: diagnostic value and neuropsychological correlates. *J. Neurol. Neurosurg. Psychiatry 55:* 967-972, 1992.

Schenk, D. Aβ immunotherapy for Alzheimer's disease: the end of the beginning. *Nat. Rev. Neurosci. 3:* 824-828, 2002.

Schenk, D., Barbour, R., Dunn, W., Gordon, G., Grajeda, H., Guido, T., Hu, K., Huang, J., Johnson-Wood, K., Khan, K., Kholodenko, D., Lee, M., Liao, Z., Lieburg, I., Motter, R., Mutter, L., Soriano, F., Shopp, G., Vasquez, N., Vandevert, C., Walker, S., Wogulis, M., Yednock, T., Games, D., Seubert, P. Immunization with Aβ attenuates Alzheimer-disease-like pathology in the PDAPP mouse. *Nature 400:* 173-177, 1999.

Schenk, D.B., Seubert, P., Grundman, M., Black, R. Aβ immunotherapy: Lessons learned for potential treatment of Alzheimer's disease. *Neurodegener. Dis. 2:* 255-260, 2005.

Scheuner, D., Eckman, C., Jensen, M., Song, X., Citron, M., Suzuki, N., Bird, T.D., Hardy, J., Hutton, M., Kukull, W., Larson, E., Levy-Lahad, E., Viitanen, M., Peskind, E., Poorkaj, P., Schellenberg, G., Tanzi, R., Wasco, W., Lannfelt, L., Selkoe, D.J., Younkin, S. Secreted amyloid β-protein similar to that in the senile plaques of Alzheimer's disease is increased *in vivo* by the Presenilin 1 and 2 and APP mutations linked to familial Alzheimer's disease. *Nat. Med. 2:* 864-870, 1996.

Schott, J.M., Fox, N.C., Frost, C., Scahill, R.I., Janssen, J.C., Chan, D., Jenkins, R., Rossor, M.N. Assessing the onset of structural change in familial Alzheimer's disease. *Ann. Neurol. 53:* 181-188, 2003.

Schwarzman, A.L., Gregori, L., Vitek, M.P., Lyubski, S., Strittmatter, W.J., Enghilde, J.J., Bhasin, R., Silverman, J., Weisgraber, K.H., Coyle, P.K., et al. Transthyretin sequesters amyloid β protein and prevents amyloid formation. *Proc. Natl. Acad. Sci. USA 91:* 8368-8372, 1994.

Seabrook, T.J., Thomas, K., Jiang, L., Bloom, J., Spooner, E., Maier, M., Bitan, G., Lemere, C.A. Dendrimeric Aβ1-15 is an effective immunogen in wildtype and APP-tg mice. *Neurobiol. Aging 28:* 813-823, 2007.

Selkoe, D.J. The origins of Alzheimer disease: a is for amyloid. *JAMA 283:* 1615-1617, 2000.

Selkoe, D.J. Alzheimer's disease: Genes, proteins, and therapy. *Physiol. Rev. 81:* 741-766, 2001a.

Selkoe, D.J. Clearing the brain's amyloid cobwebs. *Neuron 32:* 177-180, 2001b.

Selkoe, D.J. Defining molecular targets to prevent Alzheimer disease. *Arch. Neurol. 62:* 192-195, 2005.

Selkoe, D.J., Schenk, D. Alzheimer's disease: molecular understanding predicts amyloid-based therapeutics. *Annu. Rev. Pharmacol. Toxicol. 43:* 545-584, 2003.

Serpell, L.C. Alzheimer's amyloid fibrils: structure and assembly. *Biochim. Biophys. Acta 1502:* 16-30, 2000.

Sgourakis, N.G., Yan, Y., McCallum, S.A., Wang, C., Garcia, A.E. The Alzheimer's peptides Aβ40 and 42 adopt distinct conformations in water: a combined MD / NMR study. *J. Mol. Biol. 368:* 1448-1457, 2007.

Shankar, G.M., Bloodgood, B.L., Townsend, M., Walsh, D.M., Selkoe, D.J., Sabatini, B.L. Natural oligomers of the Alzheimer amyloid-β protein induce reversible synapse loss by modulating an NMDA-type glutamate receptor-dependent signaling pathway. *J. Neurosci. 27:* 2866-2875, 2007.

Shepherd, J., Blauw, G.J., Murphy, M.B., Bollen, E.L., Buckley, B.M., Cobbe, S.M., Ford, I., Gaw, A., Hyland, M., Jukema, J.W., Kamper, A.M., Macfarlane, P.W., Meinders, A.E., Norrie, J., Packard, C.J., Perry, I.J., Stott, D.J., Sweeney, B.J., Twomey, C., Westendorp, R.G. Pravastatin in elderly individuals at risk of vascular disease (PROSPER): a randomised controlled trial. *Lancet 360:* 1623-1630, 2002.

Shibata, M., Yamada, S., Kumar, S.R., Calero, M., Bading, J., Frangione, B., Holtzman, D.M., Miller, C.A., Strickland, D.K., Ghiso, J., Zlokovic, B.V. Clearance of Alzheimer's amyloid β(1-40) peptide from brain by LDL receptor-related protein-1 at the blood-brain barrier. *J. Clin. Invest. 106:* 1489-1499, 2000.

Shoghi-Jadid, K., Small, G.W., Agdeppa, E.D., Kepe, V., Ercoli, L.M., Siddarth, P., Read, S., Satyamurthy, N., Petric, A., Huang, S.C., Barrio, J.R. Localization of neurofibrillary tangles and β-amyloid plaques in the brains of living patients with Alzheimer disease. *Am. J. Geriatr. Psychiatry 10:* 24-35, 2002.

Shulman, K.I. Clock-drawing: is it the ideal cognitive screening test? *Int. J. Geriatr. Psychiatry 15:* 548-561, 2000.

Siemers, E., Skinner, M., Dean, R.A., Gonzales, C., Satterwhite, J., Farlow, M., Ness, D., May, P.C. Safety, tolerability, and changes in Aβ concentrations after administration of a γ-secretase inhibitor in volunteers. *Clin. Neuropharmacol. 28:* 126-132, 2005.

Siemers, E.R., Quinn, J.F., Kaye, J., Farlow, M.R., Porsteinsson, A., Tariot, P., Zoulnouni, P., Galvin, J.E., Holtzman, D.M., Knopman, D.S., Satterwhite, J., Gonzales, C., Dean, R.A., May, P.C. Effects of a γ-secretase inhibitor in a randomized study of patients with Alzheimer disease. *Neurology 66:* 602-604, 2006.

Silverman, D.H., Small, G.W., Chang, C.Y., Lu, C.S., Kung De Aburto, M.A., Chen, W., Czernin, J., Rapoport, S.I., Pietrini, P., Alexander, G.E., Schapiro, M.B., Jagust, W.J., Hoffman, J.M., Welsh-Bohmer, K.A., Alavi, A., Clark, C.M., Salmon, E., de Leon, M.J., Mielke, R., Cummings, J.L., Kowell, A.P., Gambhir, S.S., Hoh, C.K., Phelps, M.E. Positron emission tomography in evaluation of dementia: Regional brain metabolism and long-term outcome. *JAMA 286:* 2120-2127, 2001.

Sjogren, P., Christrup, L.L., Petersen, M.A., Hojsted, J. Neuropsychological assessment of chronic non-malignant pain patients treated in a multidisciplinary pain centre. *Eur. J. Pain 9:* 453-462, 2005.

Small, D.H. The role of the amyloid protein precursor (APP) in Alzheimer's disease: does the normal function of APP explain the topography of neurodegeneration? *Neurochem. Res. 23:* 795-806, 1998.

Small, G.W., Kepe, V., Ercoli, L.M., Siddarth, P., Bookheimer, S.Y., Miller, K.J., Lavretsky, H., Burggren, A.C., Cole, G.M., Vinters, H.V., Thompson, P.M., Huang, S.C., Satyamurthy, N., Phelps, M.E., Barrio, J.R. PET of brain amyloid and tau in mild cognitive impairment. *N. Engl. J. Med. 355:* 2652-2663, 2006.

Solomon, B. Alzheimer's disease and immunotherapy. *Curr. Alzheimer Res. 1:* 149-163, 2004.

Solomon, B., Koppel, R., Frankel, D., Hanan-Aharon, E. Disaggregation of Alzheimer β-amyloid by site-directed mAb. *Proc. Natl. Acad. Sci. USA 94:* 4109-4112, 1997.

Soto, C., Kindy, M.S., Baumann, M., Frangione, B. Inhibition of Alzheimer's amyloidosis by peptides that prevent β-sheet conformation. *Biochem. Biophys. Res. Commun. 226:* 672-680, 1996.

Soto, C., Sigurdsson, E.M., Morelli, L., Kumar, R.A., Castano, E.M., Frangione, B. β-sheet breaker peptides inhibit fibrillogenesis in a rat brain model of amyloidosis: implications for Alzheimer's therapy. *Nat. Med. 4:* 822-826, 1998.

Sparks, D.L., Connor, D.J., Sabbagh, M.N., Petersen, R.B., Lopez, J., Browne, P. Circulating cholesterol levels, apolipoprotein E genotype and dementia severity influence the benefit of atorvastatin treatment in Alzheimer's disease: results of the Alzheimer's Disease Cholesterol-Lowering Treatment (ADCLT) trial. *Acta Neurol. Scand. Suppl. 185:* 3-7, 2006a.

Sparks, D.L., Sabbagh, M., Connor, D., Soares, H., Lopez, J., Stankovic, G., Johnson-Traver, S., Ziolkowski, C., Browne, P. Statin therapy in Alzheimer's disease. *Acta Neurol. Scand. Suppl. 185:* 78-86, 2006b.

Squire, L.R., Stark, C.E., Clark, R.E. The medial temporal lobe. *Annu. Rev. Neurosci. 27:* 279-306, 2004.

Stachel, S.J., Coburn, C.A., Steele, T.G., Crouthamel, M.C., Pietrak, B.L., Lai, M.T., Holloway, M.K., Munshi, S.K., Graham, S.L., Vacca, J.P. Conformationally biased P3 amide replacements of β-secretase inhibitors. *Bioorg. Med. Chem. Lett. 16:* 641-644, 2006.

Stachel, S.J., Coburn, C.A., Steele, T.G., Jones, K.G., Loutzenhiser, E.F., Gregro, A.R., Rajapakse, H.A., Lai, M.T., Crouthamel, M.C., Xu, M., Tugusheva, K., Lineberger, J.E., Pietrak, B.L., Espeseth, A.S., Shi, X.P., Chen-Dodson, E., Holloway, M.K., Munshi, S., Simon, A.J., Kuo, L., Vacca, J.P. Structure-based design of potent and selective cell-permeable inhibitors of human β-secretase (BACE-1). *J. Med. Chem. 47:* 6447-6450, 2004.

Suo, Z.M., Humphrey, J., Kundtz, A., Sethi, F., Placzek, A., Crawford, F., Mullan, M. Soluble Alzheimers β-amyloid constricts the cerebral vasculature *in vivo. Neurosci. Lett. 257:* 77-80, 1998.

Suzuki, N., Cheung, T.T., Cai, X.-D., Odaka, A., Ötvös, L., Jr, Eckman, C., Golde, T.E., Younkin, S.G. An increased percentage of long amyloid β protein secreted by familial amyloid β protein precursor (βAPP717) mutants. *Science 264:* 1336-1340, 1994.

Takahashi, Y., Hayashi, I., Tominari, Y., Rikimaru, K., Morohashi, Y., Kan, T., Natsugari, H., Fukuyama, T., Tomita, T., Iwatsubo, T. Sulindac sulfide is a noncompetitive γ-secretase inhibitor that preferentially reduces Aβ42 generation. *J. Biol. Chem. 278:* 18664-18670, 2003.

Tamagno, E., Bardini, P., Obbili, A., Vitali, A., Borghi, R., Zaccheo, D., Pronzato, M.A., Danni, O., Smith, M.A., Perry, G., Tabaton, M. Oxidative stress increases expression and activity of BACE in NT2 neurons. *Neurobiol. Dis. 10:* 279-288, 2002.

Tan-Hehir, C., Fish, K., Siclovan, T., Smith, J., Williams, A., Agdeppa, E., Berry, J., Hughes, K., Demattos, R., Montalto, M. Discovery of a small molecule that preferentially binds the oligomeric form but not the fibrillar form of β-amyloid. Program No. 17.8. 2006 Neuroscience Meeting Planner. Atlanta, GA: Society for Neuroscience, 2006.

Tanzi, R.E., Moir, R.D., Wagner, S.L. Clearance of Alzheimer's Aβ peptide: the many roads to perdition. *Neuron 43:* 605-608, 2004.

Tariot, P.N., Farlow, M.R., Grossberg, G.T., Graham, S.M., McDonald, S., Gergel, I. Memantine treatment in patients with moderate to severe Alzheimer disease already receiving donepezil: a randomized controlled trial. *JAMA 291:* 317-324, 2004.

Teplow, D.B. Structural and kinetic features of amyloid β-protein fibrillogenesis. *Amyloid 5:* 121-142, 1998.

Terry, R.D. Alzheimer's disease and the aging brain. *J. Geriatr. Psychiatry Neurol. 19:* 125-128, 2006.

Thal, L.J., Kantarci, K., Reiman, E.M., Klunk, W.E., Weiner, M.W., Zetterberg, H., Galasko, D., Pratico, D., Griffin, S., Schenk, D., Siemers, E. The role of biomarkers in clinical trials for Alzheimer disease. *Alzheimer Dis. Assoc. Disord. 20:* 6-15, 2006.

Tierney, M.C., Szalai, J.P., Snow, W.G., Fisher, R.H., Nores, A., Nadon, G., Dunn, E., St George-Hyslop, P.H. Prediction of probable Alzheimer's disease in memory-impaired patients: A prospective longitudinal study. *Neurology 46:* 661-665, 1996.

Tjernberg, L.O., Näslund, J., Lindqvist, F., Johansson, J., Karlstrom, A.R., Thyberg, J., Terenius, L., Nordstedt, C. Arrest of β-amyloid fibril formation by a pentapeptide ligand. *J. Biol. Chem. 271:* 8545-8548, 1996.

Tomita, T., Iwatsubo, T. γ-secretase as a therapeutic target for treatment of Alzheimer's disease. *Curr. Pharm. Des. 12:* 661-670, 2006.

Townsend, M., Cleary, J.P., Mehta, T., Hofmeister, J., Lesne, S., O'Hare, E., Walsh, D.M., Selkoe, D.J. Orally available compound prevents deficits in memory caused by the Alzheimer Aβ oligomers. *Ann. Neurol. 60:* 668-676, 2006.

TransitionTherapeuticsInc. 2006, "FDA Provides Clearance to Initiate Phase I Clinical Trial with Alzheimer's Disease Drug Product AZD-103." From http://www.transitiontherapeutics.com/news/article.php.

TransTechPharma. 2005, "TTP488." From http://www.ttpharma.com/pipeline_ttp488.html.

Truelsen, T., Thudium, D., Gronbaek, M. Amount and type of alcohol and risk of dementia: the Copenhagen City Heart Study. *Neurology 59:* 1313-1319, 2002.

Tucker, H.M., Kihiko, M., Caldwell, J.N., Wright, S., Kawarabayashi, T., Price, D., Walker, D., Scheff, S., McGillis, J.P., Rydel, R.E., Estus, S. The plasmin system is induced by and degrades amyloid-β aggregates. *J. Neurosci. 20:* 3937-3946, 2000.

Tucker, H.M., Simpson, J., Kihiko-Ehmann, M., Younkin, L.H., McGillis, J.P., Younkin, S.G., Degen, J.L., Estus, S. Plasmin deficiency does not alter endogenous murine amyloid β levels in mice. *Neurosci. Lett. 368:* 285-289, 2004.

Tuszynski, M.H. Growth-factor gene therapy for neurodegenerative disorders. *Lancet Neurol. 1:* 51-57, 2002.

Tuszynski, M.H., Thal, L., Pay, M., Salmon, D.P., U, H.S., Bakay, R., Patel, P., Blesch, A., Vahlsing, H.L., Ho, G., Tong, G., Potkin, S.G., Fallon, J., Hansen, L., Mufson, E.J., Kordower, J.H., Gall, C., Conner, J. A phase 1 clinical trial of nerve growth factor gene therapy for Alzheimer disease. *Nat. Med. 11:* 551-555, 2005.

Urbanc, B., Cruz, L., Yun, S., Buldyrev, S.V., Bitan, G., Teplow, D.B., Stanley, H.E. *In silico* study of amyloid β-protein folding and oligomerization. *Proc. Natl. Acad. Sci. USA 101:* 17345-17350, 2004.

van Dyck, C.H., Lin, C.H., Smith, E.O., Wisniewski, G., Cellar, J., Robinson, R., Narayan, M., Bennett, A., Delaney, R.C., Bronen, R.A., Hoffer, P.B. Comparison of technetium-99m-HMPAO and technetium-99m-ECD cerebral SPECT images in Alzheimer's disease. *J. Nucl. Med. 37:* 1749-1755, 1996.

Van Nostrand, W.E., Porter, M. Plasmin cleavage of the amyloid β-protein: alteration of secondary structure and stimulation of tissue plasminogen activator activity. *Biochemistry 38:* 11570-11576, 1999.

Vardy, E.R., Catto, A.J., Hooper, N.M. Proteolytic mechanisms in Aβ metabolism: therapeutic implications for Alzheimer's disease. *Trends Mol. Med. 11:* 464-472, 2005.

Vassar, R. BACE1: the β-secretase enzyme in Alzheimer's disease. *J. Mol. Neurosci. 23:* 105-114, 2004.

Visser, P.J., Verhey, F.R., Hofman, P.A., Scheltens, P., Jolles, J. Medial temporal lobe atrophy predicts Alzheimer's disease in patients with minor cognitive impairment. *J. Neurol. Neurosurg. Psychiatry 72:* 491-497, 2002.

Vlasenko, A., Petit-Taboue, M.C., Bouvard, G., Morello, R., Derlon, J.M. Comparative quantitation of cerebral blood volume: SPECT versus PET. *J. Nucl. Med. 38:* 919-924, 1997.

von Arnim, C.A., Kinoshita, A., Peltan, I.D., Tangredi, M.M., Herl, L., Lee, B.M., Spoelgen, R., Hshieh, T.T., Ranganathan, S., Battey, F.D., Liu, C.X., Bacskai, B.J., Sever, S., Irizarry, M.C., Strickland, D.K., Hyman, B.T. The low density lipoprotein receptor-related protein (LRP) is a novel β-secretase (BACE1) substrate. *J. Biol. Chem. 280:* 17777-17785, 2005.

Wahlund, L.O., Julin, P., Johansson, S.E., Scheltens, P. Visual rating and volumetry of the medial temporal lobe on magnetic resonance imaging in dementia: a comparative study. *J. Neurol. Neurosurg. Psychiatry 69:* 630-635, 2000.

Walsh, D.M., Hartley, D.M., Kusumoto, Y., Fezoui, Y., Condron, M.M., Lomakin, A., Benedek, G.B., Selkoe, D.J., Teplow, D.B. Amyloid β-protein fibrillogenesis - Structure and biological activity of protofibrillar intermediates. *J. Biol. Chem. 274:* 25945-25952, 1999.

Walsh, D.M., Klyubin, I., Fadeeva, J.V., Cullen, W.K., Anwyl, R., Wolfe, M.S., Rowan, M.J., Selkoe, D.J. Naturally secreted oligomers of amyloid β protein potently inhibit hippocampal long-term potentiation *in vivo*. *Nature 416:* 535-539, 2002.

Walsh, D.M., Selkoe, D.J. Oligomers on the brain: the emerging role of soluble protein aggregates in neurodegeneration. *Protein Pept. Lett. 11:* 213-228, 2004.

Wang, D.S., Dickson, D.W., Malter, J.S. β-Amyloid Degradation and Alzheimer's Disease. *J. Biomed. Biotechnol. 2006:* 58406, 2006.

Wang, J., Dickson, D.W., Trojanowski, J.Q., Lee, V.M. The levels of soluble versus insoluble brain Aβ distinguish Alzheimer's disease from normal and pathologic aging. *Exp. Neurol. 158:* 328-337, 1999.

Wang, R., Sweeney, D., Gandy, S.E., Sisodia, S.S. The profile of soluble amyloid β protein in cultured cell media. Detection and quantification of amyloid β protein and variants by immunoprecipitation-mass spectrometry. *J Biol. Chem. 271:* 31894-31902, 1996.

Wang, X., Lee, S.R., Arai, K., Lee, S.R., Tsuji, K., Rebeck, G.W., Lo, E.H. Lipoprotein receptor-mediated induction of matrix metalloproteinase by tissue plasminogen activator. *Nat. Med. 9:* 1313-1317, 2003.

Weggen, S., Eriksen, J.L., Das, P., Sagi, S.A., Wang, R., Pietrzik, C.U., Findlay, K.A., Smith, T.E., Murphy, M.P., Bulter, T., Kang, D.E., Marquez-Sterling, N., Golde, T.E., Koo, E.H. A subset of NSAIDs lower amyloidogenic Aβ42 independently of cyclooxygenase activity. *Nature 414:* 212-216, 2001.

Wenk, G.L., Zajaczkowski, W., Danysz, W. Neuroprotection of acetylcholinergic basal forebrain neurons by memantine and neurokinin B. *Behav. Brain Res. 83:* 129-133, 1997.

Wilcock, D.M., Munireddy, S.K., Rosenthal, A., Ugen, K.E., Gordon, M.N., Morgan, D. Microglial activation facilitates Aβ plaque removal following intracranial anti-Aβ antibody administration. *Neurobiol. Dis. 15:* 11-20, 2004a.

Wilcock, D.M., Rojiani, A., Rosenthal, A., Levkowitz, G., Subbarao, S., Alamed, J., Wilson, D., Wilson, N., Freeman, M.J., Gordon, M.N., Morgan, D. Passive amyloid immunotherapy clears amyloid and transiently activates microglia in a transgenic mouse model of amyloid deposition. *J. Neurosci. 24:* 6144-6151, 2004b.

Wilcock, G.K., Black, S., Haworth, J., Laughlin, M., Hendrix, S., Binger, M.-H., Zavitz, K., Swabb, E., Hobden, A. A Placebo-controlled, Double-blind Trial of the Selective Aβ-42 Lowering Agent, Flurizan (MPC-7869, (R)-flurbiprofen) in Patients with Mild to Moderate Alzheimer's Disease. Alzheimer's Association International Conference on Prevention of Dementia, Washington, D.C., 2005.

Winblad, B., Palmer, K., Kivipelto, M., Jelic, V., Fratiglioni, L., Wahlund, L.O., Nordberg, A., Backman, L., Albert, M., Almkvist, O., Arai, H., Basun, H., Blennow, K., de Leon, M., DeCarli, C., Erkinjuntti, T., Giacobini, E., Graff, C., Hardy, J., Jack, C., Jorm, A., Ritchie, K., van Duijn, C., Visser, P., Petersen, R.C. Mild cognitive impairment--beyond controversies, towards a consensus: report of the International Working Group on Mild Cognitive Impairment. *J. Intern. Med. 256:* 240-246, 2004.

Wnendt, S., Wetzels, I., Gunzler, W.A. Amyloid β peptides stimulate tissue-type plasminogen activator but not recombinant prourokinase. *Thromb. Res. 85:* 217-224, 1997.

Wolfe, M.S. The γ-secretase complex: membrane-embedded proteolytic ensemble. *Biochemistry 45:* 7931-7939, 2006.

Wolfe, M.S., Citron, M., Diehl, T.S., Xia, W., Donkor, I.O., Selkoe, D.J. A substrate-based difluoro ketone selectively inhibits Alzheimer's γ-secretase activity. *J. Med. Chem. 41:* 6-9, 1998.

Wolozin, B., Kellman, W., Ruosseau, P., Celesia, G.G., Siegel, G. Decreased prevalence of Alzheimer disease associated with 3-hydroxy-3-methyglutaryl coenzyme A reductase inhibitors. *Arch. Neurol. 57:* 1439-1443, 2000.

Wong, G.T., Manfra, D., Poulet, F.M., Zhang, Q., Josien, H., Bara, T., Engstrom, L., Pinzon-Ortiz, M., Fine, J.S., Lee, H.J., Zhang, L., Higgins, G.A., Parker, E.M. Chronic treatment with the γ-secretase inhibitor LY-411,575 inhibits β-amyloid peptide production and alters lymphopoiesis and intestinal cell differentiation. *J. Biol. Chem. 279:* 12876-12882, 2004.

Wong, H.K., Sakurai, T., Oyama, F., Kaneko, K., Wada, K., Miyazaki, H., Kurosawa, M., De Strooper, B., Saftig, P., Nukina, N. β- Subunits of voltage-gated sodium channels are novel substrates of β-site amyloid precursor protein-cleaving enzyme (BACE1) and γ-secretase. *J. Biol. Chem. 280:* 23009-23017, 2005.

Yan, L.M., Tatarek-Nossol, M., Velkova, A., Kazantzis, A., Kapurniotu, A. Design of a mimic of nonamyloidogenic and bioactive human islet amyloid polypeptide (IAPP) as nanomolar affinity inhibitor of IAPP cytotoxic fibrillogenesis. *Proc. Natl. Acad. Sci. USA 103:* 2046-2051, 2006.

Yan, L.M., Velkova, A., Tatarek-Nossol, M., Andreetto, E., Kapurniotu, A. IAPP mimic blocks Aβ cytotoxic self-assembly: cross-suppression of amyloid toxicity of Aβ and IAPP suggests a molecular link between Alzheimer's disease and type II diabetes. *Angew. Chem. Int. Ed. Engl. 46:* 1246-1252, 2007.

Yang, D.S., Smith, J.D., Zhou, Z., Gandy, S.E., Martins, R.N. Characterization of the binding of amyloid-β peptide to cell culture-derived native apolipoprotein E2, E3, and E4 isoforms and to isoforms from human plasma. *J. Neurochem. 68:* 721-725, 1997.

Yang, F., Lim, G.P., Begum, A.N., Ubeda, O.J., Simmons, M.R., Ambegaokar, S.S., Chen, P.P., Kayed, R., Glabe, C.G., Frautschy, S.A., Cole, G.M. Curcumin inhibits formation of Aβ oligomers and fibrils, binds plaques, and reduces amyloid *in vivo*. *J. Biol. Chem. 280:* 5892-5901, 2005.

Yoon, K., Gaiano, N. Notch signaling in the mammalian central nervous system: insights from mouse mutants. *Nat. Neurosci. 8:* 709-715, 2005.

Youdim, M.B. The path from anti Parkinson drug selegiline and rasagiline to multifunctional neuroprotective anti Alzheimer drugs ladostigil and m30. *Curr. Alzheimer Res. 3:* 541-550, 2006.

Youdim, M.B., Amit, T., Bar-Am, O., Weinreb, O., Yogev-Falach, M. Implications of co-morbidity for etiology and treatment of neurodegenerative diseases with multifunctional neuroprotective-neurorescue drugs; ladostigil. *Neurotox. Res. 10:* 181-192, 2006.

Youdim, M.B., Bakhle, Y.S. Monoamine oxidase: isoforms and inhibitors in Parkinson's disease and depressive illness. *Br. J. Pharmacol. 147 Suppl 1:* S287-296, 2006.

Younkin, S.G. Evidence that Aβ42 is the real culprit in Alzheimer's disease. *Ann. Neurol. 37:* 287-288, 1995.

Zandi, P.P., Anthony, J.C., Khachaturian, A.S., Stone, S.V., Gustafson, D., Tschanz, J.T., Norton, M.C., Welsh-Bohmer, K.A., Breitner, J.C. Reduced risk of Alzheimer disease in users of antioxidant vitamin supplements: the Cache County Study. *Arch. Neurol. 61:* 82-88, 2004.

Zencir, M., Kuzu, N., Beser, N.G., Ergin, A., Catak, B., Sahiner, T. Cost of Alzheimer's disease in a developing country setting. *Int. J. Geriatr. Psychiatry 20:* 616-622, 2005.

Zhang, Y., McLaughlin, R., Goodyer, C., LeBlanc, A. Selective cytotoxicity of intracellular amyloid β peptide(1-42) through p53 and Bax in cultured primary human neurons. *J. Cell Biol. 156:* 519-529, 2002.

Zhu, G., Wang, D., Lin, Y.H., McMahon, T., Koo, E.H., Messing, R.O. Protein kinase Cε suppresses Aβ production and promotes activation of α-secretase. *Biochem. Biophys. Res. Commun. 285:* 997-1006, 2001.

Zlokovic, B.V. Clearing amyloid through the blood-brain barrier. *J. Neurochem. 89:* 807-811, 2004.

Zlokovic, B.V., Yamada, S., Holtzman, D., Ghiso, J., Frangione, B. Clearance of Aβ-peptide from brain: transport or metabolism? *Nat. Med. 6:* 718-719, 2000.

In: Research Progress in Alzheimer's Disease and Dementia   ISBN 978-1-60021-960-3
Editor: Miao-Kun Sun, pp. 251-273   © 2008 Nova Science Publishers, Inc.

Chapter IX

IN VIVO VISUALIZATION OF AMYLOID LIKE STRUCTURES WITH PET MOLECULAR IMAGING PROBES

Vladimir Kepe, Sung-Cheng Huang, Nagichettiar Satyamurthy, Gary W. Small and Jorge R. Barrio [*]

David Geffen School of Medicine at UCLA, Department of Molecular and Medical Pharmacology (V.K., S.-C.H., N.S., and J.R.B.) and Department of Psychiatry and Biobehavioral Sciences (G.W.S.); Semel Institute for Neuroscience and Human Behavior (G.W.S.); University of California at Los Angeles, Los Angeles, CA, USA.

ABSTRACT

Histochemical detection of β amyloid plaques and neurofibrillary tangles in neocortical and subcortical regions in postmortem brain tissue is necessary for definitive diagnosis of Alzheimer's disease. This chapter describes *non invasive* methods for their *in vivo* detection in the living brain of patients in early stages of the disease when neuronal loss and related functional impairment are still limited. With early detection effective therapeutic interventions are still possible. Moreover, these noninvasive methods to detect brain pathologies are potentially useful in developing surrogate markers for drug discovery and for monitoring therapeutic interventions.

Keywords: alzheimer's disease, senile plaques, neurofibrillary tangles, positron emission tomography, molecular imaging probes.

---

[*] Correspondence concerning this article should be addressed to: Dr. Jorge R. Barrio, Ph.D. David Geffen School of Medicine at UCLA, Department of Molecular and Medical Pharmacology, 10833 LeConte Avenue CHS B2-086A, Los Angeles, CA 90095. e-mail: jbarrio@mednet.ucla.edu; phone: 310-825-4167; fax: 310-825-4517.

In vivo imaging techniques are important tools in brain research providing structural (MRI, CT) and functional (PET, SPECT) information about the human brain in healthy and diseased state. Their use in medicine aids the diagnosis of a wide variety of conditions including cancer and neurodegenerative diseases. The structural and functional changes caused by neurodegenerative diseases (*e.g.* Alzheimer's disease, frontotemporal dementia, Parkinson's disease, prion diseases, etc.), can be detected and measured in the living brain of subjects suffering from these diseases. These changes are the result of pathological processes which include, among others, synaptic and neuronal degeneration in disease-specific vulnerable neuronal populations and presence of pathological intracellular and/or extracellular protein aggregates specific for each neurodegenerative disease. The ultimate goal of *in vivo* imaging is to detect these changes at very early, pre-symptomatic stages of neurodegenerative diseases, when the extent of damage is still limited and localized to few brain areas only.

In vivo imaging methods such as magnetic resonance imaging (MRI) for assessment of brain atrophy and 2-deoxy-2-[F-18]fluoro-*D*-glucose ([F-18]FDG) positron emission tomography (PET) for determination of regional brain glucose utilization have already found application in detection and diagnosis of neurodegenerative diseases such as Alzheimer's disease (AD).

Among the neurodegenerative diseases Alzheimer's disease is the most prevalent disorder associated with older age and has as such been extensively studied both at the level of molecular basis of the disease as well as by *in vivo* imaging methods. Pathological changes are found throughout the neocortex as pronounced neuronal loss as well as dense deposits of two types of insoluble protein aggregates, β-amyloid senile plaques and neurofibrillary tangles.

Neuronal loss, neuronal shrinkage, synaptic loss, and loss of neuronal projections contribute to the collapse of gray and white matter measurable as atrophy. At the same time these neuronal changes compromise the integrity of the major neuronal circuits which results in decreased function and decreased glucose utilization which is measurable with [F-18]FDG PET (Minoshima, 2003).

Intracellular and/or extracellular pathological deposits of insoluble protein aggregates are pathological hallmarks of all neurodegenerative diseases but were not considered viable targets for *in vivo* imaging due to the lack of appropriate molecular imaging probes.

In the last decade several classes of molecular imaging probes with demonstrated binding affinity for *in vitro* formed β-amyloid fibrils, and in some cases with capacity to label neurofibrillary tangles, were developed and applied for *in vivo* detection of pathological deposits in the brains of AD patients with PET. The focus of this chapter will be on use of imaging approaches for detection of these brain pathological deposits, and its application for detection of AD brain pathology.

ALZHEIMER'S DISEASE

Alzheimer's disease, the most common type of dementia among the elderly, is a progressive neurodegenerative disorder that gradually results in severe cognitive impairments leaving patients completely dependent on others (Evans, 1990). AD manifests itself clinically as impairment of a broad spectrum of cognitive processes, including verbal and nonverbal memory; language and semantic knowledge; attention and executive functions; and visuospatial abilities; all of which can be assessed with neuropsychological measures (Salmon and Lange, 2001). The prevalence of AD dramatically increases with age, from 1% in the 60-64 year group to 40% in the >85 year group (von Strauss et al., 1999) In 1990, more than 4 million Americans suffered from AD, and if current trends continue unabated an estimated 16 million will have AD by 2040 (Iqbal, 1991). The financial burden, including both direct costs (i.e., actual dollar expenditures) and indirect costs (i.e., resource losses not involving dollar expenditures), is conservatively estimated to exceed $100 billion annually in the U.S. alone (Rice et al., 2001)

Alois Alzheimer was first to describe two characteristic brain lesions, neurofibrillary tangles (NFT) and senile plaques (SP) (Vickers et al., 2000), in the brain of a patient affected by a dementia syndrome (Alzheimer, 1907). In addition to NFTs and NPs, the AD related pathological changes also include neuropil threads, hippocampal granuvacuolar degeneration and Hirano bodies, vascular changes, widespread neuronal loss and tissue atrophy, synaptic abnormalities, and activated glial cells as a result of neuroinflammation (Lantos and Cairns, 2000). SPs and NFTs are by far the most abundant neuropathological lesions found in AD, and although they can be also found in the brains of cognitively normal elderly subject as result of normal brain aging their density throughout the brain is significantly greater in AD than in normal aging or in other neurodegenerative disorders. In fully developed AD senile plaques (SP) appear throughout the neocortex and in several subcortical structures as diffuse amorphous (non-congophilic) aggregates and as dense focal (congophilic) fibrillar and dense core plaques (Dickson and Vickers, 2001). These brain lesions are found in extracellular space and are composed mainly of water insoluble β-amyloid peptide aggregates (Teplow, 1998; Selkoe, 1994). Senile plaques are often spatially co-localized with dystrophic neuritic processes which contain paired helical filaments (PHFs), fibrillar aggregates of hyperphosphorylated microtubule-associated protein tau (Lantos and Cairns, 2000; Dickson and Vickers, 2001). Such plaques are also referred to as neuritic plaques.

β-Amyloid peptides are 39 to 43 amino acid long peptides which are formed from amyloid precursor protein (APP), a large transmembrane protein, through the β- and γ-secretase mediated cleavage (Wisniewski et al., 1997). Intracellularly formed monomeric peptides are excreted into the extracellular space where they aggregate and form fibrillar and non-fibrillar deposits. Detailed structural information about β-amyloid fibrils based on the high resolution X-ray crystallography is not available due to the inability of insoluble β-amyloid fibrils to form single crystals (Lansbury, 1996) but considerable information about the fibrillar nature of *ex vivo* β-amyloid fibrils is available from X-ray diffraction experiments, which show two distinctive diffraction bands at 4.7 and 10 Å, typical of fibrils with cross-β sheets secondary structure element (Kirschner et al., 1986; Serpell, 2000; Teplow, 1998).

Aggregation of cross-β sheets leads to formation of 7-10 nm-wide straight rigid fibrils, as demonstrated by electron microscopy (Malinchik et al., 1998). Fibrils of synthetic β-amyloid(1-40), formed *in vitro*, resemble *in vivo* fibrils in terms of neurotoxic properties (Seileheimer et al., 1997) and ultrastructure (Miyakawa et al., 1986; Kirchner et al., 1987), but this may not hold true for tau aggregates.

Senile plaques are heterogeneous structures and are co-localized with a variety of proteinaceous and non-proteinaceous molecules, such as proteoglycans, inflammatory molecules, serum related amyloid P component, ubiquitin, apolipoprotein E, low density lipoprotein receptor-related protein, α2-macroglobulin, α1-antichymotripsin, and cholinesterases, among others (Atwood et al., 2002).

Neurofibrillary tangles are the second major type of pathological lesion found in AD. NFTs are intracellular lesions found in vulnerable neuronal populations throughout the neocortex and subcortical regions. NFTs are cytoskeletal structures composed of PHFs and straight filaments (SF), which are intraneuronal fibrillar aggregates of hyper-phosphorylated microtubule-associated protein tau (Lee et al., 2001a). After the NFT-laden neurons die, extracellular "tombstone" tangles remain visible, keeping the shape of neurons in which they were formed (*e.g.* typical flame-like tangles originated in pyramidal neurons) (Braak et al., 1999). Hyper-phosphorylated, microtubule-associated protein tau aggregates into PHFs – fibrillar structures 10-20 nm in width with 75-80 nm repeats – by forming cross-β sheet with tau peptide repeat domains and with the rest of the peptide forming largely unstructured "fuzzy" coats (Barghorn et al., 2004). The presence of cross-β sheets in NFTs and in the *in vitro* assembled tau polymers has also been suggested based on the X-ray diffraction experiments (Kirschner et al., 1986; von Bergen et al., 2005). NFTs undergo posttranslational modifications (e.g. proteolysis, glycation, crosslinking, amino acid racemization) and are spatially co-localized with a variety of proteins, such as ubiquitin, proteoglycans, serum amyloid P component, kinases, other MAP proteins, and apolipoprotein E, among others (Mandelkow and Mandelkow, 1998; Yen et al., 1995)

AD is a progressive disease which affects vulnerable neuronal populations throughout the neocortex and subcortical structures in a complex pattern that expands throughout the brain with worsening of symptoms. In the advanced stages of the disease, when a diagnosis of probable AD can be made, the death toll in vulnerable populations of CNS neurons is already heavy and has spread to the cortical regions beyond the hippocampus, one of the critical sites of neuronal damage leading to dementia (Braak and Braak, 1991; Price and Morris, 1999). In the cortex, the pyramidal neurons furnishing long cortico-cortical projections are thought to be particularly vulnerable to neurodegeneration, leading to disconnections of the association cortices (Morisson and Hof, 1997). By contrast, primary sensory and motor areas exhibit only limited neuronal loss. The association areas are also affected by extensive synaptic loss, which contributes to the structural disconnection of neuronal circuits leading to symptoms.

The brain areas affected by substantial neuronal loss at the earliest stages of the disease are entorhinal cortex and hippocampus. The large pyramidal neurons in CA1 and subicular regions of hippocampus, and the neurons in layers II and IV of entorhinal cortex are particularly vulnerable (Morisson and Hof, 1997; Mann, 1996; Hof, 1997). These types of neurons predominantly utilize glutamate for neurotransmission.

The extent of neuronal loss in these vulnerable populations is the best parameter to correlate with degree of dementia or cognitive decline (Bobinski et al., 1997; Gomez-Isla et al., 1997). Gomez-Isla et al. (Gomez-Isla et al., 1996) reported 57% neuronal loss of neurons in the layer II of the entorhinal cortex of patients with very mild AD. This result is in agreement with other studies reporting loss of entorhinal cortex layer II neurons (Price et al., 2001; Kordower et al., 2001). Other studies also have reported severe loss (>50%) of neurons in hippocampal CA1 field of AD patients (Price et al., 2001; Kordower et al., 2001; West et al., 1994; Fukutani et al., 1995). In severely affected AD patients, loss of CA1 neurons has been reported to reach 86% (Hof et al., 1997). The neuronal loss in CA1 field is progressive and Rössler and colleagues (Rössler et al., 2002) have determined it to be 33% at the Braak NFT stage IV and 51% at the Braak NFT stage V. These neuronal losses show significant correlations with the presence of abundant intraneuronal NFTs but not with amyloid deposition in the same areas (Braak and Braak, 1991; Rössler et al., 2002; Giannakopoulos et al., 2003).

Because of the progressive nature of AD, *in vivo* imaging of neuropathological deposits requires understanding of temporal and spatial progression of the neuropathological changes and their connections. The most important aspect of *in vivo* imaging of neuropathological deposits is its potential for detection of early changes during the pre-symptomatic stages or before dementia is clinically obvious - when brain damage is still limited and when the therapeutic interventions still have potential to protect the rest of the brain by arresting the progression of pathology and by preventing further neuronal loss.

Deposition of NFTs and β-amyloid plaques in AD has been studied extensively and separate patterns have been proposed for evolution of NFT pathology and β-amyloid plaque pathology (Braak and Braak, 1991; Delacourte et al., 1999). Braak and Braak (Braak and Braak, 1991) have proposed six stages of NFT pathology progression based on the spatial pattern of NFT distribution in the brain. In the initial stages ('transentorhinal' stages I and II), NFTs are observed only in entorhinal cortex; in the 'limbic' stages III and IV dense deposits of NFTs can be observed throughout the entire entorhinal cortex and hippocampal formation with association areas of temporal lobe, cingulate gyrus and orbito-frontal cortex having sparse deposits. In more advanced 'cortical' stages V and VI, associated with fully developed dementia, NFTs finally spread throughout the neocortex leaving only sensory motor cortex relatively spared. Delacourte and colleagues (Delacourte et al., 1999) have proposed a 10-stage system (S1-S10) of NFT progression which more clearly defines the pattern of the expansion of NFT pathology through the neocortex after it progresses from the medial temporal lobe.

β-Amyloid plaque pathology develops in a pattern different from the NFT distribution and predominantly affects neocortical regions, with hippocampus and entorhinal cortex being less affected and at later stages of β-amyloid plaque progression. Braak and Braak (Braak and Braak, 1991) have proposed three stages of β-amyloid plaque progression. In the stage A the basal portions of temporal, frontal and occipital lobes develop low densities of β-amyloid deposits. In the stage B almost all neocortical association areas develop medium densities of β-amyloid deposits. Finally, in the stage C, densely packed β-amyloid deposits can be found throughout the whole neocortex and in numerous subcortical structures with relative sparing of primary sensory-motor areas. The pathology patterns proposed by Braak and Braak match well the distribution of pathology reported in a detailed study of pathology distribution by Arnold et al. in 39 brain areas of 11 patients with moderate to severe AD (Arnold et al., 1991). Densities of NFTs and neuritic β-amyloid plaques were mapped out showing the degree of involvement of neocortex. The results correspond to Braak NFT stages V/VI and Braak β-amyloid stage C. In this study the authors observed a gradient of NFT densities decreasing in the following order: limbic lobe (hippocampus and entorhinal cortex) > temporal lobe > frontal lobe > parietal lobe > occipital lobe. All primary sensory areas were relatively spared. Neuritic β-amyloid plaques were distributed more uniformly in the neocortex with temporal, parietal, and occipital lobes having higher densities of neuritic plaques than frontal lobe. Similarly, Price et al. (Price et al., 1991) have determined in their moderately to heavily demented AD patients (CDR scores 2 and 3) in more limited number of analyzed areas that both NFTs and β-amyloid plaques are distributed densely throughout the cortex with caudate and putamen showing dense deposits of β-amyloid plaques. In mildly demented patients (CDR score 0.5) the distribution of NFTs and β-amyloid plaques matched that of more severely demented subjects yet lower densities of both pathologies were observed in all areas analyzed. The non-demented subjects did show low levels of NFTs in CA1 region of hippocampus, entorhinal cortex and in perirhinal cortex as well as in the anterior olfactory nucleus and these densities increased with age. Low densities of β-amyloid plaques were found in isolated areas of lateral temporal cortex only in a small number of non-demented cases. The authors have also presented an isolated non-demented case with NFTs and β-amyloid plaque topography and densities comparable to those observed in very mildly demented subjects.

A large scale autopsy study of 1258 brains from elderly patients with available clinical diagnosis (58 cases had AD, 1131 were not demented or were mildly impaired, the remaining cases had other types of dementias) has shown, as expected, stark differences in densities of NFTs and β-amyloid plaques between the control group and the AD group in several brain regions (CA1 region of hippocampus, inferior temporal cortex, superior frontal cortex and occipital cortex) (Giannakopoulus et al., 1994). Reflecting the finding of Braak and Braak these results have shown presence of NFTs in CA1 region of hippocampus and in the inferior temporal cortex in the vast majority of AD cases (90% and 79%, respectively). NFTs were observed in 39% of AD cases in the superior frontal cortex and in 19% of AD cases in occipital lobe. These results also point to the gradual spreading of NFTs to the neocortex beyond the temporal lobe in AD patients with the disease progression. β-Amyloid plaques were observed almost uniformly in the neocortical regions (inferior temporal cortex, superior frontal cortex, occipital cortex) in 88-95% of AD cases and β-amyloid plaques were present in the CA1 region of 85% of AD subjects.

These studies demonstrate that both types of pathology are present to different degree in the neocortex of the symptomatic AD patients with higher densities found in more severely affected subjects. Thus, interpretation of the *in vivo* imaging results requires good understanding of the spatial and temporal pattern of cortical neuropathology progression, *i.e.* topography of neurofibrillary tangles, β-amyloid plaques, and neuronal losses and their correlations with the cognitive performance and clinical symptoms of the disease.

Neuropathological and clinical research support the idea that the pathological processes leading to AD begin years before a clinical diagnosis of probable AD can be confirmed (Braak and Braak, 1991; McKhann et al., 1984). For example, Braak and Braak (Braak and Braak, 1997) have shown on a large sample of 2661 autopsy brains from the general population (age range 26 – 95 years) that NFTs are present in some individuals very early in adult life, e.g. among 141 subjects who died between ages 31 and 40 there were 34 (24%) who had at least few NFTs in entorhinal cortex. The presence of diffuse amyloid deposits in neocortex in the same group has been demonstrated only in 2 cases.

Several studies on cognitively normal control subjects have found that the majority of elderly subjects have some NFTs in the entorhinal cortex and in some cases also in perirhinal cortex (Brodman area 35) and in CA1/subicular region of hippocampus, consistent with Braak stages I-III (Price and Morris,1999; Knopman et al., 2003; Arriagada et al., 1992; Guillozet et al., 2003). The density of NFTs in these areas increases in age dependent manner but it is significantly lower than observed in AD patients. β-Amyloid plaques were observed only in a smaller subgroup of these subjects in temporal cortex and occasionally also in other neocortical areas.

Knopman et al. (Knopman et al., 2003) concluded that Braak NFT stage IV or above (i.e. spreading of NFTs to the neocortex) and presence of moderate levels of neuritic β-amyloid plaques in the neocortex (Braak amyloid stage B) should be considered as neuropathological stages associated with dementia, either in pre-clinical stages or already manifested. In similar fashion, Price and Morris (Price and Morris,1999) have reported several cases of cognitively normal subjects with CDR score 0 who displayed the pattern and densities of NFTs and β-amyloid plaques typically found in subjects with very mild dementia (CDR score 0.5) and have concluded that these were 'preclinical' AD cases.

The most important aspect of *in vivo* imaging of neuropathology in AD is to determine the pathology distribution in subjects who developed the first symptoms of AD. Mild cognitive impairment is a clinical category used to classify the subjects who display isolated impairment in the area of memory or any other cognitive function but who have otherwise preserved cognitive and functional abilities and do not meet criteria for the diagnosis of dementia (Petersen et al., 1999). This clinical category has been associated with higher rate of conversion to AD, especially among the amnestic MCI subjects. In a study on pathology distribution in amnestic MCI Petersen et al. (Petersen et al., 2006) reported that NFT pathology in hippocampus was more prevalent when compared to controls. The authors have frequently observed diffuse β-amyloid plaques, detected by Aβ immunohistochemistry, in the neocortex both in the MCI subjects and in controls but the cored and neuritic plaques were observed more infrequently. In contrast, AD patients had dense deposits of all types of β-amyloid plaques in the neocortex with NFTs distributed throughout the neocortex consistently with Braak stages IV, V, and VI. Jicha et al. (Jicha et al., 2006) reported that among the amnestic MCI subjects who developed dementia there was high prevalence of AD (71%) and that these subjects displayed the NFT brain distribution consistent with Braak NFT stages >IV.

The presence of pathological deposits by itself is not sufficient to cause dementia as demonstrated in hippocampus and entorhinal cortex in normal aging and preclinical AD cases. The pathological deposits have to be paralleled by substantial neuronal loss in in vulnerable neuronal populations for the disease symptoms to become apparent (Price et al., 2001) Neuronal loss in these vulnerable populations is the best parameter to be correlated with the degree of dementia, and the neuronal loss appears strongly correlated with NFTs (Braak and Braak, 1991; Giannakopoulos et al., 2003).

Based on the results of these studies, it is clear that temporal lobe has a very specific role in early stages of AD and that it is the area of the brain with the earliest and most pronounced pathological changes. As such it is the prime area of interest for early detection of AD based on *in vivo* imaging methods targeting pathological deposits.

Based on the pathology studies discussed in the previous section we can establish several conclusions about the spatial pattern of pathology distribution:

a) low levels of NFT pathology confined to entorhinal cortex and hippocampus (medial temporal lobe) is indicative of normal aging - *in vivo* imaging detection of low levels of probe binding only in medial temporal lobe is to be expected in some controls and its density should increase with age; b) high level of NFT pathology in the medial temporal lobe and presence of low levels of β-amyloid and NFT pathology in a number of neocortical areas is associated with preclinical AD or MCI – *in vivo* imaging detection should show high levels of probe binding in the medial temporal lobe and low level of probe binding in the affected neocortical areas; c) symptomatic AD is associated with NFTs and β-amyloid plaques distributed throughout the neocortex with higher densities of pathological deposits associated.

The progressive nature of pathology in AD presents a unique challenge for any diagnostic method based on detection of β-amyloid plaques and neurofibrillary tangles as well as for any method that would monitor therapeutic treatments targeting β-amyloid plaque and neurofibrillary tangle deposition. Such methods should possess sufficient sensitivity to detect relatively low densities of both pathological lesions in the affected areas present during the preclinical, non-symptomatic AD stages; to accurately determine their amounts; and to detect the changes in the pattern of distribution and densities resulting from spread of β-amyloid plaques and neurofibrillary tangles into additional cortical areas.

PET MOLECULAR IMAGING PROBES FOR VISUALIZATION OF NEURODEGENERATIVE CHANGES

The cognitive decline in AD is reflected in regional decreases in brain activity, which can be assessed *in vivo* with [F-18]FDG PET (Silverman et al., 2001; Silverman et al., 2003). [F-18]FDG PET has been used for the diagnosis of AD for an extended period of time and its sensitivity was determined to be 93-95% with 89-92% specificity for AD. Deactivation of temporal and parietal regions and of the posterior cingulate gyrus is the earliest sign of AD reflecting the pathological processes in neuronal circuits projecting from and to the temporal lobe (Reiman et al., 1996). [F-18]FDG provides metabolic (functional) information, but only limited information about specific brain pathologies or processes likely to be drug targets in the brain of these patients.

In addition to using [F-18]FDG for targeting neuronal glucose utilization and measuring their functional viability, there are neuronal and glial targets such as receptors, transporters, and enzymes which are specific for certain type of neurons and which can be imaged with appropriate molecular imaging probes and PET in dementia (Minoshima et al., 2004; Cohen, 2007). Although *in vivo* PET imaging of acetylcholinergic, dopaminergic, GABA-ergic, serotoninergic, and glial targets has been described in AD, their diagnostic value is limited because of limited understanding of the pathological processes which lead to the changes in these neuronal populations (Minoshima et al., 2004; Cohen, 2007).

Presence of senile plaques and NFTs in the autopsy brain samples is required for positive diagnosis of Alzheimer's disease. Although at this stage it is not clear if these lesions are the cause or the consequence of brain pathological processes, it is clear that their presence can be a sign of active neurodegenerative neurodegenerative processes.

Senile plaques and neurofibrillary tangles therefore present an excellent target for in vivo detection of neurodegeneration. Compared with receptors, transporters and enzymes, NFTs and β-amyloid plaques are inert structures largely lacking functional activity connected to the aggregated fibrils, with exception of the β-sheet forming polymerization. This lack of activity poses a serious challenge for development of molecular probes with specific binding to these structures (Shoghi-Jadid et al., 2005; Shoghi-Jadid et al., 2006).

Soluble monomeric peptides (or possibly oligomeric species) are in the equilibrium with their cross-β sheet polymerized fibrillar aggregates, which makes the monomeric peptides themselves potentially highly specific imaging agents (e.g. radiolabeled β-amyloid peptides (Kurihara and Pardridge, 2000)). An alternative approach utilizes the monoclonal antibodies directed against these peptides (e.g., Friedland et al., 1994). Due to their large size and protein nature these probes have very low capacity to penetrate the blood-brain barrier and enter the brain which seriously limits their efficiency as *in vivo* imaging probes.

The blood-brain barrier is also almost impenetrable barrier for histological dyes like Congo red and Thioflavins, histological dyes with strong anionic or cationic nature which are used as gold standards for detection of senile plaques and NFTs in post mortem AD brain tissues.

Many laboratories have attempted the development of specific small molecule imaging agents, specific for β-amyloid aggregates, with improved brain entry following various approaches. Cross-β sheet structure in the core of the amyloid fibrils with its highly ordered arrangement of peptide monomers, anchored together with the hydrogen bonds formed between the peptide backbones and with π-π stacking of the aromatic amino acid residues, as well as glutamic acid – lysine electrostatic interactions, are with high probability the targets of these ligands (Makin et al., 2005).

Three structurally distinctive groups of tracers with high affinity for *in vitro* β-amyloid fibrils (in nM range) have emerged from derivatives of Congo Red and Thioflavin T: 1) bis(styryl)benzenes, derivatives of Congo Red and Chrysamine G; 2) stilbenes and styrylheteroaromatic compounds; and 3) 2-phenylbenzothiazoles A wide variety of molecules structurally related to Thioflavins and to Congo Red,, have been prepared in forms suitable for labeling with radioisotopes for PET and SPECT. The Congo derivatives include X-34 (Styren et al., 2000), methoxy-X04 (Klunk et al., 2002), and BSB (Lee et al., 2001b). Examples of molecular probes with structures related to Thioflavines are 2-[(4'-methylamino)phenyl]-6-hydroxybenzothiazole (6-OH-BTA-1 or PIB) (Mathis et al., 2003); imidazo[1,2-*a*]pyridine derivatives (IMPY) (Kung et al., 2002; Cai et al., 2004; Zeng et al.,

2006); benzofuran derivatives (Ono et al., 2006); benzoxazole derivatives such as IBOX (Zhuang et al., 2001), styrylbenzoxazoles (Okamura et al., 2004), or BF-227 (Kudo et al., 2007); and benzothiophene derivatives (Chang et al., 2006). Styrylbenzenes and stilbenes include 4-methylamino-4'-hydroxystilbene (SB-13) (Ono et al., 2003) and its fluoroalkyl derivatives (Zhang et al., 2005a; Zhang et al., 2005b), styrylpyridines (Zhang ey al., 2007), diphenyltrienes (Zhuang et al., 2006), and diphenylacetylenes (Chandra et al., 2007). A variety of molecular imaging probes with a polyaromatic or heterocyclic core element include naphthalene ([F-18]FDDNP) (Agdeppa et al., 2003a; Kepe et al. 2006a; Liu et al., 2007), fluorenes (Lee et al., 2003), acridine (BF-108) (Suemoto et al., 2004), and thiophenes (Chandra et al., 2006). Radiofluorinated curcuminoids, natural compounds from turmeric with β-amyloid anti-aggregation properties, have been recently prepared (Ryu et al., 2006), with the purpose of *in vivo* amyloid imaging since they exhibit excellent in vitro binding properties (Ki = 0.07 nM).

Several imaging probes have also been shown to possess the capacity to label neurofibrillary tangles *in vitro* such, e.g. [F-18]FDDNP and radiolabeled quinolines and benzimidazoles (Okamura et al., 2005).

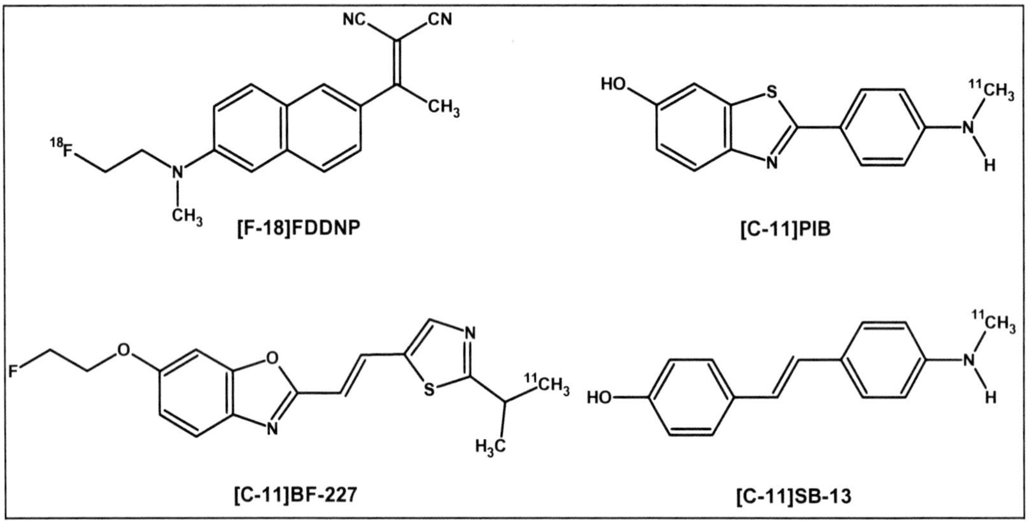

Figure 1. Chemical structures of molecular imaging probes used for clinical studies for imaging of neuropathological deposits in AD patients, controls, and in the case of [F-18]FDDNP and [C-11]PIB also in MCI subjects.

Although a variety of probes with affinity for β-amyloid aggregates and/or hyperphosphorylated has been developed, only 4 PET molecular imaging probes, [F-18]FDDNP (Shoghi-Jadid et al., 2002; Small et al., 2006), [C-11]PIB (Klunk et al., 2004; Engler et al., 2006; Mintun et al, 2006), [C-11] SB-13 (Verhoeff et al., 2004) and [C-11]BF-227 (Kudo et al., 2007), have been successfully utilized for PET imaging in human subjects with AD. Their structures are shown in Figure 1. [F-18]FDDNP and [C-11]PIB have also been applied for *in vivo* imaging of other neurodegenerative disorders. Recently, biodistribution experiments in humans and human dose estimates have also been reported for [I-123]radioiodinated IMPY, a SPECT radiolabeled molecular imaging probe for imaging of brain pathology in AD (Newberg et al., 2006). In addition to imaging of pathological brain changes in humans, [F-18]FDDNP and [C-11]PIB have also been applied for *in vivo* imaging of β-amyloid brain aggregates in transgenic animal models with microPET (Kepe et al., 2005; Toyama et al., 2005; Klunk et al., 2005).

Since the emphasis of this Chapter is on the *in vivo* PET imaging in AD we will address only the molecular imaging probes already applied for human scanning.

[F-18]FDDNP was the first molecular imaging probe reported to be effective in the visualization of neuropathology in the living brain of AD patients (Barrio et al., 1999; Agdeppa et al., 2001; Shoghi-Jadid et al., 2002). FDDNP (2-(1-{6-[(2-fluoroethyl)(methyl)amino]-2-naphthyl}ethylidene)malononitrile), a solvent viscosity and polarity sensitive fluorescent probe, is a representative of a family of substituted naphthalenes with high binding affinity for β-amyloid peptide aggregates and for NFTs (Agdeppa et al., 2003a). [F-18]FDDNP labels β-amyloid deposits and NFTs both *in vitro* and *in vivo* (Agdeppa et al., 2003a) and has proven useful to follow the neuropathology progression in the disease *in vivo*. Medial temporal lobe binding of [F-18]FDDNP was the focus of the first clinical *in vivo* imaging study in which a group of 7 AD patients and 9 controls were compared (Shoghi-Jadid et al., 2002). Significantly higher relative residence times, a measures of [F-18]FDDNP binding, were observed in AD patients when compared to the controls and were also significantly correlated with the memory MMSE scores ranging from 8 to 30 in the subject group. These results were verified by application of Logan graphical analysis with cerebellum as a reference region and significant accumulation of [F-18]FDDNP in several cortical areas in the brains of AD patients (medial and lateral temporal lobe, parietal lobe, frontal lobe, posterior cingulate gyrus), with the highest relative distribution values (DVR) observed in the medial and lateral temporal lobe reflecting high levels of β-amyloid and NFT deposition in these areas (Kepe et al., 2005; Kepe et al., 2006; Small et al., 2006). Since the medial temporal lobe is associated with initial pathology formation (Braak and Braak, 1991), [F-18]FDDNP offers an excellent opportunity for early detection (i.e., subjects at risk and patients with mild cognitive impairment).

The next successful clinical report on PET imaging using a 6-hydroxybenzothiazole derivative [C-11]-2-(4-methylaminophenyl)-6-hydroxybenzothiazole ([C-11] 6-OH-BTA or [C-11] PIB) with high *in vitro* affinity for Aβ aggregates (K_d = 4.7 nM) was reported by Klunk and colleagues (Klunk et al., 2004) in 16 AD patients and 9 controls. [C-11]PIB retention is most prominently increased in frontal cortex and parietal areas. Temporal accumulation was reported to be low, similar to that of the pons, known to lack Aβ aggregates. [C-11]PIB binding in control subjects was limited to white matter only and no binding in the grey matter areas was observed. The increases in [C-11]PIB binding found in frontal and parietal lobes in AD patients were inversely correlated with decreases in regional brain glucose utilization observed in the same AD patients (Klunk et al., 2004). In contrast, a more recent 2-year follow-up study on the same subject group has shown no changes in [C-11]PIB binding with disease progression in 4 subjects who had significant [F-18]FDG metabolic changes and for which it was concluded that their disease progressed (Engler et al., 2006). In another [C-11]PIB study (Lopresti et al., 2005) on 10 AD patients, 11 mild cognitive impairment subjects (MCI) and 6 controls the authors have found that several MCIs have distribution and levels of [C-11]PIB indistinguishable from AD, which together with the results of Engler et al. raises the question at which stage of the disease does [C-11]PIB binding reaches the plateau.

Verhoeff et al. (Verhoeff et al., 2004) reported the first human PET scanning experiments with a novel hydroxylated stilbene derivative, 4-[C-11]methylamino-4'-hydroxystylbene ([C-11]SB-13), performed in 5 AD patients and 6 controls. The most prominent tracer retention was observed in frontal and parietal areas and was significantly higher in the AD group compared to the control group. For the comparison the same subjects also received [C-11]PIB scans and both tracers have shown similar patterns of retention in the brains of AD patients.

Kudo et al. (Kudo et al., 2007) have reported a clinical PET imaging study with [C-11]BF-227 in 10 AD patients and 11 controls. The probe binding was increased in AD patients when compared to the control group most prominently in the parietal and temporal lobes and with frontal lobe showing less prominent level of binding. The authors have hypothesized that this pattern is due to their probe's preferential binding to the dense core β-amyloid plaques.

The availability of transgenic animal models of β-amyloid brain amyloidosis has also opened a new avenue for research on *in vivo* imaging of β-amyloid deposition with microPET. These models open new possibilities for testing of new molecular imaging probes for β-amyloid aggregates, validation of their efficiency through comparison with actual levels and distribution of β-amyloid deposits in the brain, and also for evaluation of new anti-aggregation therapies. [F-18]FDDNP has been successfully used for *in vivo* microPET imaging of β-amyloid brain load in the triple β-amyloid transgenic rats (Kepe et al., 2005). Parametric images based on the Logan graphical analysis with cerebellum as reference region demonstrated that [F-18]FDDNP preferentially binds to the β-amyloid rich areas of the rat brain (frontal cortex and hippocampus) when compared with cerebellum, an area almost devoid of any plaques in this animals. In contrast, microPET imaging of β-amyloid deposits in Tg2576 β-amyloid transgenic mice (Toyama et al., 2005) or PS1 and PS1/APP β-amyloid transgenic mice (Klunk et al., 2005) with [C-11]PIB did not demonstrate increased [C-11]PIB binding in β-amyloid rich areas when compared to control areas. Klunk et al. (Klunk et al., 2005) hypothesized that the reasons for this lack of [C-11]PIB binding in transgenic rodents is the significantly lower number of binding sites for [C-11]PIB on β-amyloid fibrillar deposits in the rodent brains compared to the brain β-amyloid fibrillar deposits found in the AD patients. This lack of [C-11]PIB binding is also in contrast with the initial report on multiphoton fluorescence microscopy detection of PIB binding to the brain β-amyloid plaques and β-amyloid angiopathy in the TG2576 and PSAPP β-amyloid transgenic mice (Bacskai et al., 2003).

[F-18] FDDNP as Molecular Imaging Probe for In Vitro and In Vivo Visualization of Pathological Brain Lesions

The *in vitro* binding properties of [F-18]FDDNP to synthetic Aβ(1-40) fibrils were first determined by fluorescence titration of non-radioactive FDDNP (Agdeppa et al., 2001). These experiments performed in 0.25% ethanol in PBS, yielded apparent K_D values of 0.12 nM and 1.86 nM for two binding sites. [F-18]FDDNP radioactive binding assays with brain homogenates from AD and normal control patients, performed in 1% ethanol in PBS, confirm the high affinity binding of [F-18]FDDNP to *ex vivo* β-amyloid plaques and NFTs. The resulting Scatchard plot of [F-18]FDDNP binding in AD homogenates yielded a K_D value of 0.75 nM and a B_{max} value of 144 nM with the brain sample studied (Agdeppa et al., 2003a). There was no appreciable binding of [F-18]FDDNP to homogenates from age-matched control brains. Further experiments involved digital [F-18]FDDNP autoradiography of AD and control brain samples in 1% ethanol in saline, and correlation of the autoradiography results with confocal fluorescence microscopy and immunohistochemistry in the AD brain specimens. [F-18]FDDNP binding was observed in temporal and parietal cortices matching the distribution of combined β-amyloid plaques and NFT immunostaining of adjacent slices. Fluorescence microscopy revealed that the labeling pattern in the autoradiograms and immunostained tissue originated from SPs and NFTs.

[F-18]FDDNP shares the binding site on the *in vitro* β-amyloid fibrils with several non-steroidal antiinflammatory drugs, such as naproxen and ibuprofen, but not with diclofenac, Congo red or Thioflavin T as revealed competitive binding assays (Agdeppa et al., 2003b). These results were confirmed with [F-18]FDDNP autoradiography blocking experiments on AD brain tissue samples where naproxen and ibuprofen completely blocked specific [F-18]FDDNP binding in the gray matter but no such blocking was observed with diclofenac, Congo red or Thioflavin T. These *in vitro* blocking experiments were paralleled by successful blockage of *in vivo* [F-18]FDDNP binding to β-amyloid deposits in the β-amyloid rich brains of β-amyloid triple transgenic rats by pre-treatment with naproxen (Kepe et al., 2005).

In addition, FDDNP has been demonstrated to be a useful histological dye for visualization of different types of pathological protein aggregates (Smid et al., 2006), such as prion pathology in GSS (Bresjanac et al., 2005) or a variety of neuropathological deposits in other neurodegenerative diseases. FDDNP binding was observed in majority of the fibrillar pathological aggregates which display Congo red birefringence indicative of the presence of β-sheet type of aggregation.

The *in vitro* results of all these experiments point to the conclusion that 1) *in vitro* [F-18]FDDNP binds with high affinity to one or more binding motifs present on the fibrillar protein aggregates found in β-amyloid plaques (Shoghi-Jadid et al., 2005 and 2006) and NFTs; 2) this is a specific binding which can be blocked by pre-treatment with naproxen and ibuprofen both *in vitro* and *in vivo*; 3) the pattern of [F-18]FDDNP binding closely matches the pattern of β-amyloid and NFT immunostaining in the gray matter of AD brain tissue; 4) FDDNP binds to a variety of fibrillar neuropathology deposits in various neurodegenerative diseases which form β-pleated sheets and, as result, display Congo red birefringence.

The utility of PET molecular imaging probe for visualization of pathology depends on the capacity of these probes to detect low levels of deposits at earliest stages of the disease (early diagnosis) and on the capacity to detect the changes in densities and spatial distribution of pathology over time (monitoring of disease progression and/or monitoring of therapeutic intervention). The capacity of [F-18]FDDNP to detect these early changes has been tested out in a clinical study performed in 25 AD patients, 28 mild cognitive impairment subjects (MCIs) and 30 control subjects with a subset of 12 subjects (8 controls and 4 MCIs) who received follow up [F-18]FDDNP PET scan two years (in average) after the baseline study (Small et al., 2006). Detection of the pathology pattern in MCI subjects served as the test of sensitivity of the method and the follow up study served to test the capacity of [F-18]FDDNP PET to detect the progression of pathology in subjects who experienced progression of disease between the baseline and follow-up scans. Quantitation of [F-18]FDDNP data was performed using Logan graphical analysis with cerebellum as reference region and relative distribution volume (DVR) values in different brain areas were compared in all subjects (Kepe et al., 2006b). The pattern of [F-18]FDDNP binding was increased in all cortical regions in symptomatic AD with temporal lobe strongly affected in all cases and to varying degrees in parietal and frontal areas. This stage of pathology distribution follows Braak NFT stages V/VI and β-amyloid plaque stage C in which the majority of gray matter regions shows presence of pathological deposits. The pattern of [F-18]FDDNP binding observed in the MCI group has shown more variability, yet it was more restricted than the pattern observed in AD cases with lower levels of [F-18]FDDNP binding observed in all affected areas. The study by Peterson and colleagues (Peterson et al., 2006) determined that amnestic MCI with AD pathology has higher prevalence of Braak NFT stages III and IV and amyloid stage B that the control group. We have observed that the MCI cases had increased [F-18]FDDNP binding levels in several areas with medial temporal lobe reaching the levels observed in AD and with AD level of [F-18]FDDNP binding in at least one other cortical area, e.g. often posterior cingulate gyrus or lateral temporal lobe. The cognitively normal controls have displayed uniformly low [F-18]FDDNP binding throughout the cortex, with some variability in the medial temporal lobe.

Quantitation of [F-18]FDDNP binding data (DVR values) shows that the binding of the probe in all analyzed areas (medial and lateral temporal lobe, parietal lobe, frontal lobe, posterior cingulated gyrus) were significantly elevated in the AD patients when compared with controls. An average of all areas in the same subject was used as a measure of global [F-18]FDDNP binding (global DVR). The mean [F-18]FDDNP DVR values, global and regional, differed significantly among the three diagnostic groups, the lowest in the control group and the highest in the Alzheimer's disease group. For example the global mean DVR values were 1.07±0.03 for controls, 1.12±0.01 for MCIs, and AD 1.16±0.02, (P < 0.001). The global DVR values were also correlated with lower [F-18]FDG values observed in parietal area (Spearman's rank coefficient r_s = -0.62, P<0.001) and in posterior cingulate gyrus (r_s = -0.64, P<0.001). The higher DVR values were also correlated with lower scores on several memory test, e.g. MMSE score (r_s = -0.75, P<0.001) and Digit Symbol test (r_s = -0.65, P<0.001).

In longitudinal study, the [F-18]FDDNP PET quantitation has accurately identified 4 subjects out of total 12 subjects who experienced worsening of symptoms based on the increase in the complexity of the cortical [F-18]FDDNP binding pattern. Two subjects have converted from amnestic MCI to AD and one control has converted to MCI. One control experienced some loss of function but this did not reach the level to diagnose it as an MCI. The pattern of the [F-18]FDDNP binding distribution was more complex in MCI-to-AD converters than observed in the baseline study. This is consistent with the study by Jicha and colleagues (Jicha et al., 2006) who have determined the pathological outcome in the converters from amnestic MCI to AD. An example [F-18]FDDNP binding observed at the baseline and follow-up are shown in Figure 2 for one control subjects who experienced no change in status and for one MCI subject who converted to AD at the time of follow-up.

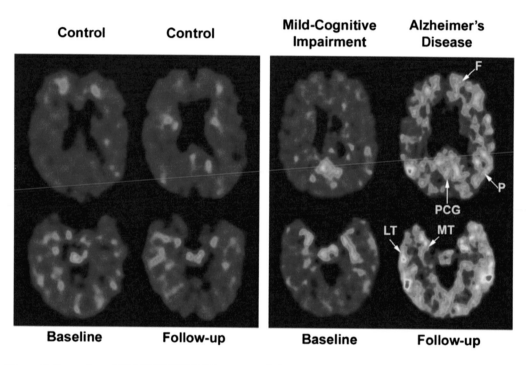

Figure 2. Examples of [F-18]FDDNP DVR parametric images are shown for two subjects who received a baseline and a follow-up [F-18]FDDNP PET study. The control subject shown on the left experienced no change in status between two imaging study. The MCI subject shown on the right progressed from MCI at the time of baseline scan to AD status at the time of follow-up scan. This worsening of the symptoms was paralleled by the spreading of pathology observed with [F-18]FDDNP. Warmed colors represent higher DVR values. Modified and reprinted with permission from Small et al., 2006. *Copyright © 2006 Massachusetts Medical Society. All rights reserved.*

A smaller imaging study compared imaging of [F-18]MPPF, a silent selective 5-HT1A receptor antagonist, with [F-18]FDDNP and [F-18]FDG in 8 AD patients, 6 MCIs and 5 controls (Kepe et al., 2006a). Decreases in hippocampal [F-18]MPPF binding were correlated with higher [F-18]FDDNP DVR values observed posterior cingulate gyrus (PCG) and medial temporal lobe (MTL) (Spearman's r_S coefficients, P values: PCG r_S=-0.71, P=0.0007; MTL r_S=-0.61, P=0.006; respectively), showing that increased pathology deposition is accompanied with decreasing 5-HT$_{1A}$ receptor concentrations resulting from pyramidal neuron loss.

CONCLUSION

From the *in vivo* imaging perspective a molecular imaging probe with binding affinity for both NFTs and β-amyloid deposits would have several advantages over an imaging probe only with binding affinity for β-amyloid deposits: 1) the earliest pathological changes in the AD brain are NFT deposits in the entorhinal cortex and hippocampus, most often without any presence of β-amyloid deposits in the neocortex, and therefore detection of the earliest pathological changes requires a molecular imaging probe with the capacity to detect increases in NFT densities; 2) NFT densities in several brain regions (entorhinal cortex, CA1 region of hippocampus, superior temporal cortex) have been correlated with neuronal loss in the same regions, with dementia severity and disease duration; 3) the gradual nature of NFT pathology accumulation makes it a good target for monitoring of disease progression, related changes in pathology densities and their spatial distribution.

PET in conjunction with a set of molecular imaging probes targeting pathological aggregates on one hand and neuronal loss on the other can provide information about very early neurodegeneration which complement the information available from [F-18]FDG PET imaging in MCI and dementia. In particular the early distribution of neurofibrillary tangle degeneration in the medial temporal lobe together with pyramidal neuronal loss in the same area can give information about the earliest pathological changes. Use of molecular imaging probes with sufficient sensitivity to detect the changes in pathology density in medial temporal lobe and to detect spreading of pathology to other areas opens the opportunity for early diagnosis and also for monitoring of disease progression and/or monitoring the efficacy of experimental therapeutic interventions.

ACKNOWLEDGMENTS

Financial support from the Department of Energy (grant DE-FC03-02ER63420) and from the National Institutes of Health (grant P01AG025831) is gratefully acknowledged.

REFERENCES

Agdeppa ED, Kepe V, Liu J, et al. Binding characteristics of radiofluorinated 6-dialkylamino-2-naphthylethylidene derivatives as positron emission tomography imaging probes for β-amyloid plaques in Alzheimer's disease. *J. Neurosci. 21:* RC189 (1-5), 2001.

Agdeppa ED, Kepe V, Shoghi-Jadid K, et al. *In vivo* and *in vitro* labeling of plaques and tangles in the brain of an Alzheimer's disease patient: a case study. *J. Nucl. Med. 42(Suppl.):* 65P, 2001.

Agdeppa ED, Kepe V, Liu J, et al. 2-Dialkylamino-6-acylmalononitrile substituted naphthalenes (DDNP Analogs): novel diagnostic and therapeutic tools in Alzheimer's disease. *Mol. Imaging Biol. 4:* 404-417, 2003a.

Agdeppa ED, Kepe V, Petrič A, et al. *In vitro* detection of (S)-naproxen and ibuprofen binding to plaques in the Alzheimer's brain using the positron emission tomography molecular imaging probe 2-(1-[6-[(2-[(18)F]fluoroethyl)(methyl)amino]-2-naphthyl]ethylidene) malononitrile. *Neuroscience 117:* 723-730, 2003.

Alzheimer A. Über eine eigenartige Erkrankung der Hirnrinde. *Allgem. Zeitschr. Psychiatrie Psychisch-Gerichtliche Medizin; 64:* 146-148, 1907. (Reprinted and translated in *Alzheimer Dis. Assoc. Disorder 1:* 3-8, 1987)

Arnold SE, Hyman BT, Flory J, Damasio AR, Van Hoesen GW. The topographical and neuroanatomical distribution of neurofibrillary tangles and neuritic plaques in the cerebral cortex of patients with Alzheimer's disease. *Cereb. Cortex 1:* 103-116, 1991.

Arriagada PV, Marzloff B, Hyman BT. Distribution of Alzheimer-type pathological changes in nondemented elderly individuals matches the pattern in Alzheimer's disease. *Neurology 42:* 1681-1688, 1992.

Atwood CS, Martins RN, Smith MA, Perry G. Senile plaque composition and posttranslational modification of amyloid-β peptide and associated proteins. *Peptides 23:* 1343-1350, 2002.

Bacskai BJ, Hickey GA, Skoch J, et al. Four-dimensional multi photon imaging of brain entry, amyloid binding, and clearance of an amyloid-β ligand in transgenic mice. *Proc. Natl. Acad. Sci. U.S.A. 100:* 12462-12467, 2003.

Barghorn S, Davies P, Mandelkow E. Tau paired helical filaments from Alzheimer's disease brain and assembled *in vitro* are based on β-structure in the core domain. *Biochemistry 43:* 1694-1703, 2004.

Barrio JR, Huang S-C, Cole G, et al. PET imaging of tangles and plaques in Alzheimer disease with a highly hydrophobic probe. *J. Labelled. Compd. Radiopharm. 42(Suppl1):* S194-S195, 1999.

Braak H, Braak E. Neuropathological stageing of Alzheimer-related changes. *Acta Neuropathol. 82:* 239-259, 1991.

Braak H, Braak E. Frequency of stages of Alzheimer-related lesions in different age categories. *Neurobiol. Aging 18:* 351-357, 1997.

Braak E, Griffing K, Arai K, Bohl J, Bratzke H, Braak H. Neuropathology of Alzheimer's disease: what is new since A. Alzheimer? *Eur. Arch. Psychiatry Clin. Neurosci. 249(Suppl 3):* 14-22, 1999.

Bresjanac M, Smid LM, Vovko TD, Petrič A, Barrio JR, Popovic M. Molecular imaging probe 2-(1-{6-[(2-fluoroethyl)(methyl)amino]-2-naphthyl}ethylidene)- malononitrile labels prion plaques *in vitro*. *J. Neurosci. 23:* 8029-8033, 2003.

Bobinski MJ, Wegiel M, Tarnawski M, et al. Relationships between regional neuronal loss and neurofibrillary changes in the hippocampal formation and duration and severity of Alzheimer disease. *J. Neuropathol. Exp. Neurol. 56:* 414-420, 1997.

Cai L, Chin FT, Pike VW, et al. Synthesis and evaluation of two 18F-labeled 6-iodo-2-(4'-N,N-dimethylamino)phenylimidazo[1,2-a]pyridine derivatives as prospective radioligands for β-amyloid in Alzheimer's disease. *J. Med. Chem. 47:* 2208-2218, 2004.

Chandra R, Kung M-P, Kung HK. Design, synthesis, and structure-activity relationship of novel thiophene derivatives for β-amyloid plaque imaging. *Bioorg. Med. Chem. Lett. 16:* 1350-1352, 2006.

Chandra R, Oya S, Kung MP, Hou C, Jin LW, Kung HF. New diphenylacetylenes as probes for positron emission tomographic imaging of amyloid plaques. *J. Med. Chem. 50:* DOI: 10.1021/jm070090j, 2007.

Chang YS, Jeong JM, Lee YS, Kim HW, Ganesha RB, Kim YJ, Lee DS, Chung JK, Lee MC. Synthesis and evaluation of benzothiophene derivatives as ligands for imaging beta-amyloid plaques in Alzheimer's disease. *Nucl. Med. Biol. 33:* 811-820, 2006.

Cohen RM. The application of positron-emitting molecular imaging tracers in Alzheimer's disease. *Mol. Imaging Biol. 9:* 204-216, 2007.

Cummings BJ, Pike CJ, Shankle R, Cotman CW. Beta-amyloid deposition and other measures of neuropathology predict cognitive status in Alzheimer's disease. *Neurobiol. Aging 17:* 921-933, 1996.

Delacourte A, David JP, Sergeant N, et al. The biochemical pathway of neurofibrillary degeneration in aging and Alzheimer's disease. *Neurology 52:* 1158-1165, 1999.

Dickson TC, Vickers JC. The morphological phenotype of β-amyloid plaques and associated neuritic changes in Alzheimer's disease. *Neuroscience 105:* 99-107, 2001.

Engler H, Forsberg A, Almkvist O, Blomquist G, Larsson E, Savitcheva I, Wall A, Ringheim A, Langstrom B, Nordberg A. Two-year follow-up of amyloid deposition in patients with Alzheimer's disease. *Brain 129:* 2856-66, 2006.

Evans DA. Estimated prevalence of Alzheimer's disease in the United States. *Milbank Q. 68:* 267-289, 1990.

Friedland RP, Majocha RE, Reno JM, Lyle LR, Marotta CA. Development of an anti-A beta monoclonal antibody for in vivo imaging of amyloid angiopathy in Alzheimer's disease. *Mol. Neurobiol. 9:* 107-113, 1994.

Fukutani Y, Kobayashi K, Nakamura I, Watanabe K, Isaki K, Cairns NJ. Neurons, intracellular and extracellular neurofibrillary tangles in subdivisions of the hippocampal cortex in normal aging and Alzheimer's disease. *Neurosci. Lett. 200:* 57-60, 1995.

Giannakopoulus P, Hof PR, Mottier S, Michel JP, Bouras C. Neuropathological changes in the cerebral cortex of 1258 cases from a geriatric hospital: retrospective clinicopathological evaluation of a 10-year autopsy population. Acta Neuropathol. *87:* 456-468, 1994.

Giannakopoulos P, Herrmann FR, Bussiere T, et al. Tangle and neuron numbers, but not amyloid load, predict cognitive status in Alzheimer's disease. *Neurology 60:* 1495-1500, 2003.

Gomez-Isla T, Price JL, McKeel DW, Morris JC, Growdon JH, Hyman BT. Profound loss of layer II entorhinal cortex neurons distinguishes very mild Alzheimer's disease from nondemented aging. *J. Neurosci. 16:* 4491-4450, 1996.

Gomez-Isla T, Hollister R, West H, et al. Neuronal loss correlates with but exceeds neurofibrillary tangles in Alzheimer's disease. *Ann. Neurol. 41:* 17-24, 1997.

Guillozet AL, Weintraub S, Mash DC, Mesulam MM. Neurofibrillary tangles, amyloid, and memory in aging and mild cognitive impairment. *Arch. Neurol. 60:* 729-736, 2003.

Hof PR. Morphology and neurochemical characteristics of the vulnerable neurons in brain aging and Alzheimer's disease. *Eur. Neurol. 37:* 71-81, 1997.

Iqbal K. *Alzheimer's Disease: Basic Mechanisms, Diagnosis, and Therapeutic Strategies.* Chichester, New York: Wiley, 1991.

Jicha GA, Parisi JE, Dickson DW, et al. Neuropathologic outcome of mild cognitive impairment following progression to clinical dementia. *Arch. Neurol. 63:* 674-681, 2006.

Kepe V, Shoghi-Jadid K, Wu H-M, et al. Global and regional [F-18]FDDNP binding as *in vivo* measure of Alzheimer's disease neuropathology. *J. Nucl. Med. 45(Suppl.):* 126P, 2004.

Kepe V, Cole GM, Liu J, et al. [F-18]MicroPET imaging of β-amyloid deposits in the living brain of triple transgenic rat model of β-amyloid deposition. *Mol. Imaging Biol. 7:* 105, 2005.

Kepe V, Huang S-C, Small GW, Satyamurthy N, Barrio JR. Visualizing pathology deposits in the living brain of patients with Alzheimer's disease. *Methods Enzymol. 412:* 144-60, 2006a.

Kepe V, Barrio JR, Huang S-C, et al. Serotonin 1A receptors in the living brain of Alzheimer's disease. *Proc. Natl. Acad. Sci. U.S.A. 103:* 702-707, 2006b.

Kirschner DA, Abraham C, Selkoe DJ. X-ray diffraction from intraneuronal paired helical filaments and extraneuronal amyloid fibers in Alzheimer disease indicates cross-beta conformation. *Proc. Natl. Acad. Sci. U.S.A. 83:* 503-507, 1986.

Kirschner DA, Inouye H, Duffy LK, Sinclair A, Lind M, Selkoe DJ. Synthetic peptide homologous to beta protein from Alzheimer disease forms amyloid-like fibrils *in vitro*. *Proc. Natl. Acad. Sci. U.S.A. 84:* 6953-6957, 1987.

Klunk W, Bacskai BJ, Mathis CA, et al. Imaging Aβ plaques in living transgenic mice with multiphoton microscopy and methoxy-X04, a systemically administered Congo Red derivative. *J. Neuropathol. Exp. Neurol. 61:* 797-805, 2002.

Klunk WE, Engler H, Nordberg A, et al. Imaging brain amyloid in Alzheimer's disease with Pittsburgh Compound-B. *Ann. Neurol. 55:* 306-319, 2004.

Klunk WE, Lopresti BJ, Ikonomovic MD, et al. Binding of the positron emission tracer Pittsburgh compound-B reflects the amount of amyloid-β in Alzheimer's disease brain but not in transgenic mouse brain. *J. Neurosci. 25:* 10598-10606, 2005.

Knopman DS, Parisi JE, Salviati A, et al. Neuropathology of cognitively normal elderly. *J. Neuropathol. Exp. Neurol. 62:* 1087-1095, 2003.

Kordower JH, Chu Y, Stebbins GT, et al. Loss and atrophy of layer II entorhinal cortex neurons in elderly people with mild cognitive impairment. *Ann. Neurol. 49:* 202-213, 2001.

Kudo Y, Okamura N, Furumoto S, Tashiro M, Furukawa K, Maruyama M, Itoh M, Iwata R, Yanai K, Arai H. 2-(2-[2-Dimethylaminothiazol-5-yl] ethenyl) -6-(2-[fluoro]ethoxy) benzoxazole: a novel PET agent for in vivo detection of dense amyloid plaques in Alzheimer's disease patients. *J. Nucl. Med. 48:* 553-61, 2007.

Kung M-P, Hou C, Zhuang, Z-P, et al. IMPY: an improved thioflavin-T derivative for *in vivo* labeling of β-amyloid plaques. *Brain Res. 956:* 202-210, 2002.

Kurihara A, Pardridge WM. Abeta(1-40) peptide radiopharmaceuticals for brain amyloid imaging: (111)In chelation, conjugation to poly(ethylene glycol)-biotin linkers, and autoradiography with Alzheimer's disease brain sections. *Bioconjug. Chem. 11:* 380-386, 2000.

Lansbury PT. A reductionist view of Alzheimer's disease. *Accounts Chem. Res. 29:* 317-321, 1996.

Lantos P, Cairns N. The neuropathology of Alzheimer's disease. In: O'Brien J, Ames D, Burns A (Eds.) *Dementia, second edition.* London, England: Arnold, 2000, pp. 443-459.

Lee VM, Goedert M, Trojanowski JQ. Neurodegenerative tauopathies. *Annu. Rev. Neurosci. 24:* 1121-1159, 2001a.

Lee C-W, Zhuang Z-P, Kung M-P, et al. Isomerization of (Z,Z) to (E,E)1-bromo-2,5-bis-(3-hydroxycarbonyl-4-hydroxy)styrylbenzene in strong base: probes for amyloid plaques in the brain. *J. Med. Chem. 44:* 2270-2275, 2001b. Lee C-W, Kung M-P, Hou C, Kung HK. Dimethylamino-fluorenes: ligands for detecting β-amyloid plaques in the brain. *Nucl. Med. Biol. 30:* 573-580, 2003.

Liu J, Kepe V, Žabjek A, Petrič A, Padgett HC, Satyamurthy N, Barrio JR. High-yield, automated radiosynthesis of 2-(1-{6-[(2-[18F]fluoroethyl)(methyl)amino]-2-naphthyl}ethylidene)malononitrile ([18F]FDDNP) ready for animal or human administration. *Mol. Imaging Biol. 9:* 6-16, 2007.

Lopresti BJ, Klunk WE, Mathis CA, et al. Simplified quantification of Pittsburgh compound B amyloid imaging PET studies: a comparative analysis. *J. Nucl. Med. 46:* 1959-1972, 2005.

Makin OS, Atkins E, Sikorsky P, Johansson J, Serpell LC. Molecular basis for amyloid fibril formation and stability. *Proc. Natl. Acad. Sci. U.S.A. 102:* 315-320, 2005.

Malinchik SB, Inouye H, Szumowski KE, Kirschner DA. Structural analysis of Alzheimer's β(1-40) amyloid: protofilament assembly of tubular fibrils. *Biophys. J.* 74:537-545, 1998.

Mandelkow EM, Mandelkow E. Tau in Alzheimer's disease. *Trends Cell Biol. 8:* 425-427, 1998.

Mann DMA. Pyramidal nerve cell loss in Alzheimer's disease. *Neurodegeneration 5:* 423-427, 1996.

Mathis CA, Wang Y, Holt DP, Huang G-F, Debnath ML, Klunk WE. Synthesis and evaluation of ^{11}C-labeled 6-substituted 2-arylbenzothiazoles as amyloid imaging agents. *J. Med. Chem. 46:* 2740-2754, 2003.

McKhann G, Drachman D, Folstein M, et al. Clinical diagnosis of Alzheimer's disease: report of the NINCDS-ADRDA Work Group under the auspices of the Department of Health and Human Services Task Force on Alzheimer's Disease. *Neurology 34:* 939-44, 1984.

Minoshima S. Imaging Alzheimer's disease: clinical applications. *Neuroimaging Clin. N. Am. 13:* 769-780, 2003.

Minoshima S, Frey KA, Cross DJ, Kuhl DE. Neurochemical imaging of dementias. *Sem. Nucl. Med. 34:* 70-82, 2004.

Mintun MA, Larossa GN, Sheline YI, Dence CS, Lee SY, Mach RH, Klunk WE, Mathis CA, DeKosky ST, Morris JC. [11C]PIB in a nondemented population: potential antecedent marker of Alzheimer disease. *Neurology 67:* 446-52, 2006.

Miyakawa T, Katsuragi S, Watanabe K, Shimoji A, Ikeuchi Y. Ultrastructural studies of amyloid fibrils and senile plaques in human brain. *Acta Neuropathol. 70:* 202-208, 1986.

Morisson JH, Hof PR. Life and death of neurons in the aging brain. *Science 278:* 412-419, 1997.

Newberg AB, Wintering NA, Plössl K, at al. Safety, biodistribution and dosimetry of ^{123}I-IMPY: a novel amyloid plaque-imaging agent for the diagnosis of Alzheimer's disease. *J. Nucl. Med. 47:* 748-754, 2006.

Okamura N, Suemoto T, Shimadzu H, et al. Styrylbenzoxazole derivatives for *in vivo* imaging of amyloid plaques in the brain. *J. Neurosci. 24:* 2535–2541, 2004.

Okamura N, Suemoto T, Furumoto S, et al. Quinoline and benzimidazole derivatives: candidate probes for in vivo imaging of tau pathology in Alzheimer's disease. *J. Neurosci. 25:* 10857-10862, 2005.

Ono M, Wilson A, Nobrega J, et al. 11C-labeled stilbene derivatives as Aβ-aggregate-specific PET imaging agents for Alzheimer's disease. *Nucl. Med. Biol. 30:* 565-571, 2003.

Ono M, Kawashima H, Nonaka A, et al. Novel benzofuran derivatives for PET imaging of β-amyloid plaques in Alzheimer's disease brains. *J. Med. Chem. 49:* 2725-2730, 2006.

Petersen R, Smith G, Waring S, Ivnik R, Tangalos E, Kokmen E. Mild cognitive impairment: clinical characterization and outcome. *Arch. Neurol. 56:* 303-308, 1999.

Petersen RC, Parisi JE, Dickson DW, et al. Neuropathologic features of amnestic mild cognitive impairment. *Arch. Neurol. 63:* 665-672, 2006.

Price JL, Davies PB, Morris JC, White DL. The distribution of tangles, plaques and related immunohistochemical markers in healthy aging and Alzheimer's disease. Neurobiol. Aging *12:* 295-312, 1991.

Price JL, Morris JC. Tangles and plaques in nondemented aging and "preclinical" Alzheimer's disease. *Ann. Neurol. 45:* 358–368, 1999.

Price JL, Ko AI, Wade MJ, et al. Neuron number in the entorhinal cortex and CA1 in preclinical Alzheimer's disease. *Arch. Neurol. 58:* 1395-1402, 2001.

Reiman EM, Caselli RJ, Yun LS, et al. Preclinical evidence of Alzheimer's disease in persons homozygous for the ε4 allele for apolipoprotein E. *N. Engl. J. Med. 334:* 752-758, 1996.

Rice DP, Fillit HM, Max W, Knopman DS, Lloyd JR, Duttagupta S. Prevalence, costs, and treatment of Alzheimer's disease and related dementia: A managed care perspective. *Am. J. Manag. Care 7:* 809-17, 2001.

Rössler M, Zarski R, Bohl J, Ohm TG. Stage-dependent and sector-specific neuronal loss in hippocampus during Alzheimer's disease. *Acta Neuropathol. 103:* 363-369, 2002.

Ryu EK, Choe YS, Lee KH, Choi Y, Kim BT. Curcumin and dehydrozingerone derivatives: synthesis, radiolabeling, and evaluation for beta-amyloid plaque imaging. *J. Med. Chem. 49:* 6111-9, 2006.

Salmon DP, Lange KL. Cognitive screening and neuropsychological assessment in early Alzheimer's disease. *Clin. Geriatr. Med. 17:* 229-254, 2001.

Seilheimer B, Bohrmann B, Nondolfi B, Muller F, Stuber D, Dobeli H. The toxicity of the Alzheimer's beta-amyloid peptide correlates with a distinct fiber morphology. *J. Struct. Biol. 119:* 59-71, 1997.

Selkoe DJ. Cell biology of the amyloid beta-protein precursor and the mechanism of Alzheimer's disease. *Annu. Rev. Cell. Biol. 10:* 373-403, 1994.

Serpell LC. Alzheimer's amyloid fibrils: structure and assembly. *Biochim. Biophys. Acta 1502:* 16-30, 2000.

Shoghi-Jadid K, Small GW, Agdeppa ED, et al. Localization of neurofibrillary tangles and beta-amyloid plaques in the brains of living patients with Alzheimer disease. *Am. J. Geriatr. Psychiatry 10:* 24-35, 2002.

Shoghi-Jadid K, Barrio JR, Kepe V, et al. Imaging beta-amyloid fibrils in Alzheimer's disease: a critical analysis through simulation of amyloid fibril polymerization. *Nucl. Med. Biol. 32:* 337-351, 2005.

Shoghi-Jadid K, Barrio JR, Kepe V, Huang SC. Exploring a mathematical model for the kinetics of beta-amyloid molecular imaging probes through a critical analysis of plaque pathology. *Mol. Imaging Biol. 8:* 151-162, 2006.

Silverman DH, Small GW, Chang CY, et al. Positron emission tomography in evaluation of dementia: Regional brain metabolism and long-term outcome. *J. Am. Med. Assoc. 286:* 2120-2127, 2001.

Silverman DH, Truong CT, Kim SK, et al. Prognostic value of regional cerebral metabolism in patients undergoing dementia evaluation: comparison to a quantifying parameter of subsequent cognitive performance and to prognostic assessment without PET. *Molec. Genetics Metab. 80:* 350-355, 2003.

Small GW, Kepe V, Ercoli L, et al. PET of brain amyloid and tau in mild cognitive impairment. *N. Engl. J. Med. 355:* 2652-2663, 2006.

Smid LM, Vovko TD, Popovic M, et al. The 2,6-disubstituted naphthalene derivative FDDNP labeling reliably predicts Congo red birefringence of protein deposits in brain sections of selected human neurodegenerative diseases. *Brain Pathol. 16:* 124-130, 2006.

Styren SD, Hamilton RL, Styren GC, Klunk WE. X-34, a fluorescent derivative of Congo Red: a novel histochemical stain for Alzheimer's disease pathology. *J. Histochem. Cytochem. 48:* 1223-1232, 2000.

Suemoto T, Okamura N, Shiomitsu T, et al. In vivo labeling of amyloid with BF-108. *Neurosci. Res. 48:* 65-74, 2004.

Teplow DB. Structural and kinetic features of amyloid beta-protein fibrillogenesis. *Amyloid 5:* 121-142, 1998.

Toyama H, Ye D, Ichise M, et al. PET imaging of brain with β-amyloid probe, [11C]6-OH-BTA-1, in a transgenic mouse model of Alzheimer's disease. *Eur. J. Nucl. Med. Mol. Imaging 32:* 593-600, 2005.

Verhoeff NP, Wilson AA, Takeshita S, et al. *In vivo* imaging of Alzheimer disease beta-amyloid with [11C]SB-13 PET. *Am. J. Geriatr. Psychiatry 12:* 584-595, 2004.

Vickers JC, Dickson TC, Adlard PA, Saunders HL, King CE, McCormack G. The cause of neuronal degeneration in Alzheimer's diseas. *Prog. Neurobiol. 60:* 139-165, 2000.

Von Bergen M, Barghorn S, Biernat J, Mandelkow EM, Mandelkow E. Tau aggregation is driven by a transition from random coil to beta sheet structure. *Biochim. Biophys. Acta 1739:* 158-166, 2005.

Von Strauss EM, Viitane D, De Ronchi D, et al. Aging and the occurrence of dementia. *Arch. Neurol. 56:* 587-592, 1999.

West MJ, Coleman PD, Flood DG, Troncoso JC. Differences in the pattern of hippocampal neuronal loss in normal aging and Alzheimer's disease. *Lancet 344:* 769-772, 1994.

Wisniewski T, Ghiso J, Frangione B. Biology of Aβ amyloid in Alzheimer's disease. *Neurobiol. Disease 4:* 313-328, 1997.

Yen S-H, Liu W-K, Hall FL, Yan S-D, Stern D, Dickson DW. Alzheimer neurofibrillary lesions: Molecular nature and potential roles of different components. *Neurobiol. Aging 16:* 381-387, 1995.

Zeng F, Southerland JA, Voll RJ, et al. Synthesis and evaluation of two ^{18}F-labeled imidazo[1,2-*a*]pyridine analogs as potential agents for imaging β-amyloid in Alzheimer's disease. *Bioorg. Med. Chem. Lett. 16:* 3015-3018, 2006. Zhuang ZP, Kung M-P, Hou C, et al. IBOX(2-(4'-dimethylaminophenyl)-6-iodobenzoxazole): a ligand imaging amyloid plaques in the brain. *Nucl. Med. Biol. 28:* 887-894, 2001.

Zhang W, Oya S, Kung M-P, Hou C, Maier DL, Kung HF. F-18 stilbenes as imaging agents for detecting β-amyloid plaques in the brain. *J. Med. Chem. 48:* 5980-5988, 2005a.

Zhang W, Oya S, Kung M-P, Hou C, Maier DL, Kung HF. F-18 Polyethyleneglycol stilbenes as PET imaging agents targeting Aβ aggregates in the brain. *Nucl. Med. Biol. 32:* 799-809, 2005b.

Zhang W, Kung M-P, Oya S, Hou C, Kung HF. 18F-labeled styrylpyridines as PET agents for amyloid plaque imaging. *Nucl. Med. Biol. 34:* 89-97, 2007.

Zhuang Z-P, Kung M-P, Kung HF. Synthesis of biphenyltrienes as probes for β-amyloid plaques. *J. Med. Chem. 49:* 2841-2844, 2006.

In: Research Progress in Alzheimer's Disease and Dementia   ISBN 978-1-60021-960-3
Editor: Miao-Kun Sun, pp. 275-302   © 2008 Nova Science Publishers, Inc.

Chapter X

CATHEPSIN B, ANTIAMYLOIDOGENESIS, AND NEUROPROTECTION

Li Gan

Gladstone Institute of Neurological Disease, Department of Neurology,
University of California, San Francisco, USA.

ABSTRACT

Alzheimer's disease (AD) is a progressive neurodegenerative disease that causes loss of cognitive functions. Amyloid beta (Aβ) peptides play a central role in AD pathogenesis by triggering neuronal and synaptic damage, and inflammatory responses, leading to cell death. The accumulation of Aβ peptides in AD brains could reflect overproduction or inefficient clearance or both. Thus, promoting Aβ degradation may represent an effective approach for reducing Aβ levels. Here I review recent evidence that cathepsin B (CatB), a cysteine protease that is localized within amyloid plaques, degrades Aβ aggregates and contributes to Aβ clearance. CatB cleaves Aβ1-42 at the C-terminus, resulting in Aβ species that are less toxic and less fibrillogenic. Genetic ablation of CatB in AD-related animal models increased plaque deposition, the relative abundance of Aβ1-42, and associated neuronal deficits, suggesting that CatB has an antiamyloidogenic and neuroprotective function in vivo. Lentiviral expression of CatB cleared existing amyloid plaques, including dense, thioflavin-S-positive plaques, further supporting the notion that promoting CatB activity reduces Aβ load in vivo. Potential strategies to enhance the activities of CatB and other Aβ-degrading enzymes and their therapeutic implications are also discussed.

ABBREVIATIONS

Aβ	amyloid beta
AD	Alzheimer's disease
APP	amyloid precursor protein
CatB	cathepsin B
CysC	cystatin C
ECE	endothelin-coverting enzyme
DG	dentate gyrus
FAD	autosomal dominated familial AD
hAPP	human APP
IDE	insulin-degrading enzyme
Lenti-CatB	lentiviral vector that encodes mouse CatB cDNA
Lenti-NEP	lentiviral vector overexpressing NEP
Lenti-shCatB	lentiviral vector encoding a small-hairpin RNA targeting CatB
NEP	neprilysin
PS1	presenilin 1

1. ALZHEIMER'S DISEASE AND THE AMYLOID HYPOTHESIS

Alzheimer's disease (AD) is a progressive neurodegenerative disease that causes loss of cognitive functions (Hardy and Selkoe, 2002; Mattson, 2004). AD is characterized by deposits of amyloid beta (Aβ) peptides surrounded by dystrophic neurites (neuritic plaques) (Hardy and Selkoe, 2002; Braak and Braak, 1991; Terry, et al., 1991). The most common dementia in the elderly, AD afflicts roughly 4.5 million Americans, a number that is predicted to more than double by 2050 if no progress is made in preventing or delaying the onset of disease (Hebert, et al., 2001). The current medical cost for AD is estimated to be $50–$100 billion per year in the United States alone, and the predicted increase in the number of cases will cause a staggering social and economic burden. Currently four drugs, including acetylcholinesterase inhibitors and the N-methyl-D-aspartate antagonist memantine, are routinely used to treat AD. However, they provide only modest benefits to a subset of patients (Lleo, et al., 2006). Clearly, new "disease-modifying" strategies are urgently needed to treat this devastating disease.

Although the cause of AD is unknown, extensive data supports the notion that Aβ peptides play a central role in AD pathogenesis. According to the "amyloid hypothesis," accumulation of Aβ peptides triggers neuronal and synaptic damage, inflammatory responses, and the formation of neurofibrillary tangles, leading to neurotransmitter deficits and cell death. Some of the most compelling evidence came from genetic analysis of a small subset of AD patients with familial mutations. Most of these mutations are associated with increased production of Aβ peptides (Citron, et al., 1992; St George-Hyslop, et al., 1992; Tanzi, et al., 1992; Younkin, 1994; Annaert, et al., 2000; Tanzi and Bertram, 2005). Strategies that reduce levels of Aβ peptides ameliorate neuronal and behavioral deficits in transgenic mice overexpressing human amyloid precursor protein (hAPP) (Janus, et al., 2000; Schenk, et al., 1999; Citron, 2002; Leissring, et al., 2003).

Recent studies implicate specific types and forms of soluble Aβ assemblies as the earliest triggers in the pathway of amyloid toxicity (Walsh and Selkoe, 2004; Klein, 2002; Kayed, et al., 2003; Lesne, et al., 2006; Bitan, et al., 2003; Chromy, et al., 2003; Jarrett, et al., 1993; Kalback, et al., 2002; Fezoui, et al., 2000; Dahlgren, et al., 2002). Neurotoxic diffusible forms of Aβ, including Aβ-derived diffusible ligands and other Aβ oligomers and protofibrils, are believed to cause neurodegeneration and deficits in synaptic transmission (Lambert, et al., 1998; Caughey and Lansbury, 2003; Hsia, et al., 1999; Wang, et al., 2002; Gong, et al., 2003; Walsh, et al., 2002). Naturally secreted Aβ oligomers, but not Aβ monomers or fibrils, markedly inhibit hippocampal long-term potentiation *in vivo* (Walsh, et al., 2002; Cleary, et al., 2005). In a transgenic AD model, age-dependent synaptic transmission deficits occur well before amyloid plaques form, suggesting that Aβ may be synaptotoxic even in the absence of plaques (Hsia, et al., 1999). These results support a plaque-independent role for Aβ in AD-related synaptic toxicity and may explain some of the discrepancies between the cognitive deficits and plaque load observed in AD.

1.1. Aβ Production and Clearance

Aβ is generated when hAPP is cleaved by β secretase and γ secretase, which is a multiprotein complex of presenilin 1 (PS1), nicastrin, PEN-2, and APH-1 (Kopan and Goate, 2002; Wolfe, et al., 1999; Vassar, et al., 1999; De Strooper, 2003; Iwatsubo, 2004; Francis, et al., 2002; Yu, et al., 2000; Selkoe and Kopan, 2003; Sisodia and St George-Hyslop, 2002). Although various Aβ peptides of 39–43 amino acids are produced in the brain (Glenner and Wong, 1984; Gouras, et al., 1998; Masters, et al., 1985), Aβ1-42 appears to be particularly critical in AD pathogenesis. Most autosomal dominated familial AD (FAD) mutations on the APP or PS1 gene increase the production or relative abundance of Aβ1-42 (Citron, et al., 1992; St George-Hyslop, et al., 1992; Tanzi, et al., 1992; Younkin, 1994; Annaert, et al., 2000; Tanzi and Bertram, 2005).

The accumulation of Aβ peptides in AD brains could reflect overproduction or inefficient clearance or both. Enormous progress has been made in understanding the complex mechanisms that regulate the production of Aβ peptides. As a result, strategies to inhibit the secretases, especially β secretase, are being actively developed as mechanism-based AD therapies (Vassar, 2001; Tsai, et al., 2002). However, overproduction of Aβ probably explains only a small number of cases of FAD (Tanzi and Bertram, 2005). In most sporadic and late-onset AD cases lacking the familial mutations of APP or PS1, Aβ production is likely to be normal throughout life, and high levels of cerebral Aβ levels may result from defects in Aβ clearance (Selkoe, 2001). The most promising strategy to promote Aβ clearance is immunization, which can prevent and even partially reverse AD-like central nervous system alterations, including neuritic dystrophy, gliosis, synaptic loss, and behavioral deficits (Janus, et al., 2000; Schenk, et al., 1999; Bard, et al., 2000; Lambert, et al., 2001; Morgan, et al., 2000; Das, et al., 2003; Buttini, et al., 2005). Aβ may also be cleared from the brain by receptor-mediated transport. The low-density lipoprotein receptor-related protein and the receptor for advanced glycation end products are involved in receptor-mediated flux of Aβ across the blood-brain barrier (Deane, et al., 2003; Shibata, et al., 2000; Deane, et al., 2004; Gopalraj, et al., 2005).

1.2. Aβ-Degrading Enzymes

Proteolytic degradation is another major pathway for Aβ clearance. Aβ-degrading enzymes include neprilysin (NEP), insulin-degrading enzyme (IDE), matrix metalloproteinases, endothelin-coverting enzyme (ECE), angiotensin-converting enzyme, the plasmin system, and cathepsin B (CatB) (Qiu, et al., 1998; Iwata, et al., 2001; Eckman, et al., 2001; Tucker, et al., 2000; Yamin, et al., 1999; Yan, et al., 2006; Mueller-Steiner, et al., 2006). Studies in knockout mice showed that NEP, IDE, ECEs, and more recently, MMP-2 or -9 are involved in degrading endogenous murine Aβ (Eckman, et al., 2001; Iwata, et al., 2000; Farris, et al., 2003). Their distinct cellular localizations may indicate complementary roles. The primary localization of NEP at the presynaptic terminals in neurons suggests that NEP is capable of degrading Aβ released from the nerve terminals (Iwata, et al., 2004). IDE is mainly cytosolic and peroxisomal (Authier, et al., 1996), but can also degrade Aβ extracellularly (Qiu, et al., 1998). MMP-2 and -9, which are secreted in a latent form from astroglia, are localized with the amyloid plaques (Yin, et al., 2006). ECEs, on the other hand, may degrade Aβ in acidic compartments represented by trans-Golgi network (Schweizer, et al., 1997). In AD-related animal models that overexpress IDE or NEP, levels of human Aβ1-42 and Aβ1-x were markedly decreased (Leissring, et al., 2003), strongly supporting effective degradation of human Aβ peptides by IDE and NEP.

Unlike murine Aβ peptides that mostly remain monomeric, human Aβ peptides, especially Aβ1-42, are prone to aggregation. In fact, small human Aβ aggregates, not Aβ monomers, are believed to be critical in inducing AD-related neuronal and cognitive deficits (Lesne, et al., 2006; Cleary, et al., 2005). However, Aβ aggregates are largely resistant to degradation. IDE and ECEs appear to target monomers exclusively, and NEP showed limited ability to degrade dimers in vitro. Although lentiviral overexpression of NEP in the brain of adult hAPP transgenic mice modestly decreased the preexisiting Aβ deposits (Marr, et al., 2003), the ability of NEP to efficiently degrade protofibrillar and fibrillar Aβ remains unclear. Plasmin, which does not appear to be involved in degrading endogenous murine Aβ, can degrade Aβ aggregates in vitro and block Aβ toxicity in primary neuronal cultures (Tucker, et al., 2000). The proteolytic efficiency with which plasmin degrades fibrillar Aβ, however, is about 1% of that for freshly dissolved Aβ (i.e., largely monomeric) (Tucker, et al., 2000). A recent study showed that MMP-2 and -9 degrade Aβ fibrils in vitro (Yan, et al., 2006). However, the ability of plasmin or MMPs to degrade Aβ aggregates in AD-related animal models is unknown.

2. CatB Degrades Aβ and Protects against Aβ-Dependent Neurodegeneration

Recently, we identified CatB as an enzyme that efficiently degrades human Aβ aggregates *in vivo* (Mueller-Steiner, et al., 2006). This chapter will focus on CatB and perspectives on promoting Aβ degradation as an anti-Aβ therapeutic strategy.

CatB is an abundant and ubiquitously expressed cysteine peptidase (clan CA) of the papain family (C1-A) (Azaryan, et al., 1985; Docherty, et al., 1983; Takio, et al., 1980; Chan, et al., 1986; Chapman, et al., 1997). It is synthesized as a glycosylated species that is proteolytically processed to both single- and double-chain forms (Kominami, et al., 1991; Rowan, et al., 1992; Keppler and Sloane, 1996). Of the lysosomal cysteine proteases, only CatB can act both as a dipeptidyl carboxypeptidase and an endopeptidase. Because of two histidine residues (His110 and His111) in a 20-residue occluding loop at the primer side of the catalytic site, CatB's carboxydipeptidic activity is greater than its endopeptidic activity (Khouri, et al., 1991; Nagler, et al., 1997; Illy, et al., 1997). In the endosomal pathway, for example, CatB catalyzes C-terminal truncations of epidermal growth factor and insulin-like growth factor and reduces their signaling (Tsujinaka, et al., 1995; Authier, et al., 1999). Active CatB is also continuously exocytosed as a single-chain 31-kDa enzyme that is active at pH 7.0 (Linebaugh, et al., 1999) and degrades E-cadherin, fibrinogen, laminin, fibronectin, collagen type IV, immunoglobulin light chain-associated amyloid proteins, and myelin basic protein (Reddy, et al., 1995; Banati, et al., 1993; Berlet and Ilzenhofer, 1985; Buck, et al., 1992; Lah, et al., 1989; Gocheva, et al., 2006). Secreted CatB from activated microglial cells damages cultured neurons (Gan, et al., 2004; Kingham and Pocock, 2001).

2.1. Localization of CatB in the Brain

At the ultrastructural level, CatB immunoreactivity in senile plaques localizes principally to lysosomal dense bodies and extracellular lipofuscin granules (Cataldo and Nixon, 1990). Thus, escape of cathepsins from the stringently regulated intracellular milieu may provide a basis for CatB-induced proteolytic activity within plaques. Moreover, in most pyramidal neurons, mature and proenzyme forms of the CatB were identified in most early endosomes in AD brains, but were detectable in only a minor proportion of endosomes in normal brain (Cataldo, et al., 1997; Tagawa, et al., 1992). In chromaffin cells, CatB colocalized with Aβ in secretory vesicles, as shown by immunoelectron microscopy (Hook, et al., 2005). The increased trafficking of CatB to endosomes, where a portion of Aβ is derived from APP, is a potential mechanism by which CatB might influence hAPP or Aβ metabolism. CatB might be involved in abnormal cleavage of APP, potentially accelerating β-amyloidogenesis in sporadic AD (Cataldo and Nixon, 1990; Hook, et al., 2005).

We characterized the association of CatB with amyloid plaques in 16–20-month-old hAPP mice. Brain sections from hAPP mice were colabeled with a CatB-specific antibody and with either 3D6, which stains both mature and diffuse Aβ deposits, or thioflavin-S, which labels the β-sheet structures in mature plaques (Figure 1A). CatB was found in a subpopulation of 3D6-positive deposits and thioflavin S-positive plaques. More thioflavin S-positive than 3D6-positive deposits were immunoreactive for CatB, indicating that CatB accumulates preferentially in mature plaques. Within neuritic plaques, CatB immunoreactivity overlapped with dystrophic neurites labeled with an anti-hAPP antibody (8E5) (Cheng, et al., 2004). These CatB-positive amyloid plaques were also associated with clusters of reactive astroglia labeled with GFAP antibody as well as microglia (data not shown). Interestingly, CatB activity was present in the supernatants of primary cultures enriched for neurons, astrocytes, or microglia; the highest levels were detected in microglial cultures (data not shown). These results suggest that extracellular CatB accumulating within neuritic plaques could be produced by all three cell types, including activated microglia surrounding the plaques. Consistent with previous findings in AD brain, CatB in hippocampal neurons of hAPP mice is colocalized with lysosomal membrane glycoprotein 1 (LAMP1), a lysosomal marker and endosome-associated autoantigen 1 (EEA-1)–positive early endosomes, a site involved in APP processing and Aβ generation. Our results suggest that CatB colocalizes with APP/Aβ both extracellularly (plaques) and intracellularly (early endosomes).

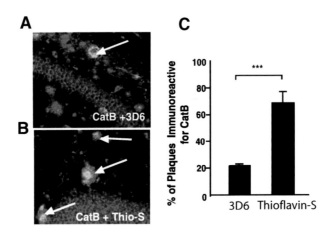

Figure 1. (A) Coimmunostaining of an anti-CatB antibody (red) with an anti-Aβ antibody (3D6, green) or thioflavin-S (green, B). Yellow signals (white arrows) in the merged images represent colocalization of CatB with Aβ peptides (A) or thioflavin-S (B). (C) The proportion of plaques immunoreactive for CatB was calculated by dividing the areas occupied by both CatB and 3D6 or thioflavin-S by the area occupied by 3D6 or thioflavin-S alone (n=5, ***, $P < 0.001$, Unpaired t test). Reproduced with permission from Cell Press.

2.2. CatB Reduces Aβ Levels in Primary Neurons

What is the exact role of CatB in modulating APP processing and Aβ metabolism? To address this question, we compared Aβ levels in the primary cortical neurons from $CatB^{-/-}$ mice and $CatB^{+/+}$ littermate controls. Aβ1-42 levels, but not total Aβ (Aβ1-x) levels, were significantly higher in the supernatants from $CatB^{-/-}$ neurons than $CatB^{+/+}$ neurons.

Expression of CatB in hAPP primary neurons was acutely inhibited with a lentiviral vector encoding a small-hairpin RNA targeting CatB (Lenti-shCatB). Inhibiting CatB significantly increased Aβ1-42 levels, suggesting that CatB negatively regulates Aβ1-42 levels. Total Aβ levels were also significantly elevated in cultures infected with Lenti-shCatB, indicating that CatB also reduces total Aβ levels. To further confirm the negative effects of CatB on Aβ levels, we increased CatB activity in primary neuronal cultures from hAPP mice with a lentiviral vector that encodes mouse CatB cDNA (Lenti-CatB). Infection with Lenti-CatB resulted in significant increase in CatB activity. Both Aβ1-42 and Aβ1-x levels were significantly reduced in cultures overexpressing CatB. Taken together, these results strongly suggest that neuronal CatB reduces Aβ levels.

2.3. CatB Truncates Aβ1-42 at the C-Terminus and Reduces Levels of Aβ Fibrils *in vitro*

Since CatB colocalizes with Aβ and reduces Aβ levels in neurons, we hypothesized that Aβ1-42 is a substrate for CatB and that CatB reduces levels of Aβ1-42 through proteolytic cleavage. Under cell-free conditions, synthetic Aβ1-42 was incubated with purified CatB at pH 6.0, a pH close to that of endosomes, where CatB is likely to encounter Aβ intracellularly (Cataldo, et al., 1997; Hook, et al., 2002). Surface-enhanced laser desorption ionization-time of flight (SELDI-TOF) mass spectrometry was used to analyze the proteolytic products. Incubating Aβ1-42 with CatB resulted in generation of Aβ1-40, Aβ1-38, and Aβ1-33 through proteolytic cleavage at Val_{40}-Ile_{41}, Gly_{38}-Gly_{39}, and Gly_{33}-Leu_{34} (Figure 2A). No truncations occurred with the inhibitor CA074 or without CatB, confirming that the truncations depended on the proteolytic activity of CatB. Consistent with its carboxydipeptidic activity, CatB cleaves Aβ1-42 at the C-terminus to generate Aβ1-40, which in turn serves as a substrate for the generation of Aβ1-38.

CatB also exerted endopeptidase activity to generate Aβ1-33 (Figures 2). Consistent with a endopeptidase activity weaker than carboxydipeptidase activity in CatB at acidic pH (4.0–6.0) (Nagler, et al., 1997; Musil, et al., 1991), higher concentrations of CatB were required to generate Aβ1-33 than to generate Aβ1-40 and Aβ1-38. Interestingly, even when Aβ1-40 was almost completely converted to Aβ1-38, no Aβ1-36 was generated from Aβ1-38, indicating that Aβ1-38 is not a substrate for CatB's carboxydipeptidic activity.

Soluble Aβ1-42 assemblies (protofibrillar) were highly toxic in cultured primary neurons (Chen, et al., 2005; Hartley, et al., 1999) and, at pH 6.0, were cleaved by CatB as efficiently as nonaggregated preparations, resulting in the same C-terminally-truncated peptides, Aβ1-40, Aβ1-38, and Aβ1-33 (Figure 2A), which are less toxic and fibrillogenic than Aβ1-42 (Iijima, et al., 2004; Zhang, et al., 2002). The generation of distinct C-terminally-truncated Aβ fragments by CatB offers a unique mechanism to modulate the levels of Aβ, especially Aβ1-42.

Although the ability of CatB to cleave Aβ, especially nonaggregated (fresh) Aβ, was markedly reduced at neutral pH (~7.0), CatB-induced cleavage of protofibrillar and fibrillar Aβ1-42 preparations resulted in the same truncated Aβ species observed at pH 6.0 (Figure 2B).

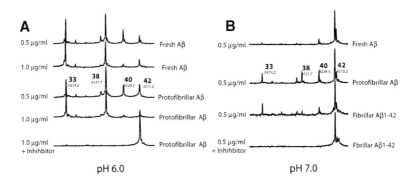

Figure 2. SELDI-TOF mass spectrometry analysis of CatB-induced cleavage of aggregated Aβ1-42 (protofibrillar and fibrillar). (A) At pH 6.0, protofibrillar Aβ1-42 was cleaved as efficiently as fresh Aβ1-42. (B) At pH 7.0, CatB induced cleavage of fresh, soluble and fibrillar Aβ1-42. Reproduced with permission from Cell Press.

Incubation of CatB induced a marked decrease in the amount of large Aβ assemblies, as shown on tricine SDS-PAGE gels. Levels of low-MW Aβ1-42 oligomers and monomers, detected with an antibody specific for Aβ1-42, were also reduced (Figure 3A). Moreover, incubation with CatB reduced fibrillar Aβ1-42 (Figure 3B). Both effects depended on the proteolytic activity of CatB, as demonstrated by inhibition with CA074. These results suggest that CatB effectively targets soluble and insoluble Aβ assemblies *in vitro*.

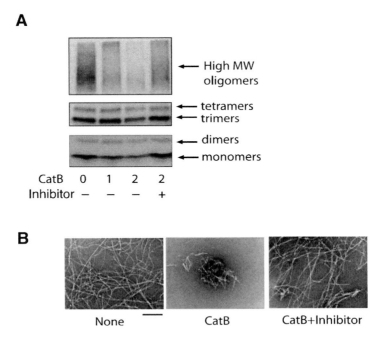

Figure 3. (A) A western blot of a tricine gel (16%) shows effects of CatB (1–2 μg/ml) on Aβ1-42 assemblies, including larger (MW) Aβ oligomers, and putative monomeric, dimeric, trimeric, and tetrameric Aβ1-42 (arrows), in the presence or absence of CA074, according to the molecular mass markers (3.5–75 kDa). (B) Electron microscopy photomicrograph of preformed Aβ1-42 fibrils incubated with CatB in the presence or absence of its inhibitor CA074. Scale bar: 200 nm. Reproduced with permission from Cell Press.

2.4. CatB Deletion Increases Plaque Deposition in AD-Related Animal Models

Transgenic mouse models have been valuable in elucidating the role of APP/Aβ in AD pathogenesis. In multiple independent transgenic lines, overexpression of FAD-mutant APP results in age-dependent plaque deposition, neuritic dystrophy, and gliosis with or without FAD-linked mutant presenilin (Hsia, et al., 1999; Games, et al., 1995; Borchelt, et al., 1997; Holcomb, et al., 1998). Despite small differences, these models share several key pathological features, including amyloid plaques, neuritic dystrophy, reactive gliosis, and loss of synapses. In the hAPP mouse model (J20 line), overexpression of hAPP carrying FAD-linked (Swedish and Indiana) mutations in neurons was achieved by using alternatively spliced minigene constructs directed by the platelet-derived growth factor β-chain promoter (Games, et al., 1995; Mucke, et al., 2000). In these mice, deficits in spatial learning and memory correlates well with relative abundance of Aβ1-42, but not with the amount of Aβ in amyloid plaques (Palop, et al., 2003), confirming the role of soluble Aβ in AD pathogenesis.

To determine the role of CatB in APP processing and Aβ metabolism *in vivo*, we examined $CatB^{-/-}$ mice crossed with hAPP mice. CatB activity was undetectable in $CatB^{-/-}$ mice and reduced to 50% of wild-type levels in heterozygotes ($CatB^{+/-}$). Western blot analyses with an antibody targeting C-terminal fragment of hAPP revealed that CatB ablation in hAPP mice did not affect levels of C-terminal fragments (CTF) of hAPP, or full-length hAPP. Levels of α-sAPP, detected with 6E10 antibody (Esposito, et al., 2004), were not affected by CatB ablation either. These results suggest that CatB does not significantly affect the processing of hAPP.

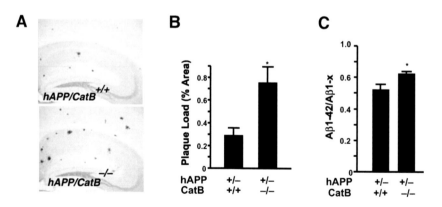

Figure 4. Genetic ablation of CatB increases plaque deposition and relative abundance of Aβ1-42. (A) Photomicrographs of 3D6 immunostaining in the hippocampus of 6–7-month-old $hAPP/CatB^{+/+}$ mice or $hAPP/CatB^{-/-}$ mice. (B) Plaque load was calculated as the percent area of the hippocampus covered by 3D6-immunoreactive material. (C) ELISA measurements of hippocampal levels of Aβ1-42 and Aβ1-x (approximates total Aβ). N=10–12 mice/genotype, * $P < 0.05$, Unpaired t test. Reproduced with permission from Cell Press.

Consistent with Aβ-reducing effects of CatB, hippocampal plaque loads were significantly higher in $hAPP/CatB^{-/-}$ mice than $hAPP/CatB^{+/+}$ mice at 6 months of age, as shown by immunostaining with an anti-Aβ antibody, 3D6 (Figure 4A). The number of neuritic plaques labeled with thioflavin-S was also significantly higher in hippocampus of *hAPP/CatB*$^{-/-}$ mice than in *hAPP/CatB*$^{+/+}$ mice (Figure 4B). In addition, more amyloid deposits were detected in the cortex of *hAPP/CatB*$^{-/-}$ mice than in *hAPP/CatB*$^{+/+}$ mice (data not shown). These results indicate that CatB is involved in reducing Aβ deposition. Using an ELISA assay for human Aβ, we next examined the effects of CatB ablation on hippocampal Aβ1-42 and Aβ1-x (approximates total Aβ) levels and found that Aβ1-42/Aβ1-x ratios were significantly higher in *hAPP/CatB*$^{-/-}$ mice than *hAPP/CatB*$^{+/+}$ mice at 6–7 months of age (Figure 4C). This result is consistent with the increased plaque deposition in 6–7-month-old *hAPP/CatB*$^{-/-}$ mice.

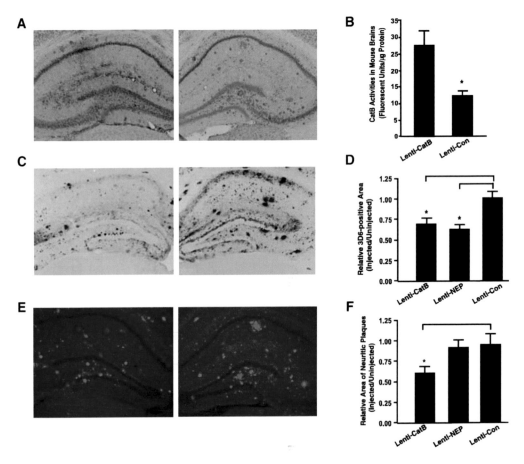

Figure 5. CatB gene transfer reduces amyloid plaques in aged hAPP mice. (A) Representative CatB immunostaining of the Lenti-CatB injected (left) and uninjected (right) hippocampus in a 12–15-month-old hAPP mouse. (B) CatB enzymatic activities in hippocampus of *CatB*$^{+/-}$ after injection of Lenti-CatB or Lenti-control (n=3 mice/group, * $P < 0.05$, Unpaired t test). (C) Representative photomicrograph of 3D6 immunostaining or thioflavin-S-positive labeling (E) of the Lenti-CatB injected (left) and uninjected (right) hippocampus. (D) Injection of Lenti-CatB or Lenti-NEP, but not Lenti-control reduced 3D6-immunoreactive Aβ deposits in the hippocampus of 12–15-month-old hAPP mice. (F) Injection of Lenti-CatB, but not Lenti-NEP or Lenti-control reduced thioflavin-S–positive plaques in the hippocampus of 12–15-month-old hAPP mice. * $P < 0.05$, Tukey Kramer *post hoc* test. Reproduced with permission from Cell Press.

2.5. CatB Gene Transfer Reduces Amyloid Plaques in aged hAPP Mice

In a clinical setting, most AD patients will be treated after cognitive dysfunction has developed. Therefore, it is important to determine if elevating CatB levels after the onset of pathology reduces preexisting pathology. To address this question, we injected Lenti-CatB into the hippocampus of 12–15-month-old hAPP mice, which have significant plaque deposition. Lenti-control, which does not encode a functional protein, served as a negative control for nonspecific viral effects. A lentiviral vector overexpressing NEP (Lenti-NEP) (Marr, et al., 2003) served as a positive control. Three weeks after the stereotaxic injections, CatB immunoreactivity (Figure 5A) and enzymatic activity (Figure 5B) were much stronger in the injected hippocampus, especially in the dentate gyrus (DG), than that in the contralateral side. Lenti-NEP also induced higher NEP immunoreactivity in the DG. Injection of Lenti-CatB (Figure 5C) or Lenti-NEP significantly reduced 3D6-postive Aβ deposits in the ipsilateral DG; control virus had no effect (Figure 5D).

These results suggest that, in aged hAPP mice, CatB reduces preexisting plaque load as effectively as NEP. Notably, CatB gene transfer markedly reduced thioflavin-S–positive neuritic plaques (Figure 5E and 5F), whereas Lenti-NEP did not (Figure 5F). Thus, CatB was more effective than NEP in removing aggregated Aβ in established dense mature amyloid plaques. The CatB-induced efficient clearance of thioflavin-S–positive neuritic plaques could be due to CatB's unique ability to target aggregated Aβ and its accumulation within neuritic plaques. Our results reinforce the notion that CatB and NEP contribute to overall Aβ degradation in the brain by targeting different forms of Aβ, reflecting their distinct proteolytic properties and subcellular localizations.

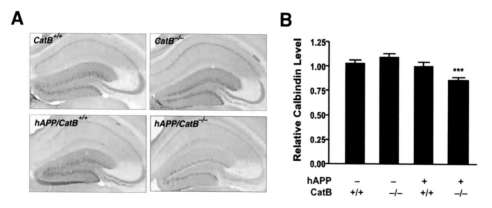

Figure 6. (A) Photomicrographs of calbindin immunostaining in the hippocampus of 6–7-month-old *hAPP/CatB*⁺ᐟ⁺ or *hAPP/CatB*⁻ mice and littermate controls (*CatB*⁺ᐟ⁺ and *CatB*⁻). (B) Calbindin levels in the DG relative to those in the CA1 regions were significantly lower in *hAPP/CatB*⁻ mice than in *hAPP/CatB*⁺ᐟ⁺ mice or controls (n=10–12/genotype, *** *P* < 0.001, Tukey Kramer *post hoc* test). Reproduced with permission from Cell Press.

2.6. CatB Protects Against Aβ-Dependent Neuronal Deficits

Learning deficits in hAPP mice are influenced by Aβ1-42 levels and, on an inbred C57BL/6 background, correlated strongly with the depletion of the calcium-binding protein calbindin-D28k in granule cells of the DG (Palop, et al., 2003; Palop, et al., 2005). Consistent with their increased levels of Aβ1-42, 6–7-month-old *hAPP/CatB$^{-/-}$* mice had significantly lower calbindin levels in the DG than age-matched *hAPP/CatB$^{+/+}$* mice (Figures 6A–B). These results suggest that CatB protects neurons against the Aβ-induced depletion of synaptic activity-dependent proteins.

3. REGULATION OF CATB

3.1. CatB is Upregulated by Aβ1-42

CatB in microglial cells is transcriptionally upregulated by exposure to Aβ1-42 (Gan, et al., 2004). In tumor progression and arthritic conditions, CatB expression is increased at both the gene and protein levels (Bien, et al., 2004). The increased gene expression results from gene amplification, elevated transcription, use of alternative promoters, and alternative splicing (Yan, et al., 2000; Yan and Sloane, 2004; Yan, et al., 2003; Berquin, et al., 1995; Zwicky, et al., 2003). These changes increased CatB protein levels, leading to redistribution, secretion, and increased activity (Sloane, et al., 2005). Post-translational factors governing the proteolytic activity of CatB include pH, redox potential, amounts of its own precursor, intracellular targeting, and cysteine protease inhibitors (Linebaugh, et al., 1999; Zeng, et al., 2006; O'Neil, et al., 2003; Turk, et al., 1995; Quraishi, et al., 1999; Cimerman, et al., 1999).

To determine if Aβ1-42 also regulates CatB in neuronal cells, where the majority of Aβ is made, we stimulated neuroblastoma (N2A) cells with increasing amounts of Aβ1-42 and Aβ1-40. CatB mRNA levels and enzymatic activities were both markedly increased by Aβ1-42; Aβ1-40 had little or no effect. Treatment with preaggregated Aβ1-40, however, induced a modest but significant increase in CatB activity, supporting the notion that regulation of CatB is influenced by the assembly states of Aβ peptides.

Do Aβ levels modulate CatB activities *in vivo*? To address this question, we compared the enzymatic activities of CatB in the hippocampus of hAPP mice with age-matched nontransgenic controls (Figure 7). CatB levels were higher in hAPP mice both before (1–3 months) and after (7–8 months) plaque deposition, suggesting that hAPP/Aβ upregulates CatB activities and that the up-regulation of CatB represents a protective mechanism. At 16–20 months, however, hAPP/Aβ failed to stimulate CatB, indicating that the protective mechanism fails with aging. Aging also reduces the levels of somatostatin, resulting in markedly decreased NEP levels in vulnerable regions of the aging brain (Iwata et al., 2004; Saito et al., 2005). Together, these studies provide evidence that aging-dependent defects in Aβ catabolism by proteolysis may underlie Aβ accumulation in late-onset sporadic AD.

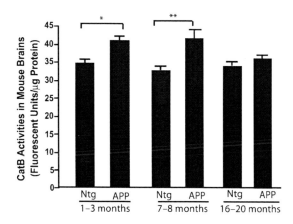

Figure 7. CatB activity levels were significantly elevated in young (1–3 months) and middle-aged (7–8 months), but not elderly (16–20 months) hAPP mice, compared with age-matched non-transgenic (ntg) controls. The bars represent means ± S.E.M. (n=8–18, *, $P < 0.05$, **, $P < 0.01$, Tukey Kramer *post hoc* test). Reproduced with permission from Cell Press.

3.2. Regulation of CatB Activity by Cystatin C (CysC)

The enzymatic activity of CatB is predominantly inhibited by CysC (Turk, et al., 1995; Cimerman, et al., 1999), a 2-member family of a super family of cysteine protease inhibitors. Although ubiquitously expressed, CysC is found at particularly high concentrations in cerebrospinal fluid (Lofberg and Grubb, 1979). Because it is a secreted protein, its major functional site is presumed to be extracellular (Chapman, et al., 1990; Warfel, et al., 1987). Polymorphism in the CysC gene has been implicated as a risk factor for sporadic late-onset AD (Beyer, et al., 2001; Crawford, et al., 2000; Finckh, et al., 2000). However, this finding is controversial, as several case-control studies failed to confirm the association in certain populations (Maruyama, et al., 2001; Dodel, et al., 2002; Roks, et al., 2001). Patients with hereditary CysC amyloid angiopathy have repeated massive brain hemorrhages (Calero, et al., 2001; Abrahamson, et al., 1992; Levy, et al., 1989) that are caused by mutant CysC (Leu68Gln) protein in the wall of the cerebral arteries (Calero, et al., 2001; Jensson, et al., 1987; Palsdottir, et al., 1988; Grubb, et al., 1984). Indeed, CysC is an amyloidogenic protein with a tendency to form very tight twofold symmetric dimers, leading to a complete loss of its inhibitory activity (Janowski, et al., 2001; Ekiel, et al., 1997).

CysC binds to CatB in two steps: an initial weak binding is followed by a conformational change in the second step that involves the dislocation of the inhibitor by the occluding loop of CatB (Illy, et al., 1997; Auerswald, et al., 1995). Extensive characterizations of the structure and function of CysC have revealed that N-terminal segment is critical for its inhibitory function (Abrahamson, et al., 1987; Abrahamson, et al., 1990). An N-terminal deletion in the mouse CysC gene (CysCΔ64–94, numbering refers to the nucleic acid) reduces this inhibitory function without affecting the normal trafficking and other biological functions (Taupin, et al., 2000) of the protein. The implications of the interaction of CatB with CysC have been extensively studied in tumor metastasis and inflammatory conditions

(Coulibaly, et al., 1999). In the cerebrospinal fluid of patients with inflammatory neurological diseases (e.g., multiple sclerosis), decreased CysC levels may be related to the high levels of CatB activity, which are believed to have crucial roles in disease initiation and progression (Nagai, et al., 2000).

CysC appears to bind specifically, saturably, and with high affinity to both Aβ1-42 and Aβ1-40, resulting in a concentration-dependent inhibition of Aβ fibril formation *in vitro* (Sastre, et al., 2004). In AD brains and hAPP mice, CysC colocalizes with Aβ in parenchymal and vascular amyloid deposits (Levy, et al., 2001). Immunoelectron microscopy with anti-CysC antibodies revealed strongly labeled pyramidal neurons that were immunopositive for intracellular Aβx-42 (Levy, et al., 2001). In a separate study in AD brains, neuronal staining of CysC was primarily limited to regions most susceptible to cell death and colocalized with CatB (Deng, et al., 2001). However, it remains to be established whether CysC plays a primary role in amyloidogenesis of AD or its association with Aβ is a late event by binding to the previously formed Aβ amyloid fibrils.

To determine the role of CysC in Aβ metabolism, CysC-null ($CysC^{-/-}$) mice were crossed with C56B/L6 wild-type mice to generate $CysC^{+/-}$ mice, which were crossed again to generate $CysC^{-/-}$ mice and littermate wild-type ($CysC^{+/+}$) controls. Hippocampal CatB activities were significantly higher in $CysC^{-/-}$ mice than in wild-type ($CysC^{+/+}$) controls, supporting the notion that CysC is the main endogenous inhibitor of CatB.

We hypothesized that inhibition of CysC might reduce Aβ levels as a result of increased CatB activity. To test this hypothesis, $CysC^{-/-}$ or $CysC^{+/+}$ cultures were infected with an adenoviral vector encoding hAPP cDNA and the supernatants were harvested for examination by Aβ ELISA. Indeed, levels of Aβ1-42, were significantly lower in the supernatants from $CysC^{-/-}$ cultures than $CysC^{+/+}$ cultures, suggesting that CysC removal reduces Aβ1-42 levels. This finding supports the notion that inhibiting CysC could reduce Aβ1-42 levels through promoting CatB activities.

4. FUTURE DIRECTIONS

Our recent studies have demonstrated that CatB plays an anti-amyloidogenic and neuroprotective function *in vivo*. In transgenic mice expressing hAPP with FAD-linked mutations in neurons, genetic ablation of CatB increased plaque deposition, as well as the relative abundance of Aβ1-42 and associated neuronal deficits. Many aspects of AD-related neuronal damage have been attributed to nonfibrillar, non-deposited Aβ, including synaptic degeneration (Mucke, et al., 2000; Takahashi, et al., 2004), deficits in synaptic transmission (Hsia, et al., 1999; Walsh, et al., 2002), depletion of activity-dependent neuronal proteins (calbindin, c-*fos*) (Palop, et al., 2003), and behavioral deficits (Lesne, et al., 2006; Cleary, et al., 2005). Although under cell-free conditions, aggregated (oligomeric and fibrillar) Aβ1-42 was effectively truncated by CatB at the C-terminus *in vitro*, resulting in Aβ species that are less toxic and less fibrillogenic (Bitan, et al., 2003), a key unaddressed question is whether CatB targets these biochemically stable structures *in vivo*. Since AD is characterized by behavioral alterations, the next step is to use behavioral tests to assess the functional effects of CatB ablation in hAPP mice.

A second key question is whether CatB can reverse plaque-independent neuronal and behavioral deficits after the onset of pathology. Our studies established that lentivirus-based gene delivery modulates CatB levels in a spatial- and temporal-specific manner. Virus-mediated CatB expression significantly reduced the amount of amyloid plaques in the DG and did so more effectively than NEP removed neuritic plaques. These findings strongly suggest that CatB can reverse plaque-dependent neuritic dystrophy in aged hAPP mice. However, oligomeric Aβ1-42 assemblies, not plaques, are critical in mediating cognitive deficits in hAPP mice. Our next step is to determine if CatB also reduces plaque-independent neuronal deficits after the onset of pathology.

The age-dependent regulation of CatB also raised intriguing questions for further investigation. For example, why is CatB stimulated in middle-aged but not old hAPP mice, although CatB immunoreactivity is present in most neuritic plaques, even in old hAPP mice? We hypothesize that CatB in neuritic plaques may lose enzymatic activity with aging, resulting in inefficient removal of amyloid in aging brain. To test this hypothesis, one needs to directly monitor the CatB activity in the context of amyloid pathology in hAPP mice. The small-molecule activity-based probes (ABPs) that target enzymatically active cathepsins (Kato, et al., 2005; Bogyo, 2005; Blum, et al., 2005) are well suited to address this important question.

5. THERAPEUTIC PERSPECTIVES

Significant progress has been made in identifying proteases that degrade Aβ in physiological and pathophysiological conditions. The specific localizations and proteolytic properties of these enzymes suggest that they may play complementary roles in regulating Aβ of different assembly states in distinct cellular compartments. A better understanding of the pathways regulating Aβ-degrading enzymes could lead to reagents that reduce Aβ levels through enhancing the expression and activation of Aβ-degrading enzymes. Promoting activities of proteases, especially those capable of degrading Aβ aggregates and oligomers, such as CatB and NEP, could represent an effective way to induce Aβ clearance and reverse Aβ-dependent pathology in AD.

Several strategies have been proposed to enhance the activities of the Aβ-degrading enzymes, a more difficult task than inhibiting protease activities. One strategy is to deliver recombinant proteases. However, this approach could be problematic: these proteases regulate levels of many peptides of important physiological functions. For example, IDEs regulates levels of insulin, which controls the glucose levels in the blood, and NEP regulates levels of atrial natriuretic peptide, which regulates blood pressure. Thus, a localized and regulated delivery to the vulnerable regions of the brain would be needed. Viral vectors overexpressing NEP and CatB have been used in experimental animal models to reduce Aβ pathology in aged mouse brain (Mueller-Steiner, et al., 2006; Iwata, et al., 2004; Marr, et al., 2003). However, extensive preclinical and clinical studies will be required to test the safety of gene therapy in humans.

In addition, a better understanding of the regulatory pathways of Aβ-degrading enzymes could lead to reagents that promote Aβ-degrading enzymes. For example, somatostatin significantly elevated neuronal NEP activity, likely by affecting protein turnover and cellular localization (Saito, et al., 2005). Agonists for somatostatin receptors might be used to augment NEP's Aβ-degrading activities (Saito, et al., 2005). Another strategy might be to down-regulate the endogenous inhibitors of proteases. We hypothesize that the balance between Aβ-degrading proteases and their endogenous inhibitors may be altered in sporadic AD, leading to deficiencies in Aβ degradation and clearance. Thus, reducing the levels/activities of the inhibitors would tip the balance in favor of Aβ degradation. For example, CatB activity might be suppressed by its endogenous inhibitor CysC (Cimerman, et al., 1999), whose levels are higher in the CSF and susceptible neurons of AD patients (Deng, et al., 2001; Carrette, et al., 2003). Ongoing studies are testing whether down-regulation of CysC will promote Aβ degradation and reduce Aβ levels in AD-related animal models. It is likely that a combination of approaches that leads to both decreased production and increased clearance would be the most effective anti-Aβ therapy.

ACKNOWLEDGMENT

The author would like to thank former and current members of the Gan laboratory in the Gladstone Institute of Neurological Disease, including Drs. S. Mueller-Steiner, Y. Zhou, H. Arai, B. Sun, J. Chen for their contribution to the work described in the chapter. The author would also like to thank L. Mucke for his insights, G. Howard and S. Ordway for editorial assistance, and K. Nelson for administrative assistance.

REFERENCES

Abrahamson, M., Jonsdottir, S., Olafsson, I., Jensson, O., Grubb, A. Hereditary cystatin C amyloid angiopathy: Identification of the disease-causing mutation and specific diagnosis by polymerase chain reaction based analysis. *Hum. Genet. 89*: 377–380, 1992.

Abrahamson, M., Olafsson, I., Palsdottir, A., Ulvsback, M., Lundwall, A., Jensson, O., Grubb, A. Structure and expression of the human cystatin C gene. *Biochem. J. 268*: 287–294, 1990.

Abrahamson, M., Ritonja, A., Brown, M.A., Grubb, A., Machleidt, W., Barrett, A.J. Identification of the probable inhibitory reactive sites of the cysteine proteinase inhibitors human cystatin C and chicken cystatin. *J. Biol. Chem. 262*: 9688–9694, 1987.

Annaert, W., Cupers, P., Saftig, P., De Strooper, B. Presenilin function in APP processing. *Ann. N. Y. Acad. Sci. 920*: 158–164, 2000.

Auerswald, E.A., Nagler, D.K., Assfalg-Machleidt, I., Stubbs, M.T., Machleidt, W., Fritz, H. Hairpin loop mutations of chicken cystatin have different effects on the inhibition of cathepsin B, cathepsin L and papain. *FEBS Lett. 361*: 179–184, 1995.

Authier, F., Metioui, M., Bell, A.W., Mort, J.S. Negative regulation of epidermal growth factor signaling by selective proteolytic mechanisms in the endosome mediated by cathepsin B. *J. Biol. Chem. 274*: 33723–33731, 1999.

Authier, F., Posner, B.I., Bergeron, J.J. Insulin-degrading enzyme. *Clin Invest Med 19*: 149–160, 1996.

Azaryan, A., Barkhudaryan, N., Galoyan, A. Some properties of human and bovine brain cathepsin B. *Neurochem. Res. 10*: 1511–1524, 1985.

Banati, R.B., Rothe, G., Valet, G., Kreutzberg, G.W. Detection of lysosomal cysteine proteinases in microglia: Flow cytometric measurement and histochemical localization of cathepsin B and L. *Glia 7*: 183–191, 1993.

Bard, F., Cannon, C., Barbour, R., Burke, R.L., Games, D., Grajeda, H., Guido, T., Hu, K., Huang, J., Johnson-Wood, K., Khan, K., Kholodenko, D., Lee, M., Lieberburg, I., Motter, R., Nguyen, M., Soriano, F., Vasquez, N., Weiss, K., Welch, B., Seubert, P., Schenk, D., Yednock, T. Peripherally administered antibodies against amyloid β-peptide enter the central nervous system and reduce pathology in a mouse model of Alzheimer disease. *Nat. Med. 6*: 916–919, 2000.

Berlet, H.H., Ilzenhofer, H. Elucidation of cathepsin B-like activity associated with extracts of human myelin basic protein. *FEBS Lett. 179*: 299–302, 1985.

Berquin, I.M., Cao, L., Fong, D., Sloane, B.F. Identification of two new exons and multiple transcription start points in the 5'-untranslated region of the human cathepsin-B-encoding gene. *Gene 159*: 143-149, 1995.

Beyer, K., Lao, J.I., Gomez, M., Riutort, N., Latorre, P., Mate, J.L., Ariza, A. Alzheimer's disease and the cystatin C gene polymorphism: An association study. *Neurosci. Lett. 315*: 17–20, 2001.

Bien, S., Ritter, C.A., Gratz, M., Sperker, B., Sonnemann, J., Beck, J.F., Kroemer, H.K. Nuclear factor-kappaB mediates up-regulation of cathepsin B by doxorubicin in tumor cells. *Mol Pharmacol 65*: 1092-1102, 2004.

Bitan, G., Kirkitadze, M.D., Lomakin, A., Vollers, S.S., Benedek, G.B., Teplow, D.B. Amyloid beta -protein (Abeta) assembly: Abeta 40 and Abeta 42 oligomerize through distinct pathways. *Proc Natl Acad Sci U S A 100*: 330-335, 2003.

Blum, G., Mullins, S.R., Keren, K., Fonovic, M., Jedeszko, C., Rice, M.J., Sloane, B.F., Bogyo, M. Dynamic imaging of protease activity with fluorescently quenched activity-based probes. *Nat Chem Biol 1*: 203-209, 2005.

Bogyo, M. Screening for selective small molecule inhibitors of the proteasome using activity-based probes. *Methods Enzymol 399*: 609-622, 2005.

Borchelt, D.R., Ratovitski, T., van Lare, J., Lee, M.K., Gonzales, V., Jenkins, N.A., Copeland, N.G., Price, D.L., Sisodia, S.S. Accelerated amyloid deposition in the brains of transgenic mice coexpressing mutant presenilin 1 and amyloid precursor proteins. *Neuron 19*: 939–945, 1997.

Braak, H., Braak, E. Neuropathological stageing of Alzheimer-related changes. *Acta Neuropathol. Berl. 82*: 239–259, 1991.

Buck, M.R., Karustis, D.G., Day, N.A., Honn, K.V., Sloane, B.F. Degradation of extracellular-matrix proteins by human cathepsin B from normal and tumour tissues. *Biochem. J. 282* (Pt 1): 273–278, 1992.

Buttini, M., Masliah, E., Barbour, R., Grajeda, H., Motter, R., Johnson-Wood, K., Khan, K., Seubert, P., Freedman, S., Schenk, D., Games, D. Beta-amyloid immunotherapy prevents synaptic degeneration in a mouse model of Alzheimer's disease. *J Neurosci 25*: 9096-9101, 2005.

Calero, M., Pawlik, M., Soto, C., Castano, E.M., Sigurdsson, E.M., Kumar, A., Gallo, G., Frangione, B., Levy, E. Distinct properties of wild-type and the amyloidogenic human cystatin C variant of hereditary cerebral hemorrhage with amyloidosis, Icelandic type. *J. Neurochem. 77*: 628–637, 2001.

Carrette, O., Demalte, I., Scherl, A., Yalkinoglu, O., Corthals, G., Burkhard, P., Hochstrasser, D.F., Sanchez, J.C. A panel of cerebrospinal fluid potential biomarkers for the diagnosis of Alzheimer's disease. *Proteomics 3*: 1486-1494, 2003.

Cataldo, A.M., Barnett, J.L., Pieroni, C., Nixon, R.A. Increased neuronal endocytosis and protease delivery to early endosomes in sporadic Alzheimer's disease: Neuropathologic evidence for a mechanism of increased β-amyloidogenesis. *J. Neurosci. 17*: 6142–6151, 1997.

Cataldo, A.M., Nixon, R.A. Enzymatically active lysosomal proteases are associated with amyloid deposits in Alzheimer brain. *Proc. Natl. Acad. Sci. USA 87*: 3861–3865, 1990.

Cataldo, A.M., Thayer, C.Y., Bird, E.D., Wheelock, T.R., Nixon, R.A. Lysosomal proteinase antigens are prominently localized within senile plaques of Alzheimer's disease: Evidence for a neuronal origin. *Brain Res. 513*: 181–192, 1990.

Caughey, B., Lansbury, P.T., Jr. Protofibrils, pores, fibrils, and neurodegeneration: Separating the responsible protein aggregates from the innocent bystanders. *Annu. Rev. Neurosci. 2003.*

Chan, S.J., San Segundo, B., McCormick, M.B., Steiner, D.F. Nucleotide and predicted amino acid sequences of cloned human and mouse preprocathepsin B cDNAs. *Proc. Natl. Acad. Sci. USA 83*: 7721–7725, 1986.

Chapman, H.A., Jr., Reilly, J.J., Jr., Yee, R., Grubb, A. Identification of cystatin C, a cysteine proteinase inhibitor, as a major secretory product of human alveolar macrophages *in vitro. Am. Rev. Respir. Dis. 141*: 698–705, 1990.

Chapman, H.A., Riese, R.J., Shi, G.P. Emerging roles for cysteine proteases in human biology. *Annu Rev Physiol 59*: 63-88, 1997.

Chen, J., Zhou, Y., Mueller-Steiner, S., Chen, L.F., Kwon, H., Yi, S., Mucke, L., Gan, L. SIRT1 Protects against Microglia-dependent Amyloid-{beta} Toxicity through Inhibiting NF-{kappa}B Signaling. *J Biol Chem 280*: 40364-40374, 2005.

Cheng, I.H., Palop, J.J., Esposito, L.A., Bien-Ly, N., Yan, F., Mucke, L. Aggressive amyloidosis in mice expressing human amyloid peptides with the Arctic mutation. *Nat Med 10*: 1190-1192, 2004.

Chromy, B.A., Nowak, R.J., Lambert, M.P., Viola, K.L., Chang, L., Velasco, P.T., Jones, B.W., Fernandez, S.J., Lacor, P.N., Horowitz, P., Finch, C.E., Krafft, G.A., Klein, W.L. Self-assembly of $A\beta_{1-42}$ into globular neurotoxins. *Biochemistry 42*: 12749–12760, 2003.

Cimerman, N., Prebanda, M.T., Turk, B., Popovic, T., Dolenc, I., Turk, V. Interaction of cystatin C variants with papain and human cathepsins B, H and L. *J. Enzyme Inhib. 14*: 167–174, 1999.

Citron, M. β-secretase as a target for the treatment of Alzheimer's disease. *J. Neurosci. Res.* *70*: 373–379, 2002.

Citron, M., Oltersdorf, T., Haass, C., McConlogue, L., Hung, A.Y., Seubert, P., Vigo-Pelfrey, C., Lieberburg, I., Selkoe, D.J. Mutation of the β-amyloid precursor protein in familial Alzheimer's disease increases β-protein production. *Nature 360*: 672–674, 1992.

Cleary, J.P., Walsh, D.M., Hofmeister, J.J., Shankar, G.M., Kuskowski, M.A., Selkoe, D.J., Ashe, K.H. Natural oligomers of the amyloid-beta protein specifically disrupt cognitive function. *Nat Neurosci 8*: 79-84, 2005.

Coulibaly, S., Schwihla, H., Abrahamson, M., Albini, A., Cerni, C., Clark, J.L., Ng, K.M., Katunuma, N., Schlappack, O., Glossl, J., Mach, L. Modulation of invasive properties of murine squamous carcinoma cells by heterologous expression of cathepsin B and cystatin C. *Int. J. Cancer 83*: 526–531, 1999.

Crawford, F.C., Freeman, M.J., Schinka, J.A., Abdullah, L.I., Gold, M., Hartman, R., Krivian, K., Morris, M.D., Richards, D., Duara, R., Anand, R., Mullan, M.J. A polymorphism in the cystatin C gene is a novel risk factor for late-onset Alzheimer's disease. *Neurology 55*: 763–768, 2000.

Dahlgren, K.N., Manelli, A.M., Stine, W.B., Jr., Baker, L.K., Krafft, G.A., LaDu, M.J. Oligomeric and fibrillar species of amyloid-β peptides differentially affect neuronal viability. *J. Biol. Chem. 277*: 32046–32053, 2002.

Das, P., Howard, V., Loosbrock, N., Dickson, D., Murphy, M.P., Golde, T.E. Amyloid-β immunization effectively reduces amyloid deposition in $FcR\gamma^{-/-}$ knock-out mice. *J. Neurosci. 23*: 8532–8538, 2003.

De Strooper, B. Aph-1, Pen-2, and nicastrin with presenilin generate an active gamma-secretase complex. *Neuron 38*: 9–12, 2003.

Deane, R., Du Yan, S., Submamaryan, R.K., LaRue, B., Jovanovic, S., Hogg, E., Welch, D., Manness, L., Lin, C., Yu, J., Zhu, H., Ghiso, J., Frangione, B., Stern, A., Schmidt, A.M., Armstrong, D.L., Arnold, B., Liliensiek, B., Nawroth, P., Hofman, F., Kindy, M., Stern, D., Zlokovic, B. RAGE mediates amyloid-beta peptide transport across the blood-brain barrier and accumulation in brain. *Nat Med 9*: 907-913, 2003.

Deane, R., Wu, Z., Zlokovic, B.V. RAGE (yin) versus LRP (yang) balance regulates alzheimer amyloid beta-peptide clearance through transport across the blood-brain barrier. *Stroke 35*: 2628-2631, 2004.

Deng, A., Irizarry, M.C., Nitsch, R.M., Growdon, J.H., Rebeck, G.W. Elevation of cystatin C in susceptible neurons in Alzheimer's disease. *Am. J. Pathol. 159*: 1061–1068, 2001.

Docherty, K., Carroll, R., Steiner, D.F. Identification of a 31,500 molecular weight islet cell protease as cathepsin B. *Proc. Natl. Acad. Sci. USA 80*: 3245–3249, 1983.

Dodel, R.C., Du, Y., Depboylu, C., Kurz, A., Eastwood, B., Farlow, M., Oertel, W.H., Muller, U., Riemenschneider, M. A polymorphism in the cystatin C promoter region is not associated with an increased risk of AD. *Neurology 58*: 664, 2002.

Eckman, E.A., Reed, D.K., Eckman, C.B. Degradation of the Alzheimer's amyloid beta peptide by endothelin-converting enzyme. *J Biol Chem 276*: 24540-24548, 2001.

Ekiel, I., Abrahamson, M., Fulton, D.B., Lindahl, P., Storer, A.C., Levadoux, W., Lafrance, M., Labelle, S., Pomerleau, Y., Groleau, D., LeSauteur, L., Gehring, K. NMR structural studies of human cystatin C dimers and monomers. *J. Mol. Biol. 271*: 266–277, 1997.

Esposito, L., Gan, L., Yu, G.Q., Essrich, C., Mucke, L. Intracellularly generated amyloid-beta peptide counteracts the antiapoptotic function of its precursor protein and primes proapoptotic pathways for activation by other insults in neuroblastoma cells. *J Neurochem 91*: 1260-1274, 2004.

Farris, W., Mansourian, S., Chang, Y., Lindsley, L., Eckman, E.A., Frosch, M.P., Eckman, C.B., Tanzi, R.E., Selkoe, D.J., Guenette, S. Insulin-degrading enzyme regulates the levels of insulin, amyloid beta-protein, and the beta-amyloid precursor protein intracellular domain in vivo. *Proc Natl Acad Sci U S A 100*: 4162-4167, 2003.

Fezoui, Y., Hartley, D.M., Harper, J.D., Khurana, R., Walsh, D.M., Condron, M.M., Selkoe, D.J., Lansbury, P.T., Jr., Fink, A.L., Teplow, D.B. An improved method of preparing the amyloid beta-protein for fibrillogenesis and neurotoxicity experiments. *Amyloid 7*: 166-178, 2000.

Finckh, U., von der Kammer, H., Velden, J., Michel, T., Andresen, B., Deng, A., Zhang, J., Muller-Thomsen, T., Zuchowski, K., Menzer, G., Mann, U., Papassotiropoulos, A., Heun, R., Zurdel, J., Holst, F., Benussi, L., Stoppe, G., Reiss, J., Miserez, A.R., Staehelin, H.B., Rebeck, G.W., Hyman, B.T., Binetti, G., Hock, C., Growdon, J.H., Nitsch, R.M. Genetic association of a cystatin C gene polymorphism with late-onset Alzheimer disease. *Arch. Neurol. 57*: 1579–1583, 2000.

Francis, R., McGrath, G., Zhang, J., Ruddy, D.A., Sym, M., Apfeld, J., Nicoll, M., Maxwell, M., Hai, B., Ellis, M.C., Parks, A.L., Xu, W., Li, J., Gurney, M., Myers, R.L., Himes, C.S., Hiebsch, R., Ruble, C., Nye, J.S., Curtis, D. aph-1 and pen-2 are required for Notch pathway signaling, gamma-secretase cleavage of betaAPP, and presenilin protein accumulation. *Dev Cell 3*: 85-97, 2002.

Games, D., Adams, D., Alessandrini, R., Barbour, R., Berthelette, P., Blackwell, C., Carr, T., Clemens, J., Donaldson, T., Gillespie, F., et al. Alzheimer-type neuropathology in transgenic mice overexpressing V717F β-amyloid precursor protein. *Nature 373*: 523–527, 1995.

Gan, L., Ye, S., Chu, A., Anton, K., Yi, S., Vincent, V.A., von Schack, D., Chin, D., Murray, J., Lohr, S., Patthy, L., Gonzalez-Zulueta, M., Nikolich, K., Urfer, R. Identification of cathepsin B as a mediator of neuronal death induced by Abeta-activated microglial cells using a functional genomics approach. *J Biol Chem 279*: 5565-5572, 2004.

Gan, L., Ye, S., Chu, A., Anton, K.E., Yi, S., Vincent, V.A., von Schack, D., Chin, D., Murray, J., Lohr, S., Patthy, L., Gonzalez-Zulueta, M., Nikolich, K., Urfer, R. Identification of cathepsin B as a mediator of neuronal death induced by Aβ-activated microglial cells using a functional genomics approach. *J. Biol. Chem. 279*: 5565–5572, 2004.

Glenner, G.G., Wong, C.W. Alzheimer's disease: initial report of the purification and characterization of a novel cerebrovascular amyloid protein. *Biochem Biophys Res Commun 120*: 885-890, 1984.

Gocheva, V., Zeng, W., Ke, D., Klimstra, D., Reinheckel, T., Peters, C., Hanahan, D., Joyce, J.A. Distinct roles for cysteine cathepsin genes in multistage tumorigenesis. *Genes Dev 20*: 543-556, 2006.

Gong, Y., Chang, L., Viola, K.L., Lacor, P.N., Lambert, M.P., Finch, C.E., Krafft, G.A., Klein, W.L. Alzheimer's disease-affected brain: Presence of oligomeric Aβ ligands

(ADDLs) suggests a molecular basis for reversible memory loss. *Proc. Natl. Acad. Sci. USA 100*: 10417–10422, 2003.

Gopalraj, R.K., Zhu, H., Kelly, J.F., Mendiondo, M., Pulliam, J.F., Bennett, D.A., Estus, S. Genetic association of low density lipoprotein receptor and Alzheimer's disease. *Neurobiol Aging 26*: 1-7, 2005.

Gouras, G.K., Xu, H., Jovanovic, J.N., Buxbaum, J.D., Wang, R., Greengard, P., Relkin, N.R., Gandy, S. Generation and regulation of beta-amyloid peptide variants by neurons. *J Neurochem 71*: 1920-1925, 1998.

Grubb, A., Jensson, O., Gudmundsson, G., Arnason, A., Lofberg, H., Malm, J. Abnormal metabolism of gamma-trace alkaline microprotein. The basic defect in hereditary cerebral hemorrhage with amyloidosis. *N. Engl. J. Med. 311*: 1547–1549, 1984.

Hardy, J., Selkoe, D.J. The amyloid hypothesis of Alzheimer's disease: Progress and problems on the road to therapeutics. *Science 297*: 353–356, 2002.

Hartley, D.M., Walsh, D.M., Ye, C.P., Diehl, T., Vasquez, S., Vassilev, P.M., Teplow, D.B., Selkoe, D.J. Protofibrillar intermediates of amyloid β-protein induce acute electrophysiological changes and progressive neurotoxicity in cortical neurons. *J. Neurosci. 19*: 8876–8884, 1999.

Hebert, L.E., Beckett, L.A., Scherr, P.A., Evans, D.A. Annual incidence of Alzheimer disease in the United States projected to the years 2000 through 2050. *Alzheimer Dis Assoc Disord 15*: 169-173, 2001.

Holcomb, L., Gordon, M.N., McGowan, E., Yu, X., Benkovic, S., Jantzen, P., Wright, K., Saad, I., Mueller, R., Morgan, D., Sanders, S., Zehr, C., O'Campo, K., Hardy, J., Prada, C.M., Eckman, C., Younkin, S., Hsiao, K., Duff, K. Accelerated Alzheimer-type phenotype in transgenic mice carrying both mutant amyloid precursor protein and presenilin 1 transgenes. *Nat. Med. 4*: 97–100, 1998.

Hook, V., Toneff, T., Bogyo, M., Greenbaum, D., Medzihradszky, K.F., Neveu, J., Lane, W., Hook, G., Reisine, T. Inhibition of cathepsin B reduces beta-amyloid production in regulated secretory vesicles of neuronal chromaffin cells: evidence for cathepsin B as a candidate beta-secretase of Alzheimer's disease. *Biol Chem 386*: 931-940, 2005.

Hook, V.Y., Toneff, T., Aaron, W., Yasothornsrikul, S., Bundey, R., Reisine, T. β-amyloid peptide in regulated secretory vesicles of chromaffin cells: evidence for multiple cysteine proteolytic activities in distinct pathways for β-secretase activity in chromaffin vesicles. *J. Neurochem. 81*: 237–256, 2002.

Hsia, A.Y., Masliah, E., McConlogue, L., Yu, G.Q., Tatsuno, G., Hu, K., Kholodenko, D., Malenka, R.C., Nicoll, R.A., Mucke, L. Plaque-independent disruption of neural circuits in Alzheimer's disease mouse models. *Proc. Natl. Acad. Sci. USA 96*: 3228–3233, 1999.

Iijima, K., Liu, H.P., Chiang, A.S., Hearn, S.A., Konsolaki, M., Zhong, Y. Dissecting the pathological effects of human Aβ40 and Aβ42 in Drosophila: A potential model for Alzheimer's disease. *Proc. Natl. Acad. Sci. USA 101*: 6623–6628, 2004.

Illy, C., Quraishi, O., Wang, J., Purisima, E., Vernet, T., Mort, J.S. Role of the occluding loop in cathepsin B activity. *J. Biol. Chem. 272*: 1197–1202, 1997.

Iwata, N., Mizukami, H., Shirotani, K., Takaki, Y., Muramatsu, S., Lu, B., Gerard, N.P., Gerard, C., Ozawa, K., Saido, T.C. Presynaptic localization of neprilysin contributes to efficient clearance of amyloid-beta peptide in mouse brain. *J Neurosci 24*: 991-998, 2004.

Iwata, N., Tsubuki, S., Takaki, Y., Shirotani, K., Lu, B., Gerard, N.P., Gerard, C., Hama, E., Lee, H.-J., Saido, T.C. Metabolic regulation of brain Aβ by neprilysin. *Science 292*: 1550–1552, 2001.

Iwata, N., Tsubuki, S., Takaki, Y., Watanabe, K., Sekiguchi, M., Hosoki, E., Kawashima-Morishima, M., Lee, H.J., Hama, E., Sekine-Aizawa, Y., Saido, T.C. Identification of the major Abeta1-42-degrading catabolic pathway in brain parenchyma: suppression leads to biochemical and pathological deposition. *Nat Med 6*: 143-150, 2000.

Iwatsubo, T. The gamma-secretase complex: machinery for intramembrane proteolysis. *Curr Opin Neurobiol 14*: 379-383, 2004.

Janowski, R., Kozak, M., Jankowska, E., Grzonka, Z., Grubb, A., Abrahamson, M., Jaskolski, M. Human cystatin C, an amyloidogenic protein, dimerizes through three-dimensional domain swapping. *Nat. Struct. Biol. 8*: 316–320, 2001.

Janus, C., Pearson, J., McLaurin, J., Mathews, P.M., Jiang, Y., Schmidt, S.D., Chishti, M.A., Horne, P., Heslin, D., French, J., Mount, H.T., Nixon, R.A., Mercken, M., Bergeron, C., Fraser, P.E., St George-Hyslop, P., Westaway, D. A beta peptide immunization reduces behavioural impairment and plaques in a model of Alzheimer's disease. *Nature 408*: 979-982, 2000.

Jarrett, J.T., Berger, E.P., Lansbury, P.T., Jr. The carboxy terminus of the beta amyloid protein is critical for the seeding of amyloid formation: implications for the pathogenesis of Alzheimer's disease. *Biochemistry 32*: 4693-4697, 1993.

Jensson, O., Gudmundsson, G., Arnason, A., Blondal, H., Petursdottir, I., Thorsteinsson, L., Grubb, A., Lofberg, H., Cohen, D., Frangione, B. Hereditary cystatin C (γ-trace) amyloid angiopathy of the CNS causing cerebral hemorrhage. *Acta Neurol. Scand. 76*: 102–114, 1987.

Kalback, W., Watson, M.D., Kokjohn, T.A., Kuo, Y.M., Weiss, N., Luehrs, D.C., Lopez, J., Brune, D., Sisodia, S.S., Staufenbiel, M., Emmerling, M., Roher, A.E. APP transgenic mice Tg2576 accumulate Abeta peptides that are distinct from the chemically modified and insoluble peptides deposited in Alzheimer's disease senile plaques. *Biochemistry 41*: 922-928, 2002.

Kato, D., Boatright, K.M., Berger, A.B., Nazif, T., Blum, G., Ryan, C., Chehade, K.A., Salvesen, G.S., Bogyo, M. Activity-based probes that target diverse cysteine protease families. *Nat Chem Biol 1*: 33-38, 2005.

Kayed, R., Head, E., Thompson, J.L., McIntire, T.M., Milton, S.C., Cotman, C.W., Glabe, C.G. Common structure of soluble amyloid oligomers implies common mechanism of pathogenesis. *Science 300*: 486–489, 2003.

Keppler, D., Sloane, B.F. Cathepsin B: Multiple enzyme forms from a single gene and their relation to cancer. *Enzyme Prot. 49*: 94–105, 1996.

Khouri, H.E., Plouffe, C., Hasnain, S., Hirama, T., Storer, A.C., Menard, R. A model to explain the pH-dependent specificity of cathepsin B-catalysed hydrolyses. *Biochem. J. 275* (Pt 3): 751–757, 1991.

Kingham, P.J., Pocock, J.M. Microglial secreted cathepsin B induces neuronal apoptosis. *J. Neurochem. 76*: 1475–1484, 2001.

Klein, W.L. Abeta toxicity in Alzheimer's disease: globular oligomers (ADDLs) as new vaccine and drug targets. *Neurochem Int 41*: 345-352, 2002.

Kominami, E., Ueno, T., Muno, D., Katunuma, N. The selective role of cathepsins B and D in the lysosomal degradation of endogenous and exogenous proteins. *FEBS Lett. 287*: 189–192, 1991.

Kopan, R., Goate, A. Aph-2/Nicastrin: An essential component of gamma-secretase and regulator of notch signaling and presenilin localization. *Neuron 33*: 321–324, 2002.

Lah, T.T., Buck, M.R., Honn, K.V., Crissman, J.D., Rao, N.C., Liotta, L.A., Sloane, B.F. Degradation of laminin by human tumor cathepsin B. *Clin. Metastasis 7*: 461–468, 1989.

Lambert, M.P., Barlow, A.K., Chromy, B.A., Edwards, C., Freed, R., Liosatos, M., Morgan, T.E., Rozovsky, I., Trommer, B., Viola, K.L., Wals, P., Zhang, C., Finch, C.E., Krafft, G.A., Klein, W.L. Diffusible, nonfibrillar ligands derived from Aβ1–42 are potent central nervous system neurotoxins. *Proc. Natl. Acad. Sci. USA 95*: 6448–6453, 1998.

Lambert, M.P., Viola, K.L., Chromy, B.A., Chang, L., Morgan, T.E., Yu, J., Venton, D.L., Krafft, G.A., Finch, C.E., Klein, W.L. Vaccination with soluble Aβ oligomers generates toxicity-neutralizing antibodies. *J. Neurochem. 79*: 595–605, 2001.

Leissring, M.A., Farris, W., Chang, A.Y., Walsh, D.M., Wu, X., Sun, X., Frosch, M.P., Selkoe, D.J. Enhanced proteolysis of β-amyloid in APP transgenic mice prevents plaque formation, secondary pathology, and premature death. *Neuron 40*: 1087–1093, 2003.

Lesne, S., Koh, M.T., Kotilinek, L., Kayed, R., Glabe, C.G., Yang, A., Gallagher, M., Ashe, K.H. A specific amyloid-beta protein assembly in the brain impairs memory. *Nature 440*: 352-357, 2006.

Levy, E., Lopez-Otin, C., Ghiso, J., Geltner, D., Frangione, B. Stroke in Icelandic patients with hereditary amyloid angiopathy is related to a mutation in the cystatin C gene, an inhibitor of cysteine proteases. *J. Exp. Med. 169*: 1771–1778, 1989.

Levy, E., Sastre, M., Kumar, A., Gallo, G., Piccardo, P., Ghetti, B., Tagliavini, F. Co-deposition of cystatin C with amyloid-β protein in the brain of Alzheimer disease patients. *J. Neuropathol. Neurol. 60*: 94–104, 2001.

Linebaugh, B.E., Sameni, M., Day, N.A., Sloane, B.F., Keppler, D. Exocytosis of active cathepsin B. Enzyme activity at pH 7.0, inhibition and molecular mass. *Eur. J. Biochem. 264*: 100–109, 1999.

Lleo, A., Greenberg, S.M., Growdon, J.H. Current pharmacotherapy for Alzheimer's disease. *Annu Rev Med 57*: 513-533, 2006.

Lofberg, H., Grubb, A.O. Quantitation of γ-trace in human biological fluids: Indications for production in the central nervous system. *Scand. J. Clin. Lab. Invest. 39*: 619–626, 1979.

Marr, R.A., Rockenstein, E., Mukherjee, A., Kindy, M.S., Hersh, L.B., Gage, F.H., Verma, I.M., Masliah, E. Neprilysin gene transfer reduces human amyloid pathology in transgenic mice. *J. Neurosci. 23*: 1992–1996, 2003.

Maruyama, H., Izumi, Y., Oda, M., Torii, T., Morino, H., Toji, H., Sasaki, K., Terasawa, H., Nakamura, S., Kawakami, H. Lack of an association between cystatin C gene polymorphisms in Japanese patients with Alzheimer's disease. *Neurology 57*: 337–339, 2001.

Masters, C.L., Simms, G., Weinman, N.A., Multhaup, G., McDonald, B.L., Beyreuther, K. Amyloid plaque core protein in Alzheimer disease and Down syndrome. *Proc Natl Acad Sci U S A 82*: 4245-4249, 1985.

Mattson, M.P. Pathways towards and away from Alzheimer's disease. *Nature 430*: 631–639, 2004.

Morgan, D., Diamond, D.M., Gottschall, P.E., Ugen, K.E., Dickey, C., Hardy, J., Duff, K., Jantzen, P., DiCarlo, G., Wilcock, D., Connor, K., Hatcher, J., Hope, C., Gordon, M., Arendash, G.W. A beta peptide vaccination prevents memory loss in an animal model of Alzheimer's disease. *Nature 408*: 982-985, 2000.

Mucke, L., Masliah, E., Yu, G.-Q., Mallory, M., Rockenstein, E.M., Tatsuno, G., Hu, K., Kholodenko, D., Johnson-Wood, K., McConlogue, L. High-level neuronal expression of $A\beta_{1-42}$ in wild-type human amyloid protein precursor transgenic mice: Synaptotoxicity without plaque formation. *J. Neurosci. 20*: 4050–4058, 2000.

Mueller-Steiner, S., Zhou, Y., Arai, H., Roberson, E.D., Sun, B., Chen, J., Wang, X., Yu, G., Esposito, L., Mucke, L., Gan, L. Antiamyloidogenic and neuroprotective functions of cathepsin B: implications for Alzheimer's disease. *Neuron 51*: 703-714, 2006.

Musil, D., Zucic, D., Turk, D., Engh, R.A., Mayr, I., Huber, R., Popovic, T., Turk, V., Towatari, T., Katunuma, N., et al. The refined 2.15 A X-ray crystal structure of human liver cathepsin B: The structural basis for its specificity. *EMBO J. 10*: 2321–2330, 1991.

Nagai, A., Murakawa, Y., Terashima, M., Shimode, K., Umegae, N., Takeuchi, H., Kobayashi, S. Cystatin C and cathepsin B in CSF from patients with inflammatory neurologic diseases. *Neurology 55:* 1828–1832, 2000.

Nagler, D.K., Storer, A.C., Portaro, F.C., Carmona, E., Juliano, L., Menard, R. Major increase in endopeptidase activity of human cathepsin B upon removal of occluding loop contacts. *Biochemistry 36*: 12608–12615, 1997.

O'Neil, J., Hoppe, G., Hoff, H.F. Phospholipids in oxidized low density lipoproteins perturb the ability of macrophages to degrade internalized macromolecules and reduce intracellular cathepsin B activity. *Atherosclerosis 169*: 215-224, 2003.

Palop, J.J., Chin, J., Bien-Ly, N., Massaro, C., Yeung, B.Z., Yu, G.Q., Mucke, L. Vulnerability of dentate granule cells to disruption of arc expression in human amyloid precursor protein transgenic mice. *J Neurosci 25*: 9686-9693, 2005.

Palop, J.J., Jones, B., Kekonius, L., Chin, J., Yu, G.-Q., Raber, J., Masliah, E., Mucke, L. Neuronal depletion of calcium-dependent proteins in the dentate gyrus is tightly linked to Alzheimer's disease-related cognitive deficits. *Proc. Natl. Acad. Sci. USA 100*: 9572–9577, 2003.

Palsdottir, A., Abrahamson, M., Thorsteinsson, L., Arnason, A., Olafsson, I., Grubb, A., Jensson, O. Mutation in cystatin C gene causes hereditary brain haemorrhage. *Lancet 2*: 603–604, 1988.

Price, D.L., Wong, P.C., Markowska, A.L., Lee, M.K., Thinakaren, G., Cleveland, D.W., Sisodia, S.S., Borchelt, D.R. The value of transgenic models for the study of neurodegenerative diseases. *Ann. N. Y. Acad. Sci. 920*: 179–191, 2000.

Qiu, W.Q., Walsh, D.M., Ye, Z., Vekrellis, K., Zhang, J., Podlisny, M.B., Rosner, M.R., Safavi, A., Hersh, L.B., Selkoe, D.J. Insulin-degrading enzyme regulates extracellular levels of amyloid β-protein by degradation. *J. Biol. Chem. 273*: 32730–32738, 1998.

Quraishi, O., Nagler, D.K., Fox, T., Sivaraman, J., Cygler, M., Mort, J.S., Storer, A.C. The occluding loop in cathepsin B defines the pH dependence of inhibition by its propeptide. *Biochemistry 38*: 5017–5023, 1999.

Reddy, V.Y., Zhang, Q.Y., Weiss, S.J. Pericellular mobilization of the tissue-destructive cysteine proteinases, cathepsins B, L, and S, by human monocyte-derived macrophages. *Proc. Natl. Acad. Sci. USA 92*: 3849–3853, 1995.

Roks, G., Cruts, M., Slooter, A.J., Dermaut, B., Hofman, A., Van Broeckhoven, C., Van Duijn, C.M. The cystatin C polymorphism is not associated with early onset Alzheimer's disease. *Neurology 57*: 366–367, 2001.

Rowan, A.D., Mason, P., Mach, L., Mort, J.S. Rat procathepsin B. Proteolytic processing to the mature form *in vitro*. *J. Biol. Chem. 267*: 15993–15999, 1992.

Saito, T., Iwata, N., Tsubuki, S., Takaki, Y., Takano, J., Huang, S.M., Suemoto, T., Higuchi, M., Saido, T.C. Somatostatin regulates brain amyloid beta peptide Abeta42 through modulation of proteolytic degradation. *Nat Med 11*: 434-439, 2005.

Sastre, M., Calero, M., Pawlik, M., Mathews, P.M., Kumar, A., Danilov, V., Schmidt, S.D., Nixon, R.A., Frangione, B., Levy, E. Binding of cystatin C to Alzheimer's amyloid β inhibits *in vitro* amyloid fibril formation. *Neurobiol. Aging 25*: 1033–1043, 2004.

Schenk, D., Barbour, R., Dunn, W., Gordon, G., Grajeda, H., Guido, T., Hu, K., Huang, J., Johnson-Wood, K., Khan, K., Kholodenko, D., Lee, M., Liao, Z., Lieberburg, I., Motter, R., Mutter, L., Soriano, F., Shopp, G., Vasquez, N., Vandevert, C., Walker, S., Wogulis, M., Yednock, T., Games, D., Seubert, P. Immunization with amyloid-β attenuates Alzheimer-disease-like pathology in the PDAPP mouse. *Nature 400*: 173–177, 1999.

Schweizer, A., Valdenaire, O., Nelbock, P., Deuschle, U., Dumas Milne Edwards, J.B., Stumpf, J.G., Loffler, B.M. Human endothelin-converting enzyme (ECE-1): three isoforms with distinct subcellular localizations. *Biochem J 328* (Pt 3): 871-877, 1997.

Selkoe, D., Kopan, R. Notch and Presenilin: Regulated intramembrane proteolysis links development and degeneration. *Annu. Rev. Neurosci. 26*: 565–597, 2003.

Selkoe, D.J. Clearing the brain's amyloid cobwebs. *Neuron 32*: 177-180, 2001.

Shibata, M., Yamada, S., Kumar, S.R., Calero, M., Bading, J., Frangione, B., Holtzman, D.M., Miller, C.A., Strickland, D.K., Ghiso, J., Zlokovic, B.V. Clearance of Alzheimer's amyloid-ss(1-40) peptide from brain by LDL receptor-related protein-1 at the blood-brain barrier. *J Clin Invest 106*: 1489-1499, 2000.

Sisodia, S.S., St George-Hyslop, P.H. γ-secretase, notch, Aβ and Alzheimer's disease: Where do the presenilins fit in? *Nat. Rev. Neurosci. 3*: 281–290, 2002.

Sloane, B.F., Yan, S., Podgorski, I., Linebaugh, B.E., Cher, M.L., Mai, J., Cavallo-Medved, D., Sameni, M., Dosescu, J., Moin, K. Cathepsin B and tumor proteolysis: contribution of the tumor microenvironment. *Semin Cancer Biol 15*: 149-157, 2005.

St George-Hyslop, P., Haines, J., Rogaev, E., Mortilla, M., Vaula, G., Pericak-Vance, M., Foncin, J.F., Montesi, M., Bruni, A., Sorbi, S. Genetic evidence for a novel familial Alzheimer's disease locus on chromosome 14. *Nat. Genet. 2*: 330–334, 1992.

Tagawa, K., Maruyama, K., Ishiura, S. Amyloid β/A4 precursor protein (APP) processing in lysosomes. *Ann. N. Y. Acad. Sci. 674*: 129–137, 1992.

Takahashi, R.H., Almeida, C.G., Kearney, P.F., Yu, F., Lin, M.T., Milner, T.A., Gouras, G.K. Oligomerization of Alzheimer's β-amyloid within processes and synapses of cultured neurons and brain. *J. Neurosci.* 24: 3592–3599, 2004.

Takio, K., Towatari, T., Katunuma, N., Titani, K. Primary structure study of rat liver cathepsin B—a striking resemblance to papain. *Biochem. Biophys. Res. Commun.* 97: 340–346, 1980.

Tanzi, R.E., Bertram, L. Twenty years of the Alzheimer's disease amyloid hypothesis: a genetic perspective. *Cell 120*: 545-555, 2005.

Tanzi, R.E., Vaula, G., Romano, D.M., Mortilla, M., Huang, T.L., Tupler, R.G., Wasco, W., Hyman, B.T., Haines, J.L., Jenkins, B.J., et al. Assessment of amyloid β-protein precursor gene mutations in a large set of familial and sporadic Alzheimer disease cases. *Am. J. Hum. Genet. 51*: 273–282, 1992.

Taupin, P., Ray, J., Fischer, W.H., Suhr, S.T., Hakansson, K., Grubb, A., Gage, F.H. FGF-2-responsive neural stem cell proliferation requires CCg, a novel autocrine/paracrine cofactor. *Neuron 28*: 385–397, 2000.

Terry, R.D., Masliah, E., Salmon, D.P., Butters, N., DeTeresa, R., Hill, R., Hansen, L.A., Katzman, R. Physical basis of cognitive alterations in Alzheimer's disease: Synapse loss is the major correlate of cognitive impairment. *Ann. Neurol. 30*: 572–580, 1991.

Tsai, J.Y., Wolfe, M.S., Xia, W. The search for gamma-secretase and development of inhibitors. *Curr Med Chem 9*: 1087-1106, 2002.

Tsujinaka, T., Ebisui, C., Fujita, J., Morimoto, T., Ogawa, A., Ishidoh, K., Kominami, E., Yano, M., Shiozaki, H., Monden, M. Autocatalytic inactivation of lysosomal cathepsins is associated with inhibition of protein breakdown by insulin-like growth factor-1 (IGF-1) in myotubes. *Biochem. Biophys. Res. Commun. 208*: 353–359, 1995.

Tucker, H.M., Kihiko, M., Caldwell, J.N., Wright, S., Kawarabayashi, T., Price, D., Walker, D., Scheff, S., McGillis, J.P., Rydel, R.E., Estus, S. The plasmin system is induced by and degrades amyloid-beta aggregates. *J Neurosci 20*: 3937-3946, 2000.

Tucker, H.M., Kihiko-Ehmann, M., Wright, S., Rydel, R.E., Estus, S. Tissue plasminogen activator requires plasminogen to modulate amyloid-beta neurotoxicity and deposition. *J Neurochem 75*: 2172-2177, 2000.

Turk, B., Bieth, J.G., Bjork, I., Dolenc, I., Turk, D., Cimerman, N., Kos, J., Colic, A., Stoka, V., Turk, V. Regulation of the activity of lysosomal cysteine proteinases by pH-induced inactivation and/or endogenous protein inhibitors, cystatins. *Biol. Chem. Hoppe Seyler 376*: 225–230, 1995.

Vassar, R. The β-secretase, BACE: A prime drug target for Alzheimer's disease. *J. Mol. Neurosci. 17*: 157–170, 2001.

Vassar, R., Bennett, B.D., Babu-Khan, S., Kahn, S., Mendiaz, E.A., Denis, P., Teplow, D.B., Ross, S., Amarante, P., Loeloff, R., Luo, Y., Fisher, S., Fuller, J., Edenson, S., Lile, J., Jarosinski, M.A., Biere, A.L., Curran, E., Burgess, T., Louis, J.C., Collins, F., Treanor, J., Rogers, G., Citron, M. β-secretase cleavage of Alzheimer's amyloid precursor protein by the transmembrane aspartic protease BACE. *Science 286*: 735–741, 1999.

Walsh, D.M., Klyubin, I., Fadeeva, J.V., Cullen, W.K., Anwyl, R., Wolfe, M.S., Rowan, M.J., Selkoe, D.J. Naturally secreted oligomers of amyloid β protein potently inhibit hippocampal long-term potentiation *in vivo*. *Nature 416*: 535–539, 2002.

Walsh, D.M., Selkoe, D.J. Deciphering the molecular basis of memory failure in Alzheimer's disease. *Neuron 44*: 181-193, 2004.

Wang, H.W., Pasternak, J.F., Kuo, H., Ristic, H., Lambert, M.P., Chromy, B., Viola, K.L., Klein, W.L., Stine, W.B., Krafft, G.A., Trommer, B.L. Soluble oligomers of β amyloid (1–42) inhibit long-term potentiation but not long-term depression in rat dentate gyrus. *Brain Res. 924*: 133–140, 2002.

Warfel, A.H., Zucker-Franklin, D., Frangione, B., Ghiso, J. Constitutive secretion of cystatin C (gamma-trace) by monocytes and macrophages and its downregulation after stimulation. *J. Exp. Med. 166*: 1912–1917, 1987.

Wolfe, M.S., Xia, W., Ostaszewski, B.L., Diehl, T.S., Kimberly, W.T., Selkoe, D.J. Two transmembrane aspartates in presenilin-1 required for presenilin endoproteolysis and γ-secretase activity. *Nature 398*: 513–517, 1999.

Wong, P.C., Cai, H., Borchelt, D.R., Price, D.L. Genetically engineered mouse models of neurodegenerative diseases. *Nat Neurosci 5*: 633-639, 2002.

Yamin, R., Malgeri, E.G., Sloane, J.A., McGraw, W.T., Abraham, C.R. Metalloendopeptidase EC 3.4.24.15 is necessary for Alzheimer's amyloid-beta peptide degradation. *J Biol Chem 274*: 18777-18784, 1999.

Yan, P., Hu, X., Song, H., Yin, K., Bateman, R.J., Cirrito, J.R., Xiao, Q., Hsu, F.F., Turk, J.W., Xu, J., Hsu, C.Y., Holtzman, D.M., Lee, J.M. Matrix metalloproteinase-9 degrades amyloid-beta fibrils in vitro and compact plaques in situ. *J Biol Chem* 2006.

Yan, S., Berquin, I.M., Troen, B.R., Sloane, B.F. Transcription of human cathepsin B is mediated by Sp1 and Ets family factors in glioma. *DNA Cell Biol. 19*: 79–91, 2000.

Yan, S., Jane, D.T., Dufresne, M.J., Sloane, B.F. Transcription of cathepsin B in glioma cells: regulation by an E-box adjacent to the transcription initiation site. *Biol Chem 384*: 1421-1427, 2003.

Yan, S., Sloane, B.F. Isolation of a novel USF2 isoform: repressor of cathepsin B expression. *Gene 337*: 199-206, 2004.

Yin, K.J., Cirrito, J.R., Yan, P., Hu, X., Xiao, Q., Pan, X., Bateman, R., Song, H., Hsu, F.F., Turk, J., Xu, J., Hsu, C.Y., Mills, J.C., Holtzman, D.M., Lee, J.M. Matrix metalloproteinases expressed by astrocytes mediate extracellular amyloid-beta peptide catabolism. *J Neurosci 26*: 10939-10948, 2006.

Younkin, S.G. The amyloid β protein precursor mutations linked to familial Alzheimer's disease alter processing in a way that fosters amyloid deposition. *Tohoku J. Med. 174*: 217–223, 1994.

Yu, G., Nishimura, M., Arawaka, S., Levitan, D., Zhang, L., Tandon, A., Song, Y.Q., Rogaeva, E., Chen, F., Kawarai, T., Supala, A., Levesque, L., Yu, H., Yang, D.S., Holmes, E., Milman, P., Liang, Y., Zhang, D.M., Xu, D.H., Sato, C., Rogaev, E., Smith, M., Janus, C., Zhang, Y., Aebersold, R., Farrer, L.S., Sorbi, S., Bruni, A., Fraser, P., St George-Hyslop, P. Nicastrin modulates presenilin-mediated notch/glp-1 signal transduction and betaAPP processing. *Nature 407*: 48-54, 2000.

Zeng, J., Dunlop, R.A., Rodgers, K.J., Davies, M.J. Evidence for inactivation of cysteine proteases by reactive carbonyls via glycation of active site thiols. *Biochem J* 2006.

Zhang, Y., McLaughlin, R., Goodyer, C., LeBlanc, A. Selective cytotoxicity of intracellular amyloid β peptide1–42 through p53 and Bax in cultured primary human neurons. *J. Cell Biol.* *156*: 519–529, 2002.

Zwicky, R., Muntener, K., Csucs, G., Goldring, M.B., Baici, A. Exploring the role of 5' alternative splicing and of the 3'-untranslated region of cathepsin B mRNA. *Biol Chem* *384*: 1007-1018, 2003.

In: Research Progress in Alzheimer's Disease and Dementia   ISBN 978-1-60021-960-3
Editor: Miao-Kun Sun, pp. 303-328   © 2008 Nova Science Publishers, Inc.

Chapter XI

ENVIRONMENTAL ENRICHMENT: FROM MOUSE AD MODEL TO AD THERAPY

Orly Lazarov[1,] and John Larson[2]*

[1]Department of Anatomy and Cell Biology, College of Medicine, University of Illinois at Chicago, Chicago, IL 60612, USA;
[2]Psychiatric Institute, Department of Psychiatry, College of Medicine, University of Illinois at Chicago, Chicago, IL 60612, USA.

Alzheimer's disease (AD), the most prevalent form of age-related dementia, is characterized by memory impairment, cognitive decline, and the appearance of specific neuropathologies including amyloid plaques and neurofibrillary tangles. Transgenic mice based on familial forms of AD develop amyloid plaques and are used as models for the disease. It is widely believed that stimulation of cognitive activity is an effective strategy to prevent the age-related neurodegeneration, including that which occurs in AD. Here we review evidence now accumulating that indicates that environmental experience can modulate the appearance of amyloid pathology in mouse models of AD. We first discuss the effects of enriched environmental experience on brain structure, function, and behavior. We then describe studies that have examined the effects of environmental enrichment on neuropathology and behavioral impairments in mouse models for AD and discuss experimental variables that may influence environmental effects on amyloid pathology. Finally, we discuss possible mechanisms for experiential modulation of amyloid metabolism. These include changes in processing of the amyloid precursor protein as well as alterations in b-amyloid peptide secretion, aggregation, degradation, and clearance. Understanding the mechanisms by which environmental stimulation can prevent, retard, or reverse neuropathology should lead to development of effective therapeutic strategies for AD and other age-related diseases.

---

* Correspondence concerning this article should be addressed to: Orly Lazarov, Department of Anatomy and Cell Biology, College of Medicine, University of Illinois at Chicago, Chicago, IL 60612, Email: olazarov@uic.edu.

INTRODUCTION

The concept of "use it or lose it" applied to the human brain makes a lot of intuitive sense. Entropy affects everything in our natural and artificial worlds; basic upkeep is necessary to prevent disorder brought about by the ravages of time. The benefits of physical fitness for prevention of age-related illnesses are undeniable and it is natural to think that mental fitness would have comparable advantages for prevention of age-related neurodegeneration. Alzheimer's disease (AD), the most prevalent form of dementia, is characterized by memory impairment and cognitive decline. Strategies for mental hygiene are in common use in hopes of preventing the occurrence of the disorder. But how do we ascertain the most effective tactics for prevention of age-related neurodegenerative disease? Controlled clinical trials are problematic for a disease that may take years to decades to become apparent and the best we can hope for from post-hoc analyses of lifestyle factors are correlations with many confounding variables. Animal models can be very useful for identification of key variables by which environment and experience affect disease occurrence and progression.

Most cases of AD occur late in life and have an unknown origin. The familial, early-onset form of Alzheimer's disease (FAD) is caused by mutations in three genes that encode the amyloid precursor protein (APP), presenilin 1 (PS1), and presenilin 2 (PS2); APP is the precursor of β-amyloid (Aβ) peptides that, under pathological circumstances, aggregate and deposit in the brains of individuals affected with the disease (Selkoe, 2001). Amyloid deposits are one of the hallmarks of AD (Price et al., 1998b). The neuropathological outcome of FAD and sporadic cases are indistinguishable. Transgenic mice expressing one or more of the FAD-linked mutant genes develop neuropathology similar to AD and are used as models for the disease (Price et al., 1998a). Recent work indicates that enriched environment experience can attenuate AD-associated pathology in transgenic mice models for AD. Specifically, experience in enriched, complex environments for prolonged periods (months) can reduce the appearance of amyloid plaques and result in lower steady-state levels of Aβ peptides in the brain. In addition, experience in enriched environmental conditions improves learning and memory in FAD-linked mice. In this chapter, we will review the evidence for experiential modification of amyloid metabolism, discuss the potential environmental factors involved, and speculate on the underlying neural mechanisms.

ENVIRONMENTAL ENRICHMENT

In *The Organization of Behavior: a Neuropsychological Theory*, Donald Hebb (1949) described an experiment in which he and his young daughters adopted seven rats at an early age (shortly after weaning) and raised them at home as pets with the rats being "out of their cages a good deal of the time and running about the house" (p. 298). A control group of 25 rats were maintained in the laboratory colony under the usual laboratory conditions (Hebb, 1949). Tests in what has come to be known as the Hebb-Williams maze (Hebb and Williams, 1946) showed the pet rats to be superior not only in the initial series of behavioral tests, but they also improved more than the controls across repeated testing sessions. Hebb's students,

Forgays and Forgays (1952) and Hymovitch (1952) conducted more controlled laboratory experiments in which several rats were reared together in a large (7500 cm²) "free environment box" containing maze elements, "playthings", inclined planes, and so forth and were compared to rats having varied forms of more restricted experience. Using the Hebb-Williams maze, they found a dramatic enhancement of learning in the rats with free environment experience (Forgays and Forgays, 1952). Significantly, rats given access to running wheels but without access to the free environment or its social stimulation had maze learning scores equivalent to rats reared in similarly restrictive cages without opportunities for voluntary exercise (Hymovitch, 1952).

These studies inspired a series of experiments conducted at the University of California at Berkeley by a group consisting primarily of Mark Rosenzweig, Edward Bennett, David Krech, and Marian Diamond. In their standard paradigm, rats given "environmental complexity" (EC) treatment were housed in large bi-level cages containing several rats together with inanimate stimulus objects (toys, running wheels, ladder, climbing platforms, etc.) that were changed every day; the rats were also allowed a period of daily exploration in a complex maze. In early experiments, EC rats were also trained extensively on complex maze problems and visual discriminations. Rats with enriched environment experience were compared with rats housed in an "impoverished condition" (IC), isolated in cages with opaque walls in a quiet room. Initially interested in neurochemical changes induced by EC experience and training (Krech et al., 1960), they soon found that changes in brain weight were confounding their measurements of acetylcholinesterase (Rosenzweig et al., 1962). A series of replications confirmed that EC experience resulted in small but highly reliable increases in the weight and thickness of the cerebral cortex (Bennett et al., 1964b). As they put it, "Our results appear to provide the first demonstration, to our knowledge, of physical changes in the brain as a consequence of modification of experience." [(Krech et al., 1960), p. 516]. The findings were apparently met with a certain amount of skepticism (Rosenzweig, 1996), but the Berkeley group conducted many replications and extensions of the original experiments (Rosenzweig et al., 1972) and sensory deprivation effects on brain development also were reported at about the same time [e.g., (Wiesel and Hubel, 1965)]. The tide turned and experience-induced brain plasticity became an accepted concept.

Over the years, the "enriched" or "complex" environment paradigm has been very extensively used to investigate brain plasticity and learning. It was originally developed in order to provide animals with more varied experience and constant opportunities for learning than would be possible in more formalized training experiments. The consequences of environmental enrichment on brain structure, function, and behavior are profound and can be induced throughout the lifespan. The effects of enrichment on brain structure are widespread but not universal: in experiments with large sample sizes, the Berkeley group found significant effects of experience on weight and thickness of all cortical areas, which they subdivided into specific samples of sensory cortex (visual and somesthetic), remaining dorsal cortex, and a ventral cortex sample including piriform cortex and the hippocampal formation [e.g., (Bennett et al., 1964a)]. However, subcortical regions were unaffected on these gross measures. At the cellular level, a series of studies by Greenough and others (Volkmar and Greenough, 1972; Greenough and Volkmar, 1973; Greenough et al., 1973; Connor et al., 1981; Wallace et al., 1992) established that enriched experience leads to more profuse dendritic branching and longer dendrites in cortical neurons. Most of the studies have focused on the occipital cortex, but changes in dendritic branching have also been observed in temporal (Greenough et al., 1973) and parietal (Leggio et al., 2005), but not frontolateral (Greenough et al., 1973) areas. Experience can induce changes specific to certain parts of a neuron, for example, basal dendrites and not apical dendrites. However, it should be kept in mind that negative results may be due to failure to detect changes that are subtle or have high variability. Selective effects may favor specific synaptic changes rather than whole-cell modifications. Measurements of spine density suggested that enrichment induces synaptogenesis (Globus et al., 1973) and electron microscopic studies confirmed that neurons in cortex of animals with enrichment experience have more synapses per neuron than their standard housing counterparts (Turner and Greenough, 1985; Jones et al., 1997; Briones et al., 2004).

The traditional interpretation of structural changes is that they reflect learning and information storage (Rosenzweig et al., 1972; Greenough, 1976). This interpretation is strengthened by the finding that similar changes (e.g., dendritic branching) can be induced by formalized training on specific behavioral tasks (Greenough et al., 1979; Chang and Greenough, 1982; Greenough et al., 1985; Withers and Greenough, 1989), although perhaps more limited in extent.

Behavioral studies confirmed the earlier reports (Hebb, 1947; Forgays and Forgays, 1952; Hymovitch, 1952) that enriched environmental experience facilitates maze learning (Krech et al., 1962). This has now been extended to many other learning tasks involving spatial memory, working memory, and problem solving [see (Renner and Rosenzweig, 1987) for review].

The mechanisms by which environmental enrichment alters brain structure and function are not well understood. As noted above, one possibility is that the enriched environment stimulates learning, and the structural changes result from synaptic plasticity associated with learning. Long-term potentiation (LTP) of synaptic efficacy is the best understood candidate mechanism for synaptic plasticity underlying learning and memory formation (Martin et al., 2000). LTP is associated with dendritic spine shape changes and synaptogenesis; these effects are consistent with the structural effects of environmental enrichment (Lee et al., 1980; Chang and Greenough, 1984; Jones et al., 1997; Harris et al., 2003). Electrophysiological studies have shown that enriched environment experience can result in potentiation of synaptic responses in the hippocampal formation (Green and Greenough, 1986; Foster et al., 1996; Foster et al., 2000; Irvine et al., 2006) and alter LTP induced by electrical stimulation (Foster et al., 1996; van Praag et al., 1999; Foster et al., 2000; Duffy et al., 2001; Irvine et al., 2006). Both the anatomical and electrophysiological findings are consistent with the hypothesis that an LTP-like learning mechanism is stimulated by environmental enrichment.

An alternative hypothesis is that enrichment promotes neural plasticity more generally. Greenough first suggested that mechanisms responsible for growth and plasticity during development may be activated in response to experience in adulthood (Greenough, 1978). Environmental enrichment has been shown to increase levels of growth factors in brain, including nerve growth factor (NGF) (Torasdotter et al., 1998; Pham et al., 1999; Ickes et al., 2000), neurotrophin-3 [NT-3;(Torasdotter et al., 1996)], and brain-derived neurotrophic factor [BDNF; (Falkenberg et al., 1992)]. Levels of immediate-early gene products c-fos

(Puurunen et al., 2001) and Arc (Pinaud et al., 2001) are also reported to increase with enriched environment experience. Arc and c-fos are both induced by stimulation patterns that induce LTP (Steward et al., 1998); inhibition of Arc or the three growth factors inhibits LTP. The two means by which enrichment could act outlined here are, of course, not mutually exclusive.

In any case, the enriched environment paradigm can be used not only to reveal mechanisms of brain plasticity engaged by environmental experience but also as a tool for activating those mechanisms in animals that have learning and memory impairments. In this context, it becomes important to identify the aspects of enrichment experience that are necessary and sufficient to reverse the impairments. This may not be easy. In an enriched environment, the animal is exposed to and can interact with a complex array of stimuli, is allowed more freedom to move and exercise, and is provided more social stimulation than animals housed in standard laboratory conditions. The essential complexity of the environment makes it difficult to specify which aspects of the environment promote distinct brain mechanisms. We will return to this issue when we discuss findings from studies of enrichment in mouse models for AD.

ENVIRONMENT, AGING AND AD

A growing body of evidence suggests that "the fountain of youth" may be the motivation to stay active. Learning and exercising are proving to be invaluable in supporting and maintaining our minds and bodies in a healthy state (Fratiglioni et al., 2004). Numerous studies report the benefits of physical activity in the elderly. These studies suggest an inverse relation between exercise and physical dysfunction, cardiovascular disorders, mortality, depression, and cognitive decline (Leon, 1985; Powell et al., 1986; Blair et al., 1989; Blumenthal et al., 1991; Paffenbarger et al., 1995; Churchill et al., 2002; Lord et al., 2003; Colcombe et al., 2004b; Colcombe et al., 2004a; Lytle et al., 2004; Taylor et al., 2004).

It has become increasingly clear that this attitude and life-style may also prevent aging-related diseases, including neurodegenerative diseases, AD in particular (Larson and Wang, 2004; Larson et al., 2006). Exercise training is reported to increase physical function and health status while decreasing depression in AD patients (Teri et al., 2003) and to increase mental and cognitive function in individuals with dementia (Heyn et al., 2004). Years of formal education and extent of AD pathology were both found to be related to level of cognitive function in the Religious Orders Study, where older Catholic clergy underwent annual cognitive function testing and brain autopsy at the time of death (Bennett et al., 2005). Previous investigations as well as other studies also support the conclusion that extent of education and high mental activity throughout life correlates with reduced risk for AD (Stern et al., 1994; Snowdon et al., 1996; Evans et al., 1997; Letenneur et al., 1999; Friedland et al., 2001; Wilson et al., 2002).

While encouraging and promising, studies performed in humans are limited in their ability to attribute cognitive effects to a specific experience, because of the complexity of the human life. In addition, these studies are restricted in their ability to correlate enriched physical and/or mental experience with progression of pathology and with neuronal and metabolic pathways affected by physical or mental activity. In these terms, behavioral studies in animal models of different neuropathologies and neurodegenerative diseases are an invaluable tool that may provide significant insight into these crucial questions. It should be noted that experience in enriched environmental conditions and exercising on the running wheel ameliorate neuropathology in several animal models of neurodegenerative diseases, such as Huntington's disease and Parkinson's disease (van Dellen et al., 2000; Hockly et al., 2002; Bezard et al., 2003; Tillerson et al., 2003; Glass et al., 2004; Spires et al., 2004; Faherty et al., 2005; Zhu et al., 2005), as well as recovery following brain trauma (Rampon et al., 2000; Kline et al., 2007; Lippert-Gruener et al., 2007; Pereira et al., 2007).

In this chapter, we focus on observations obtained in AD animal models.

ENRICHED ENVIRONMENT IN ANIMAL MODELS OF AD

The apparently beneficial effect of exercise and cognitive stimulation in humans calls for the examination of experience and environmental factors in the etiology of neurodegenerative diseases, including AD. The beneficial effect of "enriched" or "complex" environments on synaptic plasticity and cognitive function brought this experimental paradigm into focus as an appropriate model for these investigations. Several studies have been performed during the last few years examining the effect of enriched environmental experience on AD-associated neuropathology. These studies have used different genetic mouse models for AD, and the parameters of environmental experience manipulation have varied widely. It is perhaps not surprising that different studies have reported different outcomes. Nevertheless, these results inevitably emphasize the significance of environmental factors as modulators of protein metabolism, neuronal signaling pathways and gene expression, and as such, major players in the development of Alzheimer's disease-associated neuropathology. It further exemplifies the complexity of environmental factors and the multiple signaling pathways they regulate. We will first describe our own work showing that enriched environmental experience can reduce the appearance of amyloid pathology and then discuss other studies on the effects of environmental experience in animal models for AD.

Current usage of terms is anything but standard. We will refer to groups with special experience as the "experience condition" (EC) and control groups as "inexperience condition" (IC).

We used male transgenic mice harboring two FAD-linked mutant transgenes, the Swedish APP mutation (APPswe) and the PS1 exon 9 deletion (PS1ΔE9). These mice normally exhibit amyloid deposits throughout the hippocampus and cortex at four and a half to five months of age. We compared transgenic mice housed under standard conditions (IC) in groups of three or four per cage for five months immediately after weaning with transgenic mice given environmental enrichment (EC) experience. The enriched environment consisted of a large cage with two running wheels, colored tunnels, balls, nesting material, and other objects. An episodic enrichment procedure was used in which EC mice were allowed to explore the enriched environment, in groups of three or four, for three hours each day for the first month and for three hours a day, three days a week for the remaining four months.

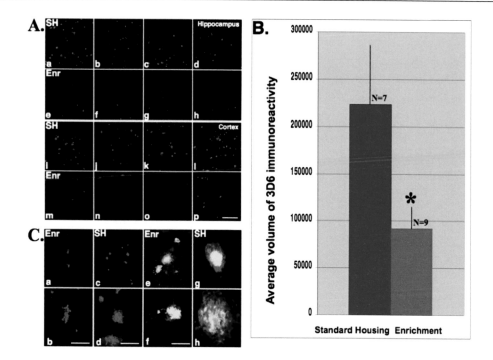

Figure 1. Reduced Amyloid Deposition in the Hippocampus and Cortex of Enriched versus Standard Housing Mice. (A) Immunohistochemical analysis of brain sections of standard housing (SH, [Aa]–[Ad], hippocampus; [Ai]–[Al], cortex) and enriched mice (Enr, [Ae]–[Ah], hippocampus; [Am]–[Ap], cortex) immunolabeled with anti-Aβ 3D6 antibodies. Pictures were taken from four enriched and four standard housing mice. Scale bar, 250μm. (B) Quantitative analysis of volume of amyloid burden in brains of standard housing and enriched mice. Volume is in arbitrary units (mean cubic pixels ± SE, ANOVA, p =0.0374). (C) Reduced number and size of thioflavine S-stained amyloid deposits in the hippocampus and cortex of enriched versus standard housing mice. Thioflavine S-positive amyloid deposits in brain sections of enriched (Enr; Ca, Cb, Ce, and Cf) and standard housing mice (SH; Cc, Cd, Cg, Ch). Size and abundance of thioflavine-positive structures in enriched (a = low power; b = high power) is reduced compared to standard housing mice (c = low power; d = high power). For (Ca) and (Cc), scale bar, 250μm. For (Cb) and (Cd), scale bar, 120μm. Double labeling with thioflavine S and anti-Aβ 3D6 antibodies reveals overlap staining at the core of the amyloid deposits, while the periphery of the deposit is stained mostly with anti-Aβ 3D6 antibodies (Cg and Ch). In contrast, the vast majority of amyloid deposits in brain sections of enriched mice had little 3D6-positive peripheral staining (Ce and Cf). Scale bar, 60μm. [Taken from (Lazarov et al., 2005a)].

Note that two hours daily enriched environment experience for as few as 30 days was shown to be sufficient to induce significant brain weight changes (Rosenzweig et al., 1968). Immunohistochemical and quantitative imaging analyses of brain sections of these animals revealed that mice with enriched environment experience exhibited significantly reduced amyloid deposition in the hippocampus and cortex compared to the standard housing group [Figure 1, (Lazarov et al., 2005a)]. Furthermore, by measuring the time mice spent in running wheels included in the enriched environments, we established a strong negative correlation between the level of motor activity and the extent of amyloid deposition in the enriched mice. We also measured steady-state levels of Aβ peptides in detergent-soluble and formic acid-soluble forebrain extracts and found them to be greatly reduced in EC mice (Figure 2). On the other hand, we found no evidence for altered APP processing in mice after enrichment experience: steady-state levels of APP, soluble APP derivatives, and membrane-tethered APP carboxyl-terminal fragments (APP-CTFs) were no different in EC and IC transgenic mice. Intriguingly, activity levels of the Aβ-degrading enzyme neprilysin [NEP, (Hersh, 2003; Marr et al., 2003; Marr et al., 2004)] were elevated in brains of enriched APPsweXPS1ΔE9 mice. Finally, microarray analysis revealed increased expression of genes implicated in learning and memory, neurogenesis, vasculogenesis and Aβ sequestration in the brains of enriched mice before the onset of amyloid deposition. These included significant elevations of messages for BDNF, the early growth response-1 (EGR-1) transcription factor, and the serum and glucocorticoid-inducible protein kinase [SGK, (Lazarov et al., 2005a)].

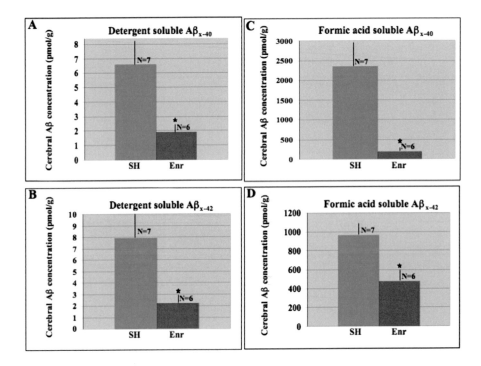

Figure 2. Reduced Steady-State Levels of Cerebral Aβ in the Brains of Enriched Mice. Cerebral steady state levels of $Aβ_{x-40/42}$ were quantified by sandwich ELISA. Levels of $Aβ_{x-40}$ and $Aβ_{x-42}$ were significantly reduced in both detergent-soluble (A and B) and formic acid-soluble (C and D) brain extracts of enriched mice (Enr) compared to standard housing (SH) mice (mean ± SE, ANOVA; for (A), p % 0.0287; for (B), p % 0.02228; for (C), p % 0.0404; for (D), p % 0.0010). [Taken from (Lazarov et al., 2005a)].

In contrast, Jankowsky and colleagues (2003) had reported that enriched environment experience *increases* amyloid pathology in transgenic mice. They compared female mice with APPswe and PS1ΔE9 transgenes that were housed in groups of three to four in standard cages (IC) from two to eight and a half months of age with similar transgenic mice given continuous enrichment experience (EC) for the same time period. EC consisted of 16 mice in a large cage with two running wheels, plastic tubes and hutches, cardboard boxes, and nesting material, all changed or rearranged once a week. Mice with enrichment experience had significantly more brain amyloid deposits and higher steady-state Aβ levels than did IC mice (Jankowsky et al., 2003).

The very different outcome of these two studies suggests that environmental experience can modify amyloid metabolism in opposite ways, depending on the nature of the experience. It therefore becomes important to consider the different aspects of enrichment paradigms that may impact on the development of pathology. One potential variable is stress: enrichment experience is generally thought to reduce stress levels, although this is usually in comparison to animals housed in isolation (Greenough, 1976). Indeed, enriched environmental experience can reverse synaptic plasticity and cognitive deficits induced in animals by stress early in life (Cui et al., 2006) and there are indications that chronic stress can exacerbate amyloid pathology in mouse models for AD (Jeong et al., 2006). It is perhaps significant that the EC mice in the Jankowsky (2003) study were not maintained as a stable group throughout the enrichment period: mice were removed for histological examination and new mice added as replacements periodically. Such group reorganization is a well-characterized model for inducing sustained social stress (Blanchard et al., 2003; Sapolsky, 1993). A more recent study by the same group (Jankowsky et al., 2005) found similar elevations of Aβ levels and amyloid deposition in APPswe/PS1ΔE9 transgenic mice housed together as a stable cohort during enrichment experience. Despite the elevation of amyloid, mice with EC experience had better scores on spatial learning tests than their IC counterparts.

A second potentially important variable is the opportunity afforded for voluntary motor activity. As noted above, we observed the lowest amyloid deposition in mice that were most active in the running wheels present in the enriched environment (Lazarov et al., 2005a). We provided a running wheel for each 1-2 mice in the enrichment cage; Jankowsky, et al. (2003; 2005) provided one wheel for every eight mice in the enriched environment. The role of motor activity was addressed directly in another study (Adlard et al., 2005b). Female TgCRND8 mice harboring an APP transgene containing both the Swedish (KM670/671NL) and Indiana (V717F) mutations were housed singly in a cage equipped with a running wheel for five months starting at one month of age (EC). They were compared with transgenic mice similarly housed in isolation but without access to a running wheel (IC). Aβ staining in cortex and hippocampus was significantly reduced in the mice with running wheel access. This decrease in amyloid deposition was paralleled by a decrease in total formic acid-extractable Aβ. Examination of the expression of APP metabolites in the brains of these mice revealed no change in levels of full-length APP or APP-CTFs. However, animals that were given access to the running wheel for only a single month showed a dramatic decrease in the levels of both α- and β-APP-CTFs. In addition, the investigators observed a large but nonsignificant decrease in formic acid-extractable Aβ $_{1-40}$ and Aβ $_{1-42}$. This decrease was not accompanied by a change in expression levels of either NEP or insulin-degrading enzyme (IDE, another enzyme implicated in Aβ degradation) in the brains of these mice. However, enzymatic activity of NEP and IDE were not assessed. Exercising animals also showed improved performance in a spatial learning task (Adlard et al., 2005b). Overall, it appears that voluntary motor activity over a prolonged period can reduce amyloid deposition to an extent similar to that we observed after EC experience. However, the effects of isolation housing should also be considered. It is possible that isolation might exacerbate amyloid deposition. If this were the case, the effect of motor activity might be to counteract, for example, the stress of isolation.

Gender may also be an important consideration. Several of the studies have used female mice to circumvent aggressive behaviors that can occur in socially-housed male mice (Jankowsky et al., 2003; Arendash et al., 2004; Jankowsky et al., 2005; Ambree et al., 2006; Costa et al., 2006; Wolf et al., 2006). It should be noted that there is a clear, but poorly understood, enhancement of amyloid burden in female transgenic mice compared to age-matched males (Wang et al., 2003), that might be related to the well-documented higher incidence of AD observed in women (Jorm et al., 1987; Katzman et al., 1989). Another important variable may be the size of the social group in the enrichment condition or group size relative to the size of the environment. Ambree and colleagues (2006) observed decreases in amyloid deposition in female TgCRND8 mice given continuous enrichment experience in groups of three to four mice each (Ambree et al., 2006). This contrasts to the large group size (16) used in the Jankowsky, et al. (2003; 2005) studies. In the Ambree et al. (2006) experiment, one-month old mice were housed in standard conditions, three to four per cage (IC), or given enrichment experience (EC) for four months. The enriched environment contained nesting material, a plastic inset, and a wooden scaffolding and a tunnel that led to a second "stimulus" cage containing novel objects such as a running wheel, ladders, ramps, tunnels, and so forth. Mice were permitted to enter the stimulus cage only at night and the objects in it were changed daily. Enriched mice had significantly fewer amyloid deposits in neocortex and hippocampus as well as reduced cerebral amyloid angiopathy. The investigators reported no changes in levels of soluble $A\beta_{1-40}$ or $A\beta_{1-42}$. Likewise, there were no changes in levels of full-length APP or APP-CTFs between EC and IC mice. Interestingly, the investigators did find an increase in levels of F4/80 antigen, a 160 KDa glycoprotein specifically expressed in microglia, in protein extracts prepared from the brains of EC mice. Microarray analysis revealed that gene products involved in the proinflammatory response such as chemokine [C–C motif] ligand 2 (*Ccl2* or *MCP-1*) were downregulated, while anti-inflammatory associated genes such as *Cd22*26 or protein tyrosine phosphatase, nonreceptor type 2 (*Ptpn2*)27 were up-regulated in brains of enriched mice. These findings suggest that experience in the enriched environment reduces "cytotoxic effects" of inflammation while increasing microglial phagocytic activity, an effect that could be beneficial for $A\beta$ clearance. Microarray analysis further revealed two hundred thirty genes that are differentially expressed in the brains of mice in the two experimental conditions. Categorizing these genes revealed that signaling pathways associated with inflammation, proteasomal degradation, and cholesterol homeostasis may be modulated in the brain following experience in the enriched environment.

Whereas Ambree et al (2006) observed similar reductions in amyloid pathology after enrichment as in our own study, two other groups have reported no change in amyloid deposition after extensive periods of enrichment experience. Costa and collaborators (2006) studied mice with APP (V717F) and PS1 (M146L) mutant transgenes, housed either in isolation as the standard housing control (IC) or in an enriched environment from weaning until 5.5-6.5 months of age. The enriched environment (EC) held 6-8 male or female mice and contained a plastic rodent house containing running wheels, platforms, toys, huts and enclosures; some of the items were changed weekly. EC mice were also removed from the EC three times a week to explore one of several novel environments for several hours. Half of the animals in each housing condition were tested in a battery of (mainly) spatial learning tasks between 4.5 and 6 months of age, while the other half remained in their respective housing conditions to control for effects of behavioral testing on neuropathology and gene expression. There were three major findings: First, EC mice performed better in the learning tasks than IC mice; indeed their performance on some tasks was indistinguishable from non-transgenic controls. Second, amyloid deposition in hippocampus and cortex was reduced in EC mice, but only those that were trained on the battery of behavioral tasks. Third, microarray analysis indicated that EC mice exhibited increased expression of genes linked to synaptic plasticity-related processes and $A\beta$ sequestration. The results of this study suggest that experience in the enriched environment can protect against Alzheimer's-like cognitive impairment, and that both amyloid-independent and amyloid-dependent mechanisms may be involved in that protection.

This fascinating study raises several important questions. First, why was there no effect of enrichment alone on amyloid deposition? The EC paradigm does not seem different in any important way from that used by Ambree et al (2006), although distinct from ours in that continuous enrichment was used. Still, both the Ambree and the Costa enrichment regimens had features that introduced episodic novelty: nocturnal access to a separate stimulus cage (Ambree et al., 2006) or periodic exploration of novel environments (Costa et al., 2006). Second, there was an interaction between EC and formal behavioral training: in terms of reduction of amyloid burden, only the EC mice benefited from training on a series of spatial learning problems. Traditionally, enrichment effects have been interpreted in terms of activating similar plasticity mechanisms as behavioral training (Rosenzweig et al., 1972). Third, variability in amyloid deposition was substantially larger in the IC groups: is this related to their isolation housing? Could there be opposing effects of training, due to the prior history (stress levels) of the animals?

In an attempt to separate cognitive and motor aspects of enrichment experience, Wolf and colleagues (2006) housed female APP23 mice (APPswe transgene) under three different conditions: one group (EC) had continuous enrichment experience as a group in a large cage with typical enrichment items such as tubes, ladders, a cardboard box, and a crawling ball, but explicitly without any running wheels; a control group (IC) was housed in standard cages without any stimulus items; the third group (RW) was housed with continuous access to a running wheel attached to the home cage. Differential housing began at 10 weeks of age and was maintained for 11 months. The mice were then tested for learning with the Morris water maze and for locomotor ability on a rotorod. After the behavioral tests, mice were returned to their differential environments and given a series of bromo-deoxyuridine (BrdU) injections for assessment of neurogenesis. Mice were sacrificed and examined histologically at 13 months of age. There were no group differences in neuritic plaque load as measured by thioflavin-S staining in hippocampal formation or cortex among the different treatment groups. Spatial learning was enhanced in the EC group but not the RW group. However, both the EC and RW groups performed better on the rotorod than the IC group. Although the treatment groups did not differ in the number of BrdU-labeled cells in dentate gyrus, the number of calretinin-expressing cells was increased in the EC group. Finally, EC mice showed increased expression of BDNF and NT-3 mRNA in hippocampus but not cortex; RW mice showed lower hippocampal fibroblast growth factor-2 (FGF-2) mRNA expression and reduced cortical BDNF, FGF-2, and NGF mRNA expression (Wolf et al., 2006).

This experiment provides evidence that behavioral improvements can be induced by enrichment without evident effect on amyloid deposition. Whether or not amyloid deposits at such late ages are sensitive enough measures to reveal effects of enrichment is yet to be determined. The lack of effect of the exercise factor is also puzzling: access to running wheels in the absence of other stimuli did not reduce amyloid deposition. At the same time, enrichment without running wheel access also had no effect on deposition.

Another factor that should be considered is duration of exposure to enriched environment and when experience in enriched environmental conditions takes place in relation to onset of deposition. Arendash and colleagues (Arendash et al., 2004) tested the effect of experience in an enriched environment on aging APPswe mice. Mice were given continuous enrichment (EC) beginning at 16 months of age, after onset of amyloid deposition. During this time, mice were also placed in novel complex environments 3 times weekly for several hours; the whole EC treatment lasted four months. Following that, animals were tested in four cognitive tests for two months. This study revealed improved cognitive function, as indicated by improved performance on the Morris water maze, circular platform, platform recognition, and radial arm water maze, in spite of no change in extent of amyloid deposition.

In summary, recent studies have documented highly beneficial effects of environmental enrichment for transgenic mice that are models for AD. A summary of these studies and their findings is presented in Table 1. Enriched environmental experience significantly improves learning and memory abilities of these mice on a number of tasks. This is exciting but perhaps not surprising, since enrichment experience has similar effects in non-transgenic mice. FAD-linked transgenic mice are impaired on a number of these behavioral tasks, so they have more room for improvement after enrichment experience. What is surprising, though, is that amyloid metabolism appears to be modulated by experience. Three studies found significant reductions in amyloid pathology in brains of transgenic mice with enrichment experience (Lazarov et al., 2005a; Ambree et al., 2006; Costa et al., 2006) and a fourth found amyloid reduction after a period of voluntary wheel running (Adlard et al., 2005b). However, decreased amyloid pathology has not always been observed after environmental enrichment (Arendash et al., 2004; Wolf et al., 2006); under certain conditions, enrichment can even increase amyloid deposition (Jankowsky et al., 2003; Jankowsky et al., 2005). Enrichment paradigms are by definition complex and it appears that the nature of the enrichment experience can have profound effects on the development of amyloid pathology. Further work will be necessary to resolve the key features of enrichment experience that protect animals from developing AD-like neuropathology.

Table 1. Effects of environmental enrichment and voluntary exercise on learning and amyloid deposition in FAD-linked transgenic mice

Subjects		Number		Enrichment Experience			Effects		
Genotype	Sex	IC	EC	Pattern	Period	Special Conditions	Amyloid deposition	Learning	Reference
APP(K670N/M671L) + PS1(dE9)	M	3-4	3-4	Episodic	1-6 mo.	2-3 running wheels; 3 hrs per day enrichment	Decrease	N.A.	Lazarov, 2005
APP(K670N/M671L) + PS1(dE9)	F	3-4	16	Continuous	2-8.5 mo.	2 running wheels; unstable population, large groups	Increase	N.A.	Jankowsky, 2003
APP(K670N/M671L) + PS1(dE9)	F	3-4	16	Continuous	2-8.5 mo.	2 running wheels; large groups	Increase	Improved	Jankowsky, 2005
APP(K670N/M671L/ V717F)	F	3-4	3-4	Continuous	1-5 mo.	Nocturnal stimulus cage	Decrease	Improved	Ambree, 2006
APP(V717F) + PS1(M146L)	MF	1	6-8	Continuous	1-6 mo.	Episodic exploration	Decrease	Improved	Costa, 2006
APP(K670N/M671L)	F	?	?	Continuous	2.5-13 mo.	No running wheel	No change	Improved	Wolf, 2006
APP(K670N/M671L)	?	4	5	Continuous	16-22 mo.	Novelty 3 times a week	No change	Improved	Arendash, 2004
APP(K670N/ M671L/V717F)	F	1	1	Continuous	1.5-6.5 mo.	Running wheel only	Decrease	Improved	Adlard, 2005

Columns under IC and EC denote number of mice housed per cage. N.A.: not applicable. Entries with question marks denote information not provided in the paper.

THE MECHANISM(S) UNDERLYING THE EFFECT OF ENRICHED ENVIRONMENT ON AD PATHOLOGY: IMPLICATIONS FOR THERAPEUTIC STRATEGIES IN HUMANS

Exposure of animals to an enriched environment promotes sensory, motor, cognitive, and social activity and facilitates or reinforces a variety of behaviors including exploration, orientation, learning, social interactions, and physical activity [For review see (van Praag et al., 2000; Benefiel et al., 2005)]. As discussed above, the mechanisms underlying experience-induced brain plasticity are not well understood. It is likely that the complexity of the environment affects multiple pathways in the brain. Indeed, environmental enrichment has been shown to have a positive impact on both morphological and physiological properties in many regions, including auditory cortex (Engineer et al., 2004), sensorimotor cortex (Coq and Xerri, 1998, 2001; Godde et al., 2002), visual cortex (Beaulieu and Cynader, 1990), associative parietal cortex (Frick et al., 2003) and the hippocampal formation (Kempermann et al., 1998; Frick et al., 2003). It would be of great interest to identify neuronal pathways and cellular mechanisms activated in the brains of AD animal models following experience in the enriched environment or voluntary exercising on the running wheel. There is general agreement that enriched environmental experience enhances cognitive function and learning ability in FAD-linked transgenic mice whether or not the experience reduces amyloid deposition. These findings are in harmony with the clinical and epidemiological studies suggesting that sustained mental and cognitive activity is self-reinforcing in humans. The effects of enrichment experience on amyloid pathology appear to be more sensitive to the nature and conditions of the experience. We have attempted to identify aspects of the enrichment experience that may be important for modulation of amyloid metabolism. It appears that the cognitive effects of enrichment are less sensitive to these variables; this may indicate that experience has more pervasive effects on cellular mechanisms of learning and memory than on the cellular mechanisms that regulate amyloid deposition. It is likely that enrichment experience in complex environments triggers cellular changes in the brain along multiple parallel pathways. A good example of this is the finding that mice lacking NMDA receptors in field CA1 have learning deficits that can be reversed by environmental enrichment (Rampon, et al., 2000). Clearly, enrichment stimulates utilization of learning mechanisms that would not be used by animals with more restricted experience. Another example is a recent study showing that exposure of CK-p25 transgenic mice exhibiting advanced neurodegeneration to enriched environment results in restoration of learning and in the ability to access long-term memory (Fischer et al., 2007). This study suggests that enriched environment induces plasticity mechanisms that can be upregulated even after synaptic and neuronal loss had already occurred, which might resemble advanced cases of AD, and that these plastic changes are sufficient to retrieve memory that could not be used otherwise.

Activation of mechanisms that can protect the brain from neurodegeneration is of the greatest interest. Although the necessary and sufficient conditions have not yet been specified, it is clear that both enriched environment and exercise on the running wheel modulate amyloid metabolism. To develop an equivalent therapeutic strategy in humans it is crucial to fully understand the aspects of enrichment experience that lead to modification of amyloid metabolism. In addition, it would be important to correlate animal behavior in the enriched environment with amyloid pathology. There appear to be important ways in which individual animals interact with the environment that influence amyloid metabolism. Information about levels of soluble-aggregated species of Aβ following experience in enriched conditions may enable us a better correlation between modulation of amyloid metabolism and learning and memory capability in AD transgenic mice (Ashe, 2006b, a; Lesne et al., 2006). This information is lacking in most studies so far, and would be valuable in future studies.

One approach to gain insight into the mechanisms underlying enrichment-induced facilitation of learning and modulation of amyloid metabolism is to assess changes in gene expression patterns following enrichment. Microarray analysis of gene expression in our young FAD-linked APPsweXPS1ΔE9 transgenic mice following experience in enriched environmental conditions revealed upregulation of genes implicated in learning and memory processes (Lazarov et al., 2005a). For example, expression of the immediate early genes (IEG) Arc, Nur77 and Zif268 were significantly higher in EC than in IC mice. Expression of these genes is markedly downregulated in FAD-linked transgenic mice harboring mutant APP and PS1 compared to nontransgenic control mice (Dickey et al., 2003; Dickey et al., 2004). In addition, increased expression of SGK was observed following enrichment (Lazarov et al., 2005a). SGK is a kinase linked to spatial learning and LTP (Ma et al., 2006). These observations provide the first clues for understanding the facilitation of learning that occurs in FAD-linked mice following experience in enriched environmental conditions (Arendash et al., 2004; Jankowsky et al., 2005; Costa et al., 2006; Wolf et al., 2006). Increased expression levels of calcium/calmodulin-dependent protein kinase II (CamKII) may also account for increased performance in learning and memory tasks (Lledo et al., 1995; Costa et al., 2006). Pharmacological inhibition of CaMKII prevents LTP induction (Malenka et al., 1989) and both LTP and spatial learning are severely disrupted in mice with targeted mutations of the CamKII α-subunit (Silva et al., 1992a; Silva et al., 1992b).

Increased expression of brain-derived neurotrophic factor (BDNF) has been observed in rodents including FAD-linked mice following exposure to different environmental conditions (Adlard et al., 2004; Adlard et al., 2005a; Lazarov et al., 2005a). BDNF is implicated in long-term synaptic plasticity in the adult hippocampus (Kovalchuk et al., 2002; Pang and Lu, 2004; Pang et al., 2004; Rex et al., 2007). Intriguingly, BDNF enhances Arc expression in synaptoneurosomes (Yin et al., 2002). In agreement with that, BDNF levels, as well as levels of IGF-1, FGF-2, VEGF, NGF and NT-3 were increased in the brains of aging FAD-linked mice following experience in enriched environmental conditions (Wolf et al., 2006). Upregulation of genes implicated in neurogenesis and vasculogenesis have also been observed in the brains of younger FAD-linked mice following environmental enrichment (Lazarov et al., 2005a).

Neurogenesis is another form or manifestation of plasticity in the adult brain. Increases in the number of new neurons are observed in the dentate gyrus following either experience in enriched environmental conditions or voluntary exercise on the running wheel. However, while environmental enrichment increases progenitor cell survival, running activity increases both proliferation and survival of newly-generated progenitor cells in mice, suggesting that the two experiential manipulations might activate different signaling pathways [For review see (van Praag et al., 2000)]. Because the hippocampus is one of the major areas affected in AD, it would be interesting to examine possible cross talk between AD pathology, and amyloidosis in particular, and hippocampal neurogenesis following enrichment. Evidence that comes from a single study examining hippocampal neurogenesis in FAD-linked mice shows increase in the number of calretinin-expressing cells in the brains of FAD-linked APP23 mice following long-term continuous environmental enrichment without running wheels (Wolf et al., 2006).

Microarray analysis in older mice that were exposed to enriched environmental conditions following onset of amyloid deposition revealed increased expression of genes encoding proteins implicated in blood brain barrier (BBB) permeability, as well as genes encoding NF-kappaB inhibitors (Costa et al., 2006). Taken together, these observations may suggest alterations in the extent of inflammatory reactions in the brain. Interestingly, Ambree and colleagues suggest that it is the phenotype of inflammatory cells that is altered following experience in an enriched environment, leading to reduced expression and secretion of cytotoxic components that may enhance $A\beta$ aggregation, and increased phagocytic activity that may result in clearance of amyloid deposits (Ambree et al., 2006).

Further evidence concerning the mechanism(s) underlying experience-induced modification of amyloid metabolism comes from Adlard and colleagues that show alterations in APP processing following exercise on the running wheel (Adlard et al., 2005b). Examination of APP processing in TgCRND8 mice that were allowed one month of voluntary exercise revealed a dramatic reduction in expression of both α- and β-APP-CTFs. This reduction was not evident in mice that experienced five months of running (Adlard et al., 2005b), suggesting a dynamic and transient effect of exercise on APP processing, ultimately leading to reductions in amyloid deposition (Adlard et al., 2005b).

It is well established that APP is transported to nerve terminals by fast axonal transport (Amaratunga and Fine, 1995; Buxbaum et al., 1998; Lazarov et al., 2005b) and that $A\beta$ is released and deposited at synaptic sites (Lazarov et al., 2002; Sheng et al., 2002). Evidence further suggests that APP metabolism, as well as $A\beta$ secretion can be modulated by synaptic activity (Nitsch et al., 1993; Huber et al., 1997; Kamenetz et al., 2003; Cirrito et al., 2005). If enhancement of synaptic activity occurs following exposure to enriched environment, it would be reasonable to speculate that this process might result in increased secretion of $A\beta$. This may lead subsequently to aggregation of $A\beta_{42}$ peptides, and as a result, to induction of NEP levels/activity, leading to increased degradation of $A\beta$ peptides. Support for this hypothesis comes from the finding that injection of aggregated $A\beta_{42}$ peptides into brains of APPswe-expressing mice leads to upregulation in endogenous NEP levels in neurons, and reduction of plaque burden in older animals (Mohajeri et al., 2002). Indeed, NEP activity levels were elevated in brains of APPsweXPS1ΔE9 mice following experience in enriched environmental conditions (Lazarov et al., 2005a). Upregulation of NEP levels may account for, at least in part, the reduction in levels of $A\beta$ observed in this study. Equally feasible is that enrichment induces NEP activity by mechanisms independent of $A\beta$ modulation. In this regard, a recent study shows that somatostatin (SST) regulates the activity of NEP (Saito et al., 2005). This finding is of interest in view of the observation that exposure of rats to an enriched environment leads to upregulation of SST expression in brain (Nilsson et al., 1993). Intriguingly, experience in enriched environmental conditions has been shown to induce activation of a variety of proteins and activities that play a role in $A\beta$ sequestration pathways, such as transthyretin (Lazarov et al., 2005a; Ambree et al., 2006). In support of the notion that $A\beta$ clearance mechanisms are modulated by experience, evidence from transgenic mice suggests that cognitive effects of environmental enrichment are influenced by expression of specific APOE isoforms (Levi et al., 2003). Taken together, this evidence suggests that experience in the enriched environment alters the equilibrium between $A\beta$ production, secretion, degradation and clearance.

In summary, studies in animal models of AD indicate that experience in enriched environments can activate signaling pathways that lead to enhanced learning and memory, reduced soluble Aβ in brain, and decreased amyloid deposition. Although further work will be necessary to characterize the aspects of enrichment experience that produce these effects and the cellular pathways that mediate them, there are indications that they involve synaptic plasticity mechanisms, Aβ processing pathways, and possibly, interactions between the two. Continued study should provide a firm empirical basis for a strategy to prevent, retard, or reverse neurodegenerative disease in old age by stimulation of cognitive activity. This could also lead to discovery of pharmacological means to enhance the process by promoting cellular mechanisms that mediate environmental effects on amyloid metabolism. Use of animal models in which other AD-related effects are pronounced such as tau pathology (Billings et al., 2007) would also be important in this regard.

REFERENCES

Adlard PA, Perreau VM, Cotman CW (2005a) The exercise-induced expression of BDNF within the hippocampus varies across life-span. *Neurobiol Aging 26*:511-520.

Adlard PA, Perreau VM, Engesser-Cesar C, Cotman CW (2004) The timecourse of induction of brain-derived neurotrophic factor mRNA and protein in the rat hippocampus following voluntary exercise. *Neurosci Lett 363*:43-48.

Adlard PA, Perreau VM, Pop V, Cotman CW (2005b) Voluntary exercise decreases amyloid load in a transgenic model of Alzheimer's disease. *J Neurosci 25*:4217-4221.

Amaratunga A, Fine RE (1995) Generation of amyloidogenic C-terminal fragments during rapid axonal transport in vivo of beta-amyloid precursor protein in the optic nerve. *J Biol Chem 270*:17268-17272.

Ambree O, Leimer U, Herring A, Gortz N, Sachser N, Heneka MT, Paulus W, Keyvani K (2006) Reduction of amyloid angiopathy and Abeta plaque burden after enriched housing in TgCRND8 mice: involvement of multiple pathways. *Am J Pathol 169*:544-552.

Arendash GW, Garcia MF, Costa DA, Cracchiolo JR, Wefes IM, Potter H (2004) Environmental enrichment improves cognition in aged Alzheimer's transgenic mice despite stable beta-amyloid deposition. *Neuroreport 15*:1751-1754.

Ashe KH (2006a) In search of the molecular basis of memory loss in Alzheimer disease. *Alzheimer Dis Assoc Disord 20*:200-201.

Ashe KH (2006b) Molecular basis of memory loss in the Tg2576 mouse model of Alzheimer's disease. *J Alzheimers Dis 9*:123-126.

Beaulieu C, Cynader M (1990) Effect of the richness of the environment on neurons in cat visual cortex. II. Spatial and temporal frequency characteristics. *Brain Res Dev Brain Res 53*:82-88.

Benefiel AC, Dong WK, Greenough WT (2005) Mandatory " enriched" housing of laboratory animals: the need for evidence-based evaluation. *Ilar J 46*:95-105.

Bennett DA, Schneider JA, Wilson RS, Bienias JL, Arnold SE (2005) Education modifies the association of amyloid but not tangles with cognitive function. *Neurology 65*:953-955.

Bennett EL, Krech D, Rosenzweig MR (1964a) Reliability and Regional Specificity of Cerebral Effects of Environmental Complexity and Training. *J Comp Physiol Psychol 57*:440-441.

Bennett EL, Diamond MC, Krech D, Rosenzweig MR (1964b) Chemical and Anatomical Plasticity Brain. *Science 146*:610-619.

Bezard E, Dovero S, Belin D, Duconger S, Jackson-Lewis V, Przedborski S, Piazza PV, Gross CE, Jaber M (2003) Enriched environment confers resistance to 1-methyl-4-phenyl-1,2,3,6-tetrahydropyridine and cocaine: involvement of dopamine transporter and trophic factors. *J Neurosci 23*:10999-11007.

Billings LM, Green KN, McGaugh JL, LaFerla FM (2007) Learning decreases Abeta*56 and tau pathology and ameliorates behavioral decline in 3xTg-AD mice. *J Neurosci 27*:751-761.

Blair SN, Kohl HW, 3rd, Paffenbarger RS, Jr., Clark DG, Cooper KH, Gibbons LW (1989) Physical fitness and all-cause mortality. A prospective study of healthy men and women. *Jama 262*:2395-2401.

Blanchard RJ, Wall PM, Blanchard DC (2003) Problems in the study of rodent aggression. *Horm Behav 44*:161-170.

Blumenthal JA, Emery CF, Madden DJ, Coleman RE, Riddle MW, Schniebolk S, Cobb FR, Sullivan MJ, Higginbotham MB (1991) Effects of exercise training on cardiorespiratory function in men and women older than 60 years of age. *Am J Cardiol 67*:633-639.

Briones TL, Klintsova AY, Greenough WT (2004) Stability of synaptic plasticity in the adult rat visual cortex induced by complex environment exposure. *Brain Res 1018*:130-135.

Buxbaum JD, Thinakaran G, Koliatsos V, O'Callahan J, Slunt HH, Price DL, Sisodia SS (1998) Alzheimer amyloid protein precursor in the rat hippocampus: transport and processing through the perforant path. *J Neurosci 18*:9629-9637.

Chang FL, Greenough WT (1982) Lateralized effects of monocular training on dendritic branching in adult split-brain rats. *Brain Res 232*:283-292.

Chang FL, Greenough WT (1984) Transient and enduring morphological correlates of synaptic activity and efficacy change in the rat hippocampal slice. *Brain Res 309*:35-46.

Churchill JD, Galvez R, Colcombe S, Swain RA, Kramer AF, Greenough WT (2002) Exercise, experience and the aging brain. *Neurobiol Aging 23*:941-955.

Cirrito JR, Yamada KA, Finn MB, Sloviter RS, Bales KR, May PC, Schoepp DD, Paul SM, Mennerick S, Holtzman DM (2005) Synaptic activity regulates interstitial fluid amyloid-beta levels in vivo. *Neuron 48*:913-922.

Colcombe SJ, Kramer AF, McAuley E, Erickson KI, Scalf P (2004a) Neurocognitive aging and cardiovascular fitness: recent findings and future directions. *J Mol Neurosci 24*:9-14.

Colcombe SJ, Kramer AF, Erickson KI, Scalf P, McAuley E, Cohen NJ, Webb A, Jerome GJ, Marquez DX, Elavsky S (2004b) Cardiovascular fitness, cortical plasticity, and aging. *Proc Natl Acad Sci U S A 101*:3316-3321.

Connor JR, Melone JH, Yuen AR, Diamond MC (1981) Dendritic length in aged rats' occipital cortex: an environmentally induced response. *Experimental neurology 73*:827-830.

Coq JO, Xerri C (1998) Environmental enrichment alters organizational features of the forepaw representation in the primary somatosensory cortex of adult rats. *Exp Brain Res 121*:191-204.

Coq JO, Xerri C (2001) Sensorimotor experience modulates age-dependent alterations of the forepaw representation in the rat primary somatosensory cortex. *Neuroscience 104*:705-715.

Costa DA, Cracchiolo JR, Bachstetter AD, Hughes TF, Bales KR, Paul SM, Mervis RF, Arendash GW, Potter H (2006) Enrichment improves cognition in AD mice by amyloid-related and unrelated mechanisms. *Neurobiol Aging.*

Cui M, Yang Y, Yang J, Zhang J, Han H, Ma W, Li H, Mao R, Xu L, Hao W, Cao J (2006) Enriched environment experience overcomes the memory deficits and depressive-like behavior induced by early life stress. *Neurosci Lett 404*:208-212.

Dickey CA, Loring JF, Montgomery J, Gordon MN, Eastman PS, Morgan D (2003) Selectively reduced expression of synaptic plasticity-related genes in amyloid precursor protein + presenilin-1 transgenic mice. *J Neurosci 23*:5219-5226.

Dickey CA, Gordon MN, Mason JE, Wilson NJ, Diamond DM, Guzowski JF, Morgan D (2004) Amyloid suppresses induction of genes critical for memory consolidation in APP + PS1 transgenic mice. *J Neurochem 88*:434-442.

Duffy SN, Craddock KJ, Abel T, Nguyen PV (2001) Environmental enrichment modifies the PKA-dependence of hippocampal LTP and improves hippocampus-dependent memory. *Learn Mem 8*:26-34.

Engineer ND, Percaccio CR, Pandya PK, Moucha R, Rathbun DL, Kilgard MP (2004) Environmental enrichment improves response strength, threshold, selectivity, and latency of auditory cortex neurons. *J Neurophysiol 92*:73-82.

Evans DA, Hebert LE, Beckett LA, Scherr PA, Albert MS, Chown MJ, Pilgrim DM, Taylor JO (1997) Education and other measures of socioeconomic status and risk of incident Alzheimer disease in a defined population of older persons. *Arch Neurol 54*:1399-1405.

Faherty CJ, Raviie Shepherd K, Herasimtschuk A, Smeyne RJ (2005) Environmental enrichment in adulthood eliminates neuronal death in experimental Parkinsonism. *Brain Res Mol Brain Res 134*:170-179.

Falkenberg T, Mohammed AK, Henriksson B, Persson H, Winblad B, Lindefors N (1992) Increased expression of brain-derived neurotrophic factor mRNA in rat hippocampus is associated with improved spatial memory and enriched environment. *Neurosci Lett 138*:153-156.

Fischer A, Sananbenesi F, Wang X, Dobbin M, Tsai LH (2007) Recovery of learning and memory is associated with chromatin remodelling.

Forgays DG, Forgays JW (1952) The nature of the effect of free-environmental experience in the rat. *J Comp Physiol Psychol 45*:322-328.

Foster TC, Gagne J, Massicotte G (1996) Mechanism of altered synaptic strength due to experience: relation to long-term potentiation. *Brain Res 736*:243-250.

Foster TC, Fugger HN, Cunningham SG (2000) Receptor blockade reveals a correspondence between hippocampal-dependent behavior and experience-dependent synaptic enhancement. *Brain Res 871*:39-43.

Fratiglioni L, Paillard-Borg S, Winblad B (2004) An active and socially integrated lifestyle in late life might protect against dementia. *Lancet Neurol* 3:343-353.

Frick KM, Stearns NA, Pan JY, Berger-Sweeney J (2003) Effects of environmental enrichment on spatial memory and neurochemistry in middle-aged mice. *Learn Mem* 10:187-198.

Friedland RP, Fritsch T, Smyth KA, Koss E, Lerner AJ, Chen CH, Petot GJ, Debanne SM (2001) Patients with Alzheimer's disease have reduced activities in midlife compared with healthy control-group members. *Proc Natl Acad Sci U S A* 98:3440-3445.

Glass M, van Dellen A, Blakemore C, Hannan AJ, Faull RL (2004) Delayed onset of Huntington's disease in mice in an enriched environment correlates with delayed loss of cannabinoid CB1 receptors. *Neuroscience 123*:207-212.

Globus A, Rosenzweig MR, Bennett EL, Diamond MC (1973) Effects of differential experience on dendritic spine counts in rat cerebral cortex. *Journal of comparative and physiological psychology 82*:175-181.

Godde B, Berkefeld T, David-Jurgens M, Dinse HR (2002) Age-related changes in primary somatosensory cortex of rats: evidence for parallel degenerative and plastic-adaptive processes. *Neurosci Biobehav Rev* 26:743-752.

Green EJ, Greenough WT (1986) Altered synaptic transmission in dentate gyrus of rats reared in complex environments: evidence from hippocampal slices maintained in vitro. *J Neurophysiol 55*:739-750.

Greenough WT (1976) Enduring brain effects of differential experience and training. In *Neural Mechanisms of Learning and Memory*. M.R.Rosenzweig and E.L.Bennett, eds. (Cambridge, MA: MIT Press):255-278.

Greenough WT (1978) Development and memory: the synaptic connection. In: *Brain and learning* (Teyler T, ed). Stamford, CT: Greylock.

Greenough WT, Volkmar FR (1973) Pattern of dendritic branching in occipital cortex of rats reared in complex environments. *Exp Neurol* 40:491-504.

Greenough WT, Volkmar FR, Juraska JM (1973) Effects of rearing complexity on dendritic branching in frontolateral and temporal cortex of the rat. *Experimental neurology 41*:371-378.

Greenough WT, Juraska JM, Volkmar FR (1979) Maze training effects on dendritic branching in occipital cortex of adult rats. *Behav Neural Biol* 26:287-297.

Greenough WT, Larson JR, Withers GS (1985) Effects of unilateral and bilateral training in a reaching task on dendritic branching of neurons in the rat motor-sensory forelimb cortex. *Behav Neur Biol 44*:301-314.

Harris KM, Fiala JC, Ostroff L (2003) Structural changes at dendritic spine synapses during long-term potentiation. *Philos Trans R Soc Lond B Biol Sci 358*:745-748.

Hebb DO (1947) The effects of early experience on problem-solving at maturity. *Am Psychol* 2:306-307.

Hebb DO (1949) The organization of Behavior. *A Neuropsychological Theory*. Wiley, New York.

Hebb DO, Williams KA (1946) A method of rating animal intelligence. *JJ Gen Psychol 34*:59-65.

Hersh LB (2003) Peptidases, proteases and amyloid beta-peptide catabolism. *Curr Pharm Des 9*:449-454.

Heyn P, Abreu BC, Ottenbacher KJ (2004) The effects of exercise training on elderly persons with cognitive impairment and dementia: a meta-analysis. *Arch Phys Med Rehabil 85*:1694-1704.

Hockly E, Cordery PM, Woodman B, Mahal A, van Dellen A, Blakemore C, Lewis CM, Hannan AJ, Bates GP (2002) Environmental enrichment slows disease progression in R6/2 Huntington's disease mice. *Ann Neurol 51*:235-242.

Huber G, Bailly Y, Martin JR, Mariani J, Brugg B (1997) Synaptic beta-amyloid precursor proteins increase with learning capacity in rats. *Neuroscience 80*:313-320.

Hymovitch B (1952) The effects of experimental variations on problem solving in the rat. *J Comp Physiol Psychol 45*:313-321.

Ickes BR, Pham TM, Sanders LA, Albeck DS, Mohammed AH, Granholm AC (2000) Long-term environmental enrichment leads to regional increases in neurotrophin levels in rat brain. *Exp Neurol 164*:45-52.

Irvine GI, Logan B, Eckert M, Abraham WC (2006) Enriched environment exposure regulates excitability, synaptic transmission, and LTP in the dentate gyrus of freely moving rats. *Hippocampus 16*:149-160.

Jankowsky JL, Xu G, Fromholt D, Gonzales V, Borchelt DR (2003) Environmental enrichment exacerbates amyloid plaque formation in a transgenic mouse model of Alzheimer disease. *J Neuropathol Exp Neurol 62*:1220-1227.

Jankowsky JL, Melnikova T, Fadale DJ, Xu GM, Slunt HH, Gonzales V, Younkin LH, Younkin SG, Borchelt DR, Savonenko AV (2005) Environmental enrichment mitigates cognitive deficits in a mouse model of Alzheimer's disease. *J Neurosci 25*:5217-5224.

Jeong YH, Park CH, Yoo J, Shin KY, Ahn SM, Kim HS, Lee SH, Emson PC, Suh YH (2006) Chronic stress accelerates learning and memory impairments and increases amyloid deposition in APPV717I-CT100 transgenic mice, an Alzheimer's disease model. *Faseb J 20*:729-731.

Jones TA, Klintsova AY, Kilman VL, Sirevaag AM, Greenough WT (1997) Induction of multiple synapses by experience in the visual cortex of adult rats. *Neurobiol Learn Mem 68*:13-20.

Jorm AF, Korten AE, Henderson AS (1987) The prevalence of dementia: a quantitative integration of the literature. *Acta Psychiatr Scand 76*:465-479.

Kamenetz F, Tomita T, Hsieh H, Seabrook G, Borchelt D, Iwatsubo T, Sisodia S, Malinow R (2003) APP processing and synaptic function. *Neuron 37*:925-937.

Katzman R, Aronson M, Fuld P, Kawas C, Brown T, Morgenstern H, Frishman W, Gidez L, Eder H, Ooi WL (1989) Development of dementing illnesses in an 80-year-old volunteer cohort. *Ann Neurol 25*:317-324.

Kempermann G, Kuhn HG, Gage FH (1998) Experience-induced neurogenesis in the senescent dentate gyrus. *J Neurosci 18*:3206-3212.

Kline AE, Wagner AK, Westergom BP, Malena RR, Zafonte RD, Olsen AS, Sozda CN, Luthra P, Panda M, Cheng JP, Aslam HA (2007) Acute treatment with the 5-HT(1A) receptor agonist 8-OH-DPAT and chronic environmental enrichment confer neurobehavioral benefit after experimental brain trauma. *Behav Brain Res 177*:186-194.

Kobayashi S, Ohashi Y, Ando S (2002) Effects of enriched environments with different durations and starting times on learning capacity during aging in rats assessed by a refined procedure of the Hebb-Williams maze task. *Journal of neuroscience research* *70*:340-346.

Kovalchuk Y, Hanse E, Kafitz KW, Konnerth A (2002) Postsynaptic Induction of BDNF-Mediated Long-Term Potentiation. *Science 295*:1729-1734.

Krech D, Rosenzweig MR, Bennett EL (1960) Effects of environmental complexity and training on brain chemistry. *Journal of comparative and physiological psychology 53*:509-519.

Krech D, Rosenzweig MR, Bennett EL (1962) Relations between chemistry and problem-solving among rats raised in enriched and impoverished environments. *J Comp Physiol Psychol 55* 801-807.

Larson EB, Wang L (2004) Exercise, aging, and Alzheimer disease. *Alzheimer Dis Assoc Disord 18*:54-56.

Larson EB, Wang L, Bowen JD, McCormick WC, Teri L, Crane P, Kukull W (2006) Exercise is associated with reduced risk for incident dementia among persons 65 years of age and older. *Ann Intern Med 144*:73-81.

Lazarov O, Lee M, Peterson DA, Sisodia SS (2002) Evidence that synaptically released beta-amyloid accumulates as extracellular deposits in the hippocampus of transgenic mice. *J Neurosci 22*:9785-9793.

Lazarov O, Robinson J, Tang YP, Hairston IS, Korade-Mirnics Z, Lee VM, Hersh LB, Sapolsky RM, Mirnics K, Sisodia SS (2005a) Environmental enrichment reduces Abeta levels and amyloid deposition in transgenic mice. *Cell 120*:701-713.

Lazarov O, Morfini GA, Lee EB, Farah MH, Szodorai A, DeBoer SR, Koliatsos VE, Kins S, Lee VM, Wong PC, Price DL, Brady ST, Sisodia SS (2005b) Axonal transport, amyloid precursor protein, kinesin-1, and the processing apparatus: revisited. *The Journal of neuroscience 25*:2386-2395.

Lee KS, Schottler F, Oliver M, Lynch G (1980) Brief bursts of high-frequency stimulation produce two types of structural change in rat hippocampus. *J Neurophysiol 44*:247-258.

Leggio MG, Mandolesi L, Federico F, Spirito F, Ricci B, Gelfo F, Petrosini L (2005) Environmental enrichment promotes improved spatial abilities and enhanced dendritic growth in the rat. *Behavioural brain research 163*:78-90.

Leon AS (1985) Physical activity levels and coronary heart disease. Analysis of epidemiologic and supporting studies. *Med Clin North Am 69*:3-20.

Lesne S, Koh MT, Kotilinek L, Kayed R, Glabe CG, Yang A, Gallagher M, Ashe KH (2006) A specific amyloid-beta protein assembly in the brain impairs memory. *Nature 440*:352-357.

Letenneur L, Gilleron V, Commenges D, Helmer C, Orgogozo JM, Dartigues JF (1999) Are sex and educational level independent predictors of dementia and Alzheimer's disease? Incidence data from the PAQUID project. *J Neurol Neurosurg Psychiatry 66*:177-183.

Levi O, Jongen-Relo AL, Feldon J, Roses AD, Michaelson DM (2003) ApoE4 impairs hippocampal plasticity isoform-specifically and blocks the environmental stimulation of synaptogenesis and memory. *Neurobiol Dis 13*:273-282.

Lippert-Gruener M, Maegele M, Garbe J, Angelov DN (2007) Late effects of enriched environment (EE) plus multimodal early onset stimulation (MEOS) after traumatic brain injury in rats: Ongoing improvement of neuromotor function despite sustained volume of the CNS lesion. *Exp Neurol 203*:82-94.

Lledo PM, Hjelmstad GO, Mukherji S, Soderling TR, Malenka RC, Nicoll RA (1995) Calcium/calmodulin-dependent kinase II and long-term potentiation enhance synaptic transmission by the same mechanism. *Proc Natl Acad Sci U S A 92*:11175-11179.

Lord SR, Castell S, Corcoran J, Dayhew J, Matters B, Shan A, Williams P (2003) The effect of group exercise on physical functioning and falls in frail older people living in retirement villages: a randomized, controlled trial. *J Am Geriatr Soc 51*:1685-1692.

Lytle ME, Vander Bilt J, Pandav RS, Dodge HH, Ganguli M (2004) Exercise level and cognitive decline: the MoVIES project. *Alzheimer Dis Assoc Disord 18*:57-64.

Ma YL, Tsai MC, Hsu WL, Lee EH (2006) SGK protein kinase facilitates the expression of long-term potentiation in hippocampal neurons. *Learn Mem 13*:114-118.

Malenka RC, Kauer JA, Perkel DJ, Mauk MD, Kelly PT, Nicoll RA, Waxham MN (1989) An essential role for postsynaptic calmodulin and protein kinase activity in long-term potentiation. *Nature 340*:554-557.

Marr RA, Rockenstein E, Mukherjee A, Kindy MS, Hersh LB, Gage FH, Verma IM, Masliah E (2003) Neprilysin gene transfer reduces human amyloid pathology in transgenic mice. *J Neurosci 23*:1992-1996.

Marr RA, Guan H, Rockenstein E, Kindy M, Gage FH, Verma I, Masliah E, Hersh LB (2004) Neprilysin regulates amyloid Beta peptide levels. *J Mol Neurosci 22*:5-11.

Martin SJ, Grimwood PD, Morris RG (2000) Synaptic plasticity and memory: an evaluation of the hypothesis. *Annu Rev Neurosci 23*:649-711.

Mohajeri MH, Wollmer MA, Nitsch RM (2002) Abeta 42-induced increase in neprilysin is associated with prevention of amyloid plaque formation in vivo. *The Journal of biological chemistry 277*:35460-35465.

Nilsson L, Mohammed AK, Henriksson BG, Folkesson R, Winblad B, Bergstrom L (1993) Environmental influence on somatostatin levels and gene expression in the rat brain. *Brain research 628*:93-98.

Nitsch RM, Farber SA, Growdon JH, Wurtman RJ (1993) Release of amyloid beta-protein precursor derivatives by electrical depolarization of rat hippocampal slices. *Proc Natl Acad Sci U S A 90*:5191-5193.

Paffenbarger RS, Jr., Wing AL, Hyde RT (1995) Physical activity as an index of heart attack risk in college alumni. 1978. *Am J Epidemiol 142*:889-903; discussion 887-888.

Pang PT, Lu B (2004) Regulation of late-phase LTP and long-term memory in normal and aging hippocampus: role of secreted proteins tPA and BDNF. *Ageing Res Rev 3*:407-430.

Pang PT, Teng HK, Zaitsev E, Woo NT, Sakata K, Zhen S, Teng KK, Yung WH, Hempstead BL, Lu B (2004) Cleavage of proBDNF by tPA/plasmin is essential for long-term hippocampal plasticity. *Science 306*:487-491.

Pereira LO, Arteni NS, Petersen RC, da Rocha AP, Achaval M, Netto CA (2007) Effects of daily environmental enrichment on memory deficits and brain injury following neonatal hypoxia-ischemia in the rat. *Neurobiol Learn Mem 87*:101-108.

Pham TM, Ickes B, Albeck D, Soderstrom S, Granholm AC, Mohammed AH (1999) Changes in brain nerve growth factor levels and nerve growth factor receptors in rats exposed to environmental enrichment for one year. *Neuroscience 94*:279-286.

Pinaud R, Penner MR, Robertson HA, Currie RW (2001) Upregulation of the immediate early gene arc in the brains of rats exposed to environmental enrichment: implications for molecular plasticity. *Brain Res Mol Brain Res 91*:50-56.

Powell KE, Spain KG, Christenson GM, Mollenkamp MP (1986) The status of the 1990 objectives for physical fitness and exercise. *Public Health Rep 101*:15-21.

Price DL, Sisodia SS, Borchelt DR (1998a) Genetic neurodegenerative diseases: the human illness and transgenic models. *Science 282*:1079-1083.

Price DL, Tanzi RE, Borchelt DR, Sisodia SS (1998b) Alzheimer's disease: genetic studies and transgenic models. *Annu Rev Genet 32*:461-493.

Puurunen K, Koistinaho J, Sirvio J, Jolkkonen J, Sivenius J (2001) Enriched-environment housing increases neuronal Fos-staining in the dentate gyrus after a water maze spatial learning task. *Neuropharmacology 40*:440-447.

Rampon C, Tang YP, Goodhouse J, Shimizu E, Kyin M, Tsien JZ (2000) Enrichment induces structural changes and recovery from nonspatial memory deficits in CA1 NMDAR1-knockout mice. *Nat Neurosci 3*:238-244.

Renner MJ, Rosenzweig MR (1987) *Enriched and Impoverished Environments. Effects on Brain and Behavior*. New York: Springer-Verlag.

Rex CS, Lin CY, Kramar EA, Chen LY, Gall CM, Lynch G (2007) Brain-derived neurotrophic factor promotes long-term potentiation-related cytoskeletal changes in adult hippocampus. *J Neurosci 27*:3017-3029.

Rosenzweig MR (1996) Aspects of the search for neural mechanisms of memory. *Ann Rev Psychol 47*:1-32.

Rosenzweig MR, Love W, Bennett EL (1968) Effects of a few hours a day of enriched experience on brain chemistry and brain weights *Physiol Beh 3*:819-825.

Rosenzweig MR, Bennett EL, Diamond MC (1972) Chemical and anatomical plasticity of brain: replications and extensions, 1970. In: *Macromolecules and Behavior* (Gaito J, ed), pp 205-227. New York: Appleton-Century-Crofts.

Rosenzweig MR, Krech D, Bennett EL, Diamond MC (1962) Effects of environmental complexity and training on brain chemistry and anatomy: a replication and extension. *J Comp Physiol Psychol 55*:429-437.

Saito T, Iwata N, Tsubuki S, Takaki Y, Takano J, Huang SM, Suemoto T, Higuchi M, Saido TC (2005) Somatostatin regulates brain amyloid beta peptide Abeta42 through modulation of proteolytic degradation. *Nature medicine 11*:434-439.

Sapolsky RM (1993) The physiology of dominance in stable versus unstable social hierarchies. In: *Primate Social Conflict*, W Mason, S Mendoza (ed) SUNY Press, NY:171.

Selkoe DJ (2001) Alzheimer's disease: genes, proteins, and therapy. *Physiol Rev 81*:741-766.

Sheng JG, Price DL, Koliatsos VE (2002) Disruption of corticocortical connections ameliorates amyloid burden in terminal fields in a transgenic model of Abeta amyloidosis. *J Neurosci 22*:9794-9799.

Silva AJ, Paylor R, Wehner JM, Tonegawa S (1992a) Impaired spatial learning in alpha-calcium-calmodulin kinase II mutant mice. *Science 257*:206-211.

Silva AJ, Stevens CF, Tonegawa S, Wang Y (1992b) Deficient hippocampal long-term potentiation in alpha-calcium-calmodulin kinase II mutant mice. *Science (New York, NY 257*:201-206.

Snowdon DA, Kemper SJ, Mortimer JA, Greiner LH, Wekstein DR, Markesbery WR (1996) Linguistic ability in early life and cognitive function and Alzheimer's disease in late life. Findings from the Nun Study. *Jama 275*:528-532.

Spires TL, Grote HE, Varshney NK, Cordery PM, van Dellen A, Blakemore C, Hannan AJ (2004) Environmental enrichment rescues protein deficits in a mouse model of Huntington's disease, indicating a possible disease mechanism. *J Neurosci 24*:2270-2276.

Stern Y, Gurland B, Tatemichi TK, Tang MX, Wilder D, Mayeux R (1994) Influence of education and occupation on the incidence of Alzheimer's disease. *Jama 271*:1004-1010.

Steward O, Wallace CS, Lyford GL, Worley PF (1998) Synaptic activation causes the mRNA for the IEG Arc to localize selectively near activated postsynaptic sites on dendrites. *Neuron 21*:741-751.

Taylor AH, Cable NT, Faulkner G, Hillsdon M, Narici M, Van Der Bij AK (2004) Physical activity and older adults: a review of health benefits and the effectiveness of interventions. *J Sports Sci 22*:703-725.

Teri L, Gibbons LE, McCurry SM, Logsdon RG, Buchner DM, Barlow WE, Kukull WA, LaCroix AZ, McCormick W, Larson EB (2003) Exercise plus behavioral management in patients with Alzheimer disease: a randomized controlled trial. *Jama 290*:2015-2022.

Tillerson JL, Caudle WM, Reveron ME, Miller GW (2003) Exercise induces behavioral recovery and attenuates neurochemical deficits in rodent models of Parkinson's disease. *Neuroscience 119*:899-911.

Torasdotter M, Metsis M, Henriksson BG, Winblad B, Mohammed AH (1996) Expression of neurotrophin-3 mRNA in the rat visual cortex and hippocampus is influenced by environmental conditions. *Neurosci Lett 218*:107-110.

Torasdotter M, Metsis M, Henriksson BG, Winblad B, Mohammed AH (1998) Environmental enrichment results in higher levels of nerve growth factor mRNA in the rat visual cortex and hippocampus. *Behav Brain Res 93*:83-90.

Turner AM, Greenough WT (1985) Differential rearing effects on rat visual cortex synapses. I. Synaptic and neuronal density and synapses per neuron. *Brain Res 329*:195-203.

van Dellen A, Blakemore C, Deacon R, York D, Hannan AJ (2000) Delaying the onset of Huntington's in mice. *Nature 404*:721-722.

van Praag H, Kempermann G, Gage FH (2000) Neural consequences of environmental enrichment. *Nat Rev Neurosci 1*:191-198.

van Praag H, Christie BR, Sejnowski TJ, Gage FH (1999) Running enhances neurogenesis, learning, and long-term potentiation in mice. *Proceedings of the National Academy of Sciences of the United States of America 96*:13427-13431.

Volkmar FR, Greenough WT (1972) Rearing complexity affects branching of dendrites in the visual cortex of the rat. *Science 176*:1445-1447.

Wallace CS, Kilman VL, Withers GS, Greenough WT (1992) Increases in dendritic length in occipital cortex after 4 days of differential housing in weanling rats. *Behavioral and neural biology 58*:64-68.

Wang J, Tanila H, Puolivali J, Kadish I, Groen T (2003) Gender differences in the amount and deposition of amyloidbeta in APPswe and PS1 double transgenic mice. *Neurobiol Dis 14*:318-327.

Wiesel TN, Hubel DH (1965) Comparison of the effects of unilateral and bilateral eye closure on cortical unit responses in kittens. *J Neurophysiol 28*:1029-1040.

Wilson RS, Bennett DA, Bienias JL, Aggarwal NT, Mendes De Leon CF, Morris MC, Schneider JA, Evans DA (2002) Cognitive activity and incident AD in a population-based sample of older persons. *Neurology 59*:1910-1914.

Withers GS, Greenough WT (1989) Reach training selectively alters dendritic branching in subpopulations of layer II-III pyramids in rat motor-somatosensory forelimb cortex. *Neuropsychologia 27*:61-69.

Wolf SA, Kronenberg G, Lehmann K, Blankenship A, Overall R, Staufenbiel M, Kempermann G (2006) Cognitive and Physical Activity Differently Modulate Disease Progression in the Amyloid Precursor Protein (APP)-23 Model of Alzheimer's Disease. *Biol Psychiatry 60*:1314-1323.

Yin Y, Edelman GM, Vanderklish PW (2002) The brain-derived neurotrophic factor enhances synthesis of Arc in synaptoneurosomes. *Proc Natl Acad Sci U S A 99*:2368-2373.

Zhu J, Apparsundaram S, Bardo MT, Dwoskin LP (2005) Environmental enrichment decreases cell surface expression of the dopamine transporter in rat medial prefrontal cortex. *J Neurochem 93*:1434-1443.

In: Research Progress in Alzheimer's Disease and Dementia   ISBN 978-1-60021-960-3
Editor: Miao-Kun Sun, pp. 329 -338   © 2008 Nova Science Publishers, Inc.

Chapter XII

FRAGILE X MENTAL RETARDATION GENE AND DEMENTIA

Maija Castrén[1],* and Seppo Kaakkola[2]

[1]Department of Medical Genetics, University of Helsinki, FIN-00014 Helsinki, Finland;
[2]Department of Neurology, University Hospital of Helsinki, Helsinki, Finland.

ABSTRACT

Mutations of the fragile X mental retardation 1 (*FMR1*) gene causing the lack or dysfunction of *FMR1* protein result in fragile X syndrome, a neurodevelopmental disorder with cognitive defects and a distinct behavioral phenotype. Recently, overexpression of *FMR1* mRNA and a late-onset neurodegenerative syndrome, fragile-X-associated tremor/ataxia syndrome (FXTAS), were found in carriers of premutation alleles. The neuropsychiatric symptoms of FXTAS include cognitive changes, which are compatible with a fronto-subcortical dementia. Thus, there is a body of evidence that aberrances of *FMR1* gene function disturb intracellular signaling cascades that are essential for normal cognitive function. Understanding of the pathogenic processes that are caused by mutations in the *FMR1* gene may give new insights into some of the networks and mechanisms underlying cognitive impairment and also mental decline in dementia.

ABBREVIATIONS:

CGG triplet repeat,	cytocine-guanine-guanine triplet repeat;
FMR1 gene,	fragile X mental retardation 1 gene;
FMRP,	fragile X mental retardation protein;

* Correspondence concerning this article should be addressed to: Maija Castrén, Department of Medical Genetics, University of Helsinki, P.O. Box 63, FIN-00014 Helsinki, Email: maija.castren@helsinki.fi.

Fmr1-KO mouse,	*Fmr1*-knockout mouse FXTAS, fragile-X-associated tremor/ataxia syndrome;
LTD,	long-term depression;
LTP,	Long-term potentiation.

MUTATIONS OF THE *FMR1* GENE

In the 5´untranslated region of the fragile X mental retardation 1 (*FMR1*) gene is a polymorphic CGG (cytocine-guanine-guanine) triplet repeat sequence, which is polymorphic in the general population (Fu YH et al., 1991; Patsalis et al., 1999; Snow et al., 1993). In normal allele, the repeat number is less than 55. Alleles with 55 to 200 CGG repeats are called "premutations" (Figure 1). The prevalence of the premutation has been estimated to be one in 813 males and one in 259 females in the general population but it may highly vary between different ethnic populations (Toledano-Alhadef et al., 2001; Dombrowski et al., 2002; Pesso et al., 2000; Rousseau et al., 1995). Recently, a unique neurodegenerative disorder, referred to as fragile-X-associated tremor/ataxia syndrome, has been characterized in premutation carriers (FXTAS, see a recent review Jacquemont S et al., 2007). The premutation allele also associates with premature ovarian failure and early menopause (Sullivan et al., 2005). In addition, emotional problems have been shown to be more common in premutation carriers than in controls (Hessl et al., 2005).

Premutation alleles are unstable and can be expanded to full mutation alleles when transmitted maternally. A full mutation of the *FMR1* gene contains over 200 CGG repeats (Figure 1). The full mutation causes transcriptional silencing of the *FMR1* gene and results in fragile X syndrome which is a common form of inherited mental retardation with a prevalence of 1/4000 in males. In females, the random inactivation of one X chromosome and the compensation provided by the unaffected X chromosome cause a larger phenotypic diversity of full mutation carriers. An exceptionally severe form of fragile X syndrome is caused by a missense mutation I304N (De Boulle et al., 1993).

DISTINCT PHENOTYPE OF FRAGILE X SYNDROME AND FXTAS

The fragile X syndrome is a neurodevelopmental disease that is characterized by cognitive defects, mild facial dysmorphology, macro-orchidism, and a distinct behavioral phenotype in males (Hagerman and Hagerman, 2002). Cognitive defects may vary from mild to severe and include deficits in visuo-spatial abilities (Crowe and Hay, 1990), short-term memory (Loesch et al., 2004), and linguistic processing (Belser and Sudhalter, 2001). The behavioral phenotype of fragile X individuals includes hyperactivity, hyperarousal, hypersensitivity to sensory stimuli, anxiety, and autistic features, such as poor eye contact and hand flapping (Backes et al., 2000; Castrén et al., 2003). Declines in IQ scores have been detected in nearly all males and in most females with fragile X syndrome (Fisch et al., 1996 and 1999). Interestingly, the decrease in IQ scores appears to precipitate in childhood (Fisch et al., 2002).

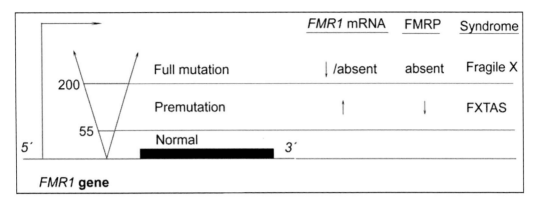

Figure 1. Schematic presentation of the repeat expansion in the 5´ untranslated region of the *FMR1* gene. The correlation of the repeat size with the gene expression is shown.

The symptoms of FXTAS appear after the age of 50 years. The FXTAS phenotype includes progressive action or intention tremor and cerebellar gait ataxia associated with intellectual decline, Parkinsonism, peripheral neuropathy, autonomic dysfunction, and limb proximal weakness (Jacquemont et al., 2003 and 2004). Cognitive changes are compatible with a dementia syndrome (Grigsby J et al., 2006). The neuropsychiatric symptoms of males with FMR1 premutation allele have been examined in detail and the symptoms appear to cluster as a fronto-subcortical dementia (Bacalman et al., 2006). Persons with FXTAS suffer particularly from impairment in executive cognitive functioning and working memory. Verbal and performance IQ as well as processing speed of these people are impaired in the context of superficially intact language. In females, the premutation allele is not associated with dementia, suggesting that the unaffected X chromosome or female hormones protect against the intellectual decline seen in permutation carrier males.

BRAIN STRUCTURE AND HISTOPATHOLOGY IN FRAGILE X SYNDROME AND FXTAS

There is evidence that diminished or absent production of FMRP has effects on the brain's structural organization (Hessl et al., 2004). Histopathological studies have demonstrated that fragile X individuals display higher dendritic spine density and more dendritic spines with an immature morphology (Irwin et al., 2001 and 2000). In neuroanatomical studies, an age-related increase in the volume of the hippocampus and a decrease in the volume of the superior temporal gyrus are found in a group of young fragile X patients when compared with a group of age- and IQ-matched controls (Reiss et al., 1994). In addition, enlarged caudate nucleus, thalamus, and ventricular volumes, but reduced posterior cerebellar vermis have been reported in subjects with fragile X syndrome (Mostofsky et al., 1998; Reiss et al., 1994; Eliez et al., 2001). In agreement with the volumetric abnormalities in the thalamus and selective visual deficits of the magnocellular pathway in fragile X syndrome, cytoarchitectual changes have been reported in the lateral geniculate nucleus (Eliez et al., 2001; Kogan et al., 2004).

Premutation alleles are associated with ubiquitin positive, eosinophilic intranuclear inclusions, both in astrocytes and in neurons in the cerebrum and brain stem of the FXTAS brain (Jacquemont et al., 2003; Tassone et al., 2007b). Symptomatic male premutation carriers show a characteristic pattern in magnetic resonance imaging (Brunberg et al., 2002). The abnormalities include increased T2 signal intensity in the middle cerebellar peduncles and deep white matter of the cerebellum. Patchy and confluent regions of increased T2 signal intensity are also more prominent in periventricular and deep white matter of the cerebral hemispheres and in the corpus callosum than in control brains. Furthermore, volume loss involving the pons, mesencephalon, cerebral and cerebellar cortex, white matter of the cerebral hemispheres, and corpus callosum are seen.

CHANGES IN *FMR1* GENE EXPRESSION BY DIFFERENT MUTATIONS

Expression levels of fragile X mental retardation protein (FMRP) encoded by the FMR1 gene correlate with the cognitive impairment of fragile X patients (Tassone et al., 1999). In most cases, the full mutation allele causes methylation of the promoter and transcriptional silencing of the *FMR1* gene which leads to the reduction of *FMR1* mRNA, and thereby, the lack of FMRP. In some fragile X males, the methylated, fully expanded alleles continue to produce *FMR1* mRNA. However, the CGG triplet expansion reduces *FMR1* mRNA translation efficiency and *FMR1* mRNA is not associated with polysomes in lymphoblastoid cells from a patient with a full mutation (Primerano et al., 2002). Premutation carriers have low FMRP levels and the reduction of the protein correlates with the repeat size (Tassone and Hagerman, 2003; Primerano et al., 2002).

The premutation carriers exhibit increased *FMR1* mRNA expression levels in peripheral blood leukocytes and cells of central nervous system (Tassone et al., 2007a; Tassone et al., 2000; Kenneson et al., 2001; Allen et al., 2004). The magnitude of the elevated mRNA levels has been shown to be as much as 10-fold and the levels correlate with the length of the CGG repeat expansion (Tassone et al., 2000; Allen et al., 2004). In individuals with the fragile X premutation, elevated *FMR1* mRNA levels but not repeat size or reduced FMRP are associated with psychological symptoms, including obsessive-compulsive symptoms and psychoticism (Hessl et al., 2005). FXTAS may also have an RNA-based pathogenesis and since the FXTAS is not seen in older individuals with fragile X syndrome, an RNA toxic gain of function model has been proposed (Hagerman et al., 2001; Greco et al., 2002; Greco et al., 2006; Hagerman and Hagerman, 2004).

FMRP AND DEMENTIA

FMRP is an RNA binding protein (Siomi et al., 1993; Ashley et al., 1993) and is highly expressed in neurons of the normal central nervous system (Hinds et al., 1993). FMRP is localized in different neuronal compartments and may play a role in regulation of transport of mRNAs and local protein synthesis, both in developing synapses and in mature dendritic spines (Castrén et al., 2001; Feng et al., 1997). It has been estimated that about 4% of human fetal brain messages, including its own mRNA, associates with FMRP and more than 500 mRNA ligands for FMRP have been identified (Brown et al., 2001; Darnell et al., 2001). A missense mutation I304N in the KH domain of FMRP reduces RNA binding (Siomi et al., 1994; Castrén et al., 2001). Since the mutation causes an exceptionally severe fragile X phenotype (De Boulle et al., 1993), the RNA binding capability is essential for the normal function of FMRP. Very recent studies showed that amyloid precursor protein is one of the targets of FMRP, suggesting that disturbances in the *FMR1* gene action may lead to pathological findings seen in Alzheimer's disease (Westmark and Malter, 2007). The decline of *Fmr1* mRNA and protein levels during aging may indicate that FMRP might be involved in normal changes of brain as function of age (Singh et al., 2006).

The absence of FMRP alters neural stem cell differentiation and the early brain development (Castrén et al., 2005). Both human and mice fragile X stem cells generate more cells responsive to metabotropic glutamate receptor activation and neurons with immature morphology. Furthermore, the neural lineage differentiation of FMRP-deficient cells takes place at the expense of glia, suggesting that glial cell disturbances may also play a role in the pathophysiology of fragile X syndrome (Castrén et al., 2005).

Studies of mouse model for fragile X syndrome, *Fmr1*-knockout (*Fmr1*-KO) mice, have shown that changes in synaptic plasticity are associated with the mental retardation caused by the absence of FMRP. Alterations particularly in metabotropic glutamate receptor-mediated plasticity appear to have a central role in several disturbances seen in *Fmr1*-KO mice (Bear et al., 2004). Long-term potentiation (LTP), a type of long-lasting synaptic plasticity, requires translation of dendritically localized mRNA for the stabilization and is affected in the cortex of *Fmr1*-KO mice (Li et al., 2002; Wilson and Cox, 2007). Changes in synaptic plasticity may be specific to different brain regions and LTP is not affected in the hippocampus where long-term depression (LTD), a synaptic depression leading to reduction in AMPA receptor signaling as a response to low synaptic activity, is augmented in the *Fmr1*-KO mice (Huber et al., 2002). Alterations in synaptic plasticity correlate with abnormalities in learning and memory, and cellular mechanisms underlying the plasticity changes in fragile X syndrome may be involved in the intracellular cascades disturbed in dementia.

CONCLUSION

Expression of *FMR1* gene is differentially disordered in fragile X syndrome caused by the lack of FMRP and FXTAS that may result from an entirely different RNA based pathogenic mechanisms. The molecular events underlying the two distinct phenotypes may, however, be at least partially overlapping. FMRP is implicated in RNA processing and cellular targeting, and regulation of translation. Since these cellular processes are also associated with mental decline, understanding the function of FMRP may provide new insights to the neuropathology of dementia.

ACKNOWLEDGEMENTS

We thank Arvo and Lea Ylppö Foundation for research grants.

REFERENCES

Allen EG, He W, Yadav-Shah M, Sherman SL. A study of the distributional characteristics of FMR1 transcript levels in 238 individuals. *Hum Genet 114*: 439-447, 2004.

Ashley CT, Jr, Wilkinson KD, Reines D, Warren ST. FMR1 Protein: Conserved RNP family domains and selective RNA binding. *Science 262*: 563-6, 1993.

Bacalman S, Farzin F, Bourgeois JA, Cogswell J, Goodlin-Jones BL, Gane LW, Grigsby J, Leehey MA, Tassone F, Hagerman RJ. Psychiatric phenotype of the fragile X-associated tremor/ataxia syndrome (FXTAS) in males: newly described fronto-subcortical dementia. *J Clin Psychiatry 67*: 87-94. 2006.

Backes M, Genc B, Schreck J, Doerfler W, Lemkuhl G, von Gontard A. Cognitive and behavioral profile of fragile X boys: correlations to molecular data. *Am J Med Genet 95*: 150-156. 2000.

Bear MF, Huber KM, Warren ST. The mGluR theory of fragile X mental retardation. *Trends Neurosci 27*: 370-377. 2004.

Belser RC, Sudhalter V. Conversational characteristics of children with fragile X syndrome: repetitive speech. *Am J Ment Retard 106*: 28-38. 2001.

Brown V, Jin P, Ceman S, Darnell JC, O'Donnell WT, Tenenbaum SA, Jin X, Feng Y, Wilkinson KD, Keene JD, Darnell RB, Warren ST. Microarray identification of FMRP-associated brain mRNAs and altered mRNA translational profiles in fragile X syndrome. *Cell 107*: 477-87. 2001.

Brunberg JA, Jacquemont S, Hagerman RJ, Berry-Kravis EM, Grigsby J, Leehey MA, Tassone F, Brown WT, Greco CM, Hagerman PJ. Fragile X premutation carriers: characteristic MR imaging findings of adult male patients with progressive cerebellar and cognitive dysfunction. *AJNR Am J Neuroradiol 23*: 1757-1766. 2002.

Castrén M, Pääkkönen A, Tarkka IM, Ryynänen M, Partanen J. Augmentation of auditory N1 in children with fragile X syndrome. *Brain Topography 15*: 165-171. 2003.

Castrén M, Haapasalo A, Oostra BA, Castrén E. Subcellular localization of fragile X mental retardation protein with the I304N mutation in the RNA-binding domain in cultured hippocampal neurons. *Cell Mol Neurobiol 21*: 29-37. 2001.

Castrén M, Tervonen T, Kärkkäinen V, Heinonen S, Castrén E, Larsson K, Bakker CE, Oostra BA, Åkerman K. Altered neuronal differentiation of human neural stem cells in fragile X syndrome. *Proc Natl Acad Sci U S A 102*: 17834-17839. 2005.

Crowe SF, Hay DA. Neuropsychological dimensions of the fragile X syndrome: support for a non-dominant hemisphere dysfunction hypothesis. *Neuropsychologia 28*: 9-16. 1990.

Darnell JC, Jensen K B, Jin P, Brown V, Warren ST, Darnell RB. Fragile X mental retardation protein targets G quartet mRNAs important for neuronal function. *Cell 107*: 489-99. (2001)

De Boulle K, Verkerk AJ, Reyniers E, Vits L, Hendrickx J, Van Roy B, Van den Bos F, de Graaff E, Oostra BA, Willems PJ. A point mutation in the FMR-1 gene associated with fragile X mental retardation. *Nat Genet 3*: 31-5. 1993.

Dombrowski C, Levesque S, Morel ML, Rouillard P, Morgan K, Rousseau F. Premutation and intermediate-size FMR1 alleles in 10572 males from the general population: loss of an AGG interruption is a late event in the generation of fragile X syndrome alleles. *Hum Mol Genet 11*: 371-378. 2002.

Eliez S, Blasey CM, Freund LS, Hastie T, Reiss AL. Brain anatomy, gender and IQ in children and adolescents with fragile X syndrome. *Brain 124*: 1610-1618. 2001.

Feng Y, Gutekunst CA, Eberhart DE, Yi H, Warren ST, Hersch SM. Fragile X mental retardation protein: nucleocytoplasmic shuttling and association with somatodendritic ribosomes. *J Neurosci 17*: 1539-47. 1997.

Fisch GS, Carpenter N, Holden JJ, Howard-Peebles PN, Maddalena A, Borghraef M, Steyaer J, Fryns JP. Longitudinal changes in cognitive and adaptive behavior in fragile X females: a prospective multicenter analysis. *Am J Med Genet 83*: 308-312. 1999.

Fisch GS, Simensen R, Tarleton J, Chalifoux M, Holden JJ, Carpenter N, Howard-Peebles PN, Maddalena A. Longitudinal study of cognitive abilities and adaptive behavior levels in fragile X males: a prospective multicenter analysis. *Am J Med Genet 1996*: 356-361. 1996.

Fisch GS, Simensen RJ, Schroer RJ. Longitudinal changes in cognitive and adaptive behavior scores in children and adolescents with the fragile X mutation or autism. *J Autism Dev Disord 32*: 107-114. 2002.

Fu YH, Kuhl DP, Pizzuti A, Pieretti M, Sutcliffe JS, Richards S, Verkerk AJ, Holden JJ, Fenwick RG Jr, Warren ST, et al. Variation of the CGG repeat at the fragile X site results in genetic instability: resolution of the Sherman paradox. *Cell 67*: 1047-1058. 1991.

Greco CM, Berman RF, Martin RM, Tassone F, Schwartz PH, Chang A, Trapp BD, Iwahashi C, Brunberg J, Grigsby J, Hessl D, Becker EJ, Papazian J, Leehey MA, Hagerman RJ, Hagerman PJ. Neuropathology of fragile X-associated tremor/ataxia syndrome (FXTAS). *Brain 129*: 243-255. 2006.

Greco CM, Hagerman RJ, Tassone F, Chudley AE, Del Bigio MR, Jacquemont S, Leehey M, and Hagerman PJ. Neuronal intranuclear inclusions in a new cerebellar tremor/ataxia syndrome among fragile X carriers. *Brain 125*: 1760-1771. 2002.

Grigsby J, Brega AG, Jacquemont S, Loesch DZ, Leehey MA, Goodrich GK, Hagerman RJ, Epstein J, Wilson R, Cogswell JB, Jardini T, Tassone F, and Hagerman PJ. Impairment in the cognitive functioning of men with fragile X-associated tremor/ataxia syndrome (FXTAS). *J Neurol Sci 248*: 227-233. 2006.

Hagerman PJ, Hagerman RJ. Fragile X-associated tremor/ataxia syndrome - an older face of the fragile X gene. *Nat Clin Pract Neurol 3*: 107-112. 2004.

Hagerman RJ, Hagerman PJ. The fragile X premutation: into the phenotypic fold. *Curr Opin Genet Dev 12*: 278-283. 2002.

Hagerman RJ, Leehey M, Heinrichs W, Tassone F, Wilson R, Hills J, Grigsby J, Gage B, Hagerman PJ. Intention tremor, parkinsonism, and generalized brain atrophy in male carriers of fragile X. *Neurology 57*: 127-130. 2001.

Hessl D, Rivera SM, Reiss AL. The neuroanatomy and neuroendocrinology of fragile X syndrome. *Ment Retard Dev Disabil Res Rev 10*: 17-24. 2004.

Hessl D, Tassone F, Loesch DZ, Berry-Kravis E, Leehey MA, Gane LW, Barbato I, Rice C, Gould E, Hall DA, Grigsby J, Wegelin JA, Harris S, Lewin F, Weinberg D, Hagerman PJ, Hagerman RJ. Abnormal elevation of FMR1 mRNA is associated with psychological symptoms in individuals with the fragile X premutation. *Am J Med Genet 139*: 115-121. 2005.

Hinds HL, Ashley CT, Sutcliffe JS, Nelson DL, Warren ST, Housman DE. Schalling M. Tissue specific expression of FMR-1 provides evidence for a functional role in fragile X syndrome. *Nat Genet 3*: 36-43. 1993.

Huber KM, Gallagher SM, Warren ST, Bear MF. Altered synaptic plasticity in a mouse model of fragile X mental retardation. *Proc Natl Acad Sci U S A 99*: 7746-7750. 2002.

Irwin SA, Galvez R, Greenough WT. Dendritic spine structural anomalies in fragile-X mental retardation syndrome. *Cereb Cortex 10*: 1038-44. 2000.

Irwin SA, Patel B, Idupulapati M, Harris JB, Crisostomo RA, Larsen BP, Kooy F, Willems PJ, Cras P, Kozlowski PB, Swain RA, Weiler IJ, Greenough WT. Abnormal dendritic spine characteristics in the temporal and visual cortices of patients with fragile X syndrome: A quantitative examination. *Am J Med Genet 98*: 161-7. 2001.

Jacquemont S, Hagerman RJ, Hagerman PJ, Leehey MA. Fragile-X syndrome and fragile X-associated tremor/ataxia syndrome: two faces of FMR1. *Lancet Neurol 6*: 45-55. 2007.

Jacquemont S, Hagerman RJ, Leehey M, Grigsby J, Zhang L, Brunberg JA, Greco C, Des Portes V, Jardini T, Levine R, Berry-Kravis E, Brown WT, Schaeffer S, Kissel J, Tassone F, Hagerman PJ. Fragile X premutation tremor/ataxia syndrome: molecular, clinical, and neuroimaging correlates. *Am J Hum Genet 72*: 869-878. 2003.

Jacquemont S, Hagerman RJ, Leehey MA, Hall DA, Levine R, Brunberg JA, Zhang L, Jardini T, Gane LW, Harris SW, Herman K, Grigsby J, Greco CM, Berry-Kravis E, Tassone F, Hagerman PJ. Penetrance of the fragile X-associated tremor/ataxia syndrome in a premutation carrier population. *JAMA 291*: 460-469. 2004.

Kenneson A, Zhang F, Hagedorn CH, Warren ST. Reduced FMRP and increased FMR1 transcription is proportionally associated with CGG repeat number in intermediate-length and premutation carriers. *Hum Mol Genet 10*: 1449-1454. 2001.

Kogan CS, Boutet I, Cornish K, Zangenehpour S, Mullen KT, Holden JJ, Der Kaloustian VM, Andermann E, Chaudhur A. Differential impact of the FMR1 gene on visual processing in fragile X syndrome. *Brain 127*: 591-601. 2004.

Li J, Pelletier M-R, Perez Velazquez JL, Carlen PL. Reduced cortical synaptic plasticity and GluR1 expression associated with fragile X mental retardation protein deficiency. *Mol Cell Neurosci 19*: 138-151. 2002.

Loesch DZ, Huggins RM, Hagerman RJ. Phenotypic variation and FMRP levels in fragile X. *Ment Retard Dev Disabil Res Rev 10*: 31-41. 2004.

Mostofsky SH, Mazzocco MM, Aakalu G, Warsofsky IS, Denckla MB, Reiss AL. Decreased cerebellar posterior vermis size in fragile X syndrome: correlation with neurocognitive performance. *Neurology 50*: 121-130. 1998.

Patsalis PC, Sismani C, Stylianou S, Ioannou P, Joseph G, Manoli P, Holden JJ, Hettinger JA. Genetic variation and intergenerational FMR1 CGG-repeat stability in 100 unrelated three-generation families from the normal population. *Am J Med Genet 84*: 217-220. 1999.

Pesso R, Berkenstadt M, Cuckle H, Gak E, Peleq L, Frydman M, Barkai G. Screening for fragile X syndrome in women of reproductive age. *Prenat Diagn 20*: 611-614. 2000.

Primerano B, Tassone F, Hagerman RJ, Hagerman P, Amaldi F, Bagni C. Reduced FMR1 mRNA translation efficiency in fragile X patients with premutations. *RNA 8*: 1482-1488. 2002.

Reiss AL, Lee J, Freund L. Neuroanatomy of fragile X syndrome: the temporal lobe. *Neurology 44*: 1317-1324. 1994.

Rousseau F, Rouillard P, Morel ML, Khandjian EW, Morgan K. Prevalence of carriers of premutation-size alleles of the FMRI gene--and implications for the population genetics of the fragile X syndrome. *Am J Hum Genet 57*: 1006-1018. 1995.

Singh K, Gaur P, Prasad S. Fragile x mental retardation (Fmr-1) gene expression is down regulated in brain of mice during aging. *Mol Biol Rep* Epub ahead of print. 2006.

Siomi H, Choi M, Siomi MC, Nussbaum RL, Dreyfuss G. Essential role for KH domains in RNA binding: Impaired RNA binding by a mutation in the KH domain of FMR1 that causes fragile X syndrome. *Cell 77*: 33-9. 1994.

Siomi H, Siomi MC, Nussbaum RL, Dreyfuss G. The protein product of the fragile X gene, FMR1, has characteristics of an RNA-binding protein. *Cell 74*: 291-8. 1993.

Snow K, Doud LK, Hagerman R, Pergolizzi RG, Erster SH, Thibodeau SN. Analysis of a CGG sequence at the FMR-1 locus in fragile X families and in the general population. *Am J Hum Genet 53*: 1217-1228. 1993.

Sullivan AK, Marcus M, Epstein MP, Allen EG, Anido AE, Paquin JJ, Yadav-Shah M, Sherman SL. Association of FMR1 repeat size with ovarian dysfunction. *Hum Reprod 20*: 402-412. 2005.

Tassone F, Beilina A, Carosi C, Albertosi S, Bagni C, Li L, Glover K, Bentley D, Hagerman PJ. Elevated FMR1 mRNA in premutation carriers is due to increased transcription. *RNA 13*: 1-8. 2007a.

Tassone F, Hagerman PJ. Expression of the FMR1 gene. *Cytogenet Genome Res 100*: 124-128. 2003.

Tassone F, Hagerman RJ, Chamberlein WD, Hagerman PJ. Transcription of the FMR1 gene in individuals with fragile X syndrome. *Am J Med Genet 97*: 195-203. 2000.

Tassone F, Hagerman RJ, Garcia-Arocena D, Khandjian EW, Greco CM, Hagerman PJ. Intranuclear inclusions in neural cells with premutation alleles in fragile X associated tremor/ataxia syndrome. *J Med Genet 41*:e43, 1-3. 2007b.

Tassone F, Hagerman RJ, Ikle DN, Dyer PN, Lampe M, Willemsen R, Oostra B, Taylor AK. FMRP expression as a potential prognostic indicator in fragile X syndrome. *Am J Med Genet 84*: 250-61. 1999.

Toledano-Alhadef H, Basel-Vanaqaite L, Maqal N, Davidov B, Ehrlich S, Drasinover V, Taub E, Halpern GJ, Ginott N, Shohat M. Fragile-X carrier screening and the prevalence of premutation and full-mutation carriers in Israel. *Am J Hum Genet 69*: 351-360. 2001.

Westmark CJ, Malter JS. FMRP Mediates mGluR5-dependent translation of amyloid precursor protein. *PLoS Biol 5*: 629-639. 2007.

Wilson BM, Cox CL. Absence of metabotropic glutamate receptor-mediated plasticity in the neocortex of fragile X mice. *Proc Natl Acad Sci U S A 104*: 2454-2459. 2007.

In: Research Progress in Alzheimer's Disease and Dementia ISBN 978-1-60021-960-3
Editor: Miao-Kun Sun, pp. 339 -365 © 2008 Nova Science Publishers, Inc.

Chapter XIII

CATEGORY LEARNING IN PARKINSON'S DISEASE

J. Vincent Filoteo[1,2,*] *and W. Todd Maddox*[3]

[1]Department of Psychiatry, University of California, San Diego, USA;
[2]Veterans Administration San Diego Healthcare System, USA;
[3]Department of Psychology, University of Texas, USA.

ABSTRACT

An understanding of the early cognitive deficits in patients with Parkinson's disease (PD) could provide better insight into the nature of the disease as well as its future course. One area of study that holds considerable promise is the study of category learning. Much research has examined the neurobiological basis of category learning and it is now well-established that multiple cognitive and brain systems are involved in learning different types of categorization tasks. One broad class of category learning tasks that have been examined include those that are learned using an explicit, verbalizable strategy, whereas another broad class includes tasks that are learned using some form of implicit learning that occurs outside of conscious awareness. This chapter reviews past research examining both explicit and implicit category learning in nondemented patients with PD. It is demonstrated that PD patients can be impaired on both explicit and implicit category learning tasks, but for very different reasons: impairment on explicit tasks appears to be related to deficits in attentional processes, whereas impairments on implicit tasks occur when the rule theoretically requires a greater degree of representation within the striatum. It is also shown that PD patients' impairment on certain implicit tasks is highly predictive of future global cognitive decline, a finding that highlights the utility of studying category learning in this disease.

* Correspondence concerning this article should be addressed to: J. Vincent Filoteo, UCSD, VASDHS 116-B, 3350 La Jolla Village Dr. San Diego, CA 92161. email: vfiloteo@ucsd.edu; phone: 858-642-1122.

INTRODUCTION

It is well accepted that, along with the classic motor symptoms (tremor, rigidity, bradykinesia, postural instability), cognitive deficits are highly prevalent in patients with Parkinson's disease (PD; Owen, 2004). Estimates of dementia range across studies, but a recent review suggests that 24-31% of patients with PD meet formal criteria for dementia at a given time (Aarsland, Zaccai, & Brayne, 2005), and other studies suggest that up to 78% of PD patients can become demented over an 8-year period (Aarsland, Andersen, Larsen, Lolk, & Kragh-Sorensen, 2003). It is also now well established that PD patients can experience significant cognitive impairment in the absence of a frank dementia. For example, relative to healthy controls, nondemented PD patients are impaired in a variety of cognitive areas, such as working memory (Gilbert, Belleville, Bherer, & Chouinard, 2005; Owen *et al.*, 1993; Owen, Iddon, Hodges, Summers, & Robbins, 1997; Postle, Jonides, Smith, Corkin, & Growdon, 1997), attention (R. G. Brown & Marsden, 1988; Filoteo & Maddox, 1999; Filoteo, Rilling, & Strayer, 2002; Sharpe, 1990), set shifting (Cools, Barker, Sahakian, & Robbins, 2001; Cronin-Golomb, Corkin, & Growdon, 1994; Hayes, Davidson, Keele, & Rafal, 1998; Owen, Roberts, Polkey, Sahakian, & Robbins, 1991), and procedural-based learning (Jackson, Jackson, Harrison, Henderson, & Kennard, 1995; Pascual-Leone *et al.*, 1993; Vakil & Herishanu-Naaman, 1998), to name a few. These deficits are often attributed to dysfunction within striatal-cortical circuits that are disrupted very early in the course of the disease (Dubois & Pillon, 1997; Muslimovic, Post, Speelman, & Schmand, 2005; Owen, 2004). Importantly, the understanding of the initial cognitive deficits in PD patients will provide a clearer picture of the nature and progression of future cognitive loss and possible dementia in this disease. Thus, the study of cognition in nondemented PD patients is crucial.

One research area that holds considerable promise in helping to better understand PD patients' early cognitive deficits is the study of category learning. Categorization is involved in learning to associate similar stimuli with one another to organize our world and help guide behavior, and as such, is highly important for our day to day activities. An important advancement over the last 10 years has been the increasing evidence for the existence of multiple category learning systems, each of which is best suited to learning a specific type of categorization problem (Ashby, Alfonso-Reese, Turken, & Waldron, 1998; Nosofsky, Palmeri, & McKinley, 1994; E. E. Smith & Sloman, 1994). Two forms of category learning that have been examined in PD are implicit and explicit category learning (see Figure 1). Past behavioral and functional neuroimaging work with normal participants and various patient populations provides extensive evidence for the distinction between implicit and explicit category learning (Ashby *et al.*, 1998; Filoteo, Maddox, Simmons *et al.*, 2005; Filoteo, Simmons, Zeithamova, Maddox, & Paulus, 2006; Knowlton & Squire, 1993; Maddox, Filoteo, Hejl, & Ing, 2004; Maddox, Filoteo, & Lauritzen, 2007; Maddox, Filoteo, Lauritzen, Connally, & Hejl, 2005; Maddox, O'Brien, Ashby, & Filoteo, 2007; Nomura *et al.*, 2007; E. E. Smith, Patalano, & Jonides, 1998; E. E. Smith & Sloman, 1994). Explicit category learning is dependent on hypothesis generation, logical reasoning, working memory and executive attention. Tasks that measure explicit category learning are often referred to as *rule-based* tasks, because there is typically a verbalizable "rule" that defines category membership. The learning of rule-based tasks is believed to be mediated within an anterior brain network that includes the dorsolateral frontal lobes and the anterior caudate nucleus (Ashby *et al.*, 1998), regions that are often impacted early in the course of PD.

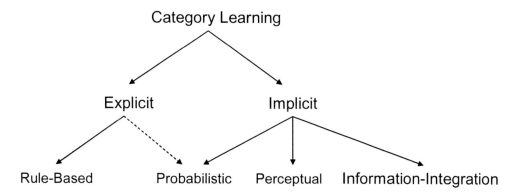

Figure 1. Classification of explicit and implicit category learning tasks.

In contrast, there are several forms of implicit category learning in which a participant can learn categories without having any conscious awareness of the category structures. Some of the tasks that have been used to examine implicit category learning in PD are *information-integration tasks, probabilistic learning tasks, prototype distortion tasks, and artificial grammar learning tasks*. Information-integration category learning tasks are thought to be learned via a procedural-based learning system that depends on a dopamine reward-mediated signal that associates a perceptual stimulus with a specific response (Wickens, 1990), and is thought to take place within a posterior brain network including the inferior temporal lobe and the posterior caudate nucleus (Ashby & Maddox, 2005; Nomura *et al.*, 2007). Probabilistic category learning tasks (e.g., the Weather Prediction Task) are also believed to depend on an implicit learning system in which information about the probability of category membership is learned across multiple trials. Prototype distortion tasks and artificial grammar learning tasks, on the other hand, are thought to be learned through a perceptual-based priming system that is mediated within posterior visual cortices (P. J. Reber & Squire, 1999; P. J. Reber, Stark, & Squire, 1998).

Given the nature and distribution of pathology in PD, it is not surprising that these patients are impaired on a variety of category learning tasks. For example, dopamine appears to be important in reward-mediated learning, so it might be expected that PD patients who, by definition, have a loss of dopamine-producing cells within the substantia nigra, would be impaired on tasks that are learned through feedback. Similarly, given the impact that PD has on striatal structures such as the caudate and putamen (via loss of dopamine input to these regions), it would not be surprising that these patients are impaired on any explicit or implicit category learning task that likely relies on those structures for learning. However, despite the finding that PD patients are impaired on a variety of category learning tasks, a number of important findings have been reported over the last 5 years that have enabled the nature of their deficits to be more clearly delineated, thus allowing one to describe in more specific terms why PD patients are impaired in some, but not all, aspects of category learning. This information has not only extended our knowledge regarding our understanding of this disease, but has also informed the cognitive neuroscience of normal category learning processes.

In this chapter, we review our previous work, and the work of other investigators, that has examined explicit and implicit category learning in nondemented patients with PD. In one section, we discuss previous studies in which explicit category learning was examined using both traditional clinical neuropsychological measures as well as experimental measures. In that section, we also address some conflicts in the literature regarding the potential underlying mechanism(s) of PD patients' explicit learning deficits. Next, we review the implicit category learning literature and address controversies regarding the conditions under which PD patients are impaired in learning implicitly based category structures. Finally, we discuss the potential clinical relevance of better understanding category learning deficits in PD.

PERCEPTUAL CATEGORIZATION TASK

In the majority of our category learning studies, we have used the perceptual categorization task first developed by Ashby and Gott (Ashby & Gott, 1988) in which individuals are presented with simple stimuli and asked to learn to categorize them into distinct groups. The stimuli often consist of lines that vary in length or orientation or Gabor patches that vary in orientation and spatial frequency (see Figures 2 and 3). In this task, participants are presented with a stimulus and are asked to categorize it into Category A or Category B. Once a response is made, the participant is given immediate corrective feedback. Prior to the experiment, a large number of stimuli are sampled randomly from specific underlying category distributions. Figure 2 displays an example of these category distributions from one of our studies in which the stimuli were Gabor patches that varied in orientation and spatial frequency. Each stimulus can be represented as a unique point in two-dimensional space. In Figure 2, the x-axis represents the spatial frequencies of the patch and the y-axis represents the orientation of the patch. Black squares represent Category A stimuli and open circles represent Category B stimuli. The arrows in Figure 2 link a sample stimulus with its representation in this two-dimensional stimulus space. In these studies, a single optimal categorization rule can be derived. The form of the rule is determined by the relationship between the two category distributions, and thus, the two stimulus attributes. The solid line in Figure 2 represents the optimal categorization rule. A participant who uses this rule will maximize long-run accuracy. Given the distribution of the Category A and B stimuli, and the optimal bound, the rule that best describes category membership in Figure 2 is a unidimensional rule in which Gabor patches with lower spatial frequencies (wider bars) are members of Category A, and patches with higher spatial frequencies (narrower bars) are members of Category B.

A major advantage in using the perceptual categorization task is that it allows us to examine different classes of categorization rules, such as implicit and explicit rules, by simply changing the distribution of the stimuli within the categories. Specifically, the rule depicted in Figure 2 is an explicit rule because the optimal rule that defines category membership (depicted as the sold line) can be easily verbalized. In essence, optimal performance requires that the participant learn to attend to only the spatial frequency of the stimuli and identify the cut-off width that best separates the two categories. This rule can be verbalized as "categorize stimuli with wide bars into Category A, and categorize stimuli with narrow bars into Category B". In contrast, Figure 3 depicts two examples of implicit rules-- a linear implicit rule (Figure 3A) and a nonlinear implicit rule (Figure 3B). In this example, the optimal rule that defines category membership is based on a relationship between the length and the orientation of the line stimuli (that is, information from the two dimensions must be integrated). Because these stimuli are in separate physical units (length and orientation), it is difficult to verbalize an optimal rule of this nature, and thus learning has to occur at an implicit level. In these examples, the rule depicted in Figure 3A is based on a linear combination of the two stimulus dimensions, whereas the rule depicted in Figure 3B is based on a nonlinear combination of the two dimensions.

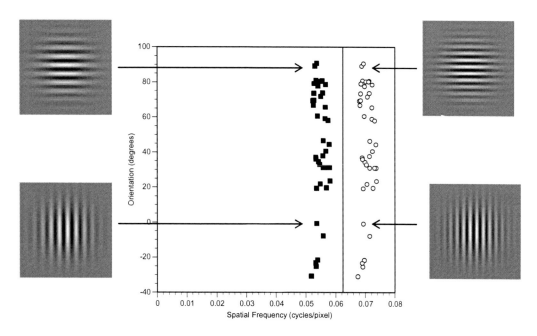

Figure 2. Stimulus distributions and sample stimuli used in the perceptual categorization task. Filled squares represent stimuli from Category A and open circles represent stimuli from Category B. The solid line represents the optimal unidimensional rule-based rule. Arrows point from specific stimulus exemplars to their location in the two-dimensional stimulus space.

Another major advantage in examining PD patients' performance on the perceptual categorization task is that it readily lends itself to the application of sophisticated quantitative models (Ashby & Waldron, 1999; Maddox, Ashby, & Bohil, 2003). These models enable one to identify the process a participant used to perform a given task (i.e., implicit vs. explicit). This is necessary because it is sometimes the case that a participant will attempt to use one approach to solve a task, such as an explicit approach, despite the fact that another approach, such as an implicit approach, is more optimal and would lead to greater levels of accuracy. Although the details of this modeling approach is beyond the scope of this chapter, we provide some discussion of how the application of these models has been invaluable in helping to better understand the nature of PD patients' category learning deficits. The interested reader is referred to other references for the details of this modeling approach (Ashby & Waldron, 1999; Ashby, Waldron, Lee, & Berkman, 2001; Maddox & Filoteo, 2007).

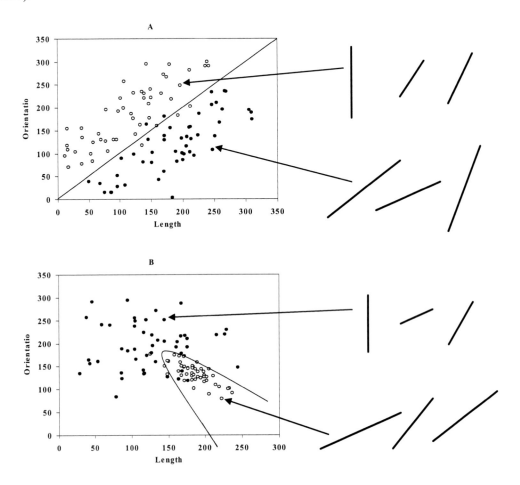

Figure 3. Sample stimuli and stimulus distributions for (A) the linear information-integration condition and (B) the nonlinear information-integration condition in which the stimuli were single lines that vary in length and orientation. Open circles represent stimuli from Category A and closed circles represent stimuli from Category B. The solid line and curve represent the optimal rules. Arrows point from specific stimulus exemplars to their location in the two-dimensional stimulus space.

EXPLICIT CATEGORY LEARNING IN PD

Rule-based measures of explicit category learning have been around since the 1920's (Weigl, 1927). The most popular rule-based clinical task that evaluates explicit category learning is the Wisconsin Card Sorting Test (WCST; Heaton, 1981). In performing the WCST, the participant has to learn a specific rule when matching cards of multiple dimensions (color, form, and number) to one of four key cards using trial-and-error feedback. Once the participant correctly classifies 10 cards in a row, the examiner changes the correct dimension (or rule) to which the participant must sort (e.g., from color to form) without informing the participant. The participant must then use the feedback to disengage from the previously correct rule in order to change to the new rule. Indices from the WCST include the number of trials it takes to achieve the first category sort, the number of categories achieved within 128 trials, the number of perseverative errors (i.e., the number of times a participant made a classification response to a previously correct dimension), and the number of set loss errors (i.e., the number of times a participant made at least 5 correct responses in a row but failed to achieve the criterion of 10 correct responses in a row). A number of studies have found that nondemented PD patients are impaired on the WCST (Azuma, Cruz, Bayles, Tomoeda, & Montgomery, 2003; Lees & Smith, 1983; Paolo, Axelrod, Troster, Blackwell, & Koller, 1996) and recent functional imaging research suggests that their deficit might be associated with decreased activation in the ventrolateral prefrontal cortex, particularly under task conditions in which the striatum is most involved (i.e., having to shift to a new dimension or rule; Monchi *et al.*, 2004; Monchi, Petrides, Mejia-Constain, & Strafella, 2007).

Despite these consistent findings of impairment on the WCST, one potential problem with establishing an explicit category learning deficit in patients with PD using this task is that the nature of their impairment does not appear to be in the *learning* of categories, but rather having to switch to a new category once a previous category has been learned. That is, nondemented PD patients tend not to be impaired in the number of trials it takes them to learn the first category on the WCST, but they tend to *perseverate* on the previously learned categorization rule when they are actually required to switch to a new rule (Paolo *et al.*, 1996). This deficit is highly consistent with PD patients' well-established impairment in set shifting (Cools *et al.*, 2001; Cronin-Golomb *et al.*, 1994; Hayes *et al.*, 1998; Owen *et al.*, 1991), particularly when having to shift from one stimulus dimension (e.g., shape) to another dimension (e.g., color; Downes *et al.*, 1989; Gauntlett-Gilbert, Roberts, & Brown, 1999). Thus, based on their performance on the WCST, nondemented PD patients do not appear to have an explicit category learning deficit *per se*, but rather their deficit on this measure appears to be more related to a deficit in set shifting.

Using other tasks, recent studies have attempted to understand the specific processes underlying explicit category learning deficits in nondemented PD patients. For example, Price (2006) administered a rule-based task to a group of nondemented PD patients in which category membership was based on a weighting of the presence of different geometric shapes. Specifically, 1-3 geometric figures were presented on each trial and participants were required to categorize the stimulus configurations into 1 of 2 categories. Each geometric figure had a specific weight assigned and category membership depended on the combination of these weights. The rule was explicit in the sense that participants could learn these weights verbally as the task proceeded. Results indicated that PD patients were impaired relative to healthy controls in learning the rule across 160 trials. In addition, Price (2006) obtained verbal reports from participants regarding how they were attempting to solve the task. An analysis of these verbal reports indicated that PD patients were less likely to use more efficient strategies that would lead to better performance, such as the possibility that a specific geometric shape was associated more with a specific category or that there was a differential weighting associated with the various geometric figures. Thus, these results suggest that PD patients are impaired in generating specific hypotheses that could be used to learn categories.

In one of our first studies examining explicit category learning in PD patients (Maddox & Filoteo, 2001), we used the perceptual categorization task (described above) in which subjects were presented with horizontal and vertical lines that varied in length. Optimal responding required the participant to categorize the stimulus into one category if the horizontal line was longer than the vertical line or into the other category if the vertical line was longer than the horizontal line. Somewhat surprisingly, the patients learned the rule at the same rate and level as control participants. To further investigate explicit category learning, we conducted a follow-up study (Ashby, Noble, Filoteo, Waldron, & Ell, 2003) in which participants categorized single cards that varied along four different binary-valued dimensions (e.g., nature of shapes, number of shapes, filling of shapes, and color of card). In the explicit condition, category membership was defined by the value on a single dimension (e.g., the color of the card). In contrast to our original finding (Maddox & Filoteo, 2001), PD patients were impaired in learning this explicit categorization rule. This finding has also been replicated in another recent study (Maddox, Aparicio, Marchant, & Ivry, 2005).

At first glance the findings from these previous studies which demonstrated a rule-based deficit in PD patients (Ashby *et al.*, 2003; Maddox, Aparicio *et al.*, 2005) seem to contradict our original finding of no deficit (Maddox & Filoteo, 2001), but one potential explanation for these discrepant results has to do with the presence or absence of irrelevant dimensional variation in the tasks used in the studies. That is, in our original study (Maddox & Filoteo, 2001), both of the stimulus dimensions (i.e., the length of the horizontal and vertical lines) were relevant to category membership, so there was no irrelevant dimensional variation. In contrast, in the other studies (Ashby *et al.*, 2003; Maddox, Aparicio *et al.*, 2005), one dimension of the stimulus was relevant and three dimensions could vary randomly from trial-to-trial. Thus, the task in the more recent studies required greater selective attention than our original study, suggesting that attentional deficits might contribute to PD patients' explicit category learning deficits.

We examined this hypothesis more directly in a follow-up study (Filoteo, Maddox, Ing, Zizak, & Song, 2005) where we systematically manipulated the selective attention requirements during the learning of an explicit task. Specifically, participants were administered a task in which they were presented with stimuli that had four binary-valued dimensions in four different conditions. Examples of representative stimuli from one stimulus set used in this study are shown in Figure 4A. For these "castle" stimuli, the potential relevant dimensions could be the shape of the foundation (diamond or square), location of the ramparts (above walls or sunken into walls), number of rings surrounding the castle (1 or 2), or the color of the drawbridge (yellow or green). In each of the four conditions, one of the binary-valued dimensions determined category membership, and zero, one, two, or three irrelevant dimensions varied from trial-to-trial. Thus, there was a systematic difference among the four conditions in terms of the degree of irrelevant dimensional variation, and thus, the amount of selective attention required. Figure 4B displays the number of trials-to-criterion (i.e., the number of trials it took subjects to obtain ten correct responses in a row correct with a greater number of trials indicative of poorer performance) for the four experimental conditions for the PD patients, a group of age-matched controls, and a group of younger controls. As can be seen, PD patients demonstrated a dramatic increase in trials-to-criterion relative to the age-matched controls when there were two irrelevant dimensions that varied across trials. Overall, these results indicated that PD patients' ability to learn the explicit categories was impacted to a much greater extent than controls as the number of varying irrelevant dimensions increased, suggesting that deficits in selective attention might contribute to the PD patients' impairment in explicit category learning. This finding is consistent with a previous study that demonstrated that PD patients are only impaired in discrimination learning when there is increased irrelevant dimensional variation (Channon, Jones, & Stephenson, 1993).

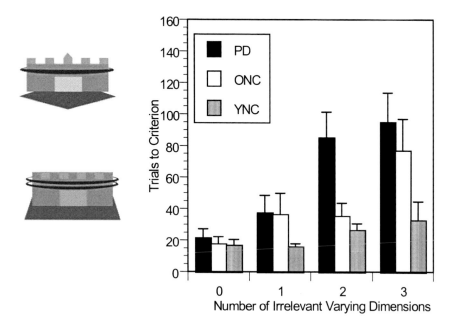

Figure 4. (A) Sample "castle" stimuli, and (B) trials-to-criterion for the PD patients, older normal controls (ONC), and younger normal controls (YNC).

Although this work supports the notion that deficits in selective attention processes might underlie the explicit category learning impairment in patients with PD, the specificity of such a deficit had not been demonstrated. In particular, PD patients had not been examined on more complex explicit category learning tasks in which other cognitive processes are also emphasized. Indeed, most past studies of explicit category learning in PD have used tasks in which only a single dimension is relevant, such as those studies that have used the WCST (Ashby et al., 2003; Paolo et al., 1996). Such tasks emphasize selective attention processes that are often found to be impaired in nondemented patients with PD (Filoteo & Maddox, 1999; Maddox, Filoteo, Delis, & Salmon, 1996; Sharpe, 1990). However, it is well known that PD patients are impaired in other cognitive processes that also likely contribute to explicit category learning. Specifically, working memory deficits have often been reported in these patients (Gilbert et al., 2005; Owen et al., 1993; Owen et al., 1997; Postle et al., 1997), and this cognitive process is likely involved in explicit category learning. For example, in learning explicit rules, participants must generate hypotheses regarding the possible rule, test such hypotheses using feedback, switch to a new hypothesis if the one currently in use is not correct, and keep track of those hypotheses that either did not work or are currently working.

Thus, it is possible that deficits in working memory might also contribute to PD patients' impairment in learning explicit categorization rules.

To examine this issue, we conducted another study in which participants were asked to learn three explicit category structures (Filoteo, Maddox, Ing, & Song, 2007). One of the conditions required participants to learn the rule depicted in Figure 2, and the other two conditions required participants to learn the rules depicted in Figure 5. The stimuli in this study consisted of Gabor patches that varied from trial-to-trial in orientation and the width of the bars. In the *unidimensional* explicit condition (Figure 2), optimal responding required that the subject set a criterion on the spatial frequency dimension and respond "A" if the bars were wide or "B" if the bars were narrow. Orientation was irrelevant in this condition although it varied from trial-to-trial. Thus, participants had to attend selectively to one stimulus dimension (the width of the bars) and ignore the other, irrelevant varying dimension (orientation). Note, as in previous studies (Ashby *et al.*, 2003; Maddox, Aparicio *et al.*, 2005), this rule required participants to learn a rule in the presence of an irrelevant dimension that varied from trial-to-trial. In the *conjunctive* explicit condition, optimal responding required the subject to respond "A" if the stimulus was more vertical *and* had narrow bars, or respond "B" if otherwise. This approach represents an explicit combination of the two features and the rule is highly verbalizable. As such, this task is considered to be explicit. The optimal rule is depicted by the solid horizontal and vertical lines in Figure 5A. In the *disjunctive* condition, the optimal rule required that the subject respond "A" if the stimulus was more vertical and had narrow bars *or* if the stimulus was more horizontal and had wide bars, or to respond "B" if the stimulus was more vertical and had wide bars *or* if the stimulus was more horizontal and had narrow bars. The optimal rule is depicted by the solid horizontal and vertical lines in Figure 5B.

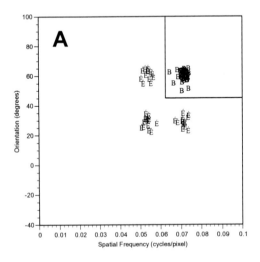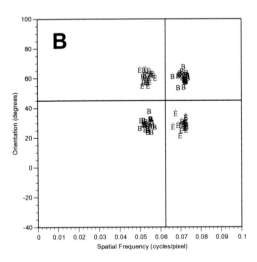

Figure 5. Stimulus distributions for (A) conjunctive, and (B) disjunctive rule-based category learning conditions. Filled squares represent stimuli from Category A and open circles represent stimuli from Category B. Solid lines represent the optimal bounds for each condition.

Note, although optimal responding in both the conjunctive and disjunctive tasks required participants to use a verbalizable combination of the two stimulus dimensions, the two tasks likely emphasize working memory to a different degree. Specifically, the logical expression associated with the disjunctive rule is much longer than the logical expression associated with the conjunctive rule, and therefore should require greater working memory. Thus, a comparison of PD patients' performances in the conjunctive and disjunctive conditions could help determine whether working memory deficits might also contribute to PD patients' explicit category learning deficits. In addition, because the conjunctive and disjunctive conditions require the participant to base their decision on both stimulus dimensions, these conditions served as an important test to determine if PD patients are impaired in all explicit tasks, or if they are impaired in only those tasks where there is irrelevant dimensional variation, such as in the unidimensional task.

Figure 6 displays the results from the three conditions. As can be seen, PD patients demonstrated a large impairment on the unidimensional explicit condition (Figure 6A), replicating previous findings (Ashby *et al.*, 2003; Maddox, Aparicio *et al.*, 2005). In contrast, the patients were not impaired in the conjunctive condition (Figure 6B) or the disjunctive condition (Figure 6C). Importantly, both groups displayed less learning in the disjunctive condition than the conjunctive condition, which was likely due to the greater working memory requirements of the former task. The pattern of PD patients' performance suggests that the explicit deficit exhibited by these patients in past studies is likely related to an impairment in selective attention. That is, the unidimensional condition placed a greater emphasis on selective attention processes because optimal responding required that the participant ignore the irrelevant variation on the orientation dimension, whereas selective attention requirements were less in the conjunctive and disjunctive conditions because optimal responding required that the participant attend to both the spatial frequency and orientation dimensions. In contrast, working memory deficits do not appear to account for their explicit category learning deficits, a view that has also been supported by previous studies (Price, 2006).

Taken together, previous work suggests that nondemented PD patients' impairments on traditional clinical rule-based tasks may be due to a deficit in shifting attentional set, whereas more recent studies that have used experimental measures suggest that their rule-based deficit may be associated with impairments in hypothesis generation and/or selective attention.

IMPLICIT CATEGORY LEARNING

As described above, three different classes of tasks have been used to investigate implicit category learning in PD patients: prototype distortion tasks and artificial grammar learning tasks; probabilistic learning tasks; and information-integration tasks. The results of studies using these three classes of tasks are discussed below.

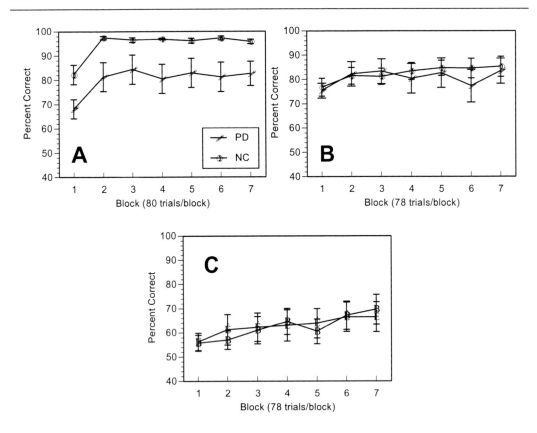

Figure 6. Accuracy for PD patients and NC subjects for (A) unidimensional, (B) conjunctive, and (C) disjunctive rule-based category learning conditions.

Prototype Distortion Learning and Artificial Grammar Learning Tasks

The first implicit tasks to be discussed are the artificial grammar task and the prototype learning task (Posner & Keele, 1968; A. S. Reber, 1967). In the artificial grammar learning task, participants are presented strings of letters that conform to a particular grammatical structure and are asked to attend to these stimuli. After having been exposed to those stimuli, participants are told that the letter strings they were shown all conformed to a particular grammatical structure and that they are now going to be shown new stimuli, with some of those conforming to the grammatical structure and the others not conforming. The participants' task is to categorize these new stimuli as either conforming or not conforming to the grammatical structure. The prototype distortion learning task is somewhat similar to the artificial grammar learning task. Specifically, participants are typically exposed to 9-dot stimuli from a single category, where the stimuli are "high distortions" of a prototype display. Participants are not required to make a response during training, but are simply told to study each of the stimuli that are presented. After their exposure to the stimuli, participants are presented with the prototype, low distortions of the prototype, high distortions of the prototype (not seen during training), and "random" stimuli (consisting of a 9-dot display that are randomly organized). The participants task is to categorize the new stimuli and decide whether each item 'is' or 'is not' a member of the previously studied category.

To our knowledge, all studies that have examined PD patients on either the artificial grammar learning or the prototype distortion learning tasks using the above methods have shown normal performances in patients relative to controls (P. J. Reber & Squire, 1999; J. Smith, Siegert, McDowall, & Abernethy, 2001; Witt, Nuhsman, & Deuschl, 2002b), although one study did report that patients were impaired after a second exposure to the test stimuli in an artificial grammar learning task (Peigneux, Meulemans, Van der Linden, Salmon, & Petit, 1999).

The finding of relatively spared performance on these tasks is consistent with the notion that learning under these conditions is primarily dependent on a perceptual priming system mediated by posterior visual cortices, including the occipital lobes and fusiform gyrus (P. J. Reber, Gitelman, Parrish, & Mesulam, 2003; Skosnik et al., 2002), brain regions that are relatively spared early in the course of PD. Such learning is believed to reflect a perceptual form of learning that is not dependent on the striatum, and thus it may not be surprising that PD patients are unimpaired on such tasks. This is especially the case when there is only one structured category and the participant's task is to state during transfer whether the test item is a member or not a member of that category (often referred to as an A/not A task) (Ashby & Maddox, 2005).

A related explanation why PD patients may not be impaired on these tasks is that they use "observational" training in that participants are not given any information regarding category membership when the stimuli are presented during training. Indeed, a recent study demonstrated that PD patients are impaired on an artificial grammar learning task when learning is based on trial-by-trial feedback, but they are not impaired after simply observing the stimuli during training (J. G. Smith & McDowall, 2006). This issue will be discussed in greater detail below.

Probabilistic Category Learning

Another form of category learning that has been studied in patients with PD is probabilistic learning, in which a set of stimuli are probabilistically related to one of two outcomes. The most popular task that has been used with PD patients is the Weather Prediction Task (WPT), which requires subjects to learn to categorize stimuli (consisting of various cue combinations) that are probabilistically associated with one of two categorical outcomes-- 'rain' or 'sunshine' (Gluck, Oliver, & Myers, 1996). Previous studies using the WPT in PD patients have yielded mixed results. For example, the first study to examine PD patients on the WPT found a deficit in these patients early in training (the first 50 trials), whereas patients were normal later in training (Knowlton, Mangels, & Squire, 1996), a finding that was later replicated by other investigators (Witt, Nuhsman, & Deuschl, 2002a). In contrast, using a slightly modified version of the WPT, another study found that PD patients were impaired both early in training (the first 50 trials) as well as later in training (trials 100-150) (Shohamy, Myers, Grossman et al., 2004). Still, other studies have only identified deficits in PD patients after extensive training (>200 trials) (Shohamy, Myers,

Onlaor, & Gluck, 2004). Finally, at least two studies have found that PD patients are not impaired on the WPT (Moody, Bookheimer, Vanek, & Knowlton, 2004; Price, 2005).

One potential explanation as to these discrepant results is the recent finding of important individual differences as to how a participant might solve the WPT. To examine this issue, Gluck and colleagues (Gluck, Shohamy, & Myers, 2002) instantiated several different strategic approaches one could use when performing the WPT and applied this strategy analysis to PD patients' performances on this task (Shohamy, Myers, Grossman *et al.*, 2004; Shohamy, Myers, Onlaor *et al.*, 2004). The results were very interesting in that both PD patients and control participants tended to learn the WPT early on by memorizing stimuli with only a single cue present (referred to as a singleton strategy). As learning progressed, however, the majority of control participants tended to switch to 'multi-cue' strategy that required the integration of multiple cues within the display. In contrast, the PD patients tended to continue to use a singleton strategy that they had adopted during the early part of learning and failed to switch away to the more advantageous multi-cue approach. Interestingly, in one study (Shohamy, Myers, Onlaor *et al.*, 2004), PD patients and controls who switched to a multi-cue strategy did not differ on the WPT, suggesting that when patients can change to a more efficient strategy, they are able to apply it just as accurately as controls.

The finding that PD patients are impaired on the WPT because of a failure to switch strategies is reminiscent of their deficit described above on the WCST. In fact, these results are in line with the finding that PD patients' deficits on the WPT have been associated with the number of perseverative errors on the WCST (Knowlton *et al.*, 1996; Price, 2005). This observation again supports the notion that PD patients' impairment on the WPT may be more a failure to switch cognitive set than to learn probabilistic categorization rules.

Another potentially important finding with the WPT comes from functional imaging data. In particular, functional imaging studies with normal participants indicate that learning the WPT is associated with activity in the striatum, medial temporal lobes, midbrain dopamine regions (i.e., the substantia nigra and ventral tegmentum), and the ventral striatum. In fact, Poldrack and colleagues (Poldrack *et al.*, 2001; Poldrack, Prabhakaran, Seger, & Gabrieli, 1999; Rodriguez, Aron, & Poldrack, 2006) demonstrated an important dynamic when normal participants learn the WPT in that, as the task is performed across time, there is a shift from greater activation of medial temporal lobe regions (which are involved in explicit memory processes) to greater activation in the striatum.

Importantly, a recent functional imaging study with PD patients performing the WPT demonstrated increased activation within the medial temporal lobe relative to controls, as well as decreased activation of the striatum (Moody *et al.*, 2004). These findings, along with the results from those studies that examined strategic approaches in learning the WPT, suggest the possibility that, early in learning, PD patients may engage an explicit approach to solving the task that is mediated within the medial temporal lobe memory system, and fail to disengage that system in order to switch to a more optimal approach that is mediated within the striatum.

Information-Integration Category Learning

As described in the previous section, past studies that have attempted to examine implicit category learning in PD patients using the WPT tasks have yielded mixed results. However, even when PD patients have been shown to be impaired on such tasks as the WPT, a more detailed analysis of their deficits suggests that they may be impaired in switching away from an explicit rule in order to adopt an implicit rule, and not in implicit learning *per se*. In our studies of category learning, the use of the perceptual categorization task has allowed us to construct the categories in a manner where we are more certain that participants use either an implicit or explicit approach, but not both. In addition, the application of quantitative models has allowed us to further determine what approach a participant takes when learning the task.

The results from one of our first category learning studies in PD indicated that nondemented patients are impaired in learning an implicit categorization rule, such as the one shown in Figure 3B (Maddox & Filoteo, 2001). However, in a subsequent study (Ashby *et al.*, 2003), we found that PD patients were normal in learning an implicit information-integration rule. One important difference between the two studies was that in the Maddox & Filoteo (2001) study, the optimal rule that defined category membership was defined by a nonlinear relationship between the stimulus dimensions. In contrast, the optimal rule that defined category membership in the Ashby et al. (2003) study was based on a linear relationship between the relevant stimulus dimensions. Thus, the linearity of the rule might account for the discrepant findings in these two studies.

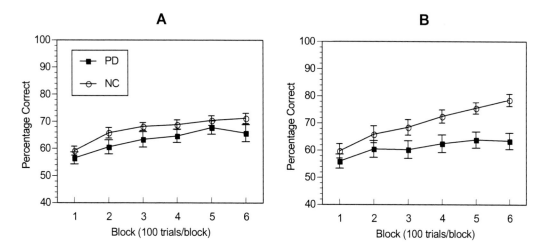

Figure 7. Percentage correct for PD patients and normal controls on (A) the linear information-integration condition and (B) the nonlinear information-integration condition.

To address this possibility, we conducted a third study in which implicit category learning in PD patients was examined using both a linear and a nonlinear rule to determine whether differences in the linearity of the categories would impact learning (Filoteo, Maddox, Salmon, & Song, 2005). In this study, we used single lines that varied in length and orientation (See Figure 3). In the nonlinear implicit condition, the optimal rule was defined by a nonlinear relationship between the length and the orientation of the line (Figure 3A), whereas in the linear implicit condition, the optimal rule was defined by a linear relationship between the two dimensions (Figure 3B). Although optimal learning for both the linear and the nonlinear categorization rules require implicit processes, it has been suggested that the nonlinear rule does so to a greater extent (Ashby *et al.*, 2001). In particular, quantitative modeling of normal participants' performance suggests that nonlinear rules might theoretically require greater involvement of the striatum than linear rules. Thus, it was anticipated that PD patients would be more impaired on the nonlinear rule than the linear rule.

The results from the two conditions are shown in Figure 7 and indicated that PD patients were impaired in the nonlinear condition (Figure 7B), but were normal in the linear condition (Figure 7A). These findings replicated our original study (Maddox & Filoteo, 2001) by identifying a deficit in PD patients in nonlinear implicit category learning. In addition, we also applied quantitative models to the participants' data in the linear and nonlinear condition to identify what approach (implicit or explicit) individuals used when learning these rules. Interestingly, only a fairly small percentage of the PD patients (55%) and control participants (65%) used an implicit approach in learning the linear rule, whereas the other participants in the two groups used an explicit approach. In contrast, most of the PD patients (80%) and the control participants (80%) used an implicit approach in learning the nonlinear rule. Importantly, when we compared the PD patients and control participants who actually used an implicit approach in the nonlinear condition, we continued to observe a deficit in the patients, whereas the two subgroups in the linear condition did not differ. Thus, unlike PD patients' past performances on the WPT, the deficits we observed on measures of information-integration category learning do indeed suggest that PD patients are impaired in learning some implicit categorization rules. This especially seems to be the case when the rule is defined by a complex (i.e., nonlinear) relationship among the stimulus attributes, and such deficits may be related to the integrity of the striatum.

Although the results of our previous studies suggest that nondemented PD patients are primarily impaired in learning nonlinear implicit categorization rules but not linear rules, two recent studies have not supported this observation. Price (Price, 2005) found that PD patients were impaired in learning a linear implicit rule, a finding that is not consistent with that of Ashby et al. (2003). Price (2005) argued that the different findings in her study and those in Ashby et al. might be due to the categories in her study being less complex as compared to the other two studies. However, this explanation does not account for the results of our studies (Filoteo, Maddox, Salmon *et al.*, 2005; Maddox & Filoteo, 2001) in which the categories were more complex than those in Price's (2005) study. As such, the nature of this discrepancy awaits further study.

Other studies have also found somewhat conflicting results. Schmitt-Eliassen and colleagues (Schmitt-Eliassen, Ferstl, Wiesner, Deuschl, & Witt, 2007) administered a nonlinear information-integration task similar to the one used by Maddox and Filoteo (2001) but, in contrast to our results, these authors did not find any differences between PD patients and controls. However, it is important to point out that neither the PD patients nor controls in the Schmitt-Eliassen et al. study displayed a large amount of learning; likely owing to the design of the study in that the task alternated blocks of trials in which feedback was either given or not give following a participant's response. This floor effect could have made it more difficult to detect differences between the PD patients and normal control participants.

The majority of the studies to date that have examined PD patients on information-integration category learning tasks have demonstrated that these patients are impaired when the rule is nonlinear. In theory, such rules likely place more demands on the striatum relative to linear rules because the former rules require a greater degree of representation, and this could explain why PD patients are primarily impaired in nonlinear learning.

Impact of Feedback on Implicit Category Learning in PD

The studies described above suggest some inconsistencies in the literature regarding whether PD patients are impaired in implicit category learning. Specifically, several studies have shown that PD patients are not impaired on prototype distortion or artificial grammar learning tasks, whereas most studies have suggested that PD patients are impaired on probabilistic and information-integration category learning tasks. One explanation that has been put forward to account for these discrepant findings is that PD patients are primarily impaired on category learning tasks in which feedback is necessary for learning (P. J. Reber & Squire, 1999). That is, tasks such as the prototype distortion or artificial grammar learning tasks do not require participants to learn based on trial-by-trial feedback, but rather participants learn under observational training conditions in which they simply view the stimuli and often perform an orienting task. In contrast, the probabilistic and information-integration category learning tasks used in past studies almost exclusively relied on trial-by-trial feedback during the acquisition of the categories. Because a dopamine reinforcement signal is believed to underlie trial-by-trial learning, and PD patients have decreased levels of dopamine, the differences in how participants are trained on these various tasks might account for these discrepant findings.

In support of this possibility, recent studies have shown that PD patients are primarily impaired on certain category learning tasks under trial-by-trial learning conditions but not under observational training conditions. For example, Shohamy and colleagues (Shohamy, Myers, Grossman et al., 2004) demonstrated that PD patients are impaired on a version of the WPT when training was done through trial-by-trial feedback, whereas their patients were normal when they observed the stimulus cues with the associated category label and were asked to explicitly remember the associations. Similarly, a recent study by Schmitt-Eliassen et al. (2007) identified normal observational learning in a PD group using the same implicit category structure as in one of our previous studies (Maddox & Filoteo, 2001). As described above, although Schmitt-Eliassen et al. did not identify any substantial learning in patients or controls using trial-by-trial feedback, our previous study demonstrated that PD patients were impaired under feedback conditions. Taken together, these studies provide support for the possibility that PD patients are primarily impaired when the acquisition of the categories is based on feedback following each response, but not when it is based on simply observing the stimuli and the associated category labels, and that these differences may be related to alterations in the dopamine system in PD.

Additional evidence suggesting a role of dopamine in feedback-based learning comes from Frank and colleagues (Frank, Seeberger, & O'Reilly R, 2004). In their study, PD patients were tested 'on' dopaminergic medication or 'off' dopaminergic medication on a probabilistic category learning task using trial-by-trial feedback. Three different pairs of individual stimuli were presented to participants during training and participants had to select one of the two stimuli as being correct. Each of the stimuli had different probabilities associated with the correct response-- importantly, for stimulus pair A-B, stimulus A was associated with the correct response 80% of the time, whereas stimulus B was associated with the correct response 20% of the time. Because of the probabilistic nature of the task, participants could potentially learn to choose stimulus A over stimulus B for the A-B pairings either because they learned from positive feedback when selecting stimulus A, or they learned from negative feedback when selecting stimulus B. To differentiate these two possibilities, the investigators presented a transfer phase in which no feedback was given and participants were shown novel pairings of stimuli in which the A and B stimuli were never presented together. If participants learned about the task during acquisition based more on the positive feedback after having selected the A stimulus, they should be more likely to select the A stimulus in the pairings presented during transfer, whereas if they learned about the task during acquisition based more on negative feedback after having selected the B stimulus, they should avoid the B stimulus during transfer and select the other stimuli that were paired with the B stimulus. Interestingly, the results of that study indicated that PD patients 'on' medication were more likely to select the A stimulus during transfer, suggesting that they learned the task during acquisition based on positive feedback. In contrast, PD patients 'off' medication were more likely to avoid the B stimulus, suggesting that they learned the task during acquisition based more on negative feedback. These results have important implications for not only understanding the potential impact that dopamine might play on various forms of category learning in PD, but also provide some insight into the complexity of the nature of feedback in category learning. Certainly, this study raises the question as to whether the category learning results described above are dependent on whether PD patients were tested when 'on' medication.

CLINICAL APPLICATIONS OF CATEGORY LEARNING TASKS IN PD

A highly important goal in determining the clinical utility of category learning in PD is to identify whether such measures are sensitive to current cognitive deficits and predictive of future cognitive decline in nondemented PD patients. Predicting the rate of cognitive decline in patients with PD can have important implications for both clinical management and treatment strategies. Most past studies have attempted to predict the rate of cognitive decline in patients with PD using a variety of symptom and disease variables including older age at disease onset, predominant rigidity/akinesia motor symptoms, and psychiatric symptoms (Aarsland *et al.*, 2001; Hobson & Meara, 2004; Levy *et al.*, 2000). Some success has been achieved in predicting cognitive decline in patients with PD on the basis of their current level of cognitive functioning. In particular, a number of studies have shown that poor performance on traditional clinical measures of executive function predicts subsequent global cognitive decline in these patients. This predictive relationship has been shown using such executive function measures as the Stroop test and measures of verbal fluency (Dujardin *et al.*, 2004; Jacobs *et al.*, 1995; Janvin, Aarsland, & Larsen, 2005; Levy *et al.*, 2002; Mahieux *et al.*, 1998). In addition, previous studies have shown that indices from the WCST can be predictive of future dementia in PD (Woods & Troster, 2003), suggesting the possibility that category learning task may be sensitive to cognitive decline in these patients.

To further determine the potential clinical utility of PD patients' category learning deficits, we re-examined their nonlinear implicit category learning deficit described above by computing the percentage of patients who were at least 1.5 standard deviations below the mean of the controls (representing at least a mild impairment) and compared this percentage to the percentage of patients who were at least 1.5 standard deviations below the standardization sample on more traditional clinical executive-function measures, such as the WCST and verbal fluency tests. As noted above, past work has shown that these measures are the best predictors of future cognitive decline and dementia in PD. The results indicated that 60% of the nondemented PD patients were at least mildly impaired on the nonlinear implicit category learning task, whereas only 6% were impaired on the WCST (perseverative errors), 0% on the letter fluency test, and 0% on the category fluency test. For the nonlinear implicit task, there was a .91 positive predictive value (i.e., the probability that an individual has PD given they are impaired on the task), and a .74 negative predictive value (i.e., the probability that an individual does not have PD given they were not impaired on the task). These findings suggest that measures of implicit category learning hold great promise for detecting subtle cognitive deficits early in the course of the PD and may be more sensitive than traditional neuropsychological measures.

At the time of our first evaluation of the PD patients on the nonlinear implicit task, we also administered the Mattis Dementia Rating Scale (MDRS; Mattis, 1988), which is a measure of global cognitive functioning that has been used successfully in this population in both clinical and research settings (G. G. Brown *et al.*, 1999). At that time, the PD patients did not differ from controls on the MDRS, despite their impairment in the nonlinear condition. To further examine the potential clinical utility of PD patients' implicit category learning deficit, we conducted a follow-up study (Filoteo, Maddox, Song, & Salmon, 2007) in which re-administered the MDRS to 85% of the patients who participated in our previous study (mean time between evaluations = 1.6 years) and examined whether performances in the nonlinear and linear conditions predicted future cognitive decline. At the time of our first evaluation, the PD patients' mean MDRS total score was 139.0 and at the time of the second evaluation, their mean score was 134.2. The results were very striking in that performance in the final block of the nonlinear condition was highly predictive ($r=-.78$; 61% of the variance) of future decline on the MDRS, whereas poorer performance on the WCST was less predictive of decline ($r=.42$; 18% of the variance). Importantly, none of the patients were considered to be demented at the time of their second evaluation and accuracy performance in the nonlinear condition did not correlate with patients' initial MDRS scores.

In a follow-up regression analysis, we also determined that performance on the nonlinear implicit task still predicted subsequent cognitive decline even after age, gender, motor impairment, mood, baseline performance on the MDRS, and performance on the WCST were taken into account. The finding that performance on the nonlinear implicit task predicted future cognitive decline above that predicted by baseline MDRS scores is important because it suggests that implicit category learning provides additional predictive value above and beyond baseline neuropsychological evaluations.

We also examined whether our quantitative analyses would provide any additional predictive information regarding global cognitive decline. We found that PD patients whose data on the nonlinear task were best fit by one of the implicit models declined less on the MDRS than those whose data were best fit by an explicit model. This difference is depicted in Figure 8. Most importantly, we determined whether the inclusion of the model-based analyses could help predict decline on the MDRS above and beyond what was predicted by accuracy performance alone. As noted above, final block accuracy in the nonlinear condition predicted 61% of the variance associated with future decline on the MDRS. To examine this issue, we conducted a stepwise regression analysis in which we predicted change on the MDRS by first entering final block accuracy and then in the next step entering whether a patient's performance was best fit by an implicit or an explicit model. The inclusion of this latter variable predicted a significant additional 15% of the variance above and beyond the 61% predicted by accuracy level alone. Thus, using a single category learning task, we were able to predict 76% of the total variance associated with future cognitive decline in a nondemented PD sample after a mean follow-up of just 1.6 years. These results clearly establish the clinical utility for the use of quantitative modeling for a better prediction of global cognitive decline in nondemented PD patients.

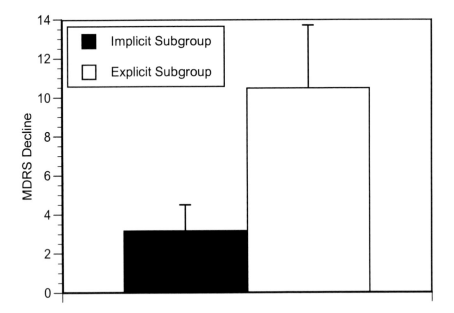

Figure 8. Decline on the Mattis Dementia Rating Scale in PD patient subgroups whose data were best fit by an implicit model or an explicit model.

Overall, these results are promising and indicate that the nonlinear implicit task is more sensitive to current and future cognitive impairment in nondemented PD patients than traditional neuropsychological tests, and that performance on at least one implicit task appears to offer unique predictive information above and beyond that which is provided by more traditional measures.

CONCLUSION

Our understanding of the nature of category learning deficits in patients with PD has not only taught us a great deal about the conditions under which these patients are impaired on such tasks, but has also informed us as to the role of various brain regions that are likely involved in normal category learning. Based on the understanding of the pathology associated with PD, it appears that the striatum plays an important role in various forms of category learning. In addition, we are now at a point where our understanding of these deficits is also starting to help us to predict future cognitive decline (and likely dementia), suggesting that a deeper understanding of the category learning impairments in these patients will likely have important clinical utility.

ACKNOWLEDGEMENTS

This research was supported, in party, by National Institute of Neurological Disorders and Stroke Grant R01 41372 to JVF and National Institute of Health Grant R01 MH59196 to WTM. Correspondence concerning this article should be addressed to J. Vincent Filoteo, UCSD, VASDHS 116-B, 3350 La Jolla Village Dr., San Diego, CA 92161 (email: vfiloteo@ucsd.edu).

REFERENCES

Aarsland, D., Andersen, K., Larsen, J. P., Lolk, A., & Kragh-Sorensen, P. (2003). Prevalence and characteristics of dementia in Parkinson disease: an 8-year prospective study. *Arch Neurol, 60*(3), 387-392.

Aarsland, D., Andersen, K., Larsen, J. P., Lolk, A., Nielsen, H., & Kragh-Sorensen, P. (2001). Risk of dementia in Parkinson's disease: a community-based, prospective study. *Neurology, 56*(6), 730-736.

Aarsland, D., Zaccai, J., & Brayne, C. (2005). A systematic review of prevalence studies of dementia in Parkinson's disease. *Mov Disord, 20*(10), 1255-1263.

Ashby, F. G., Alfonso-Reese, L. A., Turken, A. U., & Waldron, E. M. (1998). A neuropsychological theory of multiple systems in category learning. *Psychological Review, 105*(3), 442-481.

Ashby, F. G., & Gott, R. E. (1988). Decision rules in the perception and categorization of multidimensional stimuli. *J Exp Psychol Learn Mem Cogn, 14*(1), 33-53.

Ashby, F. G., & Maddox, W. T. (2005). Human category learning. *Annu Rev Psychol, 56*, 149-178.

Ashby, F. G., Noble, S., Filoteo, J. V., Waldron, E. M., & Ell, S. W. (2003). Category learning deficits in Parkinson's disease. *Neuropsychology, 17*(1), 115-124.

Ashby, F. G., & Waldron, E. M. (1999). On the nature of implicit categorization. *Psychon Bull Rev, 6*(3), 363-378.

Ashby, F. G., Waldron, E. M., Lee, W. W., & Berkman, A. (2001). Suboptimality in human categorization and identification. *Journal of Experimental Psychology: General, 130*(1), 77-96.

Azuma, T., Cruz, R. F., Bayles, K. A., Tomoeda, C. K., & Montgomery, E. B., Jr. (2003). A longitudinal study of neuropsychological change in individuals with Parkinson's disease. *Int J Geriatr Psychiatry, 18*(12), 1115-1120.

Brown, G. G., Rahill, A. A., Gorell, J. M., McDonald, C., Brown, S. J., Sillanpaa, M., & Shults, C. (1999). Validity of the Dementia Rating Scale in assessing cognitive function in Parkinson's disease. *J Geriatr Psychiatry Neurol, 12*(4), 180-188.

Brown, R. G., & Marsden, C. D. (1988). Internal versus external cues and the control of attention in Parkinson's disease. *Brain, 111 (Pt 2)*, 323-345.

Channon, S., Jones, M. C., & Stephenson, S. (1993). Cognitive strategies and hypothesis testing during discrimination learning in Parkinson's disease. *Neuropsychologia, 31*(1), 75-82.

Cools, R., Barker, R. A., Sahakian, B. J., & Robbins, T. W. (2001). Mechanisms of cognitive set flexibility in Parkinson's disease. *Brain, 124*(Pt 12), 2503-2512.

Cronin-Golomb, A., Corkin, S., & Growdon, J. H. (1994). Impaired problem solving in Parkinson's disease: impact of a set-shifting deficit. *Neuropsychologia, 32*(5), 579-593.

Downes, J. J., Roberts, A. C., Sahakian, B. J., Evenden, J. L., Morris, R. G., & Robbins, T. W. (1989). Impaired extra-dimensional shift performance in medicated and unmedicated Parkinson's disease: evidence for a specific attentional dysfunction. *Neuropsychologia, 27*(11-12), 1329-1343.

Dubois, B., & Pillon, B. (1997). Cognitive deficits in Parkinson's disease. *J Neurol, 244*(1), 2-8.

Dujardin, K., Defebvre, L., Duhamel, A., Lecouffe, P., Rogelet, P., Steinling, M., & Destee, A. (2004). Cognitive and SPECT characteristics predict progression of Parkinson's disease in newly diagnosed patients. *Journal of Neurology, 251*(11), 1383-1392.

Filoteo, J. V., & Maddox, W. T. (1999). Quantitative modeling of visual attention processes in patients with Parkinson's disease: effects of stimulus integrality on selective attention and dimensional integration. *Neuropsychology, 13*(2), 206-222.

Filoteo, J. V., Maddox, W. T., Ing, A. D., & Song, D. D. (2007). Characterizing rule-based category learning deficits in patients with Parkinson's disease. *Neuropsychologia, 45*(2), 305-320.

Filoteo, J. V., Maddox, W. T., Ing, A. D., Zizak, V., & Song, D. D. (2005). The impact of irrelevant dimensional variation on rule-based category learning in patients with Parkinson's disease. *J Int Neuropsychol Soc, 11*(5), 503-513.

Filoteo, J. V., Maddox, W. T., Salmon, D. P., & Song, D. D. (2005). Information-integration category learning in patients with striatal dysfunction. *Neuropsychology, 19*(2), 212-222.

Filoteo, J. V., Maddox, W. T., Simmons, A. N., Ing, A. D., Cagigas, X. E., Matthews, S., & Paulus, M. P. (2005). Cortical and subcortical brain regions involved in rule-based category learning. *Neuroreport, 16*(2), 111-115.

Filoteo, J. V., Maddox, W. T., Song, D., & Salmon, D. P. (2007). Implicit category learning performance predicts rate of cognitive decline in nondemented patients with Parkinson's disease. *Neuropsychology*,

Filoteo, J. V., Rilling, L. M., & Strayer, D. L. (2002). Negative priming in patients with Parkinson's disease: evidence for a role of the striatum in inhibitory attentional processes. *Neuropsychology, 16*(2), 230-241.

Filoteo, J. V., Simmons, A. N., Zeithamova, D., Maddox, W. T., & Paulus, M. P. (2006). *Change in patterns of brain activity related to early and later learning of information-integration category structures.* Paper presented at the Cognitive Neuroscience Society, San Francisco.

Frank, M. J., Seeberger, L. C., & O'Reilly R, C. (2004). By carrot or by stick: cognitive reinforcement learning in parkinsonism. *Science, 306*(5703), 1940-1943.

Gauntlett-Gilbert, J., Roberts, R. C., & Brown, V. J. (1999). Mechanisms underlying attentional set-shifting in Parkinson's disease. *Neuropsychologia, 37*(5), 605-616.

Gilbert, B., Belleville, S., Bherer, L., & Chouinard, S. (2005). Study of verbal working memory in patients with Parkinson's disease. *Neuropsychology, 19*(1), 106-114.

Gluck, M. A., Oliver, L. M., & Myers, C. E. (1996). Late-training amnesic deficits in probabilistic category learning: a neurocomputational analysis. *Learn Mem, 3*(4), 326-340.

Gluck, M. A., Shohamy, D., & Myers, C. (2002). How do people solve the "weather prediction" task?: individual variability in strategies for probabilistic category learning. *Learn Mem, 9*(6), 408-418.

Hayes, A. E., Davidson, M. C., Keele, S. W., & Rafal, R. D. (1998). Toward a functional analysis of the basal ganglia. *J Cogn Neurosci, 10*(2), 178-198.

Heaton, R. K. (1981). *Wisconsin Card Sorting Test.* Odessa, FL: Psychological Assessment Resources.

Hobson, P., & Meara, J. (2004). Risk and incidence of dementia in a cohort of older subjects with Parkinson's disease in the United Kingdom. *Movement Disorders, 19*(9), 1043-1049.

Jackson, G. M., Jackson, S. R., Harrison, J., Henderson, L., & Kennard, C. (1995). Serial reaction time learning and Parkinson's disease: evidence for a procedural learning deficit. *Neuropsychologia, 33*(5), 577-593.

Jacobs, D. M., Marder, K., Cote, L. J., Sano, M., Stern, Y., & Mayeux, R. (1995). Neuropsychological characteristics of preclinical dementia in Parkinson's disease. *Neurology, 45*(9), 1691-1696.

Janvin, C. C., Aarsland, D., & Larsen, J. P. (2005). Cognitive predictors of dementia in Parkinson's disease: a community-based, 4-year longitudinal study. *Journal of Geriatric Psychiatry and Neurology, 18*(3), 149-154.

Knowlton, B. J., Mangels, J. A., & Squire, L. R. (1996). A neostriatal habit learning system in humans. *Science, 273*(5280), 1399-1402.

Knowlton, B. J., & Squire, L. R. (1993). The learning of categories: parallel brain systems for item memory and category knowledge. *Science, 262*(5140), 1747-1749.

Lees, A. J., & Smith, E. (1983). Cognitive deficits in the early stages of Parkinson's disease. *Brain, 106 (Pt 2)*, 257-270.

Levy, G., Jacobs, D. M., Tang, M. X., Cote, L. J., Louis, E. D., Alfaro, B., Mejia, H., Stern, Y., & Marder, K. (2002). Memory and executive function impairment predict dementia in Parkinson's disease. *Movement Disorders, 17*(6), 1221-1226.

Levy, G., Tang, M. X., Cote, L. J., Louis, E. D., Alfaro, B., Mejia, H., Stern, Y., & Marder, K. (2000). Motor impairment in PD: relationship to incident dementia and age. *Neurology, 55*(4), 539-544.

Maddox, W. T., Aparicio, P., Marchant, N. L., & Ivry, R. B. (2005). Rule-based category learning is impaired in patients with Parkinson's disease but not in patients with cerebellar disorders. *J Cogn Neurosci, 17*(5), 707-723.

Maddox, W. T., Ashby, F. G., & Bohil, C. J. (2003). Delayed feedback effects on rule-based and information-integration category learning. *J Exp Psychol Learn Mem Cogn, 29*(4), 650-662.

Maddox, W. T., & Filoteo, J. V. (2001). Striatal contributions to category learning: quantitative modeling of simple linear and complex nonlinear rule learning in patients with Parkinson's disease. *Journal of the International Neuropsychological Society, 7*(6), 710-727.

Maddox, W. T., & Filoteo, J. V. (2007). Modeling visual attention and category learning in amnesiacs, striatal-damaged patients, and normal aging. In R. W. J. Neufeld (Ed.), *Advances in Clinical Cognitive Science: Formal Modeling and Assessment of Processes and Symptoms* (pp. 113-145): American Psychological Association.

Maddox, W. T., Filoteo, J. V., Delis, D. C., & Salmon, D. P. (1996). Visual selective attention deficits in patients with Parkinson's disease: A quantitative model-based approach. *Neuropsychology, 10*(2), 197-218.

Maddox, W. T., Filoteo, J. V., Hejl, K. D., & Ing, A. D. (2004). Category number impacts rule-based but not information-integration category learning: further evidence for dissociable category-learning systems. *J Exp Psychol Learn Mem Cogn, 30*(1), 227-245.

Maddox, W. T., Filoteo, J. V., & Lauritzen, J. S. (2007). Within-category discontinuity interacts with verbal rule complexity in perceptual category learning. *J Exp Psychol Learn Mem Cogn, 33*(1), 197-218.

Maddox, W. T., Filoteo, J. V., Lauritzen, J. S., Connally, E., & Hejl, K. D. (2005). Discontinuous categories affect information-integration but not rule-based category learning. *J Exp Psychol Learn Mem Cogn, 31*(4), 654-669.

Maddox, W. T., O'Brien, J. B., Ashby, F. G., & Filoteo, J. V. (2007). Dissociating stages of information-integration category learning. *Submitted for publication.*

Mahieux, F., Fenelon, G., Flahault, A., Manifacier, M. J., Michelet, D., & Boller, F. (1998). Neuropsychological prediction of dementia in Parkinson's disease. *Journal of Neurology, Neurosurgery and Psychiatry, 64*(2), 178-183.

Mattis, S. (1988). *Dementia Rating Scale*. Odessa, FL: Psychological Assessment Resources.

Monchi, O., Petrides, M., Doyon, J., Postuma, R. B., Worsley, K., & Dagher, A. (2004). Neural bases of set-shifting deficits in Parkinson's disease. *J Neurosci, 24*(3), 702-710.

Monchi, O., Petrides, M., Mejia-Constain, B., & Strafella, A. P. (2007). Cortical activity in Parkinson's disease during executive processing depends on striatal involvement. *Brain, 130*(Pt 1), 233-244.

Moody, T. D., Bookheimer, S. Y., Vanek, Z., & Knowlton, B. J. (2004). An implicit learning task activates medial temporal lobe in patients with Parkinson's disease. *Behav Neurosci, 118*(2), 438-442.

Muslimovic, D., Post, B., Speelman, J. D., & Schmand, B. (2005). Cognitive profile of patients with newly diagnosed Parkinson disease. *Neurology, 65*(8), 1239-1245.

Nomura, E. M., Maddox, W. T., Filoteo, J. V., Ing, A. D., Gitelman, D. R., Parrish, T. B., Mesulam, M. M., & Reber, P. J. (2007). Neural correlates of rule-based and information-integration visual category learning. *Cereb Cortex, 17*(1), 37-43.

Nosofsky, R. M., Palmeri, T. J., & McKinley, S. C. (1994). Rule-plus-exception model of classification learning. *Psychol Rev, 101*(1), 53-79.

Owen, A. M. (2004). Cognitive dysfunction in Parkinson's disease: the role of frontostriatal circuitry. *Neuroscientist, 10*(6), 525-537.

Owen, A. M., Beksinska, M., James, M., Leigh, P. N., Summers, B. A., Marsden, C. D., Quinn, N. P., Sahakian, B. J., & Robbins, T. W. (1993). Visuospatial memory deficits at different stages of Parkinson's disease. *Neuropsychologia, 31*(7), 627-644.

Owen, A. M., Iddon, J. L., Hodges, J. R., Summers, B. A., & Robbins, T. W. (1997). Spatial and non-spatial working memory at different stages of Parkinson's disease. *Neuropsychologia, 35*(4), 519-532.

Owen, A. M., Roberts, A. C., Polkey, C. E., Sahakian, B. J., & Robbins, T. W. (1991). Extra-dimensional versus intra-dimensional set shifting performance following frontal lobe excisions, temporal lobe excisions or amygdalo-hippocampectomy in man. *Neuropsychologia, 29*(10), 993-1006.

Paolo, A. M., Axelrod, B. N., Troster, A. I., Blackwell, K. T., & Koller, W. C. (1996). Utility of a Wisconsin Card Sorting Test short form in persons with Alzheimer's and Parkinson's disease. *Journal of Clinical and Experimental Neuropsychology, 18*(6), 892-897.

Pascual-Leone, A., Grafman, J., Clark, K., Stewart, M., Massaquoi, S., Lou, J. S., & Hallett, M. (1993). Procedural learning in Parkinson's disease and cerebellar degeneration. *Ann Neurol, 34*(4), 594-602.

Peigneux, P., Meulemans, T., Van der Linden, M., Salmon, E., & Petit, H. (1999). Exploration of implicit artificial grammar learning in Parkinson's disease. *Acta Neurol Belg, 99*(2), 107-117.

Poldrack, R. A., Clark, J., Pare-Blagoev, E. J., Shohamy, D., Creso Moyano, J., Myers, C., & Gluck, M. A. (2001). Interactive memory systems in the human brain. *Nature, 414*(6863), 546-550.

Poldrack, R. A., Prabhakaran, V., Seger, C. A., & Gabrieli, J. D. (1999). Striatal activation during acquisition of a cognitive skill. *Neuropsychology, 13*(4), 564-574.

Posner, M. I., & Keele, S. W. (1968). On the genesis of abstract ideas. *J Exp Psychol, 77*(3), 353-363.

Postle, B. R., Jonides, J., Smith, E. E., Corkin, S., & Growdon, J. H. (1997). Spatial, but not object, delayed response is impaired in early Parkinson's disease. *Neuropsychology, 11*(2), 171-179.

Price, A. L. (2005). Cortico-striatal contributions to category learning: dissociating the verbal and implicit systems. *Behav Neurosci, 119*(6), 1438-1447.

Price, A. L. (2006). Explicit category learning in Parkinson's disease: deficits related to impaired rule generation and selection processes. *Neuropsychology, 20*(2), 249-257.

Reber, A. S. (1967). Implicit learning of artificial grammars. *Journal of Verbal Learning and Verbal Behavior, 6*, 855-863.

Reber, P. J., Gitelman, D. R., Parrish, T. B., & Mesulam, M. M. (2003). Dissociating explicit and implicit category knowledge with fMRI. *J Cogn Neurosci, 15*(4), 574-583.

Reber, P. J., & Squire, L. R. (1999). Intact learning of artificial grammars and intact category learning by patients with Parkinson's disease. *Behav Neurosci, 113*(2), 235-242.

Reber, P. J., Stark, C. E., & Squire, L. R. (1998). Contrasting cortical activity associated with category memory and recognition memory. *Learn Mem, 5*(6), 420-428.

Rodriguez, P. F., Aron, A. R., & Poldrack, R. A. (2006). Ventral-striatal/nucleus-accumbens sensitivity to prediction errors during classification learning. *Hum Brain Mapp, 27*(4), 306-313.

Schmitt-Eliassen, J., Ferstl, R., Wiesner, C., Deuschl, G., & Witt, K. (2007). Feedback-based versus observational classification learning in healthy aging and Parkinson's disease. *Brain Res.*

Sharpe, M. H. (1990). Distractibility in early Parkinson's disease. *Cortex, 26*(2), 239-246.

Shohamy, D., Myers, C. E., Grossman, S., Sage, J., Gluck, M. A., & Poldrack, R. A. (2004). Cortico-striatal contributions to feedback-based learning: converging data from neuroimaging and neuropsychology. *Brain, 127*(Pt 4), 851-859.

Shohamy, D., Myers, C. E., Onlaor, S., & Gluck, M. A. (2004). Role of the basal ganglia in category learning: how do patients with Parkinson's disease learn? *Behav Neurosci, 118*(4), 676-686.

Skosnik, P. D., Mirza, F., Gitelman, D. R., Parrish, T. B., Mesulam, M. M., & Reber, P. J. (2002). Neural correlates of artificial grammar learning. *Neuroimage, 17*(3), 1306-1314.

Smith, E. E., Patalano, A. L., & Jonides, J. (1998). Alternative strategies of categorization. *Cognition, 65*(2-3), 167-196.

Smith, E. E., & Sloman, S. A. (1994). Similarity- versus rule-based categorization. *Mem Cognit, 22*(4), 377-386.

Smith, J., Siegert, R. J., McDowall, J., & Abernethy, D. (2001). Preserved implicit learning on both the serial reaction time task and artificial grammar in patients with Parkinson's disease. *Brain Cogn, 45*(3), 378-391.

Smith, J. G., & McDowall, J. (2006). When artificial grammar acquisition in Parkinson's disease is impaired: the case of learning via trial-by-trial feedback. *Brain Res, 1067*(1), 216-228.

Vakil, E., & Herishanu-Naaman, S. (1998). Declarative and procedural learning in Parkinson's disease patients having tremor or bradykinesia as the predominant symptom. *Cortex, 34*(4), 611-620.

Weigl, E. (1927). Zur Psychologie Sogenannter Abstrakionsprozesse [Translated in Journal of Abnormal Social Psychology, 36, 3-33]. *z. Psychol, 103*, 2-45.

Wickens, J. (1990). Striatal dopamine in motor activation and reward-mediated learning: steps towards a unifying model. *J Neural Transm Gen Sect, 80*(1), 9-31.

Witt, K., Nuhsman, A., & Deuschl, G. (2002a). Dissociation of habit-learning in Parkinson's and cerebellar disease. *J Cogn Neurosci, 14*(3), 493-499.

Witt, K., Nuhsman, A., & Deuschl, G. (2002b). Intact artificial grammar learning in patients with cerebellar degeneration and advanced Parkinson's disease. *Neuropsychologia, 40*(9), 1534-1540.

Woods, S. P., & Troster, A. I. (2003). Prodromal frontal/executive dysfunction predicts incident dementia in Parkinson's disease. *Journal of the International Neuropsychological Society, 9*(1), 17-24.

In: Research Progress in Alzheimer's Disease and Dementia   ISBN 978-1-60021-960-3
Editor: Miao-Kun Sun, pp. 367-380   © 2008 Nova Science Publishers, Inc.

Chapter XIV

CEREBROVASCULAR DISEASE AND DEMENTIA

*Ola A. Selnes**

Department of Neurology, Johns Hopkins University School of Medicine, USA.

ABSTRACT

The prevalence of cerebrovascular disease has been shown to increase dramatically with increasing age. Lacunar infarcts and white matter microvascular disease can be accompanied by a spectrum of neurocognitive abnormalities ranging from mild cognitive impairment to dementia. Poststroke dementia has been reported in as many as one-third of elderly patients after stroke, but some of these patients have been shown to have Alzheimer's disease rather than a pure vascular dementia syndrome. Vascular dementia unaccompanied by Alzheimer's type pathology is uncommon in most hospital-based as well as community-based autopsy series. Co-existing Alzheimer's disease and cerebrovascular disease is thought to be more common with increasing age. The presence of vascular lesions is believed to lower the threshold for the clinical expression of cognitive impairment in patients with underlying Alzheimer's pathology. Criteria for the clinical diagnosis of Alzheimer's disease with cerebrovascular disease have not yet been developed. Prospective epidemiological studies have demonstrated that subcortical small-vessel ischemic disease is a risk factor for cognitive decline and dementia. Subcortical small-vessel white matter disease is associated with a pattern of cognitive change that is characterized by decline in motor speed, executive functions, and memory. Some aspects of cognition, including recognition memory and language, tend to remain relatively preserved even with progression of the underlying disease. The pathophysiology of the cognitive decline associated with subcortical white matter disease is believed to include disruption of fronto-subcortical connections, cortical hypoperfusion, and cortical microinfarcts.

---

* Correspondence concerning this article should be addressed to: Dr. Ola A. Selnes, Ph.D. Neurology, Division of Cognitive Neuroscience, Reed Hall East – 2, 1620 McElderry St. Baltimore, MD 21287, USA. Phone: 410-955-1696; Fax: 410-614-7472.

INTRODUCTION

Our concepts of how cerebrovascular disease may lead to cognitive impairment and dementia have evolved significantly since the notion of mental impairment secondary to arteriosclerosis was first introduced by Alzheimer more than a century ago (Loeb, 1995). With the advent of new imaging techniques, the initial emphasis on "hardening of the arteries" as an explanation for late-life cognitive decline eventually shifted to a focus on the role of large vessel infarctions (Hachinski, 1983). While single or multiple large volume cerebral infarctions have long been considered to be the principal etiologies of intellectual impairment due to cerebrovascular disease, (Leys, Henon, Mackowiak-Cordoliani, & Pasquier, 2005) recent studies have also highlighted the importance of pre-existing cerebral compromise in the form of global atrophy and white matter disease as important predictors of post-stroke dementia (Lin et al., 2003; Ivan et al., 2004). The cognitive implications of subcortical small vessel ischemic disease in the absence of large volume infarction remain less well understood. Because some patients with incidental evidence of small vessel white matter disease on neuroimaging appear clinically normal (Fein et al., 1990; Duning, Kugel, & Knecht, 2005), some have argued for more limited clinical implications of subcortical white matter disease (Burns et al., 2005). More recent prospective studies of the relationship between cognition and cerebral white matter changes have reported decline in specific areas of cognition associated with small-vessel disease (Prins et al., 2005). Perhaps the most important recent development in the field of cognition and vascular disease is that the clinical distinction between vascular cognitive impairment and Alzheimer's disease (AD) may be less absolute than was previously assumed. There is increasing recognition on the basis of epidemiological as well as neuropathological studies that these conditions frequently coexist, (2001) and that concomitant cerebrovascular disease may significantly influence the clinical expression of Alzheimer's disease pathology (Snowdon et al., 1997). There are several implications of this paradigmatic shift; perhaps most important is that it opens up possibilities for primary prevention of both vascular dementia and dementia due to Alzheimer's disease. Early-life treatment of modifiable risk factors for cerebrovascular disease may substantially reduce the burden of late-life dementia as the population continues to live longer and longer (Bowler & Gorelick, 2007).

Prevalence of Clinically Asymptomatic Cerebrovascular Disease

Population-based neuroimaging studies have demonstrated that clinically asymptomatic (silent) brain lesions are surprisingly common among otherwise healthy elderly individuals. Of 3660 participants with no clinical history of stroke in the Cardiovascular Health Study, 1131 (31%) had evidence of ischemic lesions 3 mm in diameter or larger (Price et al., 1997). Factors associated with increased risk of having white matter lesions included older age, higher blood pressure and increased levels of serum creatinine. In the population based Rotterdam Study, 259 of the 1077 study participants (24%) were found to have MRI evidence of one or more infarctions (Vermeer, Koudstaal, Oudkerk, Hofman, & Breteler, 2002). Age was among the strongest predictors of having white matter lesions, with a prevalence of 8%

among participants 60-64 years old and 35% among participants 85 years or older. In studies of populations with known cardiovascular disease, such as candidates for coronary artery bypass surgery, the prevalence of silent white matter abnormalities has been found to be even higher. Goto and colleagues reported that approximately 50% of their study sample (n= 421) had either small or multiple cerebral infarctions on magnetic resonance imaging before undergoing surgery (Goto et al., 2001). There is thus considerable evidence that the prevalence of clinically asymptomatic white matter abnormalities in normal elderly individuals is high and that it increases significantly with increasing age. Although the pathophysiology of these white matter changes is not fully understood, there are several lines of evidence suggesting that chronic ischemia is an important mechanism (O'Sullivan et al., 2002; Brown, Moody, Thore, Challa, & Anstrom, 2007; Munoz, 2006).

Although MR imaging has become the standard method for quantifying the degree of vascular disease of the brain, there is evidence that routine MRI sequences may not capture the entire "burden" of cerebrovascular disease. For example, studies of the integrity of white matter tracts with using diffusion-tensor imagining (DTI) have revealed abnormalities in deep white matter areas that appear normal on standard MRI (O'Sullivan et al., 2001b). There is also evidence that markers of cerebral vascular injury other than lacunar infarcts and leukoariosis, such as microinfarcts (Koennecke, 2006) and hypoperfusion (Ruitenberg et al., 2005) may contribute to the clinical expression of vascular disease of the brain. Some have suggested that this could explain the relatively modest correlations between degree of cognitive impairment and white matter lesion-load on conventional MRI observed in some studies (Sabri et al., 1999).

CLINICAL SUBTYPES OF VASCULAR COGNITIVE IMPAIRMENT

The terminology and diagnostic criteria used to characterize the cognitive manifestations of cerebrovascular disease have evolved significantly over the past two decades. Early definitions of vascular dementia were modeled after diagnostic criteria for Alzheimer's disease, but it is now recognized that the clinical presentation as well as cognitive profiles of patients with vascular dementia differ in important ways from those of patients with AD (Knopman, 2006). The term "multi-infarct dementia" is now considered to be too restrictive, since it includes only cases with multiple large infarctions. The terms "vascular cognitive disorder" or "vascular cognitive impairment" have been proposed as umbrella terms that can be used to refer to multiple subtypes and severities of cognitive decline secondary to vascular disease of the brain (Sachdev, 1999; O'Brien et al., 2003). Whether or not all subtypes of cognitive decline due to vascular disease can be covered by a single set of criteria remains unclear, and some have suggested separate criteria for subcortical ischemic vascular dementia (Erkinjuntti et al., 2000).

Cortical Vascular Dementia

Dementia after stroke has long been considered the prototypical subtype of vascular cognitive impairment, and one might therefore expect that patients with poststroke dementia (PSD) all meet criteria for vascular dementia. Surprisingly, one-third of such patients instead have been reported to meet diagnostic criteria for Alzheimer's disease (Henon et al., 2001; Leys et al., 2005). This is consistent with the observation that a substantial number of patients diagnosed with poststroke dementia have cognitive impairment even before their stroke (Barba et al., 2000). Depending on the cohorts studied, the reported incidence of dementia after a cortical stroke ranges from a low of 6% (Madureira, Guerreiro, & Ferro, 2001) to a high of 29% (Henon et al., 2001). Elderly patients at risk for stroke are also at increased risk of dementia even in the absence of a stroke, and the availability of elderly controls is therefore very important when interpreting results of poststroke dementia studies. The most consistent demographic predictor of PSD is older age. The association with stroke risk factors appears less robust (Leys et al., 2005). Degree of pre-existing subcortical microvascular disease and global atrophy have been identified as additional predictors of poststroke dementia (Jokinen et al., 2005). Stroke characteristics, such as overall lesion volume and location, have been found to be less predictive, however, and the view that a certain volume of brain tissue loss predictably causes dementia is thus no longer widely accepted. Apolipoprotein e4 (ApoE 4) has been identified as a risk factor for Alzheimer's disease, but it does not appear to be associated with increased risk of poststroke dementia (Rowan et al., 2005).

Strategic Infarct Dementia

Strategically placed smaller infarcts, particularly those involving the deep central grey matter, may also play an important role in causing dementia (Chui, 2005). Lacunar infarcts involving the thalamus, internal capsule, and basal ganglia can be associated with widespread cognitive deficits, including confusion and memory impairment (Tatemichi et al., 1992; Vermeer et al., 2003). Infarcts involving the dorsomedial and anterior thalamus may result in executive impairment and severe amnesia, which in rare cases may be persistent (Perren, Clarke, & Bogousslavsky, 2005). Prospective studies have shown that although initially quite severe, cognitive impairment due to strategic infarcts does recover and it is often reversible by 12 months, and they are thus not a common cause of chronic dementia (Madureira, Guerreiro, & Ferro, 1999).

In summary, a cortical stroke or strategic infarct in the context of advanced age confers an increased risk of dementia, but the risk of developing dementia appears to depend more on the severity of *preexisting* white matter abnormalities, atrophy, and hemodynamic factors than the stroke characteristics themselves.

Alzheimer's Disease with Coexisting Cerebrovascular Disease

As noted in the Introduction, the usefulness of the traditional strict dichotomization between AD and vascular dementia has recently been challenged (Roman & Royall, 2004). There is accumulating evidence that AD is associated with vascular risk factors, including diabetes (Ott et al., 1999) hypertension, and smoking (Luchsinger et al., 2005). The extent to which these associations are causal or simply coincidental co-occurrences of common age-related conditions is not known. Many patients with AD, especially those 85 years or older, have significant vascular co-morbidity, and thus could be considered to have a mixed dementia syndrome of AD co-existing with cerebrovascular disease (Langa, Foster, & Larson, 2004). The determination of which vascular lesions are of importance for the clinical expression of dementia remains challenging, however (Esiri, Wilcock, & Morris, 1997). In a community-based neuropathology study of 209 elderly patients (70 – 103 years), dementia was diagnosed in 100 (48%) of the autopsy cases. Of these cases, 48% were found to have mixed vascular and AD pathology. Surprisingly, a similar degree of mixed pathology was also observed in a substantial subset (36%) of the non-demented cases (2001). Risk factors for vascular disease by themselves do not appear to have a significant influence on the rate of progression for patients with a diagnosis of AD, although cerebrovascular events do (Regan et al., 2006). Even though a mixed etiology may be more common than either pure AD or vascular dementia among very old patients, clinical criteria for antemortem diagnosis of mixed dementia are not yet available (O'Brien et al., 2003).

Subcortical Ischemic Vascular dementia

Subcortical white matter hyperintensities and lacunar infarcts demonstrated by MRI are generally considered as evidence of small vessel or microvascular ischemic disease, although some are related to dilated perivascular spaces (Chui, 2005). Pathologically, abnormalities in white matter signals on MRI reflect focal and diffuse lesions of the subcortical and periventricular white matter, as well as lacunes and micro-infarcts of the central gray matter (Udaka, Sawada, & Kameyama, 2002).

Because white matter abnormalities are common in neurologically asymptomatic individuals, they are frequently considered to be benign. There is increasing evidence, however, that white matter abnormalities on MRI are associated with an increased risk of dementia. In cross-sectional studies, those with more severe white matter disease had a two-fold increased risk of dementia (Kuller et al., 2005). In prospective studies, the presence of periventricular white matter lesions at baseline was found to double the risk of future dementia (Vermeer et al., 2003). Furthermore, progression of white matter disease is associated with decline in cognitive test performance, thus supporting an etiological link between the white matter changes and cognitive decline (Longstreth, Jr. et al., 2005; Prins et al., 2005).

Although epidemiological studies have clearly established an association of subcortical white matter lesions with worse cognitive performance, (de Groot et al., 2000) the clinical expression of subcortical small vessel disease in individual patients can be highly variable. In a patient who presents with mild cognitive impairment in the context of mild subcortical white matter lesions, the etiological consequences of the white matter lesions cannot be easily determined. Neither a history of risk factors for cerebrovascular disease nor the clinical presentation can necessarily establish that the cognitive symptoms are causally related to the white matter findings. On the one hand, there are reports of patients with MRI-proven widespread white matter disease whose cognitive functioning is normal even on formal neuropsychological testing (Duning et al., 2005). On the other hand, it is also well known that white matter abnormalities are frequently present in patients with early Alzheimer's disease (de Leeuw, Barkhof, & Scheltens, 2004).

It is unclear whether subcortical small vessel disease by itself can lead to cognitive impairment of sufficient severity to meet criteria for dementia. Overall, the cognitive expression of isolated white matter hyperintensities appears to be limited to mild psychomotor slowing and some executive impairment rather than a pervasive, severe degree of cognitive impairment (Mosley, Jr. et al., 2005). There is growing evidence, however, that the lacunar infarcts and white matter changes visualized on conventional MRI may not reflect more widespread microscopic ischemic infarcts or "covert" hypoxia-ischemia-related injury (Roman, 2004; Kalaria et al., 2001). With improvements in the ability to quantify the global burden of vascular disease of the brain, including the presence of hypoperfusion, (Takahashi, Takagi, Ide, Shohtsu, & Shinohara, 2000; Markus, Lythgoe, Ostegaard, O'Sullivan, & Williams, 2000) microinfarcts (Werring et al., 2004; Kovari et al., 2004) and amyloid angiopathy (Vinters, 2001) a more accurate assessment of the cognitive consequences of cerebrovascular disease may become possible.

NEUROPSYCHOLOGICAL FINDINGS WITH CEREBROVASCULAR DISEASE

There has been longstanding debate about the specificity of the cognitive profile associated with subcortical ischemic vascular cognitive impairment, and there are several reasons why this question has proven difficult to resolve. First, if all causes of vascular cognitive impairment are considered together, there is very little reason to expect a consistent pattern of cognitive impairment. The cognitive profile of dementia due to large cortical infarcts will depend on both the lateralization, location and overall size of the lesion, and thus be quite variable. Secondly, because comprehensive cognitive test batteries cannot easily be administered as part of large clinical or community samples, many of the studies with adequate testing have been limited by modest sample sizes (Tierney et al., 2001; Garrett et al., 2004). Third, not all cognitive domains have been assessed in sufficient detail to distinguish between the cognitive profiles in vascular and Alzheimer's type cognitive impairment. One of the remarkably consistent neuropsychological findings in patients with subcortical disease is motor and psychomotor slowing (de Groot et al., 2000) whereas patients with cortical dementias do not typically show this feature. Because many studies have not included measures of motor speed in their test battery, however, psychomotor speed has not typically been considered a unifying characteristic of vascular cognitive impairment (Garrett et al., 2004; Laukka, Jones, Small, Fratiglioni, & Backman, 2004).

Studies that have examined patients with vascular cognitive impairment of sufficient severity to meet criteria for dementia have generally reported some degree of impairment in multiple cognitive domains, with more similarities than differences from AD. It is likely, however, that these studies may have included a subset of patients with dementia of mixed etiology (Laukka et al., 2004; Fahlander, Wahlin, Almkvist, & Backman, 2002). In patients with less advanced disease, a more distinctive cognitive profile may be observed. Garrett and colleagues reported that the neurocognitive performance of a group of patients with cognitive impairment (but no dementia) was characterized by more severe deficits executive functioning and verbal retrieval (Garrett et al., 2004). Other investigators have also described a similar cognitive profile of less severe memory impairment and greater executive impairment in patients with vascular cognitive impairment (Looi & Sachdev, 1999). The pattern of memory impairment may also be somewhat different in AD and vascular cognitive impairment. Some studies have reported a profile of memory impairment that includes better preservation of recognition memory performance than of to free recall in patients with vascular cognitive impairment (Tierney et al., 2001; Traykov et al., 2002). In studies of patients with CADASIL, who are generally younger and thus less likely to have coexisting AD pathology, speed of processing has typically been identified as impaired, with somewhat less severe but significant deficits in areas of executive functioning and attention. It has been proposed that this profile of relative preservation and impairment is the essential features of the cognitive syndrome associated with small vessel subcortical ischemic disease (Peters et al., 2005; Buffon et al., 2006; O'Sullivan, Singhal, Charlton, & Markus, 2004).

Although the profile of subcortical vascular cognitive impairment may vary somewhat according to both etiology and severity of the disease, in a clinical setting the pattern of relative preservation and impairment on neuropsychological testing may nonetheless be helpful. In a patient with risk factors, imaging findings and clinical presentation consistent with subcortical ischemic vascular disease, a neuropsychological profile of relatively preserved language and recognition memory, but with motor/ psychomotor slowing and impaired executive performance, can be considered supportive of a diagnosis of probable vascular cognitive impairment, even if the clinical course is indistinguishable from that of AD. An important caveat is that the profile of the neuropsychological test findings alone cannot exclude possible coexisting AD, but if follow-up testing indicates no or only minor change over time, this can be considered additional support in favor of a vascular etiology.

Figure 1 illustrates the general pattern of relative impairment of major cognitive domains in patients with subcortical ischemic vascular disease. Speed of processing, including motor and psychomotor speed, are often among the most severely affected cognitive domains in patients with cerebrovascular disease (Almkvist, 2003). The Grooved Pegboard is a well-standardized measure for assessment of motor speed (Lezak, 1995). In addition to providing information on overall motor speed, it can also provide potential lateralizing information by identifying significant differences in speed between the right and left hand. Executive functions and working memory are also among the cognitive domains where there is decline even during early stages of the disease (Amberla et al., 2004). For some cognitive domains, including new verbal learning and memory, cognitive performance may be relatively similar in cortical and subcortical dementias. Nonetheless, some aspects of verbal recognition memory may be better preserved in patients with subcortical ischemic vascular disease

(Tierney et al., 2001; Schmidtke & Hull, 2002). The relative preservation of recognition may be somewhat test-specific, and is often most readily demonstrated on tests of forced-choice, immediate recognition memory such as the one developed by Warrington (Warrington, 1984). Delayed recall has also been shown to be somewhat less severely impaired with subcortical than with cortical dementias such as Alzheimer's disease (Libon, Price, Davis, & Giovannetti, 2004).

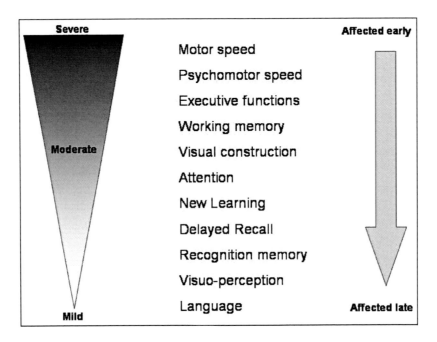

Figure 1. Relative impairment of different cognitive domains in patients with cognitive impairment secondary to subcortical vascular disease.

The pattern of performance on tests of constructional praxis, such as the Rey Complex Figure, may not differ significantly between patients with subcortical and cortical disease. Visuoperception tends to be better preserved with subcortical vascular disease, however, and this can readily be evaluated with simple tests such as having the patient tell time from pictures of clock-faces. (Figure 2) This is a task that is very sensitive to parietal lobe-type functions, because it combines perception of numbers with perception of spatial relationships of the two hands of the clock. Patients with Alzheimer's disease perform very poorly on this task, whereas patients with vascular cognitive impairment have relatively normal performance (Schmidtke et al., 2002).

Language, in particular naming performance, tends to be better preserved in patients with subcortical ischemic vascular disease. One important caveat is that some patients with subcortical disease have retrieval deficits that can mimic a language disorder (Laine, Vuorinen, & Rinne, 1997; Traykov et al., 2002). Unlike patients with a semantically based naming disorder, however, patients with retrieval deficits perform normally on a multiple-choice type test of confrontation naming.

Figure 2. Example of analog clock-face stimuli suitable for evaluating perception of time; a perceptual equivalent of clock-face drawing sensitive to parietal lobe-type impairment.

MECHANISM OF COGNITIVE IMPAIRMENT WITH SUBCORTICAL VASCULAR DISEASE

Unlike the slow, selective and progressive neuronal loss that is believed to underlie the cognitive decline of patients with AD, the mechanism of the cognitive impairment with subcortical small vessel ischemic disease remains less well understood. The pattern of motor slowing and executive impairment often observed with subcortical ischemic white matter disease has led some investigators to focus on the role of the integrity of fronto-subcortical connectivity. Several case reports have noted that subcortical lesions involving structures such as the thalamus, globus pallidus and internal capsule can produce a striking "frontal lobe syndrome" (Strub, 1989; Tatemichi et al., 1992; Bogousslavsky et al., 1988). The specifics of the clinical expression of subcortical lesions have been hypothesized to depend on which of several fronto-subcortical circuits are being interrupted (Cummings, 1993). It has also been suggested that disruption or disconnection of fronto-subcortical connections may account for decline in executive functions accompanying normal aging (O'Sullivan et al., 2001a). An alternate explanation for the disproportionate involvement of frontal or executive functions with ischemic white matter disease is that subcortical lesions may be accompanied by cortical hypoperfusion (Tullberg et al., 2004). Finally, the role of cortical microinfarcts and other vascular lesions, some of which may not be detectable by standard MR sequences, as potential mechanisms for the cognitive impairment are now beginning to be explored (Kovari et al., 2004).

CONCLUSION

Several syndromes of cognitive impairment secondary to cerebrovascular disease, ranging in severity from mild cognitive impairment to dementia, are now recognized. The risk of post-stroke dementia increases with age and with pre-existing cognitive impairment or cerebrovascular disease. Subcortical white matter small vessel disease is associated with cognitive decline, but the severity of the cognitive changes does not always correlate with the degree of white matter abnormalities observed on standard MR imaging. It has been suggested, therefore, that the subcortical white matter changes visualized on conventional MRI may be incomplete markers of the total burden of cerebrovascular disease. The cognitive profile of vascular cognitive impairment is predominantly subcortical, with prominent psychomotor slowing and executive deficits, but relatively preserved language and recognition memory. The growing recognition that vascular disease of the brain may also increase the risk of developing clinical Alzheimer's disease has led to renewed interest in early treatment of modifiable risk factors for cerebrovascular disease as a strategy for reducing the suffering, burden on caregivers, and cost associated with this disease.

ACKNOWLEDGMENTS

Supported by grant 35610 from the National Institute of Neurological Disorders and Stroke, National Institutes of Health, Bethesda, MD; by the Charles A. Dana Foundation, New York, N.Y. and the Johns Hopkins Medical Institution GCRC Grant RR 00052. Pamela Talalay, Ph.D. provided editorial assistance.

REFERENCES

Pathological correlates of late-onset dementia in a multicentre, community-based population in England and Wales. Neuropathology Group of the Medical Research Council Cognitive Function and Ageing Study (MRC CFAS) (2001). *Lancet, 357,* 169-175.

Almkvist, O. (2003). Cognitive syndrome(s) in preclinical and clinical vascular dementia. *Int.Psychogeriatr., 15 Suppl 1,* 127-131.

Amberla, K., Waljas, M., Tuominen, S., Almkvist, O., Poyhonen, M., Tuisku, S. et al. (2004). Insidious cognitive decline in CADASIL. *Stroke, 35,* 1598-1602.

Barba, R., Martinez-Espinosa, S., Rodriguez-Garcia, E., Pondal, M., Vivancos, J., & Del, S. T. (2000). Poststroke dementia : clinical features and risk factors. *Stroke, 31,* 1494-1501.

Bogousslavsky, J., Ferrazzini, M., Regli, F., Assal, G., Tanabe, H., & Delaloye-Bischof, A. (1988). Manic delirium and frontal-like syndrome with paramedian infarction of the right thalamus. *Journal of Neurology, Neurosurgery & Psychiatry, 51,* 116-119.

Bowler, J. V. & Gorelick, P. B. (2007). Advances in vascular cognitive impairment 2006. *Stroke, 38,* 241-244.

Brown, W. R., Moody, D. M., Thore, C. R., Challa, V. R., & Anstrom, J. A. (2007). Vascular dementia in leukoaraiosis may be a consequence of capillary loss not only in the lesions, but in normal-appearing white matter and cortex as well. *J Neurol.Sci.*.

Buffon, F., Porcher, R., Hernandez, K., Kurtz, A., Pointeau, S., Vahedi, K. et al. (2006). Cognitive profile in CADASIL. *J.Neurol.Neurosurg.Psychiatry, 77,* 175-180.

Burns, J. M., Church, J. A., Johnson, D. K., Xiong, C., Marcus, D., Fotenos, A. F. et al. (2005). White matter lesions are prevalent but differentially related with cognition in aging and early Alzheimer disease. *Arch.Neurol., 62,* 1870-1876.

Chui, H. (2005). Neuropathology lessons in vascular dementia. *Alzheimer Dis.Assoc.Disord.,* *19,* 45-52.

Cummings, J. L. (1993). Frontal-subcortical circuits and Human Behavior. *Arch.Neurol., 50,* 873-880.

de Groot, J. C., de Leeuw, F. E., Oudkerk, M., van Gijn, J., Hofman, A., Jolles, J. et al. (2000). Cerebral white matter lesions and cognitive function: the Rotterdam Scan Study. *Ann.Neurol., 47,* 145-151.

de Leeuw, F. E., Barkhof, F., & Scheltens, P. (2004). Alzheimer's disease--one clinical syndrome, two radiological expressions: a study on blood pressure. *J.Neurol.Neurosurg.Psychiatry, 75,* 1270-1274.

Duning, T., Kugel, H., & Knecht, S. (2005). Excellent cognitive performance despite massive cerebral white matter changes. *Neuroradiology, 47,* 749-752.

Erkinjuntti, T., Inzitari, D., Pantoni, L., Wallin, A., Scheltens, P., Rockwood, K. et al. (2000). Limitations of clinical criteria for the diagnosis of vascular dementia in clinical trials. Is a focus on subcortical vascular dementia a solution? *Ann.N.Y.Acad.Sci., 903,* 262-272.

Esiri, M. M., Wilcock, G. K., & Morris, J. H. (1997). Neuropathological assessment of the lesions of significance in vascular dementia. *J.Neurol.Neurosurg.Psychiatry, 63,* 749-753.

Fahlander, K., Wahlin, A., Almkvist, O., & Backman, L. (2002). Cognitive functioning in Alzheimer's disease and vascular dementia: further evidence for similar patterns of deficits. *J.Clin.Exp.Neuropsychol., 24,* 734-744.

Fein, G., Van, D. C., Davenport, L., Turetsky, B., Brant-Zawadzki, M., Zatz, L. et al. (1990). Preservation of normal cognitive functioning in elderly subjects with extensive white-matter lesions of long duration. *Arch.Gen.Psychiatry, 47,* 220-223.

Garrett, K. D., Browndyke, J. N., Whelihan, W., Paul, R. H., DiCarlo, M., Moser, D. J. et al. (2004). The neuropsychological profile of vascular cognitive impairment--no dementia: comparisons to patients at risk for cerebrovascular disease and vascular dementia. *Arch.Clin.Neuropsychol., 19,* 745-757.

Goto, T., Baba, T., Honma, K., Shibata, Y., Arai, Y., Uozumi, H. et al. (2001). Magnetic resonance imaging findings and postoperative neurologic dysfunction in elderly patients undergoing coronary artery bypass grafting. *Annals of Thoracic Surgery, 72,* 137-142.

Hachinski, V. (1983). Multi-infarct dementia. *Neurologic Clinics, 1,* 27-36.

Henon, H., Durieu, I., Guerouaou, D., Lebert, F., Pasquier, F., & Leys, D. (2001). Poststroke dementia: incidence and relationship to prestroke cognitive decline. *Neurology, 57,* 1216-1222.

Ivan, C. S., Seshadri, S., Beiser, A., Au, R., Kase, C. S., Kelly-Hayes, M. et al. (2004). Dementia after stroke: the Framingham Study. *Stroke, 35,* 1264-1268.

Jokinen, H., Kalska, H., Mantyla, R., Ylikoski, R., Hietanen, M., Pohjasvaara, T. et al. (2005). White matter hyperintensities as a predictor of neuropsychological deficits post-stroke. *J.Neurol.Neurosurg.Psychiatry, 76,* 1229-1233.

Kalaria, R. N., Ballard, C. G., Ince, P. G., Kenny, R. A., McKeith, I. G., Morris, C. M. et al. (2001). Multiple substrates of late-onset dementia: implications for brain protection. *Novartis.Found.Symp., 235,* 49-60.

Knopman, D. S. (2006). Dementia and cerebrovascular disease. *Mayo Clin.Proc., 81,* 223-230.

Koennecke, H. C. (2006). Cerebral microbleeds on MRI: prevalence, associations, and potential clinical implications. *Neurology, 66,* 165-171.

Kovari, E., Gold, G., Herrmann, F. R., Canuto, A., Hof, P. R., Michel, J. P. et al. (2004). Cortical microinfarcts and demyelination significantly affect cognition in brain aging. *Stroke, 35,* 410-414.

Kuller, L. H., Lopez, O. L., Jagust, W. J., Becker, J. T., Dekosky, S. T., Lyketsos, C. et al. (2005). Determinants of vascular dementia in the Cardiovascular Health Cognition Study. *Neurology, 64,* 1548-1552.

Laine, M., Vuorinen, E., & Rinne, J. O. (1997). Picture naming deficits in vascular dementia and Alzheimer's disease. *J Clin.Exp.Neuropsychol., 19,* 126-140.

Langa, K. M., Foster, N. L., & Larson, E. B. (2004). Mixed dementia: emerging concepts and therapeutic implications. *JAMA, 292,* 2901-2908.

Laukka, E. J., Jones, S., Small, B. J., Fratiglioni, L., & Backman, L. (2004). Similar patterns of cognitive deficits in the preclinical phases of vascular dementia and Alzheimer's disease. *J.Int.Neuropsychol.Soc., 10,* 382-391.

Leys, D., Henon, H., Mackowiak-Cordoliani, M. A., & Pasquier, F. (2005). Poststroke dementia. *Lancet Neurol., 4,* 752-759.

Lezak, M. (1995). *Neuropsychological Assessment.* (3 ed.) Oxford University Press: New York.

Libon, D. J., Price, C. C., Davis, G. K., & Giovannetti, T. (2004). From Binswanger's disease to leuokoaraiosis: what we have learned about subcortical vascular dementia. *Clin.Neuropsychol., 18,* 83-100.

Lin, J. H., Lin, R. T., Tai, C. T., Hsieh, C. L., Hsiao, S. F., & Liu, C. K. (2003). Prediction of poststroke dementia. *Neurology, 61,* 343-348.

Loeb, C. (1995). The history of vascular dementia. *J.Hist Neurosci., 4,* 121-126.

Longstreth, W. T., Jr., Arnold, A. M., Beauchamp, N. J., Jr., Manolio, T. A., Lefkowitz, D., Jungreis, C. et al. (2005). Incidence, manifestations, and predictors of worsening white matter on serial cranial magnetic resonance imaging in the elderly: the Cardiovascular Health Study. *Stroke, 36,* 56-61.

Looi, J. C. & Sachdev, P. S. (1999). Differentiation of vascular dementia from AD on neuropsychological tests. *Neurology, 53,* 670-678.

Luchsinger, J. A., Reitz, C., Honig, L. S., Tang, M. X., Shea, S., & Mayeux, R. (2005). Aggregation of vascular risk factors and risk of incident Alzheimer disease. *Neurology, 65,* 545-551.

Madureira, S., Guerreiro, M., & Ferro, J. M. (1999). A follow-up study of cognitive impairment due to inferior capsular genu infarction. *J.Neurol., 246,* 764-769.

Madureira, S., Guerreiro, M., & Ferro, J. M. (2001). Dementia and cognitive impairment three months after stroke. *Eur.J.Neurol., 8,* 621-627.

Markus, H. S., Lythgoe, D. J., Ostegaard, L., O'Sullivan, M., & Williams, S. C. (2000). Reduced cerebral blood flow in white matter in ischaemic leukoaraiosis demonstrated using quantitative exogenous contrast based perfusion MRI. *J.Neurol.Neurosurg.Psychiatry, 69,* 48-53.

Mosley, T. H., Jr., Knopman, D. S., Catellier, D. J., Bryan, N., Hutchinson, R. G., Grothues, C. A. et al. (2005). Cerebral MRI findings and cognitive functioning: the Atherosclerosis Risk in Communities study. *Neurology, 64,* 2056-2062.

Munoz, D. G. (2006). Leukoaraiosis and ischemia: beyond the myth. *Stroke, 37,* 1348-1349.

O'Brien, J. T., Erkinjuntti, T., Reisberg, B., Roman, G., Sawada, T., Pantoni, L. et al. (2003). Vascular cognitive impairment. *Lancet Neurol., 2,* 89-98.

O'Sullivan, M., Jones, D. K., Summers, P. E., Morris, R. G., Williams, S. C., & Markus, H. S. (2001a). Evidence for cortical "disconnection" as a mechanism of age-related cognitive decline. *Neurology, 57,* 632-638.

O'Sullivan, M., Lythgoe, D. J., Pereira, A. C., Summers, P. E., Jarosz, J. M., Williams, S. C. et al. (2002). Patterns of cerebral blood flow reduction in patients with ischemic leukoaraiosis. *Neurology, 59,* 321-326.

O'Sullivan, M., Singhal, S., Charlton, R., & Markus, H. S. (2004). Diffusion tensor imaging of thalamus correlates with cognition in CADASIL without dementia. *Neurology, 62,* 702-707.

O'Sullivan, M., Summers, P. E., Jones, D. K., Jarosz, J. M., Williams, S. C., & Markus, H. S. (2001b). Normal-appearing white matter in ischemic leukoaraiosis: a diffusion tensor MRI study. *Neurology, 57,* 2307-2310.

Ott, A., Stolk, R. P., van, H. F., Pols, H. A., Hofman, A., & Breteler, M. M. (1999). Diabetes mellitus and the risk of dementia: The Rotterdam Study. *Neurology, 53,* 1937-1942.

Perren, F., Clarke, S., & Bogousslavsky, J. (2005). The syndrome of combined polar and paramedian thalamic infarction. *Arch.Neurol., 62,* 1212-1216.

Peters, N., Opherk, C., Danek, A., Ballard, C., Herzog, J., & Dichgans, M. (2005). The Pattern of Cognitive Performance in CADASIL: A Monogenic Condition Leading to Subcortical Ischemic Vascular Dementia. *Am.J.Psychiatry, 162,* 2078-2085.

Price, T. R., Manolio, T. A., Kronmal, R. A., Kittner, S. J., Yue, N. C., Robbins, J. et al. (1997). Silent brain infarction on magnetic resonance imaging and neurological abnormalities in community-dwelling older adults. The Cardiovascular Health Study. CHS Collaborative Research Group. *Stroke, 28,* 1158-1164.

Prins, N. D., van Dijk, E. J., den, H. T., Vermeer, S. E., Jolles, J., Koudstaal, P. J. et al. (2005). Cerebral small-vessel disease and decline in information processing speed, executive function and memory. *Brain, 128,* 2034-2041.

Regan, C., Katona, C., Walker, Z., Hooper, J., Donovan, J., & Livingston, G. (2006). Relationship of vascular risk to the progression of Alzheimer disease. *Neurology, 67,* 1357-1362.

Roman, G. C. (2004). Brain hypoperfusion: a critical factor in vascular dementia. *Neurol.Res., 26,* 454-458.

Roman, G. C. & Royall, D. R. (2004). A diagnostic dilemma: is "Alzheimer's dementia" Alzheimer's disease, vascular dementia, or both? *Lancet Neurol., 3,* 141.

Rowan, E., Morris, C. M., Stephens, S., Ballard, C., Dickinson, H., Rao, H. et al. (2005). Impact of hypertension and apolipoprotein E4 on poststroke cognition in subjects >75 years of age. *Stroke, 36,* 1864-1868.

Ruitenberg, A., den, H. T., Bakker, S. L., van Swieten, J. C., Koudstaal, P. J., Hofman, A. et al. (2005). Cerebral hypoperfusion and clinical onset of dementia: the Rotterdam Study. *Ann.Neurol., 57,* 789-794.

Sabri, O., Ringelstein, E. B., Hellwig, D., Schneider, R., Schreckenberger, M., Kaiser, H. J. et al. (1999). Neuropsychological impairment correlates with hypoperfusion and hypometabolism but not with severity of white matter lesions on MRI in patients with cerebral microangiopathy. *Stroke, 30,* 556-566.

Sachdev, P. (1999). Vascular cognitive disorder. *Int.J.Geriatr.Psychiatry, 14,* 402-403.

Schmidtke, K. & Hull, M. (2002). Neuropsychological differentiation of small vessel disease, Alzheimer's disease and mixed dementia. *J.Neurol.Sci., 203-204,* 17-22.

Snowdon, D. A., Greiner, L. H., Mortimer, J. A., Riley, K. P., Greiner, P. A., & Markesbery, W. R. (1997). Brain infarction and the clinical expression of Alzheimer disease. The Nun Study. *JAMA, 277,* 813-817.

Strub, R. L. (1989). Frontal lobe syndrome in a patient with bilateral globus pallidus lesions. *Archives of Neurology, 46,* 1024-1027.

Takahashi, W., Takagi, S., Ide, M., Shohtsu, A., & Shinohara, Y. (2000). Reduced cerebral glucose metabolism in subjects with incidental hyperintensities on magnetic resonance imaging. *J.Neurol.Sci., 176,* 21-27.

Tatemichi, T. K., Desmond, D. W., Prohovnik, I., Cross, D. T., Gropen, T. I., Mohr, J. P. et al. (1992). Confusion and memory loss from capsular genu infarction: a thalamocortical disconnection syndrome? *Neurology, 42,* 1966-1979.

Tierney, M. C., Black, S. E., Szalai, J. P., Snow, W. G., Fisher, R. H., Nadon, G. et al. (2001). Recognition memory and verbal fluency differentiate probable Alzheimer disease from subcortical ischemic vascular dementia. *Arch.Neurol., 58,* 1654-1659.

Traykov, L., Baudic, S., Thibaudet, M. C., Rigaud, A. S., Smagghe, A., & Boller, F. (2002). Neuropsychological deficit in early subcortical vascular dementia: comparison to Alzheimer's disease. *Dement.Geriatr.Cogn Disord., 14,* 26-32.

Tullberg, M., Fletcher, E., DeCarli, C., Mungas, D., Reed, B. R., Harvey, D. J. et al. (2004). White matter lesions impair frontal lobe function regardless of their location. *Neurology, 63,* 246-253.

Udaka, F., Sawada, H., & Kameyama, M. (2002). White matter lesions and dementia: MRI-pathological correlation. *Ann.N.Y.Acad.Sci., 977,* 411-415.

Vermeer, S. E., Koudstaal, P. J., Oudkerk, M., Hofman, A., & Breteler, M. M. (2002). Prevalence and risk factors of silent brain infarcts in the population- based Rotterdam Scan Study. *Stroke, 33,* 21-25.

Vermeer, S. E., Prins, N. D., Den Heijer, T., Hofman, A., Koudstaal, P. J., & Breteler, M. M. (2003). Silent brain infarcts and the risk of dementia and cognitive decline. *N.Engl.J.Med., 348,* 1215-1222.

Vinters, H. V. (2001). Cerebral amyloid angiopathy: a microvascular link between parenchymal and vascular dementia? *Ann.Neurol., 49,* 691-693.

Warrington, E. K. (1984). *Recognition Memory Test.* Windsor: NFER-Nelson Publishing Co.

Werring, D. J., Frazer, D. W., Coward, L. J., Losseff, N. A., Watt, H., Cipolotti, L. et al. (2004). Cognitive dysfunction in patients with cerebral microbleeds on T2*-weighted gradient-echo MRI. *Brain, 127,* 2265-2275.

In: Research Progress in Alzheimer's Disease and Dementia   ISBN 978-1-60021-960-3
Editor: Miao-Kun Sun, pp. 381-413   © 2008 Nova Science Publishers, Inc.

Chapter XV

DEMENTIA AND HYPERTENSION

Jan A. Staessen[1,], Tom Richart[1], Lutgarde Thijs[1] and Willem H. Birkenhäger[2]*

[1]Studies Coordinating Centre, Division of Hypertension and Cardiovascular Rehabilitation, Department of Cardiovascular Diseases, University of Leuven, Belgium; [2]Erasmus University, Rotterdam, The Netherlands.

ABSTRACT

Traditional teaching subdivides the dementia syndrome into neurodegenerative Alzheimer's disease (AD), vascular dementia (VaD), and mixed variants. In spite of the vast and continuing literature on the dichotomy between AD and VaD, new emerging concepts highlight the role of cardiovascular risk factors in the pathogenesis of AD, especially in older patients. Hypertension is the major player in the pathogenesis of stroke, poststroke dementia, and VaD. AD is the most common cause of dementia, contributing from 45% to 75% of the cases in Asians and whites, respectively. This review will focus on the role of hypertension as a reversible risk factor in the development of dementia, in particular AD. To set the stage, we will first summarize current insights in the epidemiology of AD, the pathogenesis of VaD and AD, and the association between neurodegeneration and atherosclerosis.

Dementia is characterized by gradual loss of memory, inability to learn, loss of vocabulary, communication skills and abstract thinking, disorientation in time and space, indifference, depression, delusions, loss of autonomy, and ultimately depersonalization and alienation. Traditional teaching subdivides the dementia syndrome into neurodegenerative

---

[*] Correspondence concerning this article should be addressed to: Dr. Jan A. Staessen, MD, PhD, FESC, FAHA, Studies Coordinating Centre, Laboratory of Hypertension, Campus Gasthuisberg, Herestraat 49, Box 702, B-3000 Leuven, Belgium. Telephone: +32-16-34-7104 (office); +32-15-41-1747 (home); +32-47-632-4928 (mobile); Facsimile: +32-16-34-7106 (office); +32-16-34-5763 (office); +32-15-41-4542 (home); email: jan.staessen@med.kuleuven.be; voicemail: jan.staessen@proximus.be.

Alzheimer disease (AD), vascular dementia (VaD), and mixed variants. In spite of the vast literature on the "dichotomy" between AD and VaD, recent concepts highlight the role of cardiovascular risk factors in the pathogenesis of AD as well, especially in older patients [1-7]. However, the nature of the association between AD and vascular pathology awaits further elucidation. Some researchers consider AD as a secondary event related to atherosclerosis of the extracranial and intracranial arteries. An alternative hypothesis is, that AD and atherosclerosis are convergent processes, sharing common pathogenetic mechanisms in the brain and in the arterial wall, such as disturbances of cholesterol transport, inflammation, and misfolded proteins [6].

Together with smoking and dyslipidemia, hypertension explains most of the modifiable cardiovascular risk in the population at large. It is the major player in the pathogenesis of stroke, poststroke dementia, and VaD. AD is the most common cause of dementia, contributing from 45% to over 75% of the cases in Asians and North Americans, respectively [8]. This review, which has been published previously in a shorter format, [9] will focus on the role of hypertension as a potentially reversible risk factor in the development of dementia, in particular AD. To set the stage, we will first summarize current insights in the epidemiology of AD, the pathogenesis of VaD and AD, and the association between neurodegeneration and atherosclerosis.

EPIDEMIOLOGY OF DEMENTIA

Across 36 cross-sectional studies, the prevalence of dementia ranged from 0.3% to 1% in subjects aged 60 to 64 years [8]. It exponentially increased to 10% - 20% in octogenarians and to over 40% in the ninth decade of life [8]. In a systematic review of 15 longitudinal studies, the incidence of dementia showed a similar age-related dependency with rates expressed in cases per 1000 person-years ranging from 0.4 to 4 at 60–64 years and from approximately 20 to over 40 per 1000 person-years at 80–85 years [8]. The 2003 World Health Report [10] estimated that worldwide adults aged 60 years or over lost around 8.6 million Disability Adjusted Life Years (DALYs) because of AD or other dementias. In terms of millions of DALYs lost in this age group, only ischemic heart disease (31.5), cerebrovascular disease (29.6) and chronic obstructive pulmonary disease (14.4) caused more premature disability and mortality [10].

Falling birth and death rates predict an unprecedented demographic revolution. At the beginning of this century, about 600 million of the world's population was 60 years or older. This number will double by 2025 and by 2050 reach two billion, the overwhelming majority of whom will be living in developing countries. [10] Currently 24.3 million people have dementia with an annual incidence of 4.6 million new cases [11]. In view of the age dependency of cognitive impairment, the number of patients with dementia will increase twofold every 20 years to 81.1 million by 2040, with over 60% living in developing countries [11]. In the United States, the number of demented patients with roughly triple from 4.6 million in 1998 to 16 million by 2050 [12]. The interaction or convergence between disease processes leading to cardiovascular disorders and dementia hopefully holds promise toward the search for effective and common prevention of both of these disabling and burdensome conditions worldwide.

PATHOGENESIS OF DEMENTIAS

Vascular Dementia

VaD is caused by ischemic or hemorrhagic cerebrovascular disease, or by ischemic brain injury resulting from cardiovascular or circulatory disorders [13,14]. Poststroke dementia is the most common form of VaD [15]. In North American patients aged 60 years or more, the prevalence of dementia 3 months after an ischemic insult was 26.3%, about 9 times higher than in matched controls [16]. In another series of hospitalized patients with a first lacunar infarct, the 4-year incidence of dementia was 23.1% [17].

VaD may result from a single stroke interrupting brain circuits critical for memory and cognition (strategic infarct dementia) or from multiple strokes (multi-infarct dementia) [13,14]. Subcortical VaD has a more insidious character without the sensory-motor manifestations associated with stroke, but with progressive changes in personality, mood, behavior or cognition [13,14].

Alzheimer Disease

AD is a neurodegenerative disease with an inexorably progressive, disabling and fatal course (Figure 1), of which the clinically overt phase usually spans from 3 to 10 years [2]. The disease primarily affects cholinergic neurotransmission in the medial temporal lobe, the entorhinal cortex, and the hippocampus [2,18,19]. Interaction between these brain structures plays a crucial role in memory consolidation, memory optimization during sleep, and spatial orientation [20]. The prevailing viewpoint on the pathogenesis of AD rests on the extra- and intra-neuronal accumulation of misfolded protein, amyloid β-peptide (Aβ), which starts a pathogenetic cascade resulting in neurotoxicity [2,21].

Neurofibrillary tangles are the main histopathologic hallmark of AD [2,21,22]

NEURODEGENERATION AND ATHEROSCLEROSIS

Numerous neuroimaging [24-27] and post mortem histopathologic [3,23,28-30] studies indicate that up to one third of AD patients have some degree of vascular pathology, whereas in a similar proportion of VaD patients AD lesions are also present. Especially in older patients, increasing evidence suggests a strong link between AD, cardiovascular risk factors, and atherosclerosis. According to the Neuropathology Group of the Medical Research Council Cognitive and Ageing Study, [3] these observations illustrate how much present research on AD is based on a simplified view of the disorder as the conventional amyloid plaque cascade is not reflected in the brain pathology of a large number of demented people, particularly in the age groups at the highest risk. A more balanced view is that the summation of vascular brain lesions, white matter damage reflecting small vessel disease, and typical AD pathology interactively lead to dementia, even when each type of lesion, on its own, would not be severe enough to cause dementia [15]. To complete the picture, current evidence suggests that cholinergic neuronal processes are not only involved in cognition per se, but in the preservation of cerebral blood flow as well (Figure 2) [7,31-33]. Indeed, cholinergic agents stimulated regional cerebral blood flow both in human volunteers [33] and in patients with AD [31-33] or VaD [31].

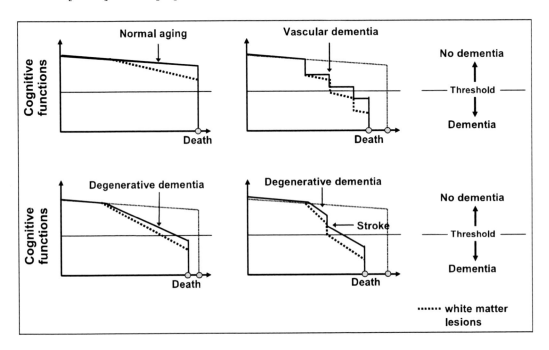

Figure 1. Time course of cognitive functions (reproduced with permission from reference 14).

Four years after two independent groups first reported an independent association between AD and the apolipoprotein E (*APOE*) ε4 allele [34,35] a quantitative overview of the literature, [36] published in 1997, and later studies [37] confirmed that the APOE ε4 allele represents a major risk factor for AD in all ethnic groups, across all ages between 40 and 90 years, and in both women and men. The ε4 allele enhances the risk threefold in heterozygotes and by a factor 15 in homozygotes [36]. The APOE ε4 allele accounts for most of the genetic risk in sporadic AD [2,6]. Here, the term sporadic is a misnomer, because late-onset AD is manifold more frequent than the familial forms of AD with onset at early age, which are due to mutations in APP or presenilin-1 [2,6].

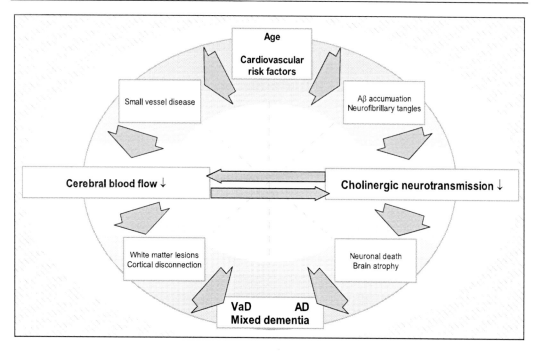

Figure 2. Overlap between neurodegenerative and vascular dementia and interaction between cholinergic factors and cerebral blood flow. Reproduced with permission from reference 9.

BLOOD PRESSURE AS RISK FACTOR FOR DEMENTIA

In middle-aged and older adults, hypertension is the predominant and most frequent cardiovascular risk factor. Any man normotensive at 50 years has a probability over 90% to become hypertensive during the remainder of his lifetime [40]. Studies on the association between cognition and blood pressure can be subdivided into those with a cross-sectional approach as opposed to those with a longitudinal design. The endpoint in these studies can be: disease outcomes, such as dementia, AD or VaD; morphologic or functional alterations of the brain as documented by modern neuroimaging techniques or histopathologic autopsy studies and cognitive function as assessed by batteries of tests each covering varying cognitive domains or more global tests of cognition, such as the Mini Mental State Examination (MMSE) or composite scores of specific tests.

CROSS-SECTIONAL STUDIES

Cross-sectional studies, in which outcome and exposure are simultaneously recorded, obviously have limited capability to assess the association between cognition and blood pressure. The extensive lag phase between the onset of hypertension and subsequent cognitive impairment together with the insidious clinical course of neurodegenerative dementia necessitate long-term prospective studies.

Longitudinal Cohort Studies

In 1996, Skoog and colleagues published a pioneering longitudinal study on the incidence of dementia in relation to blood pressure [42]. They recruited 70-year old residents (57.8% women) of Göteborg, Sweden, of whom 302, 205, and 94 were available for a re-assessment at 75, 79, and 85 years, respectively. Participants who developed dementia at age 79–85 had higher systolic blood pressure at 70 years (178 versus 164 mm Hg) and higher diastolic blood pressure at ages 70 (101 versus 92 mm Hg and 75 (97 versus 90 mm Hg) [42]. Patients specifically developing AD or VaD, had higher diastolic blood pressure at ages 70 and 75, respectively [42].

Although based on relatively few subjects, Skoog's seminal report [42] set the stage for subsequent studies published in the second half of the 1990s [43-46]. These reports confirmed that with multivariate adjustments a relatively high diastolic blood pressure (≥75 mm Hg versus ≤70 mm Hg) at age 50, [43] or a persistently elevated systolic blood pressure (≥140 mm Hg) at ages ranging from 43 [45] to 75 [44] years, or stage 2 hypertension (≥160 mm Hg systolic and ≥95 mm Hg diastolic) within the 59–71 age bracket [46] consistently predicted worse cognitive performance [43-46] or more severe white-matter lesions [45] at ages ranging from 63 [46] to 79 [45] years.

The clinical manifestations of the dementia syndrome cover a wide spectrum. Screening relies on tests of specific aspects of cognition or on global tests, such as the MMSE or composite scores of specific tests. By definition, the temporal association of cognitive decline or overt dementia with blood pressure is bound to be complex and not necessarily linear [41]. Coincident positive risk factors, such as age, a history of stroke, [47] or the number of *APOE* ε4 alleles, [48] as well as protective characteristics, such as a larger brain volume, [49] male sex, [50] moderate alcohol intake, [50] or education [50] modify the risk associated with blood pressure.

To clarify the role of blood pressure in the pathogenesis of cognitive impairment, we performed a systematic review of the prospective studies published since 2000, from which we extracted or computed summary statistics. The outcome variables were either levels of or changes in single or composite cognitive scores (Table 1), [51-62] the incidence of cognitive dysfunction, dementia, AD or VaD (Table 2), [38-40,47,48,57,63-71] or the appearance of brain lesions in histopathologic or neuroimaging studies (Table 3) [72-75]. For each of these 3 endpoints, we arranged the reports according to the age at enrolment.

TABLE 1 (starts). Association Between Cognitive Function and Blood Pressure Indexes

Study	Outcome	N	FU, y	Age, y	F, %	CVA, %	BP, mm Hg	Covariates	Effect size (95% confidence interval)	P
MLSH, 2004[51]	ΔV/FC	285	≈9.3	≈35	52	0	134/86 (56)	S, A, BMI, SMK, ALC, OCC, ED, DPR, PSM	[SP] −0.05 (−0.11 to 0.01)	≈0.13
									[DP] −0.09 (−0.19 to −0.00)	≈0.04
									[HT] −0.16 (−0.28 to −0.03)	≈0.01
Uppsala, 2000[52]	DS VF	463	20	50	0	0	≈131/83 (...)	A, DM, ED, OCC	[DP] ≈−1.00 (−1.90 to −0.10)	0.03
									[DP] ≈−0.32 (−0.65 to −0.03)	0.03
ARIC, 2001[53]	ΔDSS	10767	6.0	57	≈66		.../... (32)	C, R, A, ED, PSM	[HT] −0.40 (... to ...)	<0.05
ARIC, 2002[54]	ΔDSS	4928	6.0	≈57	≈52	0	120/72 (...)	R, A, DM, ED	[UHT] −0.90 (... to ...)	<0.05
MLSH, 2004[51]	ΔV/FC	244	≈9.3	58	51	0	152/91 (74)	S, A, BMI, SMK, ALC, OCC, ED, DPR, PSM	[SP] −0.09 (−0.14 to −0.03)	≈0.002
									[DP] −0.15 (−0.25 to −0.05)	≈0.002
									[HT] −0.24 (−0.39 to −0.08)	≈0.002
Framingham, 2003[55]	ΔSCCS	872	≈5.0	67	100	0	132/80 (...)	A, BMI, CHL, SMK, ALC, OCC, ED	[HT] −0.01 (−0.11 to −0.09)	0.88
		551		66	0	0	131/83 (...)		[HT] −0.16 (−0.30 to −0.02)	0.04
Malmö, 2003[56]	ΔSCCS	128	12.5	68	0	0	≈151/91 (16.7)	AHT, HD, PAD, DM, SMK, ALC, ED, MS, DPR	[HT2] 0.31 (0.11 to 0.51)	≈0.001
									[HT3] −0.31 (−0.54 to −0.07)	≈0.01

TABLE 1 (continues). Association Between Cognitive Function and Blood Pressure Indexes

Study	Out-come	N	FU, y	Age, y	F, %	CVA, %	BP, mm Hg	Covariates	Effect size (95% confidence interval)	P
Clergy, 2006[57]	ΔSCCS	824	6.5	70	69	...	134/75 (52.0)	S, A, ED	[SP] −0.01 (−0.03 to 0.01)	0.34
									[DP] 0.00 (... to ...)	0.76
Duke EPESE, 2002[58]	ΔSPMS	3202	3.0	73	67	6.6	143/79 (52)	R, S, A, SMK, AHT, CVA, HD, DM, ED, DPR	[HT] 0.03 (−0.10 to 0.16)	0.68
Hispanic EPESE, 2005[59]	ΔMMSE	1138 (NT)	≈7.0	73	...	4.0	124/75 (0)	S, A, BMI, ΔBMI, CVA, CVD, DM, ΔAHT, SMK, ALC, PA, ED, INC	[SP] 0.80 (−0.38 to 1.98)	≈0.18
									[ΔSP] −0.08 (−0.14 to −0.02)	0.008
		1721 (HT)	≈7.0	73	...	7.0	142/84 (100)		[SP] −0.10 (−0.49 to 0.29)	≈0.62
									[ΔSP] 0.01 (−0.30 to 0.32)	≈0.95
Chicago, 2004[60]	ΔSCCS	4284	5.3	74	62	16.0	140/77 (...)	R, S, A, BPB, ED, FU	[ΔSP] −0.00 (−0.00 to 0.00)	0.30
									[ΔDP] −0.00 (−0.00 to 0.00)	0.70
ACTIVE, 2005[61]	ΔCSR	2017	1.0	74	76	7.0	.../... (≈41)	R, S, A, BMI, CHL, CVA, HD, DM, SMK, RIG, ED	[SH1] −0.18 (−0.34 to −0.02)	0.03
									[SH2] −0.28 (−0.48 to −0.09)	0.005
OCTO, 2004[62]	ΔMMSE	258	≈6.0	≈83	≈70	10.4	160/83 (44)	S, A, SMK, HD, CVA, ED, CTB	[HT] −0.54 (−1.13 to 0.05)	≈0.07

Abbreviations: *N*=number of subjects; *FU*=average follow-up; *F*=proportion of women; *CVA*=patients with stroke; and *BP*=average blood pressure at baseline (percentage of hypertensive patients). "≈" indicates estimates derived from the total study population and taken as representative for a subgroup, statistics computed from reported data, or *P*-values computed by a normal approximation from the confidence interval. "…" represents unreported information that could not be estimated. Studies were ordered according to age at enrolment.

Acronyms: *ACTIVE*=Advanced Cognitive Training for Independent and Vital Elderly; *ARIC*=Atherosclerosis Risk in Community; *EPESE*=Established Populations for Epidemiologic Studies of the Elderly; *MLSH*=Maine-Syracuse Longitudinal Study of Hypertension; and *OCTO*=Origins of variance in the Old-Old.

Endpoints: Δ*CSR*=changes in the composite of 3 test scores reflecting reasoning; *DS*=digit span test score; Δ*DSS*=difference in change over time in the Digit Symbol Subtest of the Wechsler Adult Intelligence Test (Revised) compared to normotensive subjects; Δ*MMSE*=estimated change in the Mini Mental State Examination score over the whole follow-up period; Δ*SCCS*=annual change in standardized composite cognitive score; Δ*SPMS*=3-year change in score obtained by Short Portable Mental Status questionnaire; Δ*VI/FC*=annual change in the Visualization/Fluid Composite score as derived from the Wechsler Adult Intelligence Test; and *VF*=verbal fluency test score.

Covariates: *A*=age; *AHT*=antihypertensive drug treatment; Δ*AHT*=institution of antihypertensive treatment; *ALC*=alcohol intake; *BMI*=body mass index; Δ*BMI*=change in body mass index; *BPB*=blood pressure at baseline; *C*=center; *CHL*=hypercholesterolemia or serum cholesterol; *CTB*=cognitive tests at baseline; *CVA*=stroke; *DM*=diabetes mellitus; *DPR*=depression; *ED*=education; *FU*=follow-up duration; *HD*=heart disease; *INC*=income; *MS*=marital status; *OCC*=occupation; *PA*=physical activity; *PAD*=history of peripheral artery disease; *PSM*=psychotropic medication; *R*=race; *RIG*=randomized intervention group; *S*=sex; and *SMK*=smoking.

Blood pressure indexes at baseline: *DP/SP*=diastolic (+5 mm Hg)/systolic (+10 mm Hg) blood pressure; Δ*DP/* Δ*SP*=change from baseline in diastolic/systolic blood pressure (+1 mm Hg); *HT*= hypertension; *HT2/HT3*=stage 2/3 hypertension; and *UHT*=uncontrolled hypertension.

Effect size: score of cognitive test or change in test score associated with blood pressure indexes on a continuous or categorical scale.

All studies of cognitive function, involving subjects on average less than 70 years old at enrollment (Table 1), [51-56] uniformly showed a significantly lower performance or a more rapid decline of cognitive function with higher blood pressure, although in one cohort only for stage 3 hypertension [56]. At more advanced age, [57-62] point estimates went in the same direction, but only reached significance in the normotensive Hispanic EPESE (Established Populations for Epidemiologic Studies of the Elderly) cohort [59] and in the ACTIVE (Active Cognitive Training Independent and Vital Elderly) trial [61].

Among the studies with cognitive impairment as a categorical endpoint (Table 2) [38-40,47,48,57,63-71], those using a dichotomized test score [46,47] classified from 15% [48] to 50% [47] of the participants as cognitively impaired and reported positive associations with hypertension. Two studies [64,68] found no association of MCI with hypertension earlier in life. Studies with dementia, [38,40,66] AD, [39,40,57,63,65-67,69-71] or VaD [63,66,70] as endpoints demonstrated a significantly positive association with one or more blood pressure indexes, if follow-up started from middle age rather than old age [38,40,65,66]. Remarkably, one study involving subjects recruited at the upper end of the age spectrum found an inverse association of AD with blood pressure [67]. In keeping with the estimates listed in Table 2, the Baltimore Longitudinal Survey of Aging, based on 11 years of multivariate adjusted follow-up of 847 subjects (mean age, 70.6 years; 41% women) described age as an important modifier of the effects of blood pressure on cognition [41]. Among younger participants (60 years at baseline), those with higher systolic blood pressure performed worse on tests of nonverbal memory and confronting naming, although the test results improved over time due to a learning effect [41]. Among older participants (80 years), those with higher systolic blood pressure not only performed worse than subjects with normal blood pressure, but also experienced a decline in cognitive performance over time [41].

In summary, our overview suggests that especially hypertension in middle age adversely affects cognition later in life. In old and very old adults, the association between impaired cognition and hypertension becomes weaker and more difficult to demonstrate, perhaps because in prospective population studies diastolic blood pressure decreases after age 50, [76] or because systolic blood pressure falls in the very old [42]. Finally, 1 autopsy report [72] and 3 brain imaging studies [73-75] with longitudinal perspective observed independent and positive associations between brain lesions and blood pressure indexes (Table 3).

Low Blood Pressure as Manifestation of Dementia

Already in 1996, Skoog noticed that with advancing age all subjects in his study experienced a decrease in blood pressure, but that the fall in systolic and diastolic blood pressure was greater in patients who developed dementia than in their nondemented counterparts [42]. A retrospective review of the medical records of 1133 women (≥75 years) covering 10 years [77] revealed that systolic blood pressure increased with time in 568 unimpaired subjects, but that it increased less in 274 and 291 women who either developed cognitive impairment or became demented. Diastolic blood pressure declined significantly with time in all 3 groups [77]. In a cohort of 242 French patients with moderate AD (mean age, 78 years; 74% women) [78] blood pressure significantly fell over 1 year of follow-up, independently of sex, age, body mass index, and antihypertensive drug therapy.

Progressive physical inactivity in those blemished by advancing mental deterioration may be a substantial factor leading to a fall in blood pressure in the years immediately preceding and following overt dementia. In addition, neuronal death and defective cholinergic neurotransmission affecting the autonomic centers in the brain probably results in a dysregulation of blood pressure (Figure 2). Orthostatic or postprandial dips in blood pressure, pari passu with episodes of impaired cerebrovascular blood flow, might actually contribute to further brain damage, sustaining a perpetuating vicious circle [79].

REVERSIBILITY OF RISK ASSOCIATED WITH HYPERTENSION

Nonrandomized prospective studies and randomized clinical trials explored to what extent blood pressure lowering drugs might affect the risk of cognitive impairment or frank dementia.

Nonrandomized Observational Studies

Ten prospective studies (Table 4) [46,80-88] explored in multivariate-adjusted analyses the possible influence of antihypertensive treatment on the incidence of cognitive impairment or overt dementia. Differences in the definition of the cognitive endpoint, the wide range of age at baseline and consequent duration of follow-up, varying sampling frames, and adjustment for different sets of covariates or effect modifiers, such as the *APOE* ε4 polymorphism [46,88], turned the computation of a pooled association size into a mission impossible. Nevertheless, of the 10 studies (Table 4) [46,80-88], 8 reported that antihypertensive drug treatment lowered the risk of cognitive decline, the reduction being significant in 5 reports [80,81,84,86,87]. No single study observed a multivariate-adjusted significantly elevated risk in treated hypertensive patients. Several researchers tried to dissect the correlation between cognitive impairment and antihypertensive treatment according to the main classes of antihypertensive drugs (Table 4). Although plagued by low numbers and overexploitation of scarce data, the mainstream of these analyses suggests that diuretics [80,87] might confer particular benefit in the prevention of cognitive impairment. Two observational studies [89,90] suggested that calcium channel blockers might adversely affect cognition, but probably reflected reverse causality, patients with more severe hypertension being more likely to be treated with this potent drug class, self-selection of patients consenting to follow-up, and the arbitrary nonrandomized definition of the drug class used as reference [89]. These reports have to be viewed within the context of the controversy in former times, blaming calcium channel blockers for a wide range of adverse reactions, of which none withstood the test of randomized controlled trials [91].

Nonrandomized longitudinal studies of cognitive function have to be interpreted within the context of their well-known methodological limitations. Randomized controlled trials with a double-blind design and a predefined plan of statistical analysis protect against most of these weaknesses. Single-blind protocols or open administration of treatment with blinded endpoint evaluation [92] remove bias in the validation of events, but not in the reporting of events.

TABLE 2 (starts). Association Between Risk of Dementia and Blood Pressure Indexes

Study	Outcome	N	Events (rate per 100)	FU, y	Age, y	F, %	CVA, %	BP, mm Hg	Covariates	Relative risk (95% confidence interval)	P
KPNC, 2005[38]	DEM	8845	721 (8.2)	26.7	42	54	...	.../... (19)	R, S, A, ED	[HT] 1.24 (1.04 to 1.48)	≈0.01
Hiroshima, 2003[63]	VaD	1774	38 (2.1)	≈27	≈44	73	...	117/... (...)	S, A, MLK, ED	[SP] 1.33 (1.14 to 1.56)	<0.001
	AD		51 (2.9)						S, A, DM	[SP] ... (... to ...)	>0.05
North Karelia, 2001[64]	MCI	1409	82 (5.8)	20.9	50	62	...	144/89 (...)	A, BMI	[SH1] 0.8 (0.4 to 1.3)	≈0.36
										[SH2] 1.2 (0.7 to 2.2)	≈0.55
										[DH1] 0.9 (0.5 to 1.7)	≈0.74
										[DH2] 1.1 (0.7 to 1.9)	≈0.73
North Karelia, 2001[65]	AD	1409	48 (3.4)	20.9	50	62	...	144/89 (...)	A, BMI, SMK, ALC, CVA, HD, ED	[SH1] 2.1 (0.8 to 5.0)	≈0.09
										[SH2] 2.8 (0.1 to 7.2)	≈0.03
										[DH1] 1.4 (0.6 to 3.5)	≈0.46
										[DH2] 1.7 (0.8 to 3.6)	≈0.16
CAIDE, 2005[40]	DEM	1409	... (5.8)	21.0	50	62	7.2	144/89 (...)	S, A, BMI, CHL, ED, FU	[SH] 1.97 (1.03 to 3.77)	≈0.04
	AD		... (3.8)							[SH] 1.57 (0.78 to 3.14)	≈0.19
HAAS, 2001[48]	CASI	3605	539 (15.0)	26.0	52	0	6.2	132/82 (...)	A, BMI, SMK, ALC, ED	[SH2–E4] 1.8 (1.2 to 2.9)	≈0.01
										[SH2+E4] 2.9 (1.4 to 6.3)	≈0.006

TABLE 2 (continues). Association Between Risk of Dementia and Blood Pressure Indexes

Study	Out-come	N	Events (rate per 100)	FU, y	Age, y	F, %	CVA, %	BP, mm Hg	Covariates	Relative risk (95% confidence interval)	P
HAAS, 2000[67]	DEM	3703	197 (5.3)	27.0	53	0	6.3	131/83 (≈33)	A, SMK, ALC, E4, CVA, HD, PAD, ED	[SH1–T] 1.15 (0.62 to 2.13)	≈0.65
										[SH2–T] 3.88 (1.50 to 10.0)	≈0.004
										[DH1–T] 3.78 (1.59 to 8.95)	≈0.002
										[DH2–T] 4.00 (1.56 to 10.2)	≈0.003
	AD	3703	118 (3.2)							[SH1–T] 1.23 (0.63 to 2.43)	≈0.54
										[SH2–T] 1.22 (0.37 to 4.04)	≈0.74
										[DH1–T] 3.49 (1.28 to 9.52)	≈0.01
										[DH2–T] 4.47 (1.53 to 13.1)	≈0.005
	VaD	3703	79 (2.1)							[SH1–T] 0.81 (0.21 to 3.19)	≈0.76
										[SH2–T] 11.8 (3.52 to 39.5)	<0.001
										[DH1–T] 3.45 (0.79 to 15.0)	≈0.09
										[DH2–T] 2.49 (0.46 to 13.4)	≈0.28
Rotterdam and Gothenburg, 2001[67]	AD	4987	25 (0.5)	2.1	65	57	...	137/74 (...)	C, S, A, AHT, CVA, HD, DM, ED, CTB	[SP] 0.96 (0.80 to 1.16)	≈0.67
										[DP] 0.95 (0.81 to 1.15)	≈0.68
Clergy members, 2006[57]	AD	824	151 (18.3)	6.5	70	69	...	134/75 (52.0)	S, A, ED	[SP] 0.95 (0.82 to 1.04)	0.25
										[DP] 1.00 (0.93 to 1.08)	0.98
ILSA, 2004[68]	MCI	1445	105 (7.3)	3.5	72	56	5.7	.../... (69)	A, SMK, HD, ED	[HT] 1.20 (0.76 to 1.89)	≈0.42

TABLE 2 (continues). Association Between Risk of Dementia and Blood Pressure Indexes

Study	Outcome	N	Events (rate per 100)	FU, y	Age, y	F, %	CVA, %	BP, mm Hg	Covariates	Relative risk (95% confidence interval)	P
SOF, 2005[47]	TB	6306	≈6150 (50.0)	≈6.8	≈72	100	≈0	.../... (...)	A, CTB, FU	[HT–IS] 1.13 (1.04 to 1.22)	0.002
KAME Project, 2005[69]	AD	1859	90 (4.8)	6.0	73	56		≈140/74 (≈33.5)	E4	[SH] 1.79 (0.82 to 3.89)	0.15
SOF, 2005[47]	TB	119	76 (63.9)	8.7	75	100	0.8	148/78 (...)	A, CTB, FU	[HT+IS] 4.07 (1.37 to 12.1)	0.01
Manhattan, 2002[70]	AD VaD	1259	157 (12.5) 56 (4.4)	7.0	76	69	12.5	.../... ()	R, S, A, HD	[HT] 0.8 (0.6 to 1.1) [HT] 1.6 (0.9 to 2.9)	≈0.16 ≈0.11
Luchsinger, 2005[110]	AD	1012	246 (24.3)	≈5.5	≈76	≈70	...	.../... (≈49)	R, S, A, E4, ED	[HT] 1.5 (0.9 to 2.1)	≈0.08
CHCS, 2003[71]	DEM	2939	480 (16.3)	≈5.0	≈76	≈59	≈4.6	.../... (≈44)	R, S, A, E4, CVA, HD, DM, ED, CTB, MRI	[HT] 1.00 (0.94 to 1.27)	≈0.99
Rotterdam and Gothenburg, 2001[67]	AD	1336	68 (5.1)	2.1	79	65	...	146/72 (...)	C, S, A, AHT, CVA, HD, DM, ED, CTB	[SP] 0.95 (0.85 to 1.06) [DP] 0.98 (0.88 to 1.08)	≈0.35 ≈0.61
Rotterdam and Gothenburg, 2001[67]	AD	662	103 (15.6)	2.1	87	74	...	155/73 (...)	C, S, A, AHT, CVA, HD, DM, ED, CTB	[SP] 0.89 (0.82 to 0.97) [DP] 0.91 (0.84 to 0.98)	≈0.007 <0.001

Abbreviations: N=number of subjects; FU=average follow-up; F=proportion of women; CVA=patients with stroke; BP=average blood pressure at baseline (percentage of hypertensive patients). "≈" indicates estimates derived from the total study population and taken as representative for a subgroup, statistics computed from reported data, or P-values computed by a normal approximation from the confidence interval. "…" represents unavailable information that could not be estimated. Studies were ordered according to age at enrolment.

Acronyms: CAIDE=Cardiovascular Risk Factors, Aging and Dementia Study; CHCS=Cardiovascular Health Cognition Study; HAAS=Honolulu Asia Aging Study; ILSA=Italian Longitudinal Study on Aging; KAME=prospective study of Japanese Americans living in King County, WA; KPNC=Kaiser Permanente of Northern California; and SOF=Study of Osteoporotic Fractures

Endpoints: AD=Alzheimer disease; CASI=Cognitive Abilities Screening Instrument score below 15th percentile; DEM=dementia; MCI=mild cognitive impairment; TB=larger than median decrease in Trail B test score; and VaD=vascular dementia.

Covariates: A=age; AHT=antihypertensive drug treatment; ALC=alcohol intake; BMI=body mass index; C=cohort; CHL=hypercholesterolemia or serum cholesterol; CTB=cognitive tests at baseline; CVA=history of stroke; DM=diabetes mellitus; E4=number of APOE ε4 alleles; ED=education; FU=follow-up duration; HD=history of heart disease; MRI=brain lesions identified by magnetic resonance imaging at baseline; MLK=milk intake; PAD=history of peripheral artery disease; R=race; S=sex; and SMK=smoking.

Blood pressure indexes at baseline: DP/SP=diastolic (+5 mm Hg)/systolic (+10 mm Hg) blood pressure; DH1/DH2=diastolic blood pressure 90–94 mm Hg/≥95 mm Hg; DH1–T/ DH2–T=diastolic blood pressure 90–94/≥95 mm Hg in the absence of antihypertensive treatment; HT= hypertension; HT–IS/HT+IS=hypertension without/with intervening stroke; SH=systolic hypertension; SH1–T/SH2–T=stage 1/2 systolic hypertension; SH1/HT2=stage 1/2 systolic hypertension; SH2–E4/ SH2+E4=stage 2 systolic hypertension in absence/presence of the APOE ε4 allele.

Randomized Clinical Trials

The trial conducted by the Medical Research Council (MRC) in older adults [93] was the first outcome study that investigated the effects of antihypertensive drug treatment on cognitive function. The patients were randomized to a diuretic, (hydrochlorothiazide plus amiloride), a β-blocker (atenolol), or placebo [93]. Both active treatments reduced blood pressure below the placebo level. Over a period of 54 months, 2584 patients underwent elaborate psychometric tests [93]. No significant differences in the test scores occurred. However, follow-up of 387 surviving MRC patients for 9–12 years revealed that less decline in systolic blood pressure led to a poorer cognitive outcome, even with adjustments applied for a family history of dementia, cognitive function at baseline, increasing age, and alcohol intake [94]. Many other randomized clinical trials of short duration with small sample size that focused on single or composite cognitive scores, primarily served the marketing goals of newer classes of antihypertensive drugs [95,96], and can at best be viewed as hypothesis generating.

The MRC study [93], unfortunately, did not report on the incidence of overt dementia. In 4 outcome trials of blood pressure lowering treatment, [97-100] dementia was a secondary outcome in its own right. The double-blind placebo-controlled Systolic Hypertension in the Elderly Program [97] included 4736 patients with mean age of 72 years. SHEP failed to demonstrate a significant effect of antihypertensive treatment on the incidence of dementia (Figure 3) despite between-group blood pressure differences exceeding 10 mm Hg systolic and 4 mm Hg diastolic. The rates on placebo and active treatment were 4.2 and 3.6 cases per 1000 patient-years (relative risk reduction [RRR], 14%; 95% confidence interval [CI], −26 to 54%; $P=0.44$) [97]. Active treatment consisted of chlorthalidone with the possible addition of atenolol or reserpine. A subsequent report [101] noticed that although retention to the clinical examinations was very high, SHEP patients who missed cognitive assessments were more likely to be older, less educated, non-White, randomized to placebo, and to have a higher occurrence of nonfatal cardiovascular events before each follow-up visit. The interpretation was that selective attrition might have biased the SHEP dementia results towards the null hypothesis of no differences between the treatment groups [101].

In the double-blind placebo-controlled Systolic Hypertension in Europe (Syst-Eur) trial, active treatment consisted of the dihydropyridine calcium-channel blocker nitrendipine, which could be combined with enalapril, hydrochlorothiazide, or both add-on drugs, to achieve blood pressure control [102]. Median follow-up lasted only 2 years. The trial had to be stopped prematurely, because active treatment resulted in a 42% decrease in the primary endpoint of fatal and nonfatal stroke [102]. Of 4695 randomized patients, 2418 participated in the substudy on dementia (mean age, 70 years). Compared with placebo, active treatment reduced blood pressure by 8.3 mm Hg systolic and 3.8 mm Hg diastolic and reduced the incidence of dementia by 50% from 7.7 to 3.8 cases per 1000 patient-years [103]. After the double-blind trial had stopped in 1997, all patients were offered therapy with the same active medication. Median follow-up lengthened to 3.9 years. The number of dementia cases doubled from 32 to 64 (41 with Alzheimer's disease) [98]. Immediate compared to delayed antihypertensive therapy reduced the risk of dementia by 55% (CI, 24 to 73%; $P<0.001$) from 7.4 to 3.3 cases per 1000 patient-years (Figure 3) [98].

TABLE 3. Association Between Brain Lesion and Blood Pressure Indexes

Study	Outcome	N	FU, y	Age, y	F, %	CVA, %	BP, mm Hg	Covariates	Effect size (95% confidence interval)	P
HAAS, 2000[72]	NFTH	243	36.0	53	0	(...)	.../... (...)	A (at death), E4, AHT	[SH2] 1.41 (0.73 to 2.74)	≈0.30
									[DH2] 2.39 (1.34 to 4.26)	≈0.003
	NFTN								[SH2] 1.51 (0.60 to 3.79)	≈0.37
									[DH2] 1.66 (0.67 to 4.10)	≈0.26
	NPH								[SH2] 2.18 (1.07 to 4.46)	≈0.03
									[DH2] 0.87 (0.31 to 2.45)	≈0.79
	NPN								[SH2] 2.05 (1.00 to 4.20)	≈0.05
									[DH2] 0.69 (0.24 to 1.98)	≈0.48
Zoetermeer, 2002[73]	WMLS	514	≈20	51	53	...	131/81 (25)	S, A, BMI, SMK, DM	[HT<20] 2.9 (1.5 to 5.8)	≈0.002
									[HT>20] 2.6 (1.2 to 5.6)	≈0.01
Rotterdam, 2002[73]	WMLS	563	≈5	69	50	...	137/73 (39)	S, A, BMI, SMK, DM	[HT<5] 1.6 (0.9 to 2.9)	≈0.11
									[HT>5] 1.8 (1.1 to 3.0)	≈0.02
Rotterdam, 2003[74]	CAS	434 79	20	51	53	...	131/81 (...)	S, A, SMK	[DP−T] 0.08 (0.00 to 0.17)	≈0.05
									[DP+T] −0.02 (−0.22 to 0.19)	≈0.89
Goldstein, 2005[75]	WMH	121	5.0	66	57	0	119/72 (0)	A	[SP] 1.49 (1.10 to 2.02)	0.01
									[SPA] 1.57 (1.08 to ≈1.70)	0.02

Abbreviations: *N*=number of subjects; *FU*=average follow-up; *F*=proportion of women; *CVA*=patients with stroke; and *BP*=average blood pressure at baseline (percentage of hypertensive patients). "≈" indicates approximation from the confidence interval. "..." represents unavailable information that could not be estimated. Studies were ordered according to age at enrolment.

Study acronym: *HAAS*=Honolulu Asia Aging Study.

Endpoint: *CAS*=cortical atrophy score on magnetic resonance imaging of the brain; *NFTH/NFTN*=count ratio versus normal blood pressure for neurofibrillary tangles in hippocampus/neocortex; *NPH/NPN* =count ratio versus normal blood pressure for neuritic plaques in hippocampus/neocortex; *WMH*=white-matter hyperintensities; and *WMLS*=subcortical white matter lesions defined as the upper fifth of the distribution according to severity.

Covariates: *A*=age; *AHT*=antihypertensive drug treatment; *BMI*=body mass index; *DM*=diabetes mellitus; *E4*=number of *APOE* ε4 alleles; *S*=sex; and *SMK*=smoking.

Blood pressure indexes at baseline: *DH2*=diastolic blood pressure ≥95 mm Hg; *DP*=diastolic blood pressure (+5 mm Hg); *DP–T/ DP+T*=diastolic blood pressure (+5 mm Hg) in the absence/presence of antihypertensive treatment; *HT<5/HT<20*=hypertension present for less than 5/20 years; *HT>5,HT>20*=hypertension present for more than 5 or 20 years; *SH2*=stage 2 systolic hypertension; *SP*=systolic blood pressure (+ 10 mm Hg); and *SPA*=systolic blood pressure on daytime ambulatory measurement (+10 mm Hg).

Effect size: relative risk associated with exposure variable except for CAS, for which the difference associated with a 5 mm Hg higher diastolic blood pressure at baseline is given.

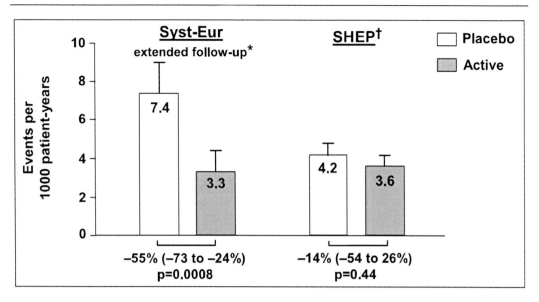

Figure 3. Incidence of dementia in the Systolic Hypertension in Europe trial (Syst-Eur132) and the Systolic Hypertension in the Elderly Program (SHEP131). In the Syst-Eur trial, the number of cases of new-onset Alzheimer disease was 29/43 and 12/21 in the patients randomized to placebo and active treatment, respectively.132 The corresponding incidence of vascular dementia was 12/43 and 7/21.132 The SHEP reports131,135 did not differentiate between Alzheimer disease and vascular dementia. Reproduced with permission from reference 9.

In the Perindopril Protection Against Recurrent Stroke Study (PROGRESS) [99], combination therapy with perindopril plus indapamide (RRR, 23%; CI, 0 to 41%, $P=0.05$), but not monotherapy with perindopril alone (RRR −8%; CI −48 to 21%, $P=0.60$), compared to placebo, reduced the incidence of dementia in 6105 patients with pre-existing cerebrovascular disease (mean age, 64 years). The systolic/diastolic blood pressure differences averaged 12/5 mm Hg and 5/3 mm Hg in the combination therapy and monotherapy arms, respectively. There was no apparent effect of active treatment among participants (16.4%) with evidence of cognitive impairment at baseline (RRR, −5%; CI, −42 to 22%; $P=0.70$), whereas among patients without such impairment (84.2%) active treatment protected against poststroke dementia (RRR, 31%; CI, 6 to 49%; $P=0.02$) [99].

The Study on Cognition and Prognosis in the Elderly (SCOPE) was set up as a double-blind placebo-controlled trial in 4964 patients (mean age, 76 years) [100]. However, open-label antihypertensive drugs, which mainly consisted of diuretics, β-blockers, or both classes of old drugs, were added to the double-blind study medication in a considerably greater proportion of the patients randomized to placebo than in those allocated candesartan [100]. The achieved blood pressure was 3.2/1.6 mm Hg lower in the candesartan group. In a post-hoc analysis [104], patients with cognitive impairment at baseline (MMSE score, 24 to 28) experienced less further decline in this test on candesartan than in the control group.

Overall, the 4 dementia trials [97-100] included 18 196 patients and 642 dementia cases. The P-value for heterogeneity across trials was not significant ($P=0.18$) [105]. Based on a fixed-effects model, the pooled odds ratio for the prevention of dementia was 0.89 (CI, 0.75 to 1.04) and did not reach statistical significance ($P =0.15$) [105]. However, sensitivity analyses revealed a difference in the pooled odds ratios, depending on whether active treatment started with an inhibitor of the renin system or not (Figure 4). The pooled odds ratios were 0.75 (CI, 0.60 to 0.94; P = 0.01) for SHEP [97], Syst-Eur [98] and the combination therapy subgroup of PROGRESS [106] and 1.08 (CI, 0.84 to 1.38; P =0.54) for SCOPE [100] and the perindopril-only subgroup of the PROGRESS trial [106]. The difference between the latter summary statistics was significant (P = 0.04) [105].

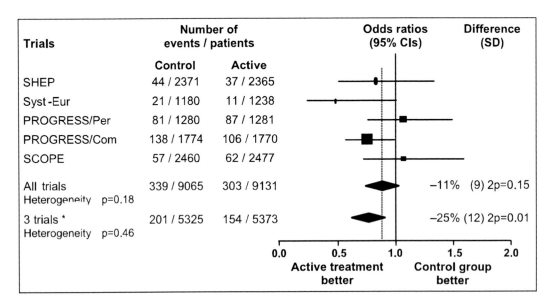

Figure 4. Effects of blood pressure lowering treatment on the incidence of dementia in placebo-controlled trials. Solid squares represent the odds ratios in individual trials and have a size proportional to the inverse of the variance of the odds ratios. Horizontal lines and diamonds denote the 95% confidence intervals for individual trials and summary statistics, respectively. Pooled estimates were computed from a fixed-effect model. The vertical dotted line marks the position of the point estimate of the pooled effect sizes for all trials combined and trials in which the active treatment included either a diuretic or a dihydropyridine calcium channel blocker. Reproduced with permission from reference 9.

Mechanism Underlying Prevention of Alzheimer Disease by Blood Pressure Lowering

The prevention of VaD or poststroke dementia by blood pressure lowering is in keeping with the well-known vascular origin of these conditions. Until now, Syst-Eur [102,103] remains the only trial that showed a significant decrease in the incidence of AD (Figure 3). At the time of the first Syst-Eur report [102], this was an unexpected observation. However, the subsequently published literature, as reviewed above, indicates that vascular factors, particularly hypertension, do play if not a causal then at least a permissive role in the pathogenesis of AD (Figure 2). On the other hand, for nearly the same blood pressure reduction, antihypertensive treatment with a thiazide did not protect against AD in the SHEP trial [97].

As we discussed elsewhere, several lines of evidence suggest that dihydropyridine calcium-channel blockers might specifically protect against neurodegeneration.

TABLE 4 (starts). Association Between Cognitive Impairment and Antihypertensive Drug Treatment in Nonrandomized Studies

Study	Out-come	N	Events (rate per 100)	FU, y	Age, y	F, %	CVA, %	Treated, %	Covariates	Effect size (95% confidence interval)	P
EVA, 1999[46]	CI	1150	98 (8.5)	4.0	65.2	58.8	...	25.6	S, A, E4, ALC, ED, MMSE, DPR	1.1 (0.7 – 1.7)	≈0.66
BLSA, 2005[85]	AD	1092	115 (10.5)	11.0	67.1	37.3	...	20.1 [C]	S, S/DBP, HD, SMK, ED	0.63 (0.31 – 1.28)	≈0.19
			6 [dC]					10.6 [Cd]		0.30 (0.07 – 1.25)	0.10
			12 [ndC]					13.0 [Cnd]		0.82 (0.37 – 1.83)	0.63
Kuopio, 2004[88]	MCI	747	66 (8.8)	3.2	≈67.8	≈61.2	≈11.1	≈33.9	S, A, E4, CVD, CVA, HT, DM, ED	1.61 (0.87 – 2.99)	≈0.12
Rotterdam, 2001[81]	DEM	6416	118 (1.8)	2.2	68.7	58.7	2.3	28.6	S, A, BMI, S/DBP, CVA, PAD, DM, SMK, ED, MMSE	0.67 (0.45 – 1.00)	≈0.046
	AD		82 (1.3)							0.77 (0.49 – 1.24)	≈0.25
	VaD		18 (0.3)							0.30 (0.09 – 0.92)	≈0.032
EPESE, 2001[82]	AD	634	99 (15.6)	4.0	72.0	63.2	4.1	33.6	S, A, SBP, SF, IS	0.66 (0.17 – 2.61)	≈0.54
								26.5 [D]		1.33 (0.68 – 2.61)	≈0.40
CSHA, 2002[83]	AD	3238	152 (4.7)	5.0	≈73.3	≈58.0	≈7.6	41.2	S, A, ED	0.91 (0.64 – 1.30)	≈0.74

TABLE 4 (continues). Association Between Cognitive Impairment and Antihypertensive Drug Treatment in Nonrandomized Studies

Study	Out-come	N	Events (rate per 100)	FU, y	Age, y	F, %	CVA, %	Treated, %	Covariates	Effect size (95% confidence interval)	P
CCS, 2006[87]	AD	3217	102 (3.17)	3.2	≈74.1	≈58.2	≈4.2	45.3	S, A, CHL, E4, CVA,	0.64 (0.41 – 0.98)	≈0.036
			26 [D]					26.5 [D]	HD, DM, ED	0.61 (0.37 – 0.98)	≈0.037
			5 [pD]					5.8 [Dp]		0.26 (0.08 – 0.64)	≈0.003
			14 [C]					14.9 [C]		0.86 (0.45 – 1.53)	≈0.60
			4 [dC]					5.8 [Cd]		0.53 (0.16 – 1.34)	≈0.17
			10 [ndC]					9.2 [Cnd]		1.16 (0.55 – 2.20)	≈0.64
			15 [A]					13.0 [A]		1.13 (0.60 – 1.98)	≈0.66
PHRSP, 2005[86]	CI	350	62 (17.7)	2.1	76.9	73.0	≈6.6	≈54.4	R, S, A, BMI, BP, CHL, CVA, DM, SMK, ALC, MMSE, FHD	0.56 (0.38 – 0.83)	0.004
Indianapolis, 2002[84]	CI	1617	288 (17.8)	≈4.7	77.7	66.5	10.8	46.6	S, A, HD, HT, ED,	0.62 (0.45 – 0.84)	0.002
								28.3 [D]	CSID	0.80 (0.58 – 1.10)	0.17
								18.2 [C]		0.86 (0.60 – 1.25)	0.44
								11.1 [Cd]		0.94 (0.60 – 1.46)	0.78
								9.5 [A]		0.64 (0.38 – 1.09)	0.002
Kungsholmen, 1999[80]	DEM	1307	224 (17.1)	3.0	82.5	76.1	≈10.0	44.9	S, A, SBP, CVA, HD,	0.7 (0.6 – 1.0)	0.03
			73 [D]					37.0 [D]	ED	0.7 (0.5 – 1.0)	0.02

Abbreviations: *N*=number of subjects; *FU*=average follow-up; *F*=proportion of women; and *CVA*=patients with stroke. "≈" indicates estimates derived from the total study population and taken as representative for subgroup, statistics computed from reported data, or *P*-values computed by a normal approximation from the confidence interval. "...." represents unavailable information that could not be estimated. Studies were ordered according to age at enrolment.

Acronyms: *BLSA*=Baltimore Longitudinal Study on Aging; *CCS*=Cache County Study; *CSHA*=Canadian Study of Health and Aging; *EPESE*= Established Populations for Epidemiologic Studies of the Elderly; *EVA*=Epidemiology of Vascular Aging Study; and *PHRSP*=Palmetto Health Richland Senior Primary Care Practice

Antihypertensive drugs: *A*=angiotensin-converting enzyme inhibitors; *C*=calcium channel blockers; *Cd*=dihydropyridine calcium channel blockers; *Cnd*=non-dihydropyridine calcium channel blockers; *D*=diuretics; and *Dp*=potassium-sparing diuretics.

Endpoints: *AD*=Alzheimer disease; *CI*=cognitive impairment defined as dementia or poor performance on screening and/or repeat cognitive testing; *DEM*=dementia; *MCI*=mild cognitive impairment; and *VaD*=vascular dementia.

Covariates: *A*=age; *ALC*=alcohol intake; *BMI*=body mass index; *BP*=blood pressure; *CHL*=total, high- and low-density lipoprotein cholesterol or hypercholesterolemia; *CSID*=score of Community Screening Instrument for Dementia at baseline; *CVA*=stroke; *CVD*=cardiovascular disease; *DM*=diabetes mellitus; *DPR*=depression; *E4*=number of *APOE* ε4 alleles; *ED*=education; *FHD*=family history of dementia; *HD*=heart disease; *HT*=hypertension; *IS*=living independently as opposed to sheltered care; *MMSE*=score of Mini Mental State Examination at baseline; *PAD*=peripheral artery disease; *R*=race; *S*=sex; *SMK*=smoking; *SF*=sampling frame; *SBP*=systolic blood pressure; and *S/DBP*=systolic and diastolic blood pressure.

Effect size: relative risk associated with antihypertensive drug treatment.

PERSPECTIVES AND CONCLUSIONS

Although hypertension has long been recognized to play a central role in the pathogenesis of VaD, its identification as an equipotent risk factor for AD had to await the final years of the twentieth century. Whether or not blood pressure lowering can prevent AD and to what extent calcium channel blockade provides specific protection against cognitive decline, is an issue with potentially far-reaching implications for public health. Medical treatment of established dementia has only marginal benefit and is not cost-effective [107]. Prevention is the only way to counteract the epidemic of AD in the world's aging populations. Public research bodies, regulators, and the pharmaceutical industry should no longer remain indifferent, but take up the challenge [108-109].

Our review also illustrates that research into dementia requires a comprehensive multidisciplinary approach. Basic researchers, neurologists, geriatricians, and cardiovascular physicians should join forces and start developing a common language transcending the one-sided container approaches of the past decennia. Reviewers and editors should facilitate this process. In scrutinizing submitted research papers, they might adhere to more stringent standards with regard to the diagnostic instruments that have been administered and check whether essential confounders have been sufficiently accounted for. Lack of standardization in the conduct and analysis of studies prevented the computation of pooled statistic from Tables 1 to 4. Finally, publication of cross-sectional and nonrandomized studies, which only provide the lowest level of scientific evidence and which can only be hypothesis generating, should be discouraged in favor of prospective surveys and randomized clinical trials, respectively.

ACKNOWLEDGEMENTS

The authors gratefully acknowledge Sandra Covens, Katrien Staessen, and Renilde Wolfs for their expert help in searching the literature and keeping the Reference Manager database updated.

SOURCES OF FUNDING

The authors did not receive any funding for writing the review. The corresponding author had full access to all data and had final responsibility for the decision to submit the manuscript for publication.

CONFLICT OF INTEREST STATEMENT

JA Staessen consulted for pharmaceutical companies and received funding for studies, seminars, and travel from manufacturers of drugs that lower blood pressure. T Richart and WH Birkenhäger have no conflict of interest to declare.

REFERENCES

[1]   Vagnucci AH, Jr., Li WW: Alzheimer's disease and angiogenesis. *Lancet.* 2003;361:605–608.

[2]   Blennow K, de Leon MJ, Zetterberg H: Alzheimer's disease. *Lancet.* 2006;368:387–403.

[3]   Neuropathology Group of the Medical Research Council Cognitive Function and Ageing Study (MRC CFAS): Pathological correlates of late-onset dementia in a multicentre, community-based population in England and Wales. *Lancet.* 2001;357:169–175.

[4]   Qiu C, Winblad B, Fastbom J, Fratiglioni L: Combined effects of *APOE* genotype, blood pressure, and antihypertensive drug use on incident AD. *Neurology.* 2003;61:655–660.

[5]   Qiu C, Winblad B, Fratiglioni L: The age-dependent relation of blood pressure to cognitive function and dementia. *Lancet Neurol.* 2005;4:487–499.

[6]   Casserly I, Topol E: Convergence of atherosclerosis and Alzheimer's disease: inflammation, cholesterol, and misfolded proteins. *Lancet.* 2004;363:1139–1146.

[7]   Román GC, Kalaria RN: Vascular determinants of cholinergic deficits in Alzheimer disease and vascular dementia. *Neurobiol Aging.* 2006 (in press).

[8]   Fratiglioni L, De Ronchi d, Agüero-Torres H: Worldwide prevalence and incidence of dementia. *Drugs Aging.* 1999;15:365–375.

[9]   Staessen JA, Richart T, Birkenhäger WH. Less atherosclerosis and lower blood pressure for a meaningful life perspective with more brain. *Hypertension* 2007;49:389-400.

[10]   Beaglehole R, A Irwin, T Prentice: *The World Health Report 2003 – Shaping the Future.* Geneva, Switzerland, World Health Organization, 2003.

[11]   Ferri CP, Prince M, Brayne C, Brodaty H, Fratiglioni L, Ganguli M, Hall K, Hasegawa K, Hendrie H, Huang Y, Jorm A, Mathers C, Menezes PR, Rimmer E, Scazufca M, for Alzheimer's Disease International: Global prevalence of dementia: a Delphi consensus study. *Lancet.* 2005;366:2112–2117.

[12]   Brookmeyer R, Gray S, Kawas C: Projections of Alzheimer's disease in the United States and the public health impact of delaying disease onset. *Am J Public Health.* 1998;88:1337–1342.

[13]   Román GC: Vascular dementia revisited: diagnosis, pathogenesis, treatment, and prevention. *Med Clin North Am.* 2002;86:477–499.

[14]   Román GC: Vascular dementia. Advances in nosology, diagnosis, treatment and prevention. *Panminerva Med.* 2004;46:207–215.

[15] Pasquier F, Leys D: Why are stroke patients prone to develop dementia? *J Neurol.* 1997;244:135–142.

[16] Tatemichi TK, Paik M, Bagiella E, Desmond DW, Stern Y, Sano M, Hauser WA, Mayeux R: Risk of dementia after stroke in a hospitalized cohort: results of a longitudinal study. *Neurology.* 1994;44:1885–1891.

[17] Loeb C, Gandolfo C, Croce R, Conti M: Dementia associated with lacunar infarction. *Stroke.* 1992;23:1225–1229.

[18] McCormick WC, Abrass IB: Shifting thinking about memory impairment. *Lancet.* 1998;352 (suppl IV):6.

[19] Cohen HJ, Feussner JR, Weinberger M, Carnes M, Hamdy RC, Hsieh F, Phibbs C, Lavori P: A controlled trial of inpatient and outpatient geriatric evaluation and management. *N Engl J Med.* 2002;346:905–912.

[20] Sargolini F, Fyhn M, Hafting T, McNaughton B, Witter MP, Moser EI, Moser MB: Conjunctive representation of position, direction, and velocity in entorhinal cortex. *Science.* 2006;312:758–762.

[21] Agamanolis DP: An Illustrated Interactive Course for Medical Students and Residents. Chapter Nine. Degenerative Diseases (accessed on August 19, 2006).

[22] Maurer K, Volk S, Gerbaldo H: Auguste D and Alzheimer's disease. *Lancet.* 2002;349:1546–1549.

[23] Jicha GA, Parisi JE, Dickson DW, Johnson K, Cha R, Ivnik RJ, Tangalos EG, Boeve BF, Knopman DS, Braak H, Petersen RC: Neuropathologic outcome of mild cognitive impairment following progression to clinical dementia. *Arch Neurol.* 2006;63:674–681.

[24] van der Flier WM, van Straaten ECW, Barkhof F, Verdelho A, Madureira S, Pantoni L, Inzitari D, Erkinjuntti T, Crisby M, Waldemar G, Schmidt R, Fazekas F, Scheltens P, on behalf of the LADIS Group: Small vessel disease and general cognitive function in nondisabled elderly. The LADIS Study. *Stroke.* 2005;36:2116–2120.

[25] Gurol ME, Irizarry MC, Smith EE, Raju S, Diaz-Arrastia R, Bottiglieri T, Rosand J, Growdon JH, Greenberg SM: Plasma □-amyloid and white matter lesions in AD, MCI, and cerebral amyloid angiopathy. *Neurology.* 2006;66:23–29.

[26] Schneider JA, Wilson RS, Bienias JL, Evans DA, Bennett DA: Cerebral infarctions and the likelihood of dementia from Alzheimer disease. *Neurology.* 2004;62:1148–1155.

[27] Nagata K, Kondo Y, Atchison R, Sato M, Satoh Y, Watanabe Y, Hirata Y, Yokoyama E: Vascular and metabolic reserve in Alzhiemer's disease. *Neurobiol Aging.* 2000;21:301–307.

[28] Snowdon DA, Greiner LH, Mortimer JA, Riley KP, Greiner PA, Markesbery WR: Brain infarction and the clinical expression of Alzheimer's disease. The nun study. *JAMA.* 1997;277:813–817.

[29] Yip AG, McKee AC, Green RC, Wells J, Young H, Cupples LA, Farrer LA: *APOE,* vascular pathology, and the AD brain. *Neurology.* 2005;65:259–265.

[30] Honig LS, Kukull W, Mayeux R: Atherosclerosis and AD. Analysis of data from the US National Alzheimer's Coordinating Center. *Neurology.* 2005;64:494–500.

[31]   Lojkowska W, Ryglewicz D, Jedrzejczak T, Minc S, Jakubowska T, Jarosz H, Bochynska A: The effect of cholinesterase inhibitors on the regional blood flow in patients with Alzheimer's disease and vascular dementia. *J Neurol Sci.* 2003;216:119– 126.

[32]   Ceravolo R, Volterrani D, Tognoni G, Dell'Agnello G, Manca G, Kiferle L, Rossi C, Logi C, Strauss HW, Mariani G, Murri L: Cerebral perfusional effects of cholinesterase inhibitors in Alzheimer disease. *Clin Neuropharmacol.* 2004;27:166– 170.

[33]   Blin J, Ivanoiu A, Coppens A, De Volder A, Labar D, Michel C, Laterre EC: Cholinergic neurotransmission has different effects on cerebral glucose consumption and blood flow in young normals, aged normals, and Alzheimer's disease patients. *Neuroimage.* 1997;6:335–343.

[34]   Corder EH, Saunders AM, Strittmatter WJ, Schmechel DE, Gaskell PC, Small GW, Roses AD, Haines JL, Pericak-Vance MA: Gene dose of apolipoprotein E type 4 allele and the risk of Alzheimer's disease in late onset families. *Science.* 1993;261:921–923.

[35]   Poirier J, Davignon J, Bouthillier D, Kogan S, Bertrand P, Gauthier S: Apolipoprotein E polymorphism and Alzheimer's disease. *Lancet.* 1993;342:697–699.

[36]   Farrer LA, Cupples LA, Haines JL, Hyman B, Kukull WA, Mayeux R, Myers RH, Pericak-Vance MA, Risch N, van Duijn CM, for the APOE and Alzheimer Disease Meta Analysis Consortium: Effect of age, sex, and ethnicity on the association between apolipoprotein E genotype and Alzheimer disease. A meta-analysis. *JAMA.* 1997;278:1349–1356.

[37]   Cui T, Zhou X, Jin W, Zheng F, Cao X: Gene polymorphism in apolipoprotein E and presenilin-1 in patients with late-onset Alzheimer's disease. *Chin Med J.* 2000;113:340–344.

[38]   Whitmer RA, Sidney S, Selby J, Johnston SC, Yaffe K: Midlife cardiovascular risk factors and risk of dementia in late life. *Neurology.* 2005;64:277–281.

[39]   Mancia G, Giannattasio C, Grassi G: Current antihypertensive treatment: can we do better? *Am J Hypertens.* 1999;12:131S–138S.

[40]   Kivipelto M, Ngandu T, Fratiglioni L, Viitanen M, Kåreholt I, Winblad B, Helkala EL, Tuomilehto J, Soininen H, Nissinen A: Obesity and vascular risk factors at midlife and the risk of dementia and Alzheimer disease. *Arch Neurol.* 2005;62:1556– 1560.

[41]   Waldstein SR, Giggey PP, Thayer JF, Zonderman AB: Nonlinear relations of blood pressure to cognitive function. The Baltimore longitudinal study of aging. *Hypertension.* 2005;45:374–379.

[42]   Skoog I, Lernfelt B, Landahl S, Palmertz B, Andreasson LA, Nilsson L, Persson G, Odén A, Svanborg A: 15-year longitudinal study of blood pressure and dementia. *Lancet.* 1996;347:1141–1145.

[43]   Kilander L, Nyman H, Boberg M, Hansson L, Lithell H: Hypertension is related to cognitive impairment. A 20-year follow-up of 999 men. *Hypertension.* 1998;31:780– 786.

[44]   Swan GE, Carmelli D, Larue A: Systolic blood pressure tracking over 25 to 30 years
        and cognitive performance in older adults. *Stroke.* 1998;29:2334–2340.

[45]   Swan GE, DeCarli C, Miller BL, Reed T, Wolf PA, Jack LM, Carmelli D:
        Association of midlife blood pressure to late-life cognitive decline and brain
        morphology. *Neurology.* 1998;51:986–993.

[46]   Tzourio C, Dufouil C, Ducimetière P, Alpérovitch A, for the EVA Study Group:
        Cognitive decline in individuals with high blood pressure. A longitudinal study in the
        elderly. *Neurology.* 1999;53:1948–1952.

[47]   Elkins JS, Yaffe K, Cauley JA, Fink HA, Hillier TA, Johnson SC: Pre-existing
        hypertension and the impact of stroke on cognitive function. *Ann Neurol.*
        2005;58:68–74.

[48]   Peila R, White LR, Petrovich H, Masaki K, Ross GW, Havlik RJ, Launer LJ: Joint
        effect of the *APOE* gene and midlife systolic blood pressure on late-life cognitive
        impairment. The Honolulu-Asia aging study. *Stroke.* 2001;32:2882–2889.

[49]   Strassburger TL, Lee HC, Daly EM, Szczepanik J, Krasuski JS, Mentis MJ, Salerno
        JA, DeCarli C, Schapiro MB, Alexander GE: Interactive effects of age and
        hypertension on volumes of brain structures. *Stroke.* 1997;28:1410–1417.

[50]   Seux ML, Thijs L, Forette F, Staessen JA, Birkenhäger WH, Bulpitt CJ, Girerd X,
        Jääskivi M, Vanhanen H, Kivinen P, Yodfat Y, Vänskä O, Antikainen R, Laks T,
        Webster JR, Hakamäki T, Lehtomäki E, Lilov E, Grigirov M, Janculova K, Halonen
        K, Kohonen-Jalonen P, Kermowa R, Nachev C, Tuomilehto J: Correlates of cognitive
        status of old patients with isolated systolic hypertension: the Syst-Eur Vascular
        Dementia Project. *J Hypertens.* 1998;16:963–969.

[51]   Elias PK, Elias MF, Robbins MA, Budge MM: Blood pressure-related cognitive
        decline: does age make a difference? *Hypertension.* 2004;44:625–630.

[52]   Kilander L, Nyman H, Boberg M, Lithell H: The association between low diastolic
        blood pressure in middle age and cognitive function in old age. A population-based
        study. *Age Ageing.* 2000;29:243–248.

[53]   Knopman D, Boland LL, Mosley T, Howard G, Liao D, Szklo M, McGovern P,
        Folsom AR: Cardiovascular risk factors and cognitive decline in middle-aged adults.
        Neurology. 2001;56:42–48.

[54]   Alves de Moraes S, Szklo M, Knopman D, Sato R: The relationship between
        temporal changes in blood pressure and changes in cognitive function:
        Atherosclerosis Risk In Communities (ARIC) Studies. *Prev Med.* 2002;35:258–263.

[55]   Elias MF, Elias PK, Sullivan LM, Wolf PA, D'Agostino RB: Lower cognitive
        function in the presence of obesity and hypertension: the Framingham Heart Study.
        Int J Obes. 2003;27:260–268.

[56]   André-Petersson L, Elmståhl S, Hagberg B, Janzon L, Reinprecht F, Steen G: Is
        blood pressure at 68 an independent predictor of cognitive decline at 81? Results
        from follow-up study 'Men born in 1914', Malmö, Sweden. *Aging Ment Health.*
        2003;7:61–72.

[57]   Shah RC, Wilson RS, Bienias JL, Arvanitakis Z, Evans DA, Bennett DA: Relation of
        blood pressure to risk of incident Alzheimer's disease and change in global cognitive
        function in older persons. *Neuroepidemiology.* 2006;26:30–36.

[58]   Bohannon AD, Fillenbaum GG, Pieper CF, Hanlon JT, Blazer DG: Relationship of race/ethnicity and blood pressure to change in cognitive function. *J Am Geriatr Soc.* 2002;50:424–429.

[59]   Insel KC, Palmer RF, Stroup-Benham CA, Markides KS, Espino DV: Association between change in systolic blood pressure and cognitive decline among elderly Mexican American: data from the hispanic established population for epidemiology study of the elderly. *Exp Aging Res.* 2005;31:35–54.

[60]   Hebert LE, Scherr PA, Bennett DA, Bienias JL, Wilson RS, Morris MC, Evans DA: Blood pressure and late-life cognitive function change. A biracial longitudinal population study. *Neurology.* 2004;62:2021–2024.

[61]   Kuo HK, Jones RN, Milberg WP, Tennstedt S, Talbot L, Morris JN, Lipsitz LA: Effect of blood pressure and diabetes mellitus on cognitive and physical functions in older adults: a longitudinal analysis of the advanced cognitive training for independent and vital elderly cohort. *J Am Geriatr Soc.* 2005;53:1154–1161.

[62]   Hassing LB, Hofer SM, Nilsson SE, Berg S, Pedersen NL, McClearn G, Johansson B: Comorbid type 2 diabetes mellitus and hypertension exacerbates cognitive decline: evidence from a longitudinal study. *Age Ageing.* 2004;33:355–361.

[63]   Yamada M, Kasagi F, Sasaki H, Masunari N, Mimori Y, Suzuki G: Assocociation between dementia and midlife risk factors: the Radiation Effects Research Foundation Adult Health Study. *J Am Geriatr Soc.* 2003;51:410–414.

[64]   Kivipelto M, Helkala EL, Hänninen T, Laakso MP, Hallikainen M, Alhainen K, Soininen H, Tuomilehto J, Nissinen A: Midlife vascular risk factors and late-life mild cognitive impairment. A population-based study. *Neurology.* 2001;56:1683–1689.

[65]   Kivipelto M, Helkala EL, Laakso MP, Hänninen T, Hallikainen M, Alhainen K, Soininen H, Tuomilehto J, Nissien A: Midlife vacsular risk factors and Alzheimer's disease in later life: longitudinal population based study. *Br Med J.* 2001;322:1447–1451.

[66]   Launer LJ, Webster Ross G, Petrovitch H, Masaki K, Foley D, White LR, Havlik RJ: Midlife blood pressure and dementia: the Honolulu-Asia Aging Study. *Neurobiol Aging.* 2000;21:49–55.

[67]   Ruitenberg A, Skoog I, Ott A, Aevarsson O, Witteman JCM, Lernfelt B, van Harskamp F, Hofman A, Breteler MMB: Blood pressure and risk of dementia: results from the Rotterdam study and the Gothenburg H-70 study. *Dement Geriatr Cogn Disord.* 2001;12:33–39.

[68]   Solfrizzi V, Panza F, Colacicco AM, D'Introno A, Capurso C, Torres F, Grigoletto F, Maggi S, Del Parigi A, Reiman EM, Caselli RJ, Scafato E, Farchi G, Capurso A, for the Italian Longitudinal study on Aging Working group: Vascular risk factors, incidence of MCI, and rates of progression to dementia. *Neurology.* 2004;63:1882–1891.

[69]   Borenstein AR, Wu Y, Mortimer JA, Schellenberg GD, McCormick WC, Bowen JD, McCurry S, Larson EB: Developmental and vascular risk factors for Alzheimer's disease. *Neurobiol Aging.* 2005;26:325–334.

[70] Posner HB, Tang MX, Luchsinger J, Lantigua R, Stern Y, Mayeux R: The relationship of hypertension in the elderly to AD, vascular dementia, and cognitive function. *Neurology*. 2002;58:1175–1181.

[71] Kuller LW, Lopez OL, Newman A, Beauchamps NJ, Burke G, Dulberg C, Fitzpatrick A, Fried L, Haan MN: Risk factors for dementia in the Cardiovascular Health Cognition Study. *Neuroepidemiology*. 2003;22:13–22.

[72] Petrovitch H, White LR, Izmirilian G, Ross GW, Havlik RJ, Markesbery W, Nelson J, Davis DG, Hardman J, Foley DJ, Launer LJ: Midlife blood pressure and neuritic plaques, neurofibrillary tangles, and brain weight at death: the HAAS. *Neurobiol Aging*. 2000;21:57–62.

[73] de Leeuw FE, de Groot JC, Oudkerk M, Witteman JCM, Hofman A, van Gijn J, Breteler MMB: Hypertension and cerebral white matter lesions in a prospective cohort study. *Brain*. 2002;125:765–772.

[74] den Heijer T, Skoog I, Oudkerk M, de Leeuw FE, de Groot JC, Hofman A, Breteler MMB: Association between blood pressure levels over time and brain atrophy in the elderly. *Neurobiol Aging*. 2003;24:307–313.

[75] Goldstein IB, Bartzokis G, Guthrie D, Shapiro D: Ambulatory blood pressure and the brain. A 5-year follow-up study. *Neurology*. 2005;64:1846–1852.

[76] Zhang H, Thijs L, Kuznetsova T, Fagard RH, Li X, Staessen JA: Progression of hypertension in the non-hypertensive participants in the Flemish Study on Environment, Genes and ealth Outcomes. *J Hypertens*. 2006;24:1719–1727.

[77] Petitti DB, Crooks VC, Buckwalter JG, Chiu V: Blood pressure levels before dementia. *Arch Neurol*. 2005;62:112–116.

[78] Hanon O, Latour F, Seux ML, Lenoir H, Forette F, Rigaud AS, the REAL.FR group: Evolution of blood pressure in patients with Alzheimer's disease: a one year survey of a French cohort (REAL.FR). *J Nutr Health Aging*. 2005;9:106–111.

[79] Kario K, Pickering TG, Matsuo T, Hoshide S, Schwartz JE, Shimada K: Stroke prognosis and abnormal nocturnal blood pressure falls in older hypertensives. *Hypertension*. 2001;38:852–857.

[80] Guo Z, Fratiglioni L, Zhu L, Fastbom J, Winblad B, Viitanen M: Occurrence and progression of dementia in a community population aged 75 years and older. Relationship with medication use. *Arch Neurol*. 1999;56:991–996.

[81] in't Veld BA, Ruitenberg A, Hofman A, Stricker BHC, Breteler MMB: Antihypertensive drugs and incidence of dementia: the Rotterdam Study. *Neurobiol Aging*. 2001;22:407–412.

[82] Morris MC, Scherr PA, Hebert LE, Glynn RJ, Bennett DA, Evans DA: Association of incident Alzheimer disease and blood pressure measured from 13 years before to 2 years after diagnosis in a large community study. *Arch Neurol*. 2001;58:1640–1646.

[83] Lindsay J, Laurin D, Verreault R, Hebert R, Helliwell B, Hill GB, McDowell I: Risk factors for Alzheimer's disease: a prospective analysis from the Canadian Study of Health and Aging. *Am J Epidemiol*. 2002;156:445–453.

[84] Murray MD, Lane KA, Gao S, Evans RM, Unverzagt FW, Hall KS, Hendrie H: Preservation of cognitive function with antihypertensive medications. A longitudinal analysis of a community-based sample of African Americans. *Arch Intern Med.* 2002;162:2090–2096.

[85] Yasar S, Corrada M, Brookmeyer R, Kawas C: Calcium channel blockers and risk of AD: the Baltimore Longitudinal Study of Aging. *Neurobiol Aging.* 2005;26:157–163.

[86] Hajjar I, Catoe H, Sixta S, Boland R, Johnson D, Hirth V, Wieland D, Eleazer P: Cross-sectional and longitudinal association between antihypertensive medications and cognitive impairment in an elderly population. *J Gerontol.* 2005;60A:67–73.

[87] Khachaturian AS, Zandi PP, Lyketsos CG, Hayden KM, Skoog I, Norton MC, Tschanz JT, Mayer LS, Welsh-Bohmer KA, Breitner J: Antihypertensive medication use and incident Alzheimer disease: the Cache County Study. *Arch Neurol.* 2006;63:686–692.

[88] Tervo S, Kivipelto M, Hänninen T, Vanhanen M, Hallikainen M, Mannermaa A, Soininen H: Incidence and risk factors for mild cognitive impairment: a population-based three-year follow-up study of cognitively healthy elderly subjects. *Dement Geriatr Cogn Disord.* 2004;17:196–203.

[89] Heckbert SR, Longstreth WT, Jr., Psaty BM, Murros KE, Smith NL, Newman AB, Williamson JD, Bernick C, Furberg CD: The association of antihypertensive agents with MRI white matter findings and the Modified Mini-Mental State Examination in older adults. *J Am Geriatr Soc.* 1997;45:1423–1433.

[90] Maxwell CJ, Hogan DB, Ebly EM: Calcium-channel blockers and cognitive function in elderly people: results from the Canadian Study of Health and Aging. *Can Med Ass J.* 1999;161:501–506.

[91] Staessen JA, Li Y, Thijs L, Wang JG: Blood pressure reduction and cardiovascular prevention: an update including the 2003-2004 secondary prevention trials. *Hypertens Res.* 2005;28:385–407.

[92] Hansson L, Hedner T, Dahlöf B: Prospective randomized open blinded end-point (PROBE) study. A novel design for intervention trials. *Blood Press.* 1992;1:113–119.

[93] Prince MJ, Bird AS, Blizard RA, Mann AH: Is the cognitive function of older patients affected by antihypertensive treatment? Results from 54 months of the Medical Research Council's treatment trial of hypertension in older adults. *Br Med J.* 1996;312:801–805.

[94] Cervilla JA, Prince M, Joels S, Lovestone S, Mann A: Long-term prediction of cognitive outcome in a cohort of older people with hypertension. *Brit J Psychiatry.* 2000;177:66–71.

[95] Fogari R, Mugellini A, Zoppi A, Marasi G, Pasotti C, Poletti L, Rinaldi A, Preti P: Effects of valsartan compared with enalapril on blood pressure and cognitive function in elderly patients with essential hypertension. *Eur J Clin Pharmacol.* 2004;59:863–868.

[96] Tedesco MA, Ratti G, Mennella S, Manzo G, Grieco M, Rainone AC, Iarussi D, Iacono A: Comparison of losartan and hydrochlorothiazide on cognitive function and quality of life in hypertensive patients. *Am J Hypertens.* 1999;12:1130–1134.

[97]   SHEP Cooperative Research Group: Prevention of stroke by antihypertensive drug treatment in older persons with isolated systolic hypertension. Final results of the Systolic Hypertension in the Elderly Program (SHEP). *JAMA.* 1991;265:3255–3264.

[98]   Forette F, Seux ML, Staessen JA, Thijs L, Babarskiene MR, Babeanu S, Bossini A, Fagard R, Gil-Extremera B, Laks T, Kobalava Z, Sarti C, Tuomilehto J, Vanhanen H, Webster J, Yodfat Y, Birkenhäger WH, for the Syst-Eur Investigators: The prevention of dementia with antihypertensive treatment. New evidence from the Systolic Hypertension in Europe (Syst-Eur) Study [erratum published in The Archives of Internal Medicine 2003, volume 163, January 27, p 241]. *Arch Intern Med.* 2002;162:2046–2052.

[99]   The PROGRESS Collaborative Group: Effects of blood pressure lowering with perindopril and indapamide therapy on dementia and cognitive decline in patients with cerebrovascular disease. *Arch Intern Med.* 2003;163:1069–1075.

[100]   Lithell H, Hansson L, Skoog I, Elmfeldt D, Hofman A, Olofsson B, Trenkwalder P, Zanchetti A, for the SCOPE Study Group: The Study on Cognition and Prognosis in the Elderly (SCOPE): principal results of a randomised double-blind intervention trial. *J Hypertens.* 2003;21:875–886.

[101]   Di Bari M, Pahor M, Franse LV, Shorr RI, Ferrucci L, Somes GW, Applegate WB: Dementia and disability outcomes in large hypertension trials: lessons learned from the Systolic Hypertension in the Elderly Program (SHEP) trial. *Am J Epidemiol.* 2001;153:72–78.

[102]   Staessen JA, Fagard R, Thijs L, Celis H, Arabidze GG, Birkenhäger WH, Bulpitt CJ, de Leeuw PW, Dollery CT, Fletcher AE, Forette F, Leonetti G, Nachev C, O'Brien ET, Rosenfeld J, Rodicio JL, Tuomilehto J, Zanchetti A, for the Systolic Hypertension in Europe (Syst-Eur) Trial Investigators: Randomised double-blind comparison of placebo and active treatment for older patients with isolated systolic hypertension [erratum published in The Lancet 1997, volume 350, November 29, p 1636]. *Lancet.* 1997;350:757–764.

[103]   Forette F, Seux ML, Staessen JA, Thijs L, Birkenhäger WH, Babarskiene MR, Babeanu S, Bossini A, Gil-Extremera B, Girerd X, Laks T, Lilov E, Moisseyev V, Tuomilehto J, Vanhanen H, Webster B, Yodfat Y, Fagard R, on behalf of the Syst-Eur Investigators: Prevention of dementia in randomised double-blind placebo-controlled Systolic Hypertension in Europe (Syst-Eur) trial. *Lancet.* 1998;352:1347–1351.

[104]   Skoog I, Lithell H, Hansson L, Elmfeldt D, Hofman A, Olofsson B, Trenkwalder P, Zanchetti A, for the SCOPE Study Group: Effect of baseline cognitive function and antihypertensive treatment on cognitive function: Study on COgnition and Prognosis in the Elderly (SCOPE). *Am J Hypertens.* 2005;18:1052–1059.

[105]   Wang JG, Staessen JA, Birkenhäger WH: Antihypertensive treatment and prevention of stroke and dementia. *Sem Cerebrovasc Dis Stroke.* 2003;3:155–164.

[106]   Tzourio C, Anderson C, Chapman N, Woodward M, Neal B, MacMahon S, Chalmers J, PROGRESS Collaborative Group: Effect of blood pressure lowering with perindopril and indapamide therapy on dementia and cognitive decline in patients with cerebrovascular disease. *Arch Intern Med.* 2003;163:1069–1075.

[107] AD2000 Collaborative Group: Long-term donepezil treatment in 565 patients with Alzheimer's disease (AD2000): randomised double-blind trial. *Lancet.* 2004;363:2105-2115.

[108] Staessen JA, Birkenhäger WH: Cognitive impairment and blood pressure. Quo usque tandem abutere patientia nostra? *Hypertension.* 2004;44:612-613.

[109] Birkenhäger WH, Staessen JA. Progress in cardiovascular diseases. Cognitive function in essential hypertension. *Progress in Cardiovascular Diseases* 2006;49:1-10.

[110] Luchsinger JA, Reitz C, Honig LS, Tang M-X, Shea S, Mayeux R. Aggregation of vascular risk factors and risk of incident Alzheimer disease. *Neurology* 2005;65:545-551.

INDEX

B

C

D

E

F

G

H

N

Q

R

T

Y

Z